LOISIR ET SOCIÉTÉ / *SOCIETY AND LEISURE*

Vol. 18, n° 1, printemps / *Spring 1995*

Loisir, santé et fonctionnement humain
Leisure, Health and Human Functioning

Éditeurs invités / *Guest Editors*

Gaétan OUELLET, Seppo ISO-AHOLA et Daniel BOISVERT

Matisse, Henri (1869-1954)
Les capucines à « la Danse », 1912
Metropolitan Museum of Art
New York

1995
Presses de l'Université du Québec
2875, boul. Laurier, Sainte-Foy (Québec)   G1V 2M3

Directeur / *Editor* : Max D'AMOURS
Éditeurs associés / *Associate Editors*
    Walter TOKARSKY, Allemagne / *Germany*
    Shinji MORINO, Japon / *Japan*
    Karla HENDERSON, États-Unis / *United States*
    Grant CUSHMAN, Nouvelle-Zélande / *New Zealand*
    Nelson MELENDEZ, Porto Rico / *Porto Rico*
Responsables des comptes rendus / *Book Review Editors* : Michel BELLEFLEUR,
    Université du Québec à Trois-Rivières, Jean HARVEY, Université d'Ottawa,
    Louis JOLIN, Université du Québec à Montréal.

Pour toute correspondance	*For any correspondance*
concernant le contenu de la revue	*about the content of the review,*
prière de s'adresser à :	*please contact* :

Loisir et Société / *Society and Leisure*
Département des sciences du loisir
Université du Québec à Trois-Rivières
C.P. 500, Trois-Rivières (Québec)
Canada   G9A 5H7

Pour toute correspondance	*For any correspondance*
concernant les abonnements,	*concerning subscriptions, copyright*
les droits d'auteur et la publicité :	*and advertizing :*

Presses de l'Université du Québec
2875, boulevard Laurier, Sainte-Foy (Québec)
Canada   G1V 2M3

Cette revue est publiée grâce à une subvention accordée par le Fonds FCAR pour l'aide aux revues scientifiques du ministère de l'Enseignement supérieur et de la Science du Québec.

Les articles sont indexés dans *Repère, Loreto, Leisure Research and Tourism Abstract, Sociological Abstract, Bulletin signalétique, SPORT Database, SPORT Discus, Social Welfare Social Planning* et *Women Stud. Abstracts / Articles are indexed in* Repère, Loreto, Leisure Research and Tourism Abstract, Sociological Abstract, Bulletin signalétique, SPORT Database, SPORT Discus, Social Welfare Social Planning *and* Women Stud. Abstracts.

Traductions anglaise et française : Diane Leclerc
Traduction espagnole : Oscar Calderon
Secrétariat : Hélène S. Dubois

ISSN 0705-3436 / ISBN 2-7605-0839-0

Dépôt légal – 2ᵉ trimestre 1995
Bibliothèque nationale du Québec
Bibliothèque nationale du Canada
Imprimé au Canada

SOMMAIRE / *CONTENTS*

ARTICLES / *ARTICLES*

PARTIE I / *PART I*
LOISIR, SANTÉ ET BIEN-ÊTRE PSYCHOLOGIQUE /
LEISURE, MENTAL HEALTH AND PSYCHOLOGICAL WELL-BEING

PARTIE II / *PART II*
LOISIR, COMPORTEMENTS À RISQUE ET SANTÉ /
LEISURE, AT-RISK BEHAVIORS AND HEALTH

8

ONT COLLABORÉ À CE NUMÉRO
CONTRIBUTORS TO THIS ISSUE

BEAUCHESNE, Micheline, Département de psychologie, Université du Québec à Trois-Rivières, C.P. 500, Trois-Rivières, Québec, Canada, G9A 5H7, téléphone (819) 376-5085, télécopieur (819) 376-5092.

BOISVERT, Daniel, Département des arts, Université du Québec à Trois-Rivières, C.P. 500, Trois-Rivières, Québec, Canada, G9A 5H7, téléphone (819) 376-5135.

BUSSER, James A., Department of Sport and Leisure Studies, University of Nevada, Las Vegas, 4505 Maryland Parkway, Las Vegas NV 89154-3035, United States, téléphone (702) 895-4192, télécopieur (702) 895-4231.

CALDWELL, Linda L., School of Hotel, Restaurant and Recreation Management, The Pennsylvania State University, United States, téléphone (814) 865-1851, télécopieur (814) 863-1307.

CALTABIANO, Marie Louise, Department of Psychology and Sociology, James Cook University of North Queensland, Townsville, Queensland 4811, Australia, téléphone 61 77 81 48 59, télécopieur 61 77 79 54 35.

CANTIN, Roger, Centre François-Charon, 525, boulevard Wilfrid-Hamel Est, Québec, Québec, Canada, G1M 2S8, téléphone (418) 529-9141, télécopieur (418) 529-3699.

CARRUTHERS, Cynthia P., Department of Sport and Leisure Studies, University of Nevada, Las Vegas, 4505 Maryland Parkway, Las Vegas NV 89154-3035, United States, téléphone (702) 895-4192, télécopieur (702) 895-4231.

DALLAIRE, Christine, Faculty of Physical Education and Receration, University of Alberta, Edmonton, Canada.

DENIS, Maire-Claude, Département de psychologie, Université du Québec à Trois-Rivières, C.P. 500, Trois-Rivières, Québec, Canada, G9A 5H7, téléphone (819) 376-5085, télécopieur (819) 376-5092.

DUBÉ, Micheline, Département de psychologie, Université du Québec à Trois-Rivières, C.P. 500, Trois-Rivières, Québec, Canada, G9A 5H7, téléphone (819) 376-5085, télécopieur (819) 376-5092.

DUPUIS, Sherry L., Department of Family Studies, University of Guelph, Guelph, Ontario, Canada, N1G 2W1.

GILLETT, James, Department of Sociology, McMaster University, Hamilton, Ontario, Canada, L8S 4K1, téléphone (416) 525-9140, télécopieur (416) 5236011.

HAWORTH, John, Psychology Department, University of Manchester, Manchester, M13 9PL, England, téléphone 44 161 275 2585, télécopieur 44 161 275 2588.

ISO-AHOLA, Seppo, College of Health and Human Performance, 2367 Health and Human Performance Building, University of Maryland at College Park, Maryland 20742, United States, téléphone, (301) 405-2450, télécopieur (301) 314-9167.

JAMET, Michel, UFR STAPS, Université P. Sabatier, 118, route de Narbonne, 31062 Toulouse Cedex, France, téléphone 33 61 55 66 32, télécopieur, 33 61 55 82 17.

MURPHY, Gilles, Centre François-Charon, 525, boulevard Wilfrid-Hamel Est, Québec, Québec, Canada, G1M 2S8, téléphone (418) 529-9141, télécopieur (418) 529-3699.

NOREAU, Luc, Centre François-Charon, 525, boulevard Wilfrid-Hamel Est, Québec, Québec, Canada, GIM 2S8, téléphone (418) 529-9141, télécopieur (418) 529-3699.

OUELLET, Gaétan, Département des sciences du loisir, Université du Québec à Trois-Rivières, C.P. 500, Trois-Rivières, Québec, Canada, G9A 5H7, téléphone (819) 376-5132, télécopieur (819) 373-1988.

ROUSSEAU, Jacques, Département de psychologie, Université du Québec à Trois-Rivières, C.P. 500, Trois-Rivières, Québec, Canada, G9A 5H7, téléphone (819) 376-5085, télécopieur (819) 376-5092.

SMALE, Brian, Department of Recreation and Leisure Studies, University of Waterloo, Ontario, Canada, N2L 3G1, téléphone (519) 888-4567, poste 5664, télécopieur (519) 746-6776.

SMITH, Edward A., Department of Health Promotion and Behavior, University of Georgia, téléphone (706) 542-4367, télécopieur (706) 542-4956.

TREMBLAY, Georges, Centre François-Charon, 525, boulevard Wilfrid-Hamel Est, Québec, Québec, Canada, GIM 2S8, téléphone (418) 529-9141, télécopieur (418) 529-3699.

WEISSINGER, Ellen M., Department of Educational Psychology, 116 Bancroft Hall, University of Nebraska, Lincoln, NE 68588-0345, United States, téléphone (402) 472-6943, télécopieur (402) 472-8317.

WHITE, Philip, Department of Kinesiology, McMaster University, Hamilton, Ontario, Canada, L8S 4K1, téléphone (416) 525-9140, poste 27014, télécopieur (416) 5236011.

YOUNG, Kevin, Department of Sociology, University of Calgary, Calgary, Alberta, Canada, T2N 1N4, téléphone (403) 220-6501, télécopieur (403) 282-9298.

INTRODUCTION
LOISIR, SANTÉ ET FONCTIONNEMENT HUMAIN

Gaétan OUELLET

Depuis le début des années 1990, l'étude des bénéfices du loisir constitue une préoccupation particulièrement importante pour les scientifiques du loisir. L'imposant volume édité par Driver, Brown et Petersen (1991)[1] concrétise cette tendance de manière significative. Au Canada, les praticiens du loisir ont entrepris un virage par l'adoption d'une approche « axée sur les bénéfices » afin de susciter la participation aux loisirs et de justifier leur intervention. Une telle orientation favorise l'utilisation plus explicite des bienfaits ou des avantages du loisir, et même la recherche des fondements scientifiques attribuables aux différents aspects du loisir et de la récréation pour les individus et la collectivité.[2]

Parmi les principaux bénéfices personnels attribués aux loisirs, on retrouve la santé physique et mentale, le développement intégral de la personne, l'acquisition de comportements sains et équilibrés. C'est pour cette raison que des interventions de récréation thérapeutique et d'éducation au loisir ont acquis une importance aussi considérable aux États-Unis depuis les 25 dernières années.

Même si ces dimensions de santé globale et de fonctionnement optimal de la personne ne sont pas toujours présentes dans les motivations conscientes des gens pour désirer des loisirs et pour participer à des activités de temps libre, on les retrouve dans les justifications parfois un peu idéalisées du loisir. Les attitudes favorables face aux loisirs tirent souvent leur origine dans les croyances selon lesquelles ces activités exerceraient une influence positive sur la santé et le bien-être des gens, qu'elles favoriseraient au maximum le développement et le fonctionnement des dimensions physiques, mentales, affectives et sociales de la personne.

Ces croyances, qu'on pourrait également qualifier de préjugés favorables, ne sont pas toutes des faits démontrés scientifiquement. En effet, il n'est pas toujours certain que les effets attribués à la participation aux loisirs existent réellement ou qu'ils soient véritablement causés par la seule participation aux loisirs ; les conditions de leur obtention ne sont guère plus sûres. Ce qui est encore moins documenté et démontré, ce sont les effets négatifs susceptibles de découler de certaines formes de loisir ou de certaines conditions de participation aux activités récréatives. Par exemple, jusqu'à quel point et dans quelles conditions certaines formes de loisirs pourraient-elles causer la maladie plutôt que la santé, la dépendance plutôt que l'autonomie, la dépression plutôt que l'optimisme, la mésadaptation plutôt que l'adaptation ?

Ce numéro thématique vise à éclairer cette problématique et rejoint une préoccupation importante dans les milieux scientifiques et professionnels du loisir. Il pourra également permettre de démystifier ou de nuancer certaines croyances relatives à des faits vraisemblables ou généralement vrais, mais pas toujours, pas pour tous les loisirs, pas pour tout le monde ou pas à n'importe quelle condition. À cet égard, il constituera un complément à l'ouvrage édité récemment par Crompton et Iso-Ahola portant sur les loisirs et la santé mentale[3].

L'ensemble des travaux rapportés ici ne saurait représenter une revue exhaustive des recherches traitant de la problématique décrite ci-dessus. Il ne s'agit pas non plus d'un échantillon représentatif des études effectuées dans ce domaine ou des préoccupations des chercheurs ou des intervenants sociaux concernés. Cependant, la diversité des populations étudiées, la variété des problématiques, des thèmes et des aspects abordés est tout de même assez vaste pour alimenter une réflexion et des discussions profitables entre les divers secteurs du loisir. De plus, la qualité des recherches retenues fournit des observations et des explications qui font avancer les connaissances et les explications à la fois au sujet du loisir, de la santé et de leurs interrelations complexes.

La *première partie* porte sur les relations entre le loisir et la santé, physique ou mentale, réelle ou perçue, chez diverses catégories de personnes. De l'ensemble de ces travaux, il ressort que le loisir aurait une relation significative avec le niveau de santé, un impact direct ou indirect sur le bon fonctionnement de l'individu.

D'abord, Weissinger, qui s'intéresse aux jeunes, trouve une relation significative entre la santé perçue (physique et mentale) et l'expérience de l'ennui en loisir. Elle conclut à l'existence potentielle d'une relation causale entre l'ennui en loisir et l'incidence de comportements de santé négatifs.

Caltabiano étudie les effets de trois types d'activités de loisir sur la santé d'une population d'adultes. Certaines activités sont bénéfiques pour la santé, soit directement, soit indirectement, par la réduction des symptômes du stress. Certaines formes d'activités peuvent cependant comporter des éléments qui augmentent le niveau de stress.

Pour sa part, Haworth démontre comment les catégories d'expérience importantes pour la santé mentale peuvent être obtenues par le loisir, et non seulement par le travail, comme le prétend Jahoda dans sa théorie. De plus, certaines données de ses recherches révèlent que le loisir aurait tendance à augmenter le locus de contrôle « interne » des personnes, ce qui favoriserait une meilleure santé mentale.

Dupuis et Smale, de même que l'équipe dirigée par Rousseau, ont pour leur part étudié le rôle de l'activité et du loisir chez les personnes âgées. Leurs recherches permettent de dégager les influences de l'implication active et autodéterminée sur les niveaux d'autonomie, de résignation apprise, de dépression et de bien-être psychologique.

La *deuxième partie* regroupe deux articles portant sur divers comportements à risque et leur relation avec le loisir. D'abord, Carruthers et Busser démontrent que la consommation d'alcool peut varier en fréquence et en quantité selon les activités et les contextes de loisir des individus. Leurs données révèlent que les activités récréatives saines ne constituent pas toujours une solution de rechange à la consommation ou à l'abus d'alcool. Caldwell et Smith étudient ensuite les comportements de santé de jeunes qui sont aliénés dans leurs loisirs ; les comportements à haut niveau de risque pour la santé se retrouvent plus souvent dans leurs loisirs.

La *troisième partie* traite des valeurs et des pratiques sociales associées à l'activité physique. White, Young et Gillett remettent en question les valeurs attribuées au conditionnement physique, la façon dont on en a fait la promotion en créant des relations de domination et d'inégalité, et en associant de façon abusive les notions d'exercice, de forme physique et de santé.

Pour sa part, Jamet étudie l'évolution des politiques et de l'intervention de l'État français en matière d'activité physique.

Une *note de recherche* de Noreau, Murphy, Tremblay et Cantin trace finalement le portrait des pratiques d'activités de loisir chez un groupe de personnes atteintes de déficiences motrices. Cette étude s'intéresse particulièrement à la participation aux loisirs ainsi qu'aux contraintes qui y sont associées.

Tous ces articles représentent des contributions jugées importantes et valables par les évaluateurs, les coéditeurs invités et le comité éditorial de la revue. Ils font avancer l'état des connaissances dans un domaine de pointe et en plein essor ; ils favorisent également la conceptualisation, la description et l'explication des relations entre le loisir et le fonctionnement de la personne. Nous désirons remercier tous ceux et celles qui ont contribué à ce numéro : les nombreux chercheurs qui ont soumis des manuscrits, les experts qui ont été sollicités pour procéder à des évaluations, les membres du comité éditorial ainsi que les coéditeurs, Seppo Iso-Ahola et Daniel Boisvert.

Notes

1. Driver, B.L., Brown, P.J., Petersen, G.L. (Éds), (1991). *Benefits of Leisure,* State College, PA : Venture

2. Fédération des parcs et des loisirs de l'Ontario (1992). *Catalogue des avantages des parcs et des loisirs,* North York, Ont. : The Parks and Recreation of Ontario

3. Crompton. D.W., Iso-Ahola, S. (Éds), (1994). *Leisure and Mental Health, Volume One,* Park City, UT : Family Development Resources Inc.

INTRODUCTION
LEISURE, HEALTH AND HUMAN FUNCTIONING

Gaétan OUELLET

Since the early 1990s, the study of the benefits of leisure has been a particular focus for leisure experts. The sizable publication edited by Driver, Brown and Peterson (1991)[1] is a concrete example of this trend. Canadian leisure specialists have changed direction by adopting a benefit-oriented approach in order to encourage participation in leisure activities and to justify their intervention in this area. This type of approach favours a more explicit use of the benefits of leisure as well as the search for scientific foundations that can be attributed to the various ways in which leisure and recreation benefits both individuals and the community as a whole.[2]

Among the main personal benefits attributed to leisure activities are physical and mental health, complete development of the individual and the acquisition of healthy and stable behaviors. It is because of these benefits that therapeutic recreation and leisure education have taken on such importance in the United States over the last 25 years.

While overall improved health and optimal functioning are not always part of a person's conscious reasons for desiring leisure activities and for participating in activities in his or her free time, these dimensions are sometimes found in somewhat idealized justifications of leisure. Favourable attitudes towards leisure often originate in the belief that these activities have a positive impact on an individual's health and well-being, and that they are conducive to the maximum development and functioning of the physical, mental, emotional and social dimensions of an individual.

These beliefs, which could be also be called favourable prejudices, are not all scientifically demonstrated facts. It is not always certain that the effects attributed to participation in leisure activities actually exist or that they are caused solely by participation; the conditions for obtaining these effects are no more certain. Even less documented and demonstrated are the negative effects likely to result from certain forms of leisure or certain conditions for participating in recreational activities. For example, to what extent and under what conditions could certain forms of leisure cause sickness rather than health, dependency rather than autonomy, depression rather than optimism, maladjustment rather than adjustment?

The present issue aims at shedding light on the above questions and reflects an important preoccupation on the part of recreation specialists and researchers. It may also serve to demystify or clarify certain beliefs relating to some facts that are probable or generally true, but not all the time, not for all leisure activities, not for everyone and not under every condition. This issue is therefore intended to serve as a complement to the work edited by Crompton and Iso-Ahola on leisure and mental health[3].

The research presented here does not represent an exhaustive review of the studies dealing with the abovementioned issues. Neither is it a representative sample of either investigations carried out in this area or preoccupations of the researchers or social experts concerned. However, the diversity of the populations studied, the variety of the problems, themes and aspects examined is wide enough to provide food for thought and valuable discussion between researchers in the various areas of the leisure field. In addition, the quality of the papers provides observations and explanations that contribute to furthering our understanding of leisure, health and the complex interrelationship between the two.

The *first part* examines the relationships between leisure and both real and perceived physical and mental health in a variety of groups of individuals. The papers suggest the existence of a significant relationship between leisure and health, and that leisure has a direct or indirect influence on the adequate functioning of an individual.

Firstly, Weissinger, who studies young people, found a significant relationship between perceived health (physical and mental) and boredom experienced in leisure. She concluded that a causal relationship potentially exists between boredom in leisure and the incidence of negative health behaviors.

Caltabiano studied the effects of three types of leisure activities on the health of an adult population. Certain activities were found to be beneficial to health, either directly or indirectly, in that they reduce the stress symptoms. Certain forms of leisure activities can, however, involve components that increase the level of stress.

Hayworth showed how the categories of experience that are important for mental health can be provided by leisure, and therefore not only by work as suggested by Jahoda. In addition, some research data indicates that leisure has a tendency to increase the "internal" locus of control of individuals, which would favor better mental health.

Dupuis and Smale, as well as the research group headed by Rousseau, studied the role played by leisure and activity for older adults. Their research brought out the effects that active and self-determined implication has on levels of autonomy, learned resignation, depression and psychological well-being.

The *second part* is made of two papers that discuss various risk behaviors and their relation to leisure. Firstly, Carruthers and Busser show that alcohol consumption can vary in frequency and in quantity depending on the type of activity and the context within which the leisure activity takes place. Their results suggest that healthy recreational activities do not always provide an alternative to alcohol consumption or abuse. Caldwell and Smith then studied the health behaviors of young people who have been alienated in their leisure activities; high-risk health behaviors are found more often in their leisure activities.

The *third part* deals with values and social practices associated with physical activity. White, Young and Gillett question the values attributed to physical fitness and the way in which physical fitness is promoted by creating relationships of domination and inequality and by excessively associating the notions of exercise, physical fitness and health.

In another study, Jamet examined the evolution of the policies and actions taken by the French government regarding sports and physical education.

Finally, a *research note* by Noreau, Murphy, Tremblay and Cantin describes the leisure activities of a group of individuals with motor disabilities. This study specifically examines participation in leisure activities and the constraints associated with them.

All the above papers were deemed significant and valid by the referees, guest coeditors and the journal's editorial staff. They favor the advancement of knowledge in a rapidly growing study area. In addition, they contribute to the conceptualization, description and explanation of the relationships between leisure and human functioning. We would like to thank everyone who contributed to this issue: all the researchers who submitted manuscripts, experts who participated in the evaluation process, the editorial staff and the coeditors, Seppo Iso-Ahola and Daniel Boisvert.

NOTES

1. Driver, B.L., Brown, P.J., Petersen, G.L. (Éds), (1991). *Benefits of Leisure,* State College, PA : Venture

2. Parks and Recreation Federation of Ontario (1992). *Catalogue of the Benefits of Parks and Recreation,* North York, Ont. : The Parks and Recreation of Ontario

3. Crompton. D.W., Iso-Ahola, S. (Éds), (1994). *Leisure and Mental Health, Volume One*, Park City, UT : Family Development Resources Inc.

PARTIE I / *PART I*

LOISIR, SANTÉ
ET BIEN-ÊTRE PSYCHOLOGIQUE

LEISURE, MENTAL HEALTH
AND PSYCHOLOGICAL WELL-BEING

EFFECTS OF BOREDOM
ON SELF-REPORTED HEALTH

Ellen WEISSINGER
Department of Educational Psychology
University of Nebraska
Lincoln, United States

Introduction

Related Literature

Gitelson and Thomason (1992) found that the college environment may have a unique influence on leisure behavior, including different patterns of free time availability and new activity acquisition. For many young adults, the college years are time of expanding freedom and focusing interests. This is a developmental stage characterized by lifestyle and role establishment, during which the leisure repertoire of newly autonomous young adults is importantly constructed (Kleiber & Kelly, 1980; Freysinger & Ray, 1994).

As a result, the antecedents and consequences of leisure behavior may hold important implications during this life stage. If creating a functional leisure lifestyle is an important task at this age, then what happens to young adults who fail to develop the ability to make satisfying and meaningful choices in their leisure time? Gabriel (1988) notes that problems with boredom in later adulthood may be the result of failure, during critical periods of development, to learn how to direct behavior in ways that meaningfully satisfy needs. She further states that bored individuals are likely to "seek relief from the unpleasantness of this repression by entertaining various methods of discharge, e.g., food, drink, drugs and sex" (p. 158). This implies that young adults who perceive their leisure time as "boring" may be at risk of developing and *establishing* a pattern of leisure choices that will negatively impact mental and physical well being. Thus, the relationship between boredom and health in the college population would seem to be worthy of investigation.

Loisir et société / *Society and Leisure*
Volume 18, numéro 1, printemps 1995, pp. 21-32 • © Presses de l'Université du Québec

Research on young adults and late adolescents demonstrates that boredom during leisure time is associated with high-risk health behaviors such as substance abuse (Iso-Ahola & Crowley, 1991; Johnston & O'Malley, 1986; Orcutt, 1984), cigarette smoking (Smith & Caldwell, 1989), and eating disorders (Abramson & Stinson, 1977; Leon & Chamberlain, 1973; Mehrabian & Riccioni, 1986; Rodin, 1975). Boredom proneness has also been shown to be correlated with various forms of mental distress (Farmer & Sundberg, 1986), such as apprehension (McGiboney & Carter, 1988), alienation (Tolor, 1989), loneliness (Ragheb, 1993), shyness (Morolo, 1986), social incompetence (Oppenheim, 1984), and negative affect (Vodanovich, Verner, & Gilbride, 1991). Boredom has, in fact, been called "the most prevalent American disease" (Ramey, 1988, p. 12). Taken together, the existing literature would seem to suggest that investigation of the relationship between boredom and generalized perceptions of health is warranted.

Statement of the Problem

The present analyses are focused on the following research question: "Do traditionally aged college students who score in the upper and lower quartiles on the *Leisure Boredom Scale* differ in their self-reports of mental and physical health?" Based on the preceding review of literature, it was hypothesized that persons lower in boredom would report more positive levels of physical and mental health. Data from two studies are presented.

Method

Study One

Subjects

The first study reported here is a secondary analysis of a dataset originally collected as part of a methodological investigation (Weissinger, Caldwell & Mobily, 1992). A sample of 447 college undergraduates was administered a questionnaire packet containing self-report instruments. The subjects represent a convenience sample in which students were contacted in classroom settings at two US universities and one Canadian university. The subjects had a mean age of 20.9 years. The sample was 42% female and 58% male. Included were 34% freshmen, 21% sophomores, 21% juniors and 24% seniors; mean GPA for the sample was 2.9 on a 4.0 point scale. The study was approved by the human subject review board at the university of the lead investigator. All subjects were informed of the purpose of the study and voluntarily completed the questionnaires.

Variables and Measures

The independent variable in the present analysis, *boredom in leisure time,* was measured with Iso-Ahola and Weissinger's (1990) sixteen item scale (5 point Likert, 1 = low boredom). Iso-Ahola and Weissinger conceptualized boredom in leisure time as a trait characterized by "the subjective perception that available leisure experiences are not sufficient to instrumentally satisfy needs for optimal arousal [...] Leisure boredom is a mismatch between de*sired* arousal producing characteristics of leisure experiences, and perceptual or actual *availability* of such leisure experiences" (1990, pp. 4-5). They report Cronbach's alpha coefficients ranging from .85 to .88, and offer data from three studies that support the construct validity and unidimensional factor structure of the scale.

The conceptual dependent variable, *physical and mental health,* was operationalized by six single-item indicators, three focused on mental health and three on physical health. Respondents were asked to rate their *satisfaction* with physical and mental health (5 point scale, 5 = very satisfied), the degree to which they *worry* about their physical and mental health (4 point scale, 4 = no worry at all), and to rate their *level* of physical and mental health as compared to other people their age (4 point scale, 4 = excellent). No previous reliability or validity data are available for these items.

Study Two

Subjects

A second dataset was collected to replicate the findings of the secondary analysis. Study Two included 332 college undergraduates contacted in 12 sections of a senior level applied statistics class at a large midwestern US university. Average age for the sample was 20.3 years, with 58 % females. Included were 10 % freshmen, 33 % sophomores, 29 % juniors and 28 % seniors. Students completed the measures in their classrooms. All participation was voluntary and the study was approved by the IRB of the author's university.

Variables and Measures

Subjects completed a questionnaire packet including the Leisure Boredom Scale, the six dependent variable items, and demographics. Also included were two single-item indicators of the frequency ("How often are you bored in your free time ?") and depth ("When you are bored in free time, how deeply bored are you ?") of free time boredom. The frequency item used a four point response scale (1 = never to 4 = almost always). The depth item used a four point scale (1 = hardly bored at all to 4 = very deeply bored). These items were included in order to provide construct validity data for the Boredom Scale.

Results

Partitioning Boredom Scores

Boredom scores were calculated by taking the average across all 16 items, and therefore could vary between 1.0 (low boredom) and 5.0 (high boredom). In order to construct two comparison groups in each sample, scores on the boredom scale were divided at the upper and lower quartiles. This formed two groups, each representing 25 % of the sample with the lowest boredom scores or the highest boredom scores. The mean scores on the boredom scale for the two total samples were 2.04 and 2.10 respectively; mean scores for the lower quartile groups were 1.42 and 1.52; mean scores for the upper quartile groups were 2.68 and 2.71 (Table 1).

Reliability and Validity

Reliability analysis for the Boredom Scale in the two samples revealed Cronbach's alphas of .86 and .85, respectively. Correlations among the six dependent variable items ranged from .13 to .65 in Study One and .14 to .63 in Study Two, with an average inter-item correlation of .39 in Study One and .40 on Study Two (Table 2). Cronbach's alpha coefficients for the health items in the two samples were .79 and .80, respectively. In order to assess construct validity of the Boredom Scale, two single item indicators of the reported frequency and depth of boredom in free time were included in Study Two. Total score on the Boredom Scale was significantly correlated with both frequency ($r = .50$) and depth ($r = .36$) of boredom in free time.

TABLE 1

**Partitioning Scores to Form Higher
and Lower Boredom Groups.**

	Study One	Study Two
Higher Boredom Group (Highest Quartile)	n = 106	n = 77
	X = 2.68	X = 2.71
Lower Boredom Group (Lowest Quartile)	n = 109	n = 78
	X = 1.42	X = 1.52
Total Sample	n = 447	n = 332
	X = 2.04	X = 2.10

TABLE 2

Pearson Product-Moment Correlations
for Studies One and Two (in parentheses).

	Bore	MH	PH	MHS	PHS	MHW
MH	-.15 (-.23)					
PH	-.28 (-.32)	.23 (.40)				
MHS	-.17 (-.16)	.65 (.63)	.25 (.29)			
PHS	-.23 (-.21)	.29 (.32)	.63 (.62)	.43 (.53)		
MHW	-.09* (-.13)	.56 (.54)	.12 (.14)	.57 (.58)	.24 (.25)	
PHW	-.10* (-.18)	.25 (.28)	.43 (.43)	.30 (.23)	.49 (.42)	.37 (.39)

Bore = Boredom Scale

MH, PH = mental, physical health rating items

MHS, PHS – mental, physical health satisfaction items

MHW, PHW = mental, physical health worry items

* not significant beyond $p < .05$, all other correlations are significant.

MANOVA Analyses, Study One

In order to test for extraneous variables in the relationship between boredom and health, a 4-way MANOVA was run using boredom group (low/high), gender, sample (universities 1, 2, 3), and major (recreation/non-recreation) as independent variables. Results indicated that the main effects for gender, sample and major were not significant, nor were any 2- 3- or 4-way interactions significant. That is, subjects of different genders, majors or universities did not differ significantly on health scores, nor did these variables interact with boredom scores to change the relationship between boredom and health. Based on these results, a MANOVA was run using boredom group as the only independent variable, in order to "conserve" degrees of freedom.

MANOVA analysis from Study One is reported in Table 3. The omnibus F test was significant, therefore six univariate follow-ups were conducted. To control for the inflation of study-wise type I error that results from the use of multiple univariate tests, a Bonferroni correction was utilized (Bray & Maxwell, 1982). Total alpha (.05) was divided by the number of univariate tests (6) to produce a new pair-wise alpha level (.008). Based on this conservative alpha level, the boredom groups differed significantly on four of the six dependent variable items: satisfaction with physical and mental health, and physical and mental health rating as compared to others. As predicted, persons in the lower boredom group reported more positive mental and physical health. The two boredom groups did not differ significantly on the "worry" variables.

MANOVA Analysis, Study Two

The analysis strategy for Study Two was similar to the first study. In order to identify confounding variables, an initial MANOVA was run using gender and section (12 course sections were surveyed) as additional independent variables. Main effects for gender and section were not significant, nor were any of the interaction terms. Therefore a MANOVA was run using boredom group as the only independent variable. The omnibus F was significant (Table 4). After Bonferroni correction, univariate follow-ups revealed that the groups differed in the hypothesized direction on the three of the six dependent variable items: physical health satisfaction, physical health rating and physical health worry.

TABLE 3

MANOVA and ANOVA Analyses for Boredom Groups, Study One (n = 215).

| | Boredom Groups | | | | | |
| | Lower | | Higher | | | |
Dependent Variable	Mean	SD	Mean	SD	F	p <
Phy. Health Sat.	3.92	.939	3.29	1.129	19.88	.001*
Men. Health Sat.	4.21	.762	3.86	.946	8.31	.004*
Phy. Health Rating	3.33	.641	2.85	.679	27.99	.001*
Mcn. Health Rating	3.42	.550	3.15	.620	10.95	.001*
Phy. Health Worry	1.91	.779	2.11	.767	3.51	.060
Men. Health Worry	3.34	.764	3.20	.781	1.60	.200

Pillais value = .148 ; F(6,208) = 5.94 ; p < .001

* significant after Bonferroni correction

TABLE 4

**MANOVA and ANOVA Analyses for Boredom Groups,
Study Two (n = 155).**

| | Boredom Groups | | | | | |
| | Lower | | Higher | | | |
Dependent Variable	Mean	SD	Mean	SD	F	p <
Phy. Health Sat.	3.86	1.028	3.42	.923	7.97	.005*
Men. Health Sat.	4.27	.801	3.99	.966	3.92	.049
Phy. Health Rating	3.37	.584	2.90	.736	19.91	.001*
Men. Health Rating	3.57	.497	3.23	.724	6.49	.012
Phy. Health Worry	3.10	.831	2.75	.876	11.87	.001*
Men. Health Worry	3.33	.816	3.01	.873	5.12	.025

Pillais value = .151 ; $F(6,148) = 4.37$; $p < .001$
* significant after Bonferroni correction

Discussion

Results confirmed the proposed hypothesis. The slightly differing pattern of significance in the univariate follow-ups is not surprising, and probably due to sampling error. Given the substantial intercorrelations among the six dependent variables, the omnibus F test is a better global indicator of the differences between the high and low boredom groups (Haase & Ellis, 1987; Harwell, 1988). In both studies, persons in the lower boredom group reported more positive mental and physical health than persons in the higher boredom group.

Three methodological cautions are in order before interpreting the results. First, self-reports of health are certainly less valid and reliable than carefully controlled behavioral and clinical health measures. However, Pol and Thomas (1992) note a considerable number of studies showing significant correlations between self-report and clinical health measures, and also observe the widespread use of self-reports in the epidemiological literature (e.g., Kempen, 1992). Nonetheless, the present data should be carefully interpreted as dealing with self-reported health. Second, it is important to notice that both the "higher" and "lower" boredom groups reported relatively low levels of boredom. This actually makes the findings more conservative, in that the effect on health was found even in groups with lower levels of boredom. The nature of the boredom-health relationship in groups experiencing very high levels of boredom remains to be investigated. Third, although the present hypothesis assumed that the causal link between boredom and health was unidirectional, it is possible that this relation-ship is actually reciprocal. That is, lower levels of perceived health may also influence the likelihood of boredom.

Does boredom in leisure time cause poorer health? Although boredom has been associated with the occurrence of several negative health behaviors, it is likely that the relationship is more complex than that. It is possible to speculate that college students who are failing to develop a satisfying leisure lifestyle are also experiencing broader life adjustment problems that are associated with attitudes and behaviors that create low levels of well-being (Gabriel, 1988). In other words, reports of higher levels of leisure boredom in the college student cohort, whose primary developmental task is constructing an adult identity, may reflect a generalized difficulty to develop a satisfying and functional lifestyle. Reports of boredom, therefore, would serve as a "marker" for other variables.

This line of reasoning is similar to the argument presented by Coleman and Iso-Ahola (1993) and Coleman (1993), who posit that leisure-related disposi-tions serve to buffer the stress-illness relationship. Specifically, they hypothesize that self-determination and competence (primary intrinsic motives) contribute to coping abilities that moderate the effects of stress. Consistent with this, Weissinger, Caldwell and Bandalos (1992) found that boredom in leisure time could be usefully conceptualized as a breakdown of the intrinsic motivation process, and that low levels of self-determination and competence were related to the occurrence of boredom. Similarly, Iso-Ahola and Weissinger (1987) reported that lack of awareness of intrinsic motives was the prime cause of boredom in their sample.

Taken together, these findings would seem to hint that the boredom in leisure time influences health in at least two ways. First, there may be a direct causal relationship between boredom and the incidence of negative health behaviors such as substance abuse, smoking, alienation, etc. Second, boredom may be related to dispositional states that produce less "buffering" of the effects of life stress. Whatever the mechanism might be, the present analyses consistently indicate a significant relationship between boredom and health in college undergraduates. Given the conservative nature of the analyses, these findings should not be ignored. Further investigation of the role that boredom plays in well being is warranted.

References

ABRAMSON, E.E. & STINSON, S.G. (1977). Boredom and eating in obese and nonobese individuals. *Addictive Behaviors, 2,* 181-185.

BRAY, G. & MAXWELL, S.E. (1982). Analyzing and interpreting significant MANOVA's. *Review of Educational Research, 52,* 340-367.

COLEMAN, D. (1993). Leisure based social support, leisure dispositions and health. *Journal of Leisure Research, 25,* 350-361.

COLEMAN, D. & ISO-AHOLA, S.E. (1993). Leisure and health : The role of social support and self-determination. *Journal of Leisure Research, 25,* 111-128.

ELLIS, L. & THOMPSON, R. (1989). Relating religion, crime, arousal and boredom. *Sociology and Social Research, 73,* 132-135.

FARMER, R. & SUNDBERG, N.D. (1986). Boredom proneness : The development and correlates of a new scale. *Journal of Personality Assessment, 50,* 4-17.

FREYSINGER, V.J., & RAY, R. O. (1994). The activity involvement of women and men in young and middle adulthood : A panel study. *Leisure Sciences, 16,* 193-217.

GABRIEL, M.A. (1988). Boredom : Exploration of a developmental perspective. *Clinical Social Work Journal, 16,* 156-164.

GIBONEY, G.W. & CARTER, C. (1988). Boredom proneness and adolescent's personalities. *Psychological Reports, 63,* 741-742.

GITELSON, R. & THOMASON, P. (1992, October). *An exploratory analysis of the impact of attending college on leisure behavior.* Paper presented at the SPRE Leisure Research Symposium, Cincinnati, OH.

HAASE, R.F. & ELLIS, M.V. (1987). Multivariate analysis of variance. *Journal of Counseling Psychology, 34,* 404-413.

HARWELL, M.R. (1988). Univariate and multivariate tests : ANOVA versus MANOVA. *Educational Research Quarterly, 12,* 21-28.

ISO-AHOLA, S.E. & CROWLEY, E.D. (1991). Adolescent substance abuse and leisure boredom. *Journal of Leisure Research, 23,* 260-271.

ISO-AHOLA, S.E. & WEISSINGER, E. (1987). Leisure and boredom. *Journal of Social and Clinical Psychology, 5,* 356-364.

ISO-AHOLA, S.E. & WEISSINGER, E. (1990). Perceptions of boredom in leisure : Conceptualization, reliability and validity of the leisure boredom scale. *Journal of Leisure Research, 22,* 1-17.

JOHNSTON, L.D. & O'MALLEY, P.M. (1986). Why do the nation's students use drugs and alcohol ? Self-reported reasons from nine national surveys. *Journal of Drug Issues, 16,* 29-66.

KEMPEN, G.I.J.M. (1992). The MOS short form general health survey : Single item vs multiple item measures of health related quality of life nuances. *Psychological Reports, 70,* 608-610.

KLEIBER, D.A. & KELLY, J.R. (1980). Leisure, socialization and the life cycle. In S.E. Iso-Ahola (Ed.), *Social psychological perspectives on leisure and recreation* (pp. 91-137). Springfield, IL : Charles Thomas.

LEON, G.R. & CHAMBERLAIN, K. (1973). Emotional arousal, eating patterns, and body image as differential factors associated with varying success in maintaining a weight loss. *Journal of Counseling and Clinical Psychology, 40,* 474-480.

MEHRABIAN, A. & RICCIONI, M. (1986). Measures of eating related characteristics for the general population: Relationships with temperament. *Journal of Personality Assessment, 50*, 610,629.

MOROLDO, G.K. (1986). Shyness, boredom and grade point average among college students. *Psychological Reports, 59*, 395-398.

OPPENHEIM, J.S. (1984). *Perceived social competence, boredom, and capacity for self-entertainment.* Unpublished masters thesis, University of Maryland, College Park, MD.

ORCUTT, J.D. (1984). Contrasting the effects of two kinds of boredom on alcohol use. *Journal of Drug Issues, 14*, 161-173.

POL, L.G. & THOMAS, R.K. (1992). *The demography of health and health care.* New York: Plenum Press.

RAGHEB, M. (1993, October). *A multiple regression analysis of the contribution of campus recreation, leisure satisfaction, loneliness, and a set of satisfactions to students.* Paper presented at the SPRE Leisure Research Symposium, San Jose, CA.

RAMEY, E.R. (1974). Boredom: The most prevalent American disease. *Harpers*, November, 12-18.

RODIN, J. (1975). Causes and consequences of time perception differences in overweight and normal weight people. *Journal of Personality and Social Psychology, 31*, 898-904.

SMITH, E.A. & CALDWELL, L.L. (1989). The perceived quality of leisure experiences among smoking and nonsmoking adolescents. *Journal of Early Adolescence, 9*, 153-162.

TOLOR, A. (1989). Boredom as related to alienation, assertiveness, internal-external expectancy and sleep patterns. *Journal of Clinical Psychology, 45*, 260-265.

VODANOVICH, S.J., VERNER, K.M., & GILBRIDE, T.V. (1991). Boredom proneness: Its relationship to positive and negative affect. *Psychological Reports, 69*, 1139-1146.

WEISSINGER, E., CALDWELL, L.L., & BANDALOS, D.L. (1992). Relation between intrinsic motivation and boredom in leisure time. *Leisure Sciences, 14*, 317-325.

WEISSINGER, E., CALDWELL, L.L., & MOBILY, K.E. (1992). Use of recreation majors as research subjects: Differences between majors and nonmajors on leisure related variables. *Leisure Sciences, 14*, 327-335.

Ellen WEISSINGER
Les effets de l'ennui sur l'autodescription de la santé

RÉSUMÉ

Deux analyses ont été effectuées afin de déterminer si les personnes qui obtiennent des résultats situés dans les quartiles supérieur et inférieur de l'*Échelle de l'ennui au loisir* (*Leisure Boredom Scale*) se distinguent des autres sujets dans l'autodescription de leur santé physique et mentale. L'hypothèse était que les résultats plus élevés à cette échelle se concrétiseraient par des descriptions plus négatives de la santé. Deux échantillons d'étudiants de premier cycle (*n* total = 779) ont servi à l'étude. Des tests *F* multivariés se sont révélés significatifs et ont confirmé l'hypothèse. Après correction de l'erreur de type *I* rattachée à l'étude, on constate que les groupes manifestant un haut degré et un bas degré d'ennui se distinguent dans quatre des six indicateurs de santé dans l'étude n° 1, et dans trois des indicateurs de l'étude n° 2. L'auteur discute ces résultats par comparaison avec ceux d'autres études relatives à la relation entre les comportements de santé négatifs et l'ennui au loisir.

Ellen WEISSINGER
Effects of Boredom on Self-Reported Health

ABSTRACT

Two analyses were conducted to determine whether persons scoring in the upper and lower quartiles on the *Leisure Boredom Scale* would differ in their self-reports of mental and physical health. It was hypothesized that higher boredom scores would result in more negative self-reports of health. Data from two samples of college undergraduates were reported (total $n = 779$). Multivariate F tests were significant, supporting the hypothesis. After correcting for study-wise type *I* error inflation, high and low boredom groups differed on four of the six health indicators in Study One, and three of the indicators in Study Two. Results were discussed in the context of other literature concerning the relationship between negative health behaviors and leisure boredom.

Ellen WEISSINGER
Los efectos del tedio sobre la autodescripción de la salud

RESUMEN

Dos análisis se han realizado afín de determinar si las personas que obtienen resultados situados en los cuartiles superiores e inferiores de la escala del tedio a las diversiones (Leisure Boredom Scale) se distinguen de los otros sujetos en la autodescripción de su salud física y mental. La hipótesis suponía que los resultados más elevados en dicha escala se concretizarían por descripciones más negativas de la salud. Dos muestras de estudiantes de primer ciclo (n total = 779) sirvieron para efectuar el estudio. Pruebas F multivariadas se revelaron significativas y confirmaron la hipótesis. Después de la corrección del error de tipo I ligada al estudio, se constata que los grupos que manifiestan un alto grado y un bajo grado de tedio se distinguen en cuatro de los seis indicadores de salud en el estudio N° 1, y en tres de los indicadores en el estudio N° 2. El autor discute estos resultados comparándolos con otros estudios realizados relativos a la relación entre los comportamientos negativos para la salud y el tedio a las diversiones.

MAIN AND STRESS-MODERATING HEALTH BENEFITS OF LEISURE

Marie Louise CALTABIANO

Department of Psychology and Sociology
James Cook University of North Queensland
Townsville, Australia

It has long been recognized that leisure has salutary benefits for individuals. This notion has been reflected in theoretical arguments since the writings of Pieper (1963) and Dumazedier (1967). More recently, an entire volume has been devoted to the benefits of leisure (Driver, Brown, & Peterson, 1991) including the psychophysiological concomitants of leisure involvement. Increasingly, it is being acknowledged that leisure as a lifestyle factor plays a vital role in health promotion and disease prevention (Paffenbarger, Hyde, & Dow, 1991). Psychological benefits of leisure include a sense of well-being, increased self-esteem, and the development of adaptive personality resources (Coleman & Iso-Ahola, 1993; Tinsley & Tinsley, 1986). Physiological benefits of leisure include elevated endorphin levels, catecholamine changes and improved cardiorespiratory output (Wankel & Berger, 1991). Leisure may further exert stress-modulation effects on humoral and cellular immunity (Ulrich, Dimberg, & Driver, 1991).

Analyses of the leisure-health relationship have offered several mechanisms by which leisure can affect health. Leisure can exert a direct influence on health or it can have a stress-moderating effect (Caltabiano, 1988; Coleman & Iso-Ahola, 1993). This direct effect hypothesis, which postulates a beneficial effect of leisure on health (either psychological, physiological or spiritual) without reference to the presence of stressful life experiences, is argued in several theories. Neulinger (1982) proposed that perceived freedom in leisure and intrinsic leisure motivation contributed to an individual's psychological health. "Leisure lack" was equated with a state of diminished well-being. Weissinger and Iso-Ahola (1984) proposed that leisure, as intrinsically motivated behaviour, could optimize health. Tinsley and Tinsley (1986) argued that satisfaction of an individual's psychological needs through the leisure experience has an effect on physical health, mental health and consequently life satisfaction and personal growth.

Most leisure theory, however, has implicated stress either implicitly or explicitly in its discussion of health benefits. Driver and Tocher (1975) proposed the motivation to escape a structured life space as underlying the restorative aspects of the recreational behavioural continuum. The notion that leisure was a mode of coping or stress-reducer could be inferred from Iso-Ahola's (1989) explanation of leisure motives which incorporated an escape dimension. Iso-Ahola and Weissinger (1984) argued that socialization into satisfying leisure could contribute to the predisposition towards intrinsic motivation, which has been found by Maddi and Kobasa (1981) to act as a stress-resistance resource. In a more recent paper by Coleman and Iso-Ahola (1993), more explicit reference was made to a stress-moderating effect of leisure on health. Along with the leisure-generated disposition of self-determination, leisure-based social support was seen as exerting a moderating or buffering influence on the effects of stress on illness.

A vast body of literature exists which attests to the deleterious effects of stressful life events for health (Sarason, Sarason, & Johnson, 1985). Two components of life events were found to be predictive of somatic disease and psychological disorder. These were the amount of life change necessitated by the event, and the amount of distress associated with the life event (Dohrenwend & Dohrenwend, 1969; Paykel, Prusoff, & Uhlenhuth, 1971).

Psychosocial moderators of the relationship between life event stress and illness have been documented extensively, and include factors such as social support (Cohen & Wills, 1985) and coping resources (Pearlin & Schooler, 1978). Personality variables such as hardiness (Kobasa, Maddi, & Kahn, 1982), type A behaviour pattern, and hostility (Booth-Kewley & Friedman, 1987) have likewise been acknowledged as stress moderators.

The behavioural medicine area of research has been slower to acknowledge or investigate any moderating influence of leisure on the stress-health linkage. Recognition of the contributions of leisure by health psychologists, in a broader understanding of the effects of stress on health, may have been impeded by unfamiliarity with leisure theory and research. This may be due to such researchers equating leisure with escapist, avoidant or self-indulgent consummatory responses to stress. Leisure, however, may contribute to inner-directed coping strategies essential to action-focused coping, by providing for the development of new skills, behaviours and resources useful in solving a problem (Ulrich et al., 1991). Leisure theorists (Driver & Tocher, 1975; Iso-Ahola, 1989) see much of leisure behaviour as purposive, action-oriented and goal-directed, irrespective of associated motivations for the behaviour (e.g., relaxation and escape from stress, often considered as a means of coping with distressful emotions). Furthermore, these theorists have more readily incorporated research findings from the health area to extend leisure theory, and provide a health directive for much research.

Evidence has demonstrated the physiological and psychological benefits of movement aspects of leisure, in particular, sport, exercise and fitness. Sport participation has been found to be negatively related to number of reported symptoms of physical disease (Gratton & Tice, 1989), and reduced dysphoric emotions (Thorlindsson, Vilhjalmsson, & Valgeirsson, 1990). Sports-centered leisure was found to be associated with the highest health scores among both employed and unemployed respondents in a British study of 4,554 persons (Roberts, Lamb, Dench, & Brodie, 1989). Compared to quiet rest whose effect on blood pressure dissipated after 20 minutes, subjects in an exercise treatment condition experienced a reduction in systolic and diastolic blood pressure as long as three hours later (Raglin & Morgan, 1987). Exercise has been linked to reductions in depression (Wankel & Berger, 1991), and reduced anxiety 15 months after participating in a jogging program (Long, 1985). Physical fitness has been found to be related to lower heart rate, increased oxygen consumption, reduced risk of myocardial infarction and longevity in post myocardial infarction patients (Froelicher & Froelicher, 1991).

Social leisure has been investigated for its health benefits and stress-moderating effects. Discretionary forms of social contact through leisure were reported by Bolger and Eckenrode (1991) to be more beneficial to health than obligatory contacts at work and school. Companionship, an often-cited leisure motive, has been found to buffer the effects of daily hassles and enhance psychological well-being (Rook, 1987). Life satisfaction has been linked with socializing activities for males aged between 40 and 65 years of age (Steinkamp & Kelly, 1987).

Passive forms of recreation have been shown to be associated with a physiological response of relaxation, and reported positive mood (Ulrich *et al.,* 1991). Using electrocortical activity as a measure of physiological arousal, Ulrich (1981) found that exposure to slides of natural landscapes resulted in higher alpha brain wave levels typical of a relaxed state. Studies of the motivational basis of leisure choice have consistently reported mood enhancement and relaxation for natural areas (Hull, 1991). Whether the same physiological indicators of benefits occur for other forms of passive leisure such as hobbies/crafts or cultural pursuits remains unresearched.

Passive modes of leisure may interact with stress to affect health outcome. An experimental study by Heywood (1978) demonstrated that the stress of an arithmetic task was relieved to a greater extent by passive forms of leisure such as music, reading and television viewing which were perceived as recreative.

Stress relief was indicated by reductions in heart rate, skin conductance, upper back muscle tension and respiration. Ulrich and Simons (1986) demonstrated that stress recovery from viewing a stressful movie was faster for subjects exposed to videotapes of natural settings. Hartig, Mang and Evans (1990) found that subjects in the experimental condition of a 40 minute nature walk recovered faster following exposure to a stressor than did subjects in the urban walk and magazine/music relaxation conditions. Post-operative recovery rates have likewise been higher when patients have rooms with views of trees rather than buildings (Ulrich, 1984).

Leisure perceptions in addition to participation could be crucial to stress-moderating effects of leisure. Stress recovery in Heywood's (1978) study was influenced by a perception of the leisure as a recreative experience. Leisure activities may vary in individual perceptions of stress-reduction benefits. Caltabiano (1988, 1994) addressed this issue in a principal components analysis of 83 leisure activities rated for their perceived stress-reducing usefulness. Three factors were identified, namely, outdoor-active sport (swimming, bush walking, horseback riding, team sports, squash, water skiing), social (visiting/entertaining friends, partying, dining out, chatting/conversing) and cultural-hobbies activities (concert/symphony/ballet attendance, visiting libraries/museums, public lectures, creative crafts). Activities within a factor were perceived as equivalent in potential to reduce stress.

In examining the relationship between leisure and health, definitional and causal implications need to be considered. Health can be defined in the bio-medical sense of the absence of physiological disorder, physical symptoms or other debilitating conditions. At a deeper level of analysis, immunological status would need to be monitored. A biopsychosocial approach to defining health would emphasize psychological/emotional well-being and adaptive functioning within social systems, in addition to physical health indicators. The relationship between leisure and health is bidirectional with leisure affecting health and health affecting leisure opportunity (Coleman & Iso-Ahola, 1993). In the present study, health was defined as the absence of physical and psychological illness symptoms.

Another consideration which warrants attention in studying the stress-moderating effect of leisure on health concerns the predisposing effect on illness, of certain socio-demographic characteristics such as gender, age and socio-economic indicators. A differential exposure explanation (Dohrenwend & Dohrenwend, 1969; Wheaton, 1978) maintains that because of their day to day experiences, members of the lower class and females are more likely to be exposed to stressful situations which result in illness. A competing explanation for the observed variability in illness symptoms comes from the differential responsiveness perspective (Brown & Harris, 1978; Kessler, 1979) which contends that the context within which events occur influences the short-term and long-term responses to events. Support exists for differential exposure (Thoits & Hannan, 1979) and differential responsiveness (Kessler, 1979).

Differential responsiveness in the form of leisure-generated social support, sport and fitness may explain demographic-related differences in illness symptomatology. In support of this argument are research findings of gender-related differences in leisure (Deem, 1986; Shaw, 1985; Stamps & Stamps, 1985), socio-economic differences (Parker, 1976) and leisure variation across the life span (Iso-Ahola, Jackson, & Dunn, 1992). Accordingly, in examining the relation between leisure and health, the effect of sociodemographic variables should be held constant.

This study examined the main effect and buffering effect hypotheses of leisure's influence on illness symptoms. Three types of leisure were considered: outdoor active sport, social leisure and cultural-hobbies activity. The main effect hypothesis argues that leisure will have a beneficial effect on health irrespective of the extent of stressful life events. The buffering effect hypothesis argues that leisure exerts its beneficial effects on health only in the presence of stressful life events. Thus, if persons have been exposed to a large number of stressful life events, or events that are particularly stressful, but have many leisure experiences, then the buffering hypothesis would predict few symptoms. It was hypothesized that leisure may interact differently with life change and distress components of life events, in affecting health.

Method

Sample

The data for the study came from a survey of residents of the city of Cairns, Australia. The State Electoral Rolls for the districts of Cairns and the Barron River constituted the sampling frame for the selection of respondents. A survey response rate of 63.4% was obtained. Of the 340 respondents interviewed, 159 were males and 181 were females. Respondents were predominantly Australian born, and their ages ranged from 18 to 81 years. The majority were married (63%). Most did not have any tertiary education (52%) but some had tertiary qualifications (22%). Of the respondents, 45% were employed, 19% were unemployed, and 35% were housewives. A comparison of various sample demographics with population distributions for Cairns and Australia (based on the Census of *Population and Housing* for 1994) indicated that the data closely represented the local community and approximated national figures.

Interview Schedule

Life Events Measure

Stressful life events experienced were measured from Tennant and Andrews' (1976) *Life Events Inventory* which weights events for both life change and the amount of distress caused by the event. Tennant and Andrews' scale is an extension of work by Holmes and Rahe (1967) and Paykel *et al.* (1971). Events in the scale relate to health, bereavement, family and social, friends and relatives, education, work and moving house. Sets of events applicable only to males, females, the single, those who are, or were married, and those who have, or have had children, are incorporated in the scale. The events are worded so as to minimize the likelihood of confounding with stress reactions. The Life *Events Inventory* has good validity and is suitable for an Australian urban sample.

Respondents checked those events which they had experienced within the previous 12 months. Separate total life change and distress scores were computed for each respondent, by adding the weights corresponding to the life events checked. Respondents had experienced more life event change ($\overline{X} = 129.67$) than events which were distressful ($\overline{X} = 78.35$). This would seem to support the notion that life change and distress are different components of life events which warrant separate analyses (Dohrenwend & Dohrenwend, 1969; Paykel et al., 1971; Tennant & Andrews, 1976).

The Symptom Checklist

The list of illness symptoms was adopted from O'Brien (1978). The 70 illness symptoms were either physical (organic) or non-physical in nature. Respondents were asked to indicate any of the symptoms they had experienced during the previous 12 months. The symptoms checklist was scored by the total number of symptoms reported. Additionally, respondents were asked if they had a physical disability or illness condition which might influence participation in any leisure activity. No respondent reported any limiting health condition.

The Leisure Variable

Respondents were given the *Less Stress Inventory* (Caltabiano, 1988, 1994), designed by the author to assess the perceived stress-reducing quality of leisure. Additionally, they were asked to indicate those leisure activities which they had engaged in on a frequent basis during the last year. Selected activities within each factor (Outdoor-active sport, Social, Cultural-hobbies) were weighted for perceived stress-reducing benefits, to derive stress-reducing participation scores. This weighted leisure participation index allowed perceptions of the stress-reducing benefits of individual activities to be taken into account, in addition to actual participation. Separate scores were derived for outdoor-active sport, social leisure and cultural-hobbies activities. Higher leisure scores indicate a greater number of stress-reducing participation units for a particular group of activities.

Analysis and Discussion

Main and stress-moderating benefits of outdoor-active sport, social leisure and cultural-hobbies activities were examined using product-term regression analysis (Cohen & Cohen, 1975). Only significant outcomes are reported here. The order of entry of variables into each regression analysis was life event component, then leisure and lastly the interaction term (stress x leisure), controlling for sociodemographic variables. Separate regression analyses were conducted for each combination of leisure (outdoor-active sport, social and cultural-hobbies activities), and stressful life event components (life change, distress).

Where significant interactive effects occurred for leisure and components of stressful life events (life change, distress), these were plotted at the mean of sociodemographic variables such as education, age and income of respondents. Gender being a nominal variable, the interactions were presented separately for males and females.

The interaction effect in product-term regression where the moderator variable is interval or ratio would give a family of regression lines (Cohen & Cohen, 1975). In order to allow for a diagramatic representation of the interactive effects, the leisure variables were treated as categorical. The effect of life change/distress on illness symptoms could thus be observed at different levels of the leisure moderator variable. Stress-reducing participation scores for outdoor-active sport, social, and cultural-hobbies leisure were dichotomized using a median split into absent/present and low versus high participation. Except where indicated, all analyses discussed here are for stress-reducing leisure participation being absent versus present. Unstandardized regression coefficients are reported, as these are the more useful indicators of relative importance of variables in product-term regression (Cohen & Cohen, 1975). The significance of these coefficients is given by the F test.

A significant main effect on illness symptoms was observed for the presence of stress-reducing outdoor-sport participation, when life change (B = -.891, $F = 4.57$, $df = 2,196$, $p < .01$) was in the regression, and for the analysis with distress (B = -1.496, $F = 8.18$, $df = 2,196$, $p < .001$). No significant interactive effect was found for sport and either life change or distress. Fewer physical and psychological illness symptoms were reported by respondents who engaged in stress-reducing outdoor-active sports, irrespective of the level of stressful life circumstances. This finding is consistent with studies which have reported physiological benefits of engaging in sport (Gatton & Tice, 1989 ; Roberts *et al.*, 1989), and is in keeping with views that recreation of a physical nature promotes good health (Haun, 1973) and has psychological benefits (Iso-Ahola, 1980). Physical activity has health benefits in general, by increasing cardiorespiratory fitness.

Participation in stress-reducing social leisure did not have a main effect on symptoms. Merely engaging in these activities in the absence of stressful life events was not associated with health. Rather, overall health appeared to depend on a combination of factors working together. Although there was no interaction when life event change was used, a significant interaction was observed for life event distress and stress-reducing social leisure ($F = 4.18$, $df = 1,197$, $p < .05$). The relationship between life event distress and symptoms was found to differ for those with, versus without social leisure. The presence of social leisure buffered the respondent from the deleterious effects of distressful events ($B = -.022$). From Figure 1, it can be seen that those respondents with stress-reducing social leisure showed only a slight increase in illness symptoms as life event distress increased. Those for whom stress-reducing social leisure was absent, in contrast, showed a considerable increase in illness with increased distress.

FIGURE 1

The interactive effect of life event distress and social leisure (absence/presence) on symptoms, plotted for males and females at the mean of other sociodemographic variables

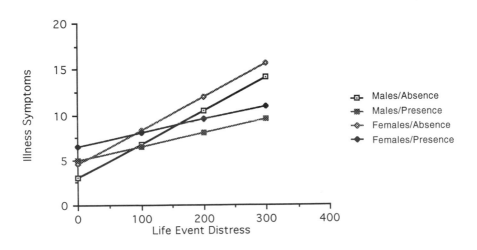

That social leisure did not interact with life change in a similar manner points up a basic difference between these two dimensions of stressful life events. When individuals undergo high levels of change, social leisure does not have an ameliorative effect, possibly because it only serves to create more activity and adjustment. However, when events of a distressful nature have occurred for the individual, the mere presence of social leisure had a dampening effect. Social leisure most likely facilitates well-being in the presence of distress because such activities involve other persons with whom problems can be discussed (Coleman & Iso-Ahola, 1993). It is the social element of such activities which is of importance. Persons under distress are able to self-disclose and receive emotional support.

In order to further explore this buffering relationship between social leisure and distressful life experiences on illness symptoms, respondents were categorized as being high or low in stress-reducing social participation. It was hypothesized that those with higher levels of such social activity would be at more of an advantage in lessening susceptibility to illness from distressful experiences. A significant interactive effect was recorded for level of social activity and distressful life events in predicting symptoms ($F = 5.63$, df $= 1,117$, $p < .05$), though not in the direction anticipated. Figure 2 indicates that for both male and female respondents with high levels of social leisure, illness symptoms increased with an increase in life event distress. Engaging in many social activities was thus found to exacerbate the effects of distress ($B = .029$). This finding does not agree with the buffering hypothesis.

FIGURE 2

The effect of life event distress on illness symptoms at low and high levels of social leisure, plotted for males and females at the mean of all other sociodemographic variables

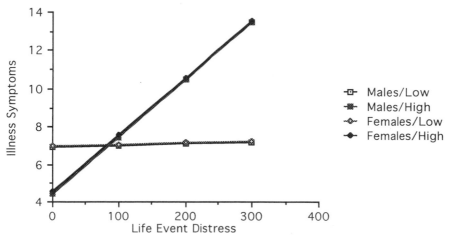

Coleman and Iso-Ahola (1993) have argued that leisure-based social support has dialectical functions, in that the presence of others is sought in times of stress. These leisure theorists also acknowledged that high levels of social support may be associated with reduced benefits from a perceived lack of control and personal competence. Social support can have an adverse effect if it offers contradictory alternatives, conveys to the recipient that they are incapable of making their own decision, or if the recipient feels compelled to act on advice (Taylor, 1991). A study by Meyerowitz (1983) reported a curvilinear relationship between social support and depression.

The presence of cultural-hobbies leisure was found to exhibit a significant interactive effect with life event change, though not in the predicted direction (B = .002, F = 5.76, df = 1,197, p < .05). Figure 3 shows the interactive effect of cultural-hobbies leisure and life event change plotted for males and females at the mean of all other socio-demographic variables. From Figure 3, it can be observed that for both male and female respondents who engaged in cultural-hobbies activities perceived as stress-reducing, more illness symptoms were reported as life change increased. When cultural-hobbies leisure was present, the relationship between life event change and illness symptoms was stronger than when absent. This counters the buffering effect hypothesis.

FIGURE 3

The interactive effect of life change and cultural-hobbies leisure (absence/presence) on illness symptoms, plotted for males and females at the mean of other sociodemographic variables

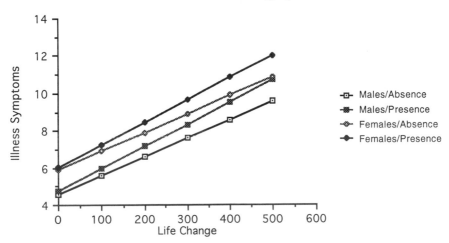

Passive activities typical of the cultural-hobbies factor were expected to lessen the impact of life change by being sedentary or untaxing in nature. Under such circumstances leisure could be thought to act as an emotion-focused coping behaviour (Lazarus & Folkman, 1984). Behaviour aimed at coping with stress through escape or fantasy is less effective in combating stress when some action is required by the individual to change a stressful situation (Folkman, 1979). Events high in life change or readjustment require an action-oriented coping approach rather than emotion regulation. This would explain the stress-exacerbating effect of cultural-hobbies leisure on life change.

Moderating effects of cultural-hobbies leisure (absence/presence) were, however, found for life event distress (F = 6.75, df = 1,197, p < .01). Those respondents with cultural-hobbies leisure perceived as having stress-reducing benefits reported having experienced less symptoms. Stress-reducing cultural-hobbies leisure protected these individuals from the adverse affects of distress (B = -.008). Figure 4, which presents a graphic representation of this interaction, demonstrates that when stress-reducing cultural-hobbies activities were absent, for both males and females, the relationship between illness symptoms and life event distress was stronger. When stress-reducing cultural-hobbies leisure was present, the relationship between life event distress and symptoms was reduced. In cultural-hobbies leisure, the individual is either transported to a fantasy world of the cinema, opera or dance, or is engaged in some hobby which is intrinsically satisfying. The flow experience (Csikszentmihalyi, 1975) is most likely associated with the latter type of activity. Cultural-hobbies activities may also serve to distract the individual from the source of distress. Evidence exists for distraction to be an effective mode of coping with stress (Kleinke, 1991). Cultural-hobbies activities provide the individual with a means of escape which reduces the emotional impact of distressing life events. Involvement in cultural-hobbies leisure appears to be an effective emotion-focused coping behaviour. This finding is in keeping with Pearlin and Schooler (1978) and Schill, Adams and Bekker (1982) who reported that emotion-focused coping lessened the impact of distressful life events.

Engagement in cultural-hobbies activities exerts different effects on health via life change and distress components of life events. This finding reinforces the distinction made in the stress literature (Dohrenwend & Dohrenwend, 1969; Paykel et al., 1971; Tennant & Andrews, 1976) between these two components which make life events stressful.

FIGURE 4

The interactive effect of life event distress and cultural-hobbies leisure (absence/presence) on illness symptoms, plotted for males and females at the mean of other sociodemographic variables

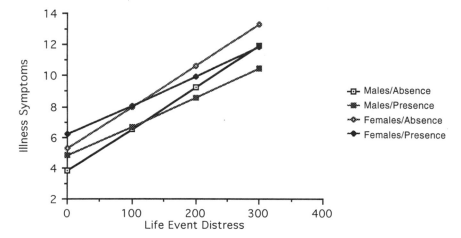

Conclusion

In summary, one could conclude that the stress-reducing capacity of the presence of outdoor-sport participation appears beneficial for health, irrespective of the extent of stressful life events. Buffering effects are more apparent when the distress associated with life events is considered. The impact of distressful life events on health is moderated by the presence of stress reducing involvement in both cultural-hobbies leisure and social leisure. High levels of social activity, though, do not provide a more protective buffer against life stress. When the life change component of stressful life circumstances is considered, different interactions are apparent. The negative influence of life change on health is increased in the presence of cultural-hobbies activity.

The finding that the mere presence of stress-reducing involvement in outdoor-active sport has a beneficial direct effect on health, independent of life stress, can be understood if the physiological consequences of sport, exercise and fitness are considered. Physical activity results in a lowered pulse rate, the body's ability to utilize oxygen is enhanced through improved functioning of the lungs and circulatory system, serum cholesterol level is decreased, body muscles, including the heart muscle are strengthened, blood pressure stabilises to normal, and calories are burned up to control weight. These physiological outcomes of physical fitness have benefits for reduced risk of heart disease, hypertension, diabetes, and mortality in general (Kleinke, 1991). The release of endorphins and the production of norepinephrine in exercise, cited as possible physiological mechanisms in mood enhancement (Thorlindsson *et al.*, 1990), additionally, may provide direct benefits for psychological health.

From the findings, it appears that certain kinds of leisure activities provide effective buffers against stress when there is a close match between the demands made by stressful events and opportunity to meet these demands. Leisure which involves acquisition of new skills, competition, or an adaptive response by the person only serves to exacerbate the stress of life change. The distress of events is moderated by leisure which allows for provision of support, information or distraction from the stressor. It is advocated that future studies look at the moderating effects of variables on different stressor categories in order to make them relevant to certain types of life events.

The main and stress-moderating effects of leisure found here have applications in the areas of stress-management, leisure counselling and the design of individualized leisure packages. It is advocated that counsellors ask clients to rate the leisure activities for personal usefulness in reducing stress. A stress-reduction leisure package may then be devised according to the needs of the individual.

Some of the stress-exacerbating effects observed in the product-term regressions highlight some interesting points about leisure. Leisure activities themselves may involve an element of stress. Ulrich et al. (1991) alluded to this in relation to immediate deleterious influences of challenging outdoor recreation on the cardiovascular system and catecholamine levels. Social leisure also can be stressful in that it involves change, whether this be establishing new relationships or accommodating to new social settings, a finding borne out by the absence of an interactive effect between life change and social leisure. Future research could explore social elements of different leisure activities which induce stress and how this relates to overall health.

Much headway has been made in the area of health benefits of leisure. The majority of these studies have focussed on the effects of physical fitness and exercise on cardiovascular parameters and psychological health indicators of diminished anxiety and depression. Laboratory research on physiological impacts of exposure to slides of natural settings has benefit implications for outdoor recreation. As Ulrich et al. (1991) argue, more research is needed of a quasi-experimental nature in the field setting to overcome problems of ecological validity. The major consideration in a physiological assessment of short-term stress-reduction benefits (lower blood pressure, positive mood) of exposure to nature in active outdoor recreation relates to confounding effects of physical exertion on these measures. According to Ulrich et *al.* (1991), the challenge is to "hold physical exertion constant while relating possible variations in physiological indicators to systematic changes in other components of the leisure experience" (Ulrich *et al.*, 1991, p. 86).

It is timely for leisure research to utilize prospective research designs in assessing stress-moderating and health benefits. Such research would point to the long-term consequences of leisure activity in lessening predisposition to certain illness categories. Another direction that this research could take is to study the interactive effect of leisure, with known risk factors for illness (e.g., diet, genetics, smoking).

The importance of leisure for immunological status is an area that is increasingly emphasized by researchers (Iso-Ahola, 1994; Ulrich et al., 1991). Immunological competence has been found to correlate with positive mood (Stone, Cox, Valdimarsdottir, Jandorf, & Neale, 1987). Both leisure and intrinsically motivated activity have been reported to induce positive mood. Intrinsic motivation is also one of the major components of the leisure experience (Iso-Ahola, 1980; Neulinger, 1982).

The present research has provided some insights into the role of leisure in the stress process and health outcome. It demonstrates that leisure's contribution, for the most part, is not direct, but depends on the level of stress in people's lives. Furthermore, the moderation of the impact of stress on health by leisure is complex, depending on the nature and level of leisure participation. It is hoped that subsequent studies pursue this area of inquiry in order to further elucidate the nature of interrelationships between stress, leisure and health.

References

BOLGER, N. & ECKENRODE, J. (1991). Social relationships, personality and anxiety during a major stressful event. *Journal of Personality and Social Psychology, 61*, 440-449.

BOOTH-KEWLEY, S. & FRIEDMAN, H.S. (1987). Psychological predictors of heart disease: A quantitative review. *Psychological Bulletin, 101*(3), 343-362.

BROWN, G.W. & HARRIS, T. (1978). *Social origins of depression: A study of psychiatric disorder in women.* New York: Wiley.

CALTABIANO, M.L. (1988). *The effect of predisposing variables and leisure on the relationship between stressful life events and illness symptomatology.* Unpublished doctoral dissertation, James Cook University, Townsville.

CALTABIANO, M.L. (1994). Measuring the similarity among leisure activities based on a perceived stress-reduction benefit. *Leisure Studies, 13*, 17-31.

COHEN, J. & COHEN, P. (1975). *Applied multiple regression/correlation analysis for the Behavioral Sciences.* Hillsdale, New Jersey: Lawrence Erlbaum.

COHEN, S. & WILLS, T.A. (1985). Stress, social support, and the buffering hypothesis. *Psychological Bulletin, 98*(2), 310-357.

COLEMAN, D. & ISO-AHOLA, S.E. (1993). Leisure and health: The role of social support and self-determination. *Journal of Leisure Research, 25*(2), 111-128.

CSIKSZENTMIHALYI, M. (1975). *Beyond boredom and anxiety.* San Francisco: Jossey-Bass.

DEEM, R. (1986). *All work and no play: The sociology of women and leisure.* Milton Keynes: Open University Press.

DOHRENWEND, B.P. & DOHRENWEND, B.S. (1969). *Social status and psychological disorders.* New York: Wiley.

DRIVER, B.L. , BROWN, P.J., & PETERSON, G.L. (Eds.), (1991). *Benefits of leisure.* Pennsylvania: Venture.

DRIVER, B.L. & TOCHER, S.R. (1975). Toward a behavioral interpretation of recreational engagements, with implications for planning. *In* B.L. Driver (Ed.), *Elements of outdoor recreation planning,* (pp. 9-28). Ann Arbor, Michigan: University of Michigan Press.

DUMAZEDIER, J. (1967). *Toward a society of leisure.* New York :Free Press.

FOLKMAN, S.K. (1979). *An analysis of coping in normal adults: A naturalistic investigation.* Unpublished Doctoral Dissertation, University of California, Berkeley.

FROELICHER, V.F. & FROELICHER, E.S. (1991). Cardiovascular benefits of physical activity. *In* B.L. Driver, P.J. Brown, & G.L. Peterson (Eds.), *Benefits of leisure,* (pp. 59-72). Pennsylvania: Venture.

GATTON, C. & TICE, A. (1989). Sports participation and health. *Leisure Studies, 8,* 77-92.

HARTIG, T., MANG, M., & EVANS, G.W. (1990). Perspectives on wilderness: Testing the theory of restorative environments. *In* A.T. Easley, J. Passineau, & B.L. Driver (Eds.), *The use of widerness for personal growth, therapy and education.* USDA Forest Service, Fort Collins, CO: Rocky Mountain Forest and Range Experiment Station.

HAUN, P. (1973). *Recreation: A medical viewpoint.* New York: Teachers College Press, Columbia University.

HEYWOOD, L.A. (1978). Perceived recreative experience and the relief of tension. *Journal of Leisure Research, 10*(2), 86-97.

HOLMES, T.H. & RAHE, R.H. (1967). The social readjustment rating scale. *Journal of Psychosomatic Research , 11,* 213 218.

HULL, R B. (1991). Mood as a product of leisure: Causes and consequences. *In* B.L. Driver, P.J. Brown, & G.L. Peterson (Eds.), *Benefits of leisure,* (pp. 249-261). Pennsylvania: Venture.

ISO-AHOLA, S.E. (1980). *The social psychology of leisure and recreation.* Dubuque: William C. Brown.

ISO-AHOLA, S.E. (1989). Motivation for leisure. *In* E.L. Jackson & T.L. Burton (Eds.), *Understanding leisure and recreation : Maping the past, charting the future.* Pennsylvania: Venture.

ISO-AHOLA, S.E. (1994). Leisure lifestyle and health. *In* D.M. Compton & S.E. Iso-Ahola (Eds.), *Leisure and mental health,* vol. 1. Park City, Utah: Family Development Resources.

ISO-AHOLA, S.E., JACKSON, E.L., & DUNN, E. (1992). *Starting, replacing and ceasing leisure activity participation across the human lifespan.* Paper presented at the NRPA Symposium on Leisure Research, Cincinnati, Ohio, October 16, 1992.

ISO-AHOLA, S.E. & WEISSINGER, E. (1984, June). Leisure and well-being: Is there a connection. *Parks and Recreation*, 40-44.

KESSLER, R.C. (1979). Stress, social status, and psychological distress. *Journal of Health and Social Behavior, 20*, 259-272.

KLEINKE, C.L. (1991). *Coping with life challenges*. Pacific Grove: Brooks/Cole.

KOBASA, S.C., MADDI, S.R., & KAHN, S. (1982). Hardiness and health: A prospective study. *Journal of Personality and Social Psychology, 42*(1), 168-177.

LAZARUS, R.S. & FOLKMAN, S. (1984). *Stress, appraisal and coping*. New York: Springer.

LONG, B.C. (1985). Stress-management interventions: A 15 month follow-up of aerobic conditioning and stress inoculation training. *Cognitive Therapy and Research, 9*, 471-478.

MADDI, S.R. & KOBASA, S.C. (1981). Intrinsic motivation and health. *In* H.I. Day (Ed.), *Advances in Intrinsic Motivation and Aesthetics*, (pp. 299-321). New York: Plenum Press.

MEYEROWITZ, B.E. (1983). Postmastectomy coping strategies and the quality of life. *Health Psychology, 2*, 117-132.

NEULINGER, J. (1982). Leisure lack and the quality of life: The broadening scope of the leisure professional. *Leisure Studies ,1*, 53-63.

O'BRIEN, G.E. (1978). *Adjustment of the unemployed* (Working Paper No 29). Bedford Park: Flinders University of South Australia, National Institute of Labour Studies.

PAFFENBARGER, R.S., HYDE, R.T., & DOW, A. (1991). Health benefits of physical activity. *In* B.L. Driver, P.J. Brown, & G.L. Peterson (Eds.), *Benefits of leisure*, (pp. 49-57). Pennsylvania: Venture.

PARKER, S. (1976). *The sociology of leisure*. London: George Allen and Unwin.

PAYKEL, E.S., PRUSOFF, B.A., & UHLENHUTH, E.H. (1971). Scaling of life events. *Archives of General Psychiatry, 25*, 340-347.

PEARLIN, L.I. & SCHOOLER, C. (1978). The structure of coping. *Journal of Health and Social Behavior, 19*, 2-21.

PIEPER, J. (1963). *Leisure, the basis of culture*. New York: The New American Library.

RAGLIN, J.S. & MORGAN, W.P. (1987). Influence of exercise and quiet rest on state anxiety and blood pressure. *Medicine and Science in Sports and Exercise, 19*, 456-463.

ROBERTS, K., LAMB, K.L., DENCH, S., & BRODIE, D.A. (1989). Leisure patterns, health status and employment status. *Leisure Studies, 8*, 229-235.

ROOK, K.S. (1987). Social support versus companionship: Effects on life stress, loneliness and evaluations by others. *Journal of Personality and Social Psychology, 52*, 1132-1147.

SARASON, I.G., SARASON, B.R., & JOHNSON, J.H. (1985). Stressful life events: Measurement, moderators and adaptation. *In* S.R. Burchfield (Ed.), *Stress: Psychological and physiological interactions*, (pp. 241-261). Washington, DC: Hemisphere.

SCHILL, T., ADAMS, A.E., & BEKKER, D. (1982). Repression-sensitization and coping with stressful life events. *Psychological Reports, 50*, 602.

SHAW, S.M. (1985). Gender and leisure : Inequality in the distribution of leisure time. *Journal of Leisure Research, 17*(4), 266-282.

STAMPS, S.M. & STAMPS, M.B. (1985). Race, class and leisure activities of urban residents. *Journal of Leisure Research, 17*(1), 40-56.

STEINKAMP, M.W. & KELLY, J.R. (1987). Social integration, leisure activity and life satisfaction in older adults : activity theory revisited. *International Journal of Aging and Human Development, 25*(4), 293-307.

STONE, A.A , COX, D.S. , VALDIMARSDOTTIR, H., JANDORF, L., & NEALE, J.M. (1987). Evidence that secretory IgA antibody is associated with daily mood. *Journal of Personality and Social Psychology, 52*, 988-993.

TAYLOR, S. (1991). *Health psychology.* New York : McGraw-Hill.

TENNANT, C. & ANDREWS, G. (1976). A scale to measure the stress of life events. *Australian and New Zealand Journal of Psychiatry, 10*(1),27-32.

THORLINDSSON, T., VILHJALMSSON, R., & VALGEIRSSON, G. (1990). Sport participation and perceived health status : A study of adolescents. *Social Science and Medicine, 31*, 551-556.

THOITS, P. & HANNAN, P. (1979). Income and psychological distress : The impact of an income- maintenance experiment. *Journal of Health and Social Behavior, 20*, 120-138.

TINSLEY, H.E.A. & TINSLEY, D.J. (1986). A theory of the attributes, benefits and causes of leisure experience. *Leisure Sciences, 8*(1), 1-45.

ULRICH, R.S. (1981). Natural versus urban scenes : Some psychophysiological effects. *Environment and Behavior, 13*, 523-556.

ULRICH, R.S. (1984). View through a window may influence recovery from surgery. *Science, 224*, 420-421.

ULRICH, R.S. & SIMONS, R.F. (1986). Recovery from stress during exposure to everyday outdoor environments. *In* J. Wineman, R. Barnes, & C. Zimring (Eds.), *Proceedings of the seventeenth annual conference of the environmental design research association,* (pp. 115-122), April, 1986, Atlanta. Washington, DC : EDRA.

ULRICH, R.S., DIMBERG, U., & DRIVER, B.L. (1991). Psychophysiological indicators of leisure benefits. *In* B.L. Driver, P.J. Brown, & G.L. Peterson (Eds.), *Benefits of leisure,* (pp. 73-89). Pennsylvania : Venture.

WANKEL, L.M. & BERGER, B.G. (1991). The personal and social benefits of sport and physical activity. *In* B.L. Driver, P.J. Brown, & G.L. Peterson (Eds.), *Benefits of leisure ,* (pp. 121-144). Pennsylvania : Venture.

WEISSINGER, E. & ISO-AHOLA, S.E. (1984). Intrinsic leisure motivation, personality and physical health. *Society and Leisure, 7*(1), 217-228.

WHEATON, B. (1978). The sociogenesis of psychological disorder : Reexamining the causal issues with longitudinal data. *American Sociological Review, 43*, 383-403.

Marie Louise CALTABIANO
*Effets principaux et effets de protection contre le stress
associés au loisir par rapport à la santé*

RÉSUMÉ

L'analyse porte, d'une part, sur les effets principaux, et, d'autre part, sur les effets de protection contre le stress, de trois types de loisir sur les symptômes de maladies physiques et psychologiques. Ces types de loisirs sont : les sports de plein air actifs, les activités sociales et les activités culturelles et de passe-temps. Les données proviennent d'une enquête effectuée auprès de 340 habitants de la ville de Cairns (159 hommes et 181 femmes). Les activités ont été préclassées en fonction de la perception de leurs effets sur la réduction du stress. Il ressort de cette étude qu'en l'absence d'événements stressants, la participation aux sports de plein air comporte des effets bénéfiques pour la santé par la réduction du stress qu'elle procure. Les changements qui surviennent dans la vie et la détresse provoquée par les divers événements interagissaient différemment avec les facteurs de loisir en ce qui a trait à la santé. Les activités de loisir social semblent diminuer la relation entre la détresse engendrée par les événements de la vie et les symptômes de détresse. Ces effets de protection contre le stress des activités de loisir social ne sont cependant pas apparus lorsque les niveaux d'activité sociale étaient élevés. Dans de tels cas, les effets de la détresse sur les symptômes étaient amplifiés. Par ailleurs, les activités culturelles et de passe-temps diminuaient les effets de la détresse, mais amplifiaient les effets des changements de la vie. Les résultats de cette recherche pourront servir dans les domaines de la gestion du stress, du counseling en loisir et de la conception de programmes de loisir adaptés aux personnes.

Marie Louise CALTABIANO
Main and Stress-Moderating Health Benefits of Leisure

ABSTRACT

Main and stress-moderating effects of three types of leisure (Outdoor-Active Sport, Social, Cultural-Hobbies activities) on physical and psychological illness symptoms were examined. A survey of 340 Cairns residents (159 males and 181 females) provided data for the study. Leisure activities were prescaled for perceived stress-reducing benefits. The stress-reducing capacity of outdoor sport participation was beneficial for health in the absence of stressful life events. Life change and distress components of life events interacted differently with leisure factors in affecting health. The presence of social leisure was found to moderate the relationship between life event distress and symptoms. These stress-buffering effects of social leisure were not found to hold at high levels of social activity. Rather, high levels of social leisure exacerbated the effects of distress on symptoms. The presence of stress-reducing cultural-hobbies leisure moderated the effects of distress, but exacerbated the effects of life change. The research findings have implications for stress-management, leisure counselling and the design of individualized leisure packages.

Marie Louise CALTABIANO
Efectos principales y efectos de protección contra la tensión asociada a las diversiones con relación a la salud

RESUMEN

El análisis trata, por una parte, sobre los efectos principales, y por otra, sobre los efectos de protección contra la tensión ; de tres tipos de diversiones sobre los síntomas de enfermedades físicas y psicológicas. Estos tipos de diversiones son : los deportes activos al aire libre, las actividades sociales y las actividades culturales y pasatiempos. Los datos provienen de una encuesta realizada sobre 340 habitantes de la ciudad de Cairns (159 hombres y 181 mujeres). Las actividades fueron preclasificadas en función de la percepción de sus efectos sobre la reducción de la tensión. Este estudio destaca que en la ausencia de sucesos que causen tensión, la participación en los deportes al aire libre causa efectos benéficos para la salud debido a la reducción de la tensión que ésta provoca. Los cambios que sobrevienen en la vida y la angustia provocada por los diversos sucesos interactuanban diferentemente con los factores de diversiones en lo que respecta a la salud. Las actividades de diversión social, parecen disminuir la relación entre la angustia engendrada por los sucesos de la vida y los síntomas de angustia. Estos efectos de protección contra la tensión de las actividades de diversión social no aparecieron sin embargo, cuando los niveles de actividad social eran elevados. En tales casos, los efectos de la angustia sobre los síntomas se amplificaban. Por otra parte, las actividades culturales y los pasatiempos disminuían los efectos de la angustia, pero amplificaban los efectos de los cambios de la vida. Los resultados de esta investigación podrán servir en los dominios de la gestión de la tensión, del consejo de diversiones y a la concepción de programas de recreación adaptados a las personas.

LEISURE AND CATEGORIAL MODELS
OF MENTAL HEALTH

John HAWORTH

Psychology Department
University of Manchester
Manchester, England

Introduction

The study of the contribution of leisure to health is a complex undertaking. Leisure is generally viewed as the principal life domain for positive experiences, such as enjoyment, interest, relaxation and freedom of choice or intrinsic motivation. Studies using the experience sampling method, where individuals answer questions in diaries in response to programmed signals from radio pagers or watches, have shown the importance of leisure for these positive states, while also showing the importance of work, (Csikszentmihalyi & Csikszentmihalyi 1988; Haworth & Hill, 1992; Haworth, 1993). Although leisure is viewed as providing many benefits, including the now well documented importance of exercise for physical health, attempts to fully document the psychological and social benefits remain contentious, with many claims still being speculative (Mannell & Stynes, 1991). In reviewing an important collection of papers in this area, commissioned by Driver, Brown and Peterson (1991), Mannell and Stynes highlight the importance of undertaking research into the processes or mechanisms linking leisure to benefits. They cite Hull (1991) who argues that while temporary and transient mood states are benefits of leisure, they are not the primary outcome but rather intervening variables between leisure and cognition and a variety of social behaviours such as learning, helping behaviour, self-concept and health. They also cite Driver, Tinsley and Manfredo (1991) who note that leisure benefits are causally chained and that need gratification through leisure experience can best be seen as an intervening variable with the consequences being such benefits as life satisfaction and physical health.

This recognition of the potentially important indirect benefits as well as the direct benefits of leisure requires that the world of leisure is not considered exclusively from other life domains, including the world of work. Driver et al. give a hypothetical example of a worker on a boring job realising from leisure the gratification of the need to experience something new which can lead to better mental health, which in turn may enhance job performance, salary and perceptions of economic stability, which is an important contributor to the end state benefit of life satisfaction. Kabonof and O'Brien (1980) and Kabonof (1982) in their studies of work-leisure relationships in workers in different occupations found evidence for both 'spillover' of work attributes into leisure and 'compensation' by leisure for 'needs' not satisfied in work.

Research into the effects of leisure on well-being and health also has to take into account the multifaceted nature of 'wellness'. Brief, Butcher, George and Link (1993) in their studies of subjective well-being state that no longer can it be assumed that if a factor influences one aspect of subjective well-being it will also influence other aspects. They claim that different facets of subjective well-being, such as positive affect and life satisfaction, can be affected differentially by different personality factors, situational circumstances, and their interaction. Research into the processes or mechanisms linking leisure to benefits, such as health, called for by Mannell and Stynes (1991), will thus require a detailed consideration of the influence on health, measured on a range of dimensions, of both situational factors, and person factors, as well as their interaction. This is the goal and line of the research being pursued at Manchester, which is summarised in this paper. The situational factors studied are the 'categories of experience' proposed as important for mental health and well-being by Warr (1987) and Jahoda (1982). The person factor studied is 'locus of control' (Rotter 1966, 1982, 1990) shown in many studies to be associated with aspects of well-being.

Environmental Categorical Models Of Mental Health

In his categorical, situation-centred model of mental health, Warr (1987) proposes nine principal environmental influences (PEIs), or environmental categories of experience, as having a significant non-linear influence on mental health reconceptualised into 5 components. These PEIs are: opportunity for control, opportunity for skill use, externally generated goals, variety, environmental clarity, availability of money, physical security, opportunity for interpersonal contact, and valued social position. Warr suggests that, like vitamins, these features have non-linear effects, some improving mental health up to a certain point and then having no further effects, others producing benefits up to a certain level but beyond which increases would be detrimental. These features are proposed as determinants of mental health in all kinds of environments, including work and leisure. They are considered to be properties that an environment has relative to the capabilities and requirements of human beings (Warr 1987, p. 281). Warr also recognises that individuals can influence environments, and that different individuals can have different enduring characteristics which may moderate the relationship between the principal environmental influences and mental health. The model is thus concerned with processes and person-situation interactions, as well as categorical features.

Warr's model incorporates the environmental categorical model proposed by Jahoda (1982) which indicates that the five categories of experience of time structure, activity, social contact, collective purpose, and social identity or status, are imposed by work and are important for well-being. This model 'emphasises the habitual use people make of social institutions in meeting some psychological need' (Jahoda 1992, p. 356). Leisure activities from television to sports to self-improvement are considered to be fine in themselves as a complement to employment, but are not considered to be functional alternatives since leisure lacks the compelling manifest function of earning a living. Where deprivation of these categories occurs in unemployment it is considered to give rise to negative psychological symptoms.

Warr indicates that the division of the environment into nine principal categories which facilitate or constrain personal processes and activities important for mental health, appears to be appropriately precise for most purposes, but that it is a matter of judgement, partly relating to applications, whether fewer or more categories would be preferable. He considers that 'the evidence proposed for the nine factors is as convincing as that for other models' (p. 283). The strength of his categorical model, he considers, is that it applies to any kind of environment and that it has considerable heuristic value, lending itself to application and development. Warr also notes that the term mental health is difficult to specify and that no universally accepted definition is available. He proposes five principal components of mental health which he considers would be accepted as important by most western theorists. These are affective well-being, competence, autonomy, aspiration and integrated functioning. Integrated functioning is concerned with the multiple relationships between the other four components and, as yet, does not have questionnaire measures. The most comprehensive measures are for affective well-being which can be measured on three principal axes: the 'pleasure axis' (measuring displeasure to pleasure in context free situations), the 'anxiety-contentment' axis, and the 'depressed enthusiasm' axis, which have been used in the context specific situations of work and leisure (Warr 1989,1990,1993).

Research at Manchester

A study by Evans (1986) used a questionnaire to measure access to the categories of experience (ACE) described by Jahoda, in samples of employed and unemployed young people. The study (also reported in Evans & Haworth, 1991) showed that the categories of experience can be obtained by the unemployed and that those with better access had better psychological well-being. However, ACE and psychological well-being was limited when compared to that obtained by the people in the structured situation of employment. This could be because employment provides more money which enable individuals to gain ACE outside of employment. Financial resources are obviously important. Nevertheless, just over half the unemployed sample had a main activity, either work based, leisure based or general social interaction, which gave them a chance to use their abilities and be creative. These individuals had levels of self-esteem similar to the employed sample. However, they had worse affective well-being, life satisfaction and happiness, and less access to the categories of experience of status, social contact and time structure than the employed group. The main activities of the unemployed did not seem to be embedded in informal institutional support systems, and it is an open question as to whether or not this group of people would have had access to all the categories of experience and better psychological well-being if their main activity had been located in a valued social structure. Perhaps if they had been engaged in serious leisure (Stebbins, 1982) in a leisure social world (Buchanan, 1985) which was given high status by the community, this would have enhanced psychological well-being and supported the effort necessary to sustain commitment to pursuits.

Another study (Haworth & Ducker 1991) on unemployed young people used questionnaires and the experience sampling method (ESM). Respondents answered a series of questions in a diary eight times a day for one week in response to signals from an electronic pager. Results showed that a sub-group with higher ACE scores engaged in more work like and active leisure activities than a sub-group with lower ACE scores who engaged in more passive leisure; and that the higher ACE group had statistically significant better scores on measures of self esteem, life satisfaction and enjoyment. The results also showed that hope for the future (questionnaire measure) and enjoyment (ESM measure) were significantly correlated with scores on the ACE scales.

The result from this study are interesting in that they suggest that respondents with better access to the five categories of experience participate in more positive and engaging activities, or in the terminology of White (1959) more 'competence' serving activities, than the low ACE group. It could thus be expected that the high ACE group would have better self-esteem and general levels of psychological well-being, as was borne out by the results. The findings showing that both enjoyment and hope for the future are significantly associated with Jahoda's categories of experience indicate, perhaps, in line with Fryer and McKenna (1989), that personal agency is an important route into gaining access to these categories of experience. At the same time it may be that the relationship of enjoyment with access to categories of experience represents a dynamic intertwining between the person and the situation. For some situations engagement in activities and other categories of experience could provide enjoyment, whilst at the same time enjoyment could provide the stimulus to continue with engagement in pursuits. Csikszentmihalyi (1982) and Csikszentmihalyi and Csikszentmihalyi (1988) emphasize the pivotal role of enjoyment in psychological well-being. The results from this study of unemployed people may indicate one route by which this pivotal role is achieved.

Access to categories of experience and enjoyment were also investigated as part of a study of work and leisure in a sample of young employed adults by Haworth and Hill (1992). This study used questionnaires, and the experience sampling method over a one week period. ACE was measured separately for work and leisure, and showed interesting results. While there were some correlations between ACE at work and psychological well-being, there was a range of correlations with ACE in leisure. Social contact, collective purpose, status, and a composite measure of the five categories of experience termed 'total access', all correlated significantly with a measure of life satisfaction. Social contact and collective purpose also correlated significantly with happiness in daily life measured by ESM. Status, time structure, and total access all correlated significantly with a measure of self-esteem. Variations in access to categories of experience in the leisure time of employed people thus appear to be important in relation to well-being, contrary to Jahoda's predictions. It may well be that for some people there is not a strict division between the important categories of experience obtained in work and those obtained in leisure.

However, it may be that the mechanisms vary for obtaining ACE in work and leisure. When the seven individuals with the highest and lowest total ACE scores in both work and leisure were compared, the individuals with high ACE in leisure had significantly higher mean enjoyment scores than the individuals with low ACE in leisure, though this was not the case in work. Perhaps ACE at work can be provided to some extent irrespective of enjoyment, as Jahoda (1986) appears to indicate. Whereas, perhaps ACE in leisure requires more individual effort, reflected in higher enjoyment scores in leisure.

Another study of the importance of ACE in work and leisure for mental health was undertaken on a sample of managers by Haworth and Paterson (1995). The results from multiple regression analysis showed that 'collective purpose' and 'status' in both work and leisure had moderate to large B coefficients, indicative of their potential influence, for a considerable range of measures of mental health covering freedom from negative mental health and the presence of positive mental health. 'Activity' and 'Social Contact' in leisure were also important for aspects of positive mental health. In this study the Principal Environmental Influences (PEIs) were also measured for both work and leisure. The PEI 'valued social position' incorporates the ACE measures of 'collective purpose' and 'status'. Analysis of the PEIs, which constitute a broader range of variables than ACE and which potentially reduces specification error, showed that valued social position remained a significant statistical predictor of a wide range of measures of mental health. Other interesting results from this finer grain analysis showed that use of existing skills in leisure had large B weights associated with total life satisfaction and highly enjoyable challenging experiences. 'Social Contact' in leisure did not remain significant. Inspection of the regression analysis suggested that the influence of 'Social Contact' in leisure on mental health in this sample may be through a range of other variables including 'variety', 'control', 'valued social position' and 'skill use'.

While the statistical association between two variables may reflect bidirectional causal influence, the study has important practical implications. For a company to try and maintain the mental health of managers, it would seem important to reinforce valued social position at work. Equally, time for leisure pursuits in the everyday life of busy managers is not, it would seem, a peripheral consideration, one which can be forfeited without cost.

The final study to be summarised is one focusing on person-situation interactions in a sample of working women, who were primarily office workers (Haworth, Jarman & Lee, 1995). The study measured locus of control (Rotter, 1966), as a person centred variable, PEIs and various facets of mental health; and, using the experience sampling method for one week, activities, enjoyment, interest, motivation and feelings of control. The B weights from multiple regression analysis highlighted the potential importance of 'money' for total life satisfaction and pleasure, and 'clarity' at work for total life satisfaction and affective well-being in work and leisure. 'Valued social position' in both work and leisure also had large B weights for a number of positive states. Locus of control was significantly associated with a wide range of measures of well-being, with 'internals' having more favourable scores. Respondents were divided into two groups on the basis of the locus of control scores. Analysis showed the more 'internal' locus of control group to have significantly better scores on several PEIs including 'clarity' in both work and leisure. Conceivably, while locus of control could have a direct influence on well-being, through feelings of control, 'internals', who have a greater learned expectancy for reinforcements to be contingent upon their own behaviour than 'externals', could have better well-being through the indirect path of greater access to principal environmental influences. While path analysis gave some indication of this being the case, it did not hold for each measure of well-being. However, further research is needed using larger samples.

Analysis of the ESM data showed that 'internals' had greater levels of enjoyment, interest and control for the week of the study. They also reported more of their activities as intrinsically motivated than the 'external' locus of control group. Leisure, in comparison to work, provided significantly greater levels of enjoyment and feelings of control, but not interest. In leisure, social interaction, spectating, reading, hobbies, shopping and self-maintenance had above average levels of enjoyment, with many of these activities also showing above average levels of interest and control. Chores, and domestic activities, including washing, cooking and general housework, were also high on the positive experience of control, even though below average on enjoyment and interest. Work also provided several areas where control was high, and also some of the most enjoyable activities.

Rotter (1966, 1990) emphasises that locus of control is a learned expectancy. Spector (1982) points to an interactive relationship between locus of control and experience, in that locus of control may affect behaviour and the consequences of behaviour may in turn affect locus of control. Parkes (1989) notes that internal locus of control is reciprocally related to skill use at work. The results from the present study of working women suggest the possibility of positive subjective states in leisure being reciprocally related to internal locus of control. Enjoyment and feelings of control in leisure may enhance locus of control, which in turn may lead to enhanced mental health either directly, or indirectly through greater access to principal environmental influences, in work or leisure.

Future Research.

Warr (1987) notes that the strength of his situational model is that it applies to any kind of environment and that it has considerable heuristic value, lending itself to application and development. In order to tease out the relative importance of different principal environmental influences for people with different enduring characteristics, Warr stresses the necessity for large scale survey research including longitudinal studies and multivariate analysis. The model emphasises the importance of studying the processes involved in person-situation interactions important for mental health, for which questionnaire research using causal modelling will be important.

Warr also notes that 'more descriptive and interpretive research is now required, which can elucidate the processes whereby particular sets of environmental features work together to have their environmental effects' (p. 290), and also that it is 'essential that we study the interaction defined in a processual sense, seeking to deepen our understanding of the models of person-situation interactions across time' (p. 291).

The research summarised in this paper shows that the categorical models of Warr and Jahoda are useful in studying focused samples where the aim is to get information of practical value for a particular type of group in a particular situation. Such information could help managers and policy makers concerned with work or leisure in their understanding of factors associated with well-being and health. Focused studies examining the processes and dynamics underpinning different person-situation interactions in work, leisure and well-being may also help in the construction of more general theory. Warr's model provides one overall perspective from which to develop this research. Equally, other variables and methods could be used in conjunction with questionnaire studies of the model. The importance of enjoyment has been highlighted in the present research. Enjoyment may play a pivotal role in gaining access to categories of experience, either through the direct effects of rewards, or through enhancing internal locus of control. Research using these variables could also be broadened further to include the study of life themes (Csikszentmihalyi & Beattie, 1979), and a personal history approach, including the study of subconscious processes of interaction with the environment, (Haworth, 1986).

The role of subconscious processes, including 'Unintended Thought', in the moderation of stress is now the subject of extensive enquiries (Uleman & Bargh, 1989). Concepts and approaches in this area could be useful additions in the study of what Rotter (1982) has termed 'enhancement behaviours'. These are 'specific cognitive activities that are used to enhance and maintain good feelings' which may help to explain why 'there are people who are happy, content and in a good mood much of the time, and that the objective circumstances of such people may not differ markedly from those of others who are mildly unhappy, discontent, or worried about bad things that might happen', (p. 339). In the complex interweaving of simultaneous interactions between the person and the environment (Warr 1987, p. 138), the role of activity may be critical to the subconscious and conscious processes involved in well-being. The philosopher Merleau-Ponty (1962) has highlighted the primacy of activity in the generation of consciousness, claiming that we come to know things primarily by doing, by lived experience, which can produce knowledge below the level of conscious thought, although this can be recovered by reflection. On this model, positive experiences in leisure may have a critical part to play in the chain of events associated with well-being. In investigating these complex areas, small scale questionnaire studies could be combined with more in-depth methods, including the ESM, interviews, and descriptive accounts, to form an empirical and experiential ethnography of leisure and health.

References

BUCHANAN, T. (1985). Commitment and leisure behaviour: a theoretical perspective. *Leisure Sciences, 7, 401-420.*

BRIEF, A.P., BUTCHER, A.H., GEORGE, J.M., & LINK, K.E. (1993). Integrating bottom-up and top-down theories of subjective well-being: the case of health. *Journal of Personality and Social Psychology. 64* (4), 646-653.

CSIKSZENTMIHALYI, M. (1982). Towards a psychology of optimal experience. *In* L. Wheeler (Éd.), *Review of Personality and Social Psychology (Vol. 2),* Beverley Hills, CA: Sage

CSIKSZENTMIHALYI, M. & Beattie, O. (1979). Life themes: a theoretical and empirical exploration of their origins and effects. *Journal of Humanistic Psychology, 19,* 45-63.

CSIKSZENTMIHALYI, M. & CSIKSZENTMIHALYI, I.S. (1988). *Optimal Experience,* Cambridge: Cambridge University Press.

DRIVER, B.L., BROWN, P.J., & PETERSON, G.L. (Éd.), (1991). *Benefits of Leisure.* Pennsylvania, Venture Publishing Inc.

DRIVER, B.L., TINSLEY, E.A.H., & MANFREDO, M.J. (1991). The paragraphs about Leisure and recreation experience preference scales: results from two inventories designed to assess the breadth of the perceived psychological benefits of leisure. *In* B.L. Driver *et al.* (Éd.), *Benefits of Leisure,* 263-286. Pennsylvania, Venture Publishing Inc.

EVANS, S.T. (1986). *Variations in activity and psychological well-being in unemployed young adults.* Unpublished Ph. D. thesis: University of Manchester.

EVANS, S.T. & HAWORTH, J.T. (1991). Variations in personal activity, access to categories of experience and psychological well-being in unemployed young adults. *Leisure Studies, 10,* 249-264.

FRYER, D. & McKENNA, S. (1989). Redundant skills: temporary unemployment and mental health. *In* M. Patrickson (Éd.), *Readings in Organisational Behaviour.* New South Wales: Harper & Row.

HAWORTH, J.T. (1986). Meaningful activity and psychological models of non-employment. *Leisure Studies, 5,* 281-297.

HAWORTH, J.T. (1993). Skill-challenge relationships and psychological well-being in everyday life. *Society and Leisure. 16* (1), 115-128.

HAWORTH, J.T. & DUCKER, J. (1991). Psychological well-being and access to categories of experience un unemployed young adults. *Leisure Studies, 10,* 265-274.

HAWORTH, J.T. & HILL, S. (1992). Work, leisure and psychological well-being in a sample of young adults. *Journal of Community and Applied Social Psychology, 2,* 147-160.

HAWORTH, J.T. & PATERSON, F. (1995). Access to categories of experience and mental health in a sample of managers. *Journal of Applied Social Psychology.* In press.

HAWORTH, J.T., JARMAN, M., & LEE, S. (1995). *Positive subjective states in the daily life of a sample of working women.* Paper submitted to the Journal of Applied Social Psychology.

62   John HAWORTH

HULL, RB. IV (1991). Mood as a product of Leisure: Causes and consequences. *In* B.L. Driver *et al.* (Éd.), Benefits of Leisure 249-262. Pennsylvania, Venture Publishing Inc.

JAHODA, M. (1982). *Employment and unemployment: a social psychological analysis.* Cambridge: Cambridge University Press.

JAHODA, M. (1992). Reflections on Marienthal and after. *Journal of Occupational and Organisational Psychology, 65*, 355-358.

KABONOV, B. (1982). Occupational and sex differences in leisure needs and leisure satisfaction. *Journal of Occupational Behaviour, 3*, 233-245.

KABONOV, B. & O'BRIEN, G.E. (1980). Work and Leisure: a task attributes analysis. *Journal of Applied Psychology. 65*, 5, 596-609.

MANNELL, R C. & STYNES, D.J. (1991). Retrospective: the benefits of leisure. *In* B.L. Driver *et al.* (Éd.), *Benefits of leisure* (401-473). Pennsylvania: Venture Publishing Inc.

MERLEAU-PONTY, M. (1962). *Phenomenology of perception.* London: Routledge and Kegan Paul.

PARKES, K.R. (1984). Locus of control, cognitive appraisal and coping in stressful episodes. *Journal of Personality and Social Psychology, 46*, 3, 655-668.

ROTTER, J.B. (1966). Generalised expectancies for internal versus external control of reinforcement. *Psychological Monographs, 80* (whole no.), 609.

ROTTER, J.B. (1982). *The development and applications of social learning theory.* N.Y.: Praeger.

ROTTER, J.B. (1990). Internal versus external locus of control of reinforcement: a case history of a variable. *American Psychologist, 45* (4), 489-493.

SPECTOR, P. (1982). Behaviour in organisations as a function of employee's locus of control. *Psychological Bulletin, 91*, 482-497.

STEBBINS, R.A. (1982). Serious leisure: a conceptual statement. *Pacific Sociological Review, 25*, 251-272.

ULEMAN, J.S. & BARGH, J.A. (Éd.) (1989). *Unintended thought.* N.Y.: The Guilford Press.

WARR, P. (1987). *Work, unemployment and mental health.* Oxford: Clarendon Press.

WHITE, R.W. (1959). Motivation reconsidered: the concept of competence. *Psychological Review, 66*, 297-333.

John HAWORTH
Loisir et modélisation par catégories de la santé mentale

RÉSUMÉ

Le présent article souligne la complexité de l'étude du loisir et de la santé. Il traite plus particulièrement d'un courant de recherche qui montre l'importance des divers aspects de la situation (les catégories de l'expérience), de la personne (locus de contrôle) et de leur interaction pour la santé mentale (mesurée en fonction d'une variété de dimensions). Il décrit deux modèles de santé mentale centrés sur les catégories de l'expérience fournies par l'environnement et reflétant les besoins humains. Il s'agit du modèle de Warr (1987), qui propose neuf principales catégories d'expériences environnementales (PEI) regroupées en cinq composantes. Ces catégories exerceraient une influence non linéaire sur la santé mentale. Ce modèle reconnaît également l'influence importante que les personnes peuvent exercer sur leurs environnements ; il s'intéresse aux processus et interactions entre la personne et la situation ainsi qu'aux éléments des catégories. Il intègre le modèle de Jahoda (1982) selon lequel les cinq catégories d'expériences considérées importantes pour la santé mentale sont imposées par le travail. Ces catégories sont : la structure du temps, l'activité, le contact social, l'intérêt commun et l'identité ou le statut social. L'auteur fait ensuite état de la recherche entreprise à l'Université de Manchester, centrée sur cette modélisation par catégories. Ces études révèlent que, contrairement aux théories de Jahoda, le loisir peut donner accès aux cinq catégories de l'expérience – bien que peut-être pas dans la même mesure que le travail –, et qu'un meilleur accès au loisir est relié à un mieux-être psychologique dans bon nombre de dimensions. Elles indiquent également que les mécanismes permettant l'obtention de ces catégories de l'expérience peuvent différer pour le travail et le loisir. Une recherche qui utilisait les neuf PEI a confirmé l'importance de ces cinq catégories de l'expérience pour le bien-être, et a aussi permis d'analyser plus finement l'importance du loisir. Enfin, une étude des interactions entre la personne et la situation, à partir de l'échelle de locus de contrôle et des neuf PEI, a révélé que les personnes dotées d'un locus de contrôle « interne » obtiennent des scores significativement plus élevés à plusieurs mesures de la santé mentale et de PEI au travail et au loisir. Elle a aussi montré que les variations des PEI sont associées à un bien-être supérieur. Ces personnes semblent jouir davantage de la vie, avoir le sentiment de mieux la contrôler et s'intéresser davantage à la vie quotidienne, tel que l'a démontré la méthode d'échantillonnage de l'expérience. On note la possibilité que le loisir améliore le locus de contrôle, qui, à son tour, peut entraîner l'amélioration de la santé mentale, de manière directe ou indirecte, par un meilleur accès à des PEI au travail ou au loisir. L'auteur fournit en conclusion des pistes de recherche intéressantes pour l'avenir.

John HAWORTH
Leisure And Categorical Models Of Mental Health

ABSTRACT

The paper briefly notes the complexity of the study of leisure and health. A line of research is then examined which emphasises the importance for mental health, measured on a range of dimensions, of aspects of the situation (categories of experience) and the person (locus of control), and their interaction. Two related models of mental health are outlined which focus on environmentally provided categories of experience reflective of human needs. The model proposed by Warr (1987) suggests nine principal environmental influences (PEIs) as having a significant non-linear influence on mental health, reconceptualised into five components. The model also recognises the important influence which persons can have on environments, and is thus concerned with processes and person-situation interactions as well as categorical features. This model incorporates that proposed by Jahoda (1982) which indicates that five categories of experience considered important for mental health are imposed by work, these being: time structure, activity, social contact, collective purpose and social identity or status. Research undertaken at Manchester University using these categorical models is then summarised. This shows that contrary to Jahoda's theories, leisure can provide access to these five categories of experience, although not perhaps to the same extent as employment, and that better access in leisure is associated with better psychological well-being on a range of dimensions. The studies also suggest that the mechanisms for obtaining these categories of experience may differ in work and leisure. Research using the nine PEIs was found to substantiate the importance of the five categories of experience for well-being, and also provided a finer grain analysis of the importance of leisure. Finally, a study of person-situation interactions using the locus of control scale and the nine PEIs showed that 'internals' had significantly better scores on a number of measures of mental health and PEIs in both work and leisure, and that variations in PEIs were associated with better well-being. 'Internals' were also shown to have more enjoyment, feelings of control and interest in daily life, measured by the experience sampling method. The possibility is noted that leisure may enhance internal locus of control, which in turn may lead to enhanced mental health either directly, or indirectly through greater access to PEIs, in work or leisure. The paper concludes by making some suggestions for future research.

John HAWORTH
Diversión y modelos por categorías de la salud mental.

RESUMEN

El presente artículo recalca la complejidad del estudio de las actividades de recreo y de la salud. Trata, particularmente, de una corriente de investigación que muestra la importancia de los diversos aspectos de la situación (las categorías de la experiencia), de la persona (locus de control) y de su interacción para la salud mental (medida en función de una variedad de dimensiones). Describe dos modelos de salud mental centrados sobre las categorías de la experiencia dadas por el entorno y que reflejan las necesidades humanas. Se trata del modelo de Warr (1987), que propone nueve categorías principales de experiencias del medio circundante (PEI) reagrupadas en cinco componentes. Estas categorías ejercerían una influencia non lineal sobre la salud mental. El modelo reconoce igualmente la influencia importante que las personas pueden ejercer sobre su medio; se interesa a los procesos e interacciones entre la persona y la situación, así que a los elementos de las categorías. Este modelo integra el modelo de Jahoda (1982), según el cual las cinco categorías de experiencias, consideradas importantes para la salud mental, son impuestas por el trbajo. Estas categorías son: la estructura del tiempo, la actividad, el contacto social, el interés común y la identidad o la posición social. Enseguida, el autor tiene en cuenta la investigación emprendida en la Universidad de Manchester, que enfoca los modelos por categorías. Estos estudios revelan que, contrariamente a las teorías de Jahoda, la actividad recreativa puede dar acceso a las cinco categorías de la experiencia –aunque tal vez no en la misma medida que en el trabajo–, y que un mejor acceso a la actividad recreativa está ligado a un mejor bienestar psicológico dentro de un buen número de dimensiones. El estudio sugiere igualmente que los mecanismos que permiten la obtención de estas categorías de la experiencia pueden diferir en el trabajo y en la actividad recreativa. Una investigación que utilizaba las nueve PEI, confirmó la importancia de estas cinco categorías de la experiencia para el bienestar, y permitió también analizar más concienzudamente la importancia de la actividad recreativa. Para terminar, un estudio de las interacciones entre la persona y la situación, a partir de la escala de locus de control y de las nueve PEI, reveló que las personas dotadas de un locus de control «interno» obtienen resultados significativamente más elevados que muchas otras medidas de la salud mental y de las PEI en el trabajo y en la actividad recreativa. También mostró que la variaciones de las PEI están asociadas con un bienestar superior. Estas personas parecen gozar más de la vida, tener el sentimiento de controlarla mejor e interesarse más a la vida cotidiana, tal que demostrado por le método de muestreo de la experiencia. Se nota la posibilidad que la actividad recreativa mejore el locus de control, que, a su vez, puede ocasionar un mejoramiento de la salud mental, de manera directa o indirecta, por un mejor acceso a las PEI en el trabajo o en la actividad recreativa. El autor proporciona, en conclusión, pistas interesantes de investigación para el porvenir.

_____

An Examination of Relationship Between Psychological Well-Being and Depression and Leisure Activity Participation Among Older Adults

Sherry L. DUPUIS

Department of Family Studies
University of Guelph
Ontario, Canada

Bryan J.A. SMALE

Department of Recreation and Leisure Studies
University of Waterloo
Ontario, Canada

Background

Considerable evidence in the literature has been provided in recent years to support the proposition that leisure activity participation is related to improved physical and psychological well-being. However, the research addressing the link between participation in leisure activities and well-being specifically for the older adult population has been limited. Moreover, many of the studies examining the relationship between leisure activity participation and the well-being of older adults have concentrated on physiological outcomes (see McPherson, 1990) or on the relationship between leisure activity participation and the broader concept of life satisfaction (e.g., Kelly & Ross, 1989; Riddick, 1985a, 1985b; Riddick & Daniel, 1984; Sneegas, 1986; Steinkamp & Kelly, 1987; Zuzanek & Box, 1988). Research addressing the link between participation in leisure activities and psychological well-being for the older adult population has been much less extensive. Fewer studies still have looked at the relationship between leisure activity participation and depression.

Loisir et société / *Society and Leisure*
Volume 18, numéro 1, printemps 1995, pp. 67-92 • © Presses de l'Université du Québec

An examination of the literature regarding psychological well-being reveals several inconsistencies in how it has been defined and how it has been measured. There is, however, general agreement that psychological well-being "falls within a broad area of study that examines quality of life issues" (Kozma, Stones, & McNeil, 1991, p. 1). Part of the difficulty in grasping a deeper understanding of the concept psychological well-being is due to the wide variety of concepts that have been used interchangeably in the literature. Concepts such as "well-being", "happiness" (Bradburn, 1969), "life satisfaction" (Wood, Wylie, & Sheafor, 1969), "morale" (Lawton, 1972), "quality of life", "mental" or "emotional health", "subjective well-being", "mood", and "affect" (Kozma, Stones, & McNeil, 1991) have all been used synonymously with psychological well-being. Stull (1987), however, pointed out that while these concepts are related they are not identical. Several researchers (e.g., Andrews & McKennel, 1980; Campbell, Converse, & Rodgers, 1976; McKennell, 1978; McKennell & Andrews, 1980) "have argued that life satisfaction has a more cognitive component to it, while happiness has a more affective or emotional component to it" (Stull, 1987, p. 56). Bradburn (1969) suggested that happiness – as an indicator of psychological well-being – was a function of the balance between positive affect and negative affect. Life satisfaction and psychological well-being also differ temporally (Stull, 1987) with psychological well-being reflecting an assessment of the current state of affairs whereas life satisfaction measuring an overall assessment of one's life which may include a comparison of aspirations with achievements (Campbell, Converse, & Rodgers, 1976; Stull, 1987).

A related and more complex psychological state that is negatively related to psychological well-being is depression. As an appropriate or excessive response to losses, depression is typically defined as "a state of lowered self-esteem, with associated feelings of hopelessness and helplessness" (Parker, 1978, p. 7). Some of the principal features of depression include: expressions of hopelessness or despair; a change (usually a decrease) in physical activity, eating, sleeping, or sexual activity; continual questioning of self-esteem; a real or imagined feeling of failure; and an inability to concentrate on reading, writing or conversation (Gordon, 1987, p. 210). Several authors have noted that depression is unique from other mental disorders as well as other concepts such as unhappiness particularly because of its association with self-depreciation and self-destruction (Levitt, Lubin, & Brooks, 1983; Zimmer & Foy, 1959). Depression is also distinct temporally in that it tends to be more enduring over time than the typically briefer feelings of unhappiness and that its intensity is greater (Winokur, 1981). Further, later life depression have also been shown to be qualitatively different from depression in earlier life (Stoudemire & Blazer, 1985).

There is a particular need for research which examines the relationship between leisure activity participation and psychological well-being and depression considering the many losses associated with the aging process – loss of spouse, home, income, work and family roles, health, friends, and independence (Garrigan, 1986; Stoudemire & Blazer, 1985). These losses can often lead to isolation, loneliness, depression, low self-concept, and a deprivation of basic psychological needs. In fact, depression is considered to be the most common mental health disorder among the entire senior population (Knight, 1986; Weinstein & Khanna, 1986). Several researchers have suggested that the many stresses and losses associated with aging may have a damaging and negative effect on an older adult's self-identity and thus contribute to depressive states (Busse & Pfeiffer, 1973; Garrigan, 1986; Rosow, 1973). Furthermore, the failure to satisfy basic psychological needs can be detrimental to both emotional and physical health (Tinsley & Tinsley, 1986).

Studies that have focused on psychological benefits suggest that older adults who are more actively involved in leisure activity participation may have higher psychological well-being (e.g., Brown, Frankel, & Fennell, 1991), reduced feelings of loneliness (Lee & Ishii-Kuntz, 1987; Mullins & Mushel, 1992), higher morale (Lee & Ishii-Kuntz, 1987; Tinsley, Colbs, Teaff, & Kaufman, 1987), increased total perceived wellness (Ragheb, 1993), and are better able to cope with the consequences of aging (Kelly, Steinkamp, & Kelly, 1986; Steinkamp & Kelly, 1987). However, the types of leisure activities chosen have varied greatly across these studies and it remains unclear if different types of leisure pursuits are more or less related to these psychological states.

Of the activities examined in these studies, most have concentrated on the relationship between physical activity and psychological well-being or depression (e.g., Bennett, Carmack, & Gardner, 1992; Emery & Gatz, 1990; McTeer & Curtis, 1990; Morgan, et al., 1991). However, the results of these studies have been inconsistent. In a study of older adults living in England, for example, Morgan et al. (1991, p. 399) concluded: "that among the present cohort of retired and elderly people, relationships between customary physical activity levels and psychological well-being [were] weak, indirect and gender-specific". Similarly, McTeer and Curtis (1990) found a modest, positive relationship between physical activity and psychological well-being for males 20 years of age and older, but not for females. Nonetheless, they suggest that "the physical activity/psychological well-being relationship is largely a direct relationship" (p. 341). Bennett, Carmack and Gardner (1982) utilized an experimental design to examine the effects of an exercise program on the depression levels of older adults living in a community setting and those living in a nursing home. Older adults displaying symptoms of depression showed significant improvement following their participation in the exercise program. Emery and Gatz (1990), on the other hand, found that an aerobics class did not appear to contribute significantly to improvements in measures of depression, anxiety, and avowed happiness among older adults based in the community.

In another part of the literature, the focus has been on the links between social activities and various psychological indicators (e.g., Larson, Mannell, & Zuzanek, 1986; Lee & Ishii-Kuntz, 1987; Mullins & Mushel, 1992). Of this research, few studies have found a significant relationship between the psychological well-being of older adults and the frequency with which they interact with family, and when significant relationships are found, they are quite small (see Morgan, 1976; Elwell & Maltbie-Crannell, 1981). In contrast, most previous research supports the assumption that interaction with friends is correlated to the well-being of older adults (see Larson, 1978; Larson, Mannell & Zuzanek, 1986; Mullins & Mushel, 1992; Okun, Stock, Haring, & Witter, 1984). Furthermore, Lee and Ishii-Kuntz (1987) found that interaction with friends, interaction with neighbours, and participation in voluntary associations were each significantly correlated to lower loneliness and higher morale among the elderly. Nonetheless, Larson, Zuzanek, and Mannell (1985) suggest that older adults spend very little time with friends or neighbours. In their study, only 9 per cent of the average respondent's time was spent with friends and neighbours, and over 50 per cent of their waking hours were spent alone.

Ironically, even though there is evidence that suggests older adults engage in fewer structured leisure pursuits and more home-centred and passive activities as they age (Zuzanek & Box, 1988), very little research has focused specifically on the relationship between passive activities and well-being. Kelly and Ross (1989, p. 54) found that: "home-based activity is strongly and negatively related to satisfaction for those in their twenties, but is the most important contributor [to life satisfaction] for those over 74". Other researchers have found that solitary activities such as reading and hobbies have a positive relationship with life satisfaction (see Sauer, 1977; Palmore & Kivett, 1977); however, it is unclear whether this positive relationship also holds true for psychological well-being and depression. Related to specific passive activities, researchers have also found a significant negative relationship between television viewing and psychological well-being across the lifespan (Kubey & Csikscentmihalyi, 1990; Smalc & Dupuis, 1993).

Those studies that include a variety of leisure pursuits tend to define leisure activity in its broadest context (e.g., George, 1978; Riddick, 1985a, 1985b; Riddick & Daniel, 1984; Sneegas, 1986; Steinkamp & Kelly, 1987) or include several different activity categories (e.g., Brown, Frankel, & Fennell, 1991; Kelly & Ross, 1989; Lomranz, Bergman, Eyal, & Shmotkin, 1988; Peppers, 1976; Ragheb & Griffith, 1982; Ragheb, 1993). Of those studies that have focused specifically on psychological or emotional well-being, George (1978) examined the impact of general activity level on psychological well-being and concluded that there was no significant, predictable relationship between activity levels and psychological well-being. Brown, Frankel and Fennell (1991) employed a life-course perspective and found that among eight leisure activity categories, social and outdoor activities showed the highest correlations with psychological well-being for the total sample. However, the relationship between participation in leisure activities and well-being appeared to vary by age and by sex. For those respondents between 50 and 64 years of age, there was a significant relationship between social activity participation and psychological well-being for both males and females. In addition, there were also significant, positive relationships between psychological well-being and outdoor activity involvement for men, and sedentary, informal and physical activity involvement for women. The significant correlation between outdoor activity and psychological well-being for men also was present among those between 65 and 69 years, but no significant correlations appeared for women in this age group. After the age of 69, there did not appear to be a significant relationship between any of the leisure categories and well-being for either sex.

Lomranz, Bergman, Eyal and Shmotkin (1988), in a study of Israelian older adults, found that activities performed outside the home were more strongly related to psychological well-being and depression than indoor activities, although again, the relationship varied for men and women. These results suggest that certain activities may be more strongly related to psycho-logical well-being than are others. At present, however, our understanding of which individual or types of activities may be more or less strongly related to higher psychological well-being and lower depression levels is not well developed. Researchers also have found a significant correlation between leisure diversity or repertoire – the total number of different activities in which an individual is engaged– and life satisfaction (Peppers, 1976; Zuzanek & Box, 1988). These studies generally suggest that the more leisure activities in which older adults are involved, the more satisfied they are with their lives. Whether this relationship also holds true for psychological well-being and leisure diversity has not been fully explored.

Finally, the results from some of the aforementioned studies also suggest that certain demographic variables may play a role in the relationship between leisure activity participation and well-being. Nonetheless, few researchers have examined the mediating effect of demographic variables on this relationship, and among those that have, their findings thus far have been inconsistent. For example, Brown, Frankel, and Fennell (1991) employed regression analysis and found that age and sex play significant roles in the psychological well-being/ leisure participation relationship. They conclude:

> [...] important differences persist between men and women and [...] these differences are amplified by the inclusion of a statistical control for age [...] The fact that age itself makes a significant contribution underlies the

importance of the control. Not only do the relationships between partici-
pation in leisure activities and well-being vary by age, the relative contri-
butions of the activities to well-being also vary [by] age, and age itself is
related to well-being for women (Brown, Frankel, & Fennell, 1991, p. 385).

In contrast, McTeer and Curtis (1990) found that although the relationship varied by sex, other demographic factors did not appear to modify the relationship between leisure activity participation and psychological well-being.

Lomranz, Bergman, Eyal, and Shmotkin (1988) and Morgan *et al.* (1991) focused on older adults in their examinations of the relationship between leisure activity participation and psychological well-being and/or depression levels and also found sex differences. The Morgan *et al.* (1991) study employed data gathered in Nottingham, England and examined the ability of certain variables to predict the presence or absence of dysphoria and depression. For women, once other factors such as age and health were taken into account, customary physical activity did not emerge as a significant discriminating variable in classifying emotional disturbance. For men, on the other hand, "home maintenance" physical activities played a significant role in identifying dysphoria/depression.

In summary, although a substantial body of research has investigated the relationship between leisure activity participation and the life satisfaction of older adults, research examining the association between activity participation and psychological well-being and/or depression has been much less extensive. Furthermore, the research that has examined the relationship between leisure participation and psychological variables has tended to measure participation on the basis of activity categories rather than specific leisure activities. Fewer still have investigated the psychological well-being/leisure diversity relationship. Finally, although there is some evidence that certain demographic variables may play a mediating role in the relationship between leisure activity participation and psychological well-being and/or depression, the findings have been inconsistent and may not be generalisable to older adults.

Purpose of the Study

The purpose of this study was to investigate the relationship between selected leisure activities and both psychological well-being and depression specifically for an older adult population. In addition, the role that selected demographic variables play in this relationship was examined. The research objectives which guided this study were as follows:

1. to examine the relationship between both psychological well-being and depression and participation in selected leisure activities for older adults;

2. to examine the roles that sex, age, and marital status play in the relationship between psychological well-being and depression and leisure activity participation for older adults;

3. to determine whether participation in certain leisure activities were more strongly related to psychological well-being and depression than others; and

4. to examine the relationship between psychological well-being and depression and leisure diversity for older adults.

Methods

Data Source

Data were drawn from the Campbell's *Survey on Well-Being in Canada* which was conducted in the spring of 1988 by the Canadian Fitness and Lifestyle Research Institute with the purpose of updating information collected in the 1981 *Canadian Fitness Survey*. The 1988 Campbell's Survey gathered information on patterns of leisure activity participation and physical fitness in the Canadian population; their motivations, incentives, and perceived barriers to participation; social circumstances, as well as the demographic profile of the respondents (Stephens & Craig, 1990, p. 1). A stratified, multi-stage cluster sample of Canadian families generated 4,345 respondents seven years of age and older. For the purpose of this study, only those respondents 55 years of age and older ($n = 743$) were used in the subsequent analyses.

Selected Variables

Three principal groups of variables were drawn from the data set to satisfy the research objectives. The first group of variables was comprised of two measures, one related to psychological well-being and one related to depression. The second group of variables dealt with leisure activity participation in selected passive, social, and physically active activities. Sex, age and marital status were included in the third group of variables – the moderating variables in the relationships between psychological well-being and depression and participation in leisure activity.

Psychological well-being was measured using the *Bradburn Affect Balance Scale* which consists of 10 items describing positive and negative emotional status. Each respondent was asked to indicate along a 3-point scale from "never" to "often" how often he or she had felt a certain way (i.e., "on top of the world", "excited", "bored", "lonely"). Negative scores were subtracted from positive scores to achieve an overall score of psychological well-being ranging from a high of 21 to a low of 1. The Bradburn scale has received considerable use and scrutiny in the literature and has demonstrated its validity (Bild & Havighurst, 1976; George & Bearon, 1980). Test-retest reliability of the scale has been quite high, typically with alphas ranging between 0.80 and 0.97 (Bowling, 1991; Moriwaki, 1974), and although not originally intended for use with older adults, has shown to be effective for this group (Bowling, 1991).

Depression was measured using the *Centre for Epidemiological Studies Depression Scale (CES-D Scale)*, a 20-item Likert-type scale that assesses depressive symptomatology (Radloff & Locke, 1986). Respondents were asked to report how often in the past week they had felt a certain way (i.e., "depressed", "hopeful about the future", "fearful", "restless", "happy"). Each item was measured on a 4-point scale ranging from "less than one day" to "5 to 7 days". The overall scores ranged from 0 to 60, with higher scores indicating more severe levels of depressive symptoms. The *CES-D Scale* is one of the most widely used measures of depression (George, 1989) and field testing has demonstrated high levels of consistency among a variety of general populations with alphas approximating 0.85 (Radloff & Locke, 1986).

The correlation between the two scales for older adults was -0.509 ($n = 638$; $p < .01$) which is slightly lower than the findings of previous studies of the relationship between these and various other measures of psychological states (Bowling, 1991). Although statistically significant, only about one quarter of the joint variation is explained ($r^2 = 0.259$) and this confirms the underlying distinction, especially for older adults, in the constructs being measured.

The Campbell's Survey gathered information on a wide array of leisure activities using different measures to indicate frequency of participation. In order to broadly represent various forms of leisure when specific activities were selected for examination, three general categories of leisure activity were created: (1) passive activities which are characterised by their predominantly non-physical and solitary nature; (2) social activities which involved interaction with friends as their primary purpose; and (3) physically active pursuits which included sports, fitness, and similar forms of physical activity. Two activities were selected to represent each category based on an adequate number of individuals in each of the participation categories for each age group considered. The passive activities selected were television viewing and hobbies and crafts; the social activities included visiting with friends and participation in social clubs and organisations; and the physically active pursuits were walking for exercise and swimming.

The frequency of participation in the passive and the social activities considered here were measured along a 6-point ordinal scale ranging from 0 hours per week to 15 hours per week. Respondents were asked to select the category best describing the typical number of hours per week spent on each of the activities. The physically active activities were measured in terms of the frequency, duration, and intensity of participation in each of the activities. For frequency of participation, respondents were asked to indicate whether or not they had participated in any of the listed physical activities in the past 12 months. Consequently, to facilitate comparisons across activity types in the analyses, the ordinal measures of frequency of participation for all activities except swimming were standardized along a simpler ordinal scale with three categories: (1) none or little participation, (2) moderate participation, and (3) regular participation. Due to the small number of older adult swimmers, swimming was reorganized into two categories: (1) participants, and (2) non-participants. An examination of the distribution of participation patterns in each activity on the original measures facilitated the creation of these categories and ensured for the analyses an adequate number of cases in each subgroup.

Leisure diversity was measured by summing up the total number of activities of all types in which the respondents indicated they had participated during the past year. Higher values of the resultant indicator therefore reflected a greater repertoire of leisure involvements if not the intensity of those involvements. A total of 29 activities were included in the survey – ten of the activities were associated with passive and social forms of leisure, and nineteen of the activities dealt with physically active forms of leisure.

The demographic variables considered for their moderating effects were age, sex and marital status. Three age categories were created: (1) pre-retired (55 to 64 years), (2) young old (65 to 74 years), and (3) old old (75 years and older). The three marital status categories included: (1) married, (2) widowed, and (3) single (including divorced and separated).

Analysis Procedures

The analyses of the data were carried out in three stages. First, an examination of the simple relationship between psychological well-being and depression and activity participation in each of the individual leisure activities, and for sex, age, and marital status was conducted using one-way analysis of variance. This initial step helped to clarify the nature of the direct relationship between the independent variables and the dependent variables. Second, using factorial analysis of variance, and multiple classification analysis (MCA) for descriptive purposes, the relationship between psychological well-being and depression and participation in each of the leisure activities was examined in conjunction with sex, age, and marital status to determine whether any interaction effects would be revealed. MCA is useful for describing the independent affects of each variable in the relationship and especially when there are no interaction effects revealed in the factorial analysis of variance. By calculating the standardised deviations from the grand mean of the criterion variable, direct comparisons among the key factors in the relationships can be made.

Based on McTeer and Curtis' (1990) work, it was expected that even after controlling for these factors, a positive relationship would remain between activity involvement and well-being. It is at this stage that the beta values generated from the MCA were compared in order to determine if certain variables were more strongly related to psychological well-being and depression than others. Finally, the role that leisure diversity plays in these relationships was investigated using Pearson correlation coefficients.

Results

The demographic characteristics of the sample and their participation patterns are shown in Tables 1 and 2. The majority of the respondents were female (57.5%), were between the ages of 55 and 64 years (50.9%), and were married (68.2%). Visiting friends showed the lowest level of non-participation while participation in social clubs or organizations had the highest levels (*see Table 2*). The most regularly participated in activity was walking for exercise with 53.5% of the sample participating on a regular basis. In contrast, less than a quarter of the sample participated in swimming (22.7%). Not unexpectedly, over three-quarters of the respondents (78.6%) watched television at moderate or regular levels. Similar proportions of the sample were included in each of the three levels of participation in hobbies and crafts.

TABLE 1

Characteristics of Older Adult Sample (n = 743)

Characteristic Category	n	Pct.
Sex		
Females	427	57.5
Males	316	42.5
Age Group		
55 to 64 years	378	50.9
65 to 74 years	255	34.3
75 years or older	110	14.8
Marital Status		
Married	503	68.2
Widowed	156	21.2
Single/Div./Sep.	78	10.6

TABLE 2

**Level of Participation by Older Adults
in Selected Leisure Activities**

Activity	Level of Participation[a]		
Activity	None/little	Moderate	Regular
Passive			
Television viewing	21.4	45.7	32.9
Hobbies/crafts	35.0	30.4	34.7
Social			
Social clubs/org.	70.5	11.7	17.8
Visiting friends	19.9	56.8	23.2
Physical			
Walking for exercice	29.5	17.0	53.5
Swimming[b]	Do participate = 22.7		

[a] participation reported as a percentage of the total sample
[b] due to low overall participation, sample separated between swimmers and non-swimmers

The Relationship Between Well-Being and Activity Participation

Three of the six activities selected for this study were significantly related to psychological well-being (*see Table 3*). Participation in hobbies and crafts, visiting friends, and swimming all showed positive relationships to psychological well-being. Those who participated regularly in hobbies and crafts had significantly higher psychological well-being than those who participated at moderate levels or not at all. In addition, respondents who participated even at a moderate level demonstrated significantly higher psychological well-being than those who participated very little if at all. Similarly, older adults who visited friends regularly had significantly higher levels of psychological well-being than those who visited very little or moderately. Finally, swimmers displayed significantly higher psychological well-being scores than non-swimmers. Television viewing was the only activity negatively related to psychological well-being, however, the differences between the participation categories were not significant.

An examination of the relationship between depressive symptoms and leisure activity participation revealed similar results (*see Table 4*). Again, participation in hobbies and crafts, visiting friends, and swimming were negatively related to levels of depressive symptoms. The older adults who participated in hobbies and crafts on a regular basis were significantly less depressed than those who participated moderately or very little. Those who did not visit friends or visited very little appeared to be significantly more depressed than those who visited either on a moderate or regular basis. As well, swimmers were significantly less depressed than non-swimmers. Interestingly, both increased television viewing and walking for exercise were related to somewhat higher levels of depressive symptoms, albeit the differences were not significant. With two of the three significant results reported in Table 4 showing test statistics quite close to the critical value, the possibility of making a Type-I error must be considered. However, the patterns of these results are so strikingly consistent with expectations and the previous analyses, as well as with the existing literature, that some confidence can be taken in their importance.

TABLE 3

Relationship Between Psychological Well-Being and Participation in Selected Leisure Activities

Activity	Psych. Well-Being				
Participation	n	Mean	Std. Dev.	F	p
Television viewing					
None/little	139	14.66	2.80		
Moderate	301	14.54	3.07	0.6494	.5227
Regular	215	14.32	2.87		
Hobbies/crafts					
None/little	225	13.72[a]	3.22		
Moderate	195	14.60[b]	2.88	14.2656	.0000**
Regular	222	15.17[c]	2.56		
Visiting friends					
None/little	131	13.96[a]	3.11		
Moderate	369	14.46[a]	2.81	5.3163	.0051**
Regular	150	15.09[b]	3.04		
Social clubs/org.					
None/little	455	14.35	2.90		
Moderate	78	15.00	2.82	1.8620	.1562
Regular	116	14.65	3.13		
Walking for exercise					
None/little	186	14.39	3.19		
Moderate	113	14.39	2.84	0.3208	.7257
Regular	348	14.58	2.85		
Swimming					
Non-participants	503	14.31a	3.04	8.2636	.0042**
Participants	149	15.10b	2.52		

*   significant difference between groups at 0.05 level
**   significant difference between groups at 0.01 level
Note : superscripts indicate groups significantly different from one another using post hoc
Student-Newman-Keuls procedure

TABLE 4

**Relationship Between Depression
and Participation in Selected Leisure Activities**

Activity		Depression			
Participation	n	Mean	Std. Dev.	F	p
Television viewing					
None/little	137	6.66	7.12		
Moderate	293	7.30	7.38	0.3975	.6722
Regular	211	7.23	6.97		
Hobbies/crafts					
None/little	217	8.16[a]	8.34		
Moderate	191	7.52[a]	7.57	6.0365	.0025**
Regular	221	5.84[b]	5.37		
Visiting friends					
None/little	127	8.55[a]	7.73		
Moderate	363	7.06[b]	7.39	4.1229	.0166*
Regular	148	6.08[b]	5.91		
Social clubs/org.					
None/little	446	7.26	7.21		
Moderate	78	7.77	8.09	1.3384	.2630
Regular	113	6.20	6.48		
Walking for exercise					
None/little	183	6.75	6.72		
Moderate	107	7.10	6.81	0.3247	.7229
Regular	342	7.28	7.50		
Swimming					
Non-participants	491	7.46a	7.33	5.5252	.0190*
Participants	147	5.88b	6.33		

*   significant difference between groups at 0.05 level
** significant difference between groups at 0.01 level
Note : superscripts indicate groups significantly different from one another using post hoc
    Student-Newman-Keuls procedure

Among the demographic variables, no differences were revealed between males and females ($F_{1.654} = 0.051$, $p = 0.821$), each of the three age groups ($F_{2.653} = 0.727$, $p = 0.484$), nor each of the three marital status groups ($F_{2.653} = 1.926$, $p = 0.147$) with respect to their psychological well-being. There also were no significant differences among the three age groups in their levels of depressive symptoms ($F_{2.641} = 0.467$, $p = 0.627$). On the other hand, females were significantly more depressed than males ($F_{1.642} = 16.096$, $p < .001$) and married older adults were significantly less depressed than widows and widowers and those who were single, divorced or separated ($F_{2.641} = 4.840$, $p = .008$). These results are consistent with the findings of others which suggest that females are at higher risk of depression than males (Kane, Ouslander, & Abrass, 1984; Williamson, 1974). The literature also suggests that married older adults have significantly higher scores on life satisfaction, morale, psychological adjustment, and happiness, and lower levels of depression than do widows or widowers (e.g., Bradburn, 1969; Essex & Nam, 1987; Lopata, Heinemann, & Baum, 1982; MacRae, 1990; Rice, 1989).

The Effect of Selected Demographic Variables

The introduction of controls for sex, age, and marital status had little consequence on the relationships associated with leisure activity participation and psychological well-being and depression. Of the 36 separate analyses undertaken (six activities by three demographic factors by two psychological states), a significant interaction effect appeared in only one instance. Age significantly moderated the relationship between psychological well-being and visiting friends ($F_{8,641} = 2.650$, p = .032). In this particular case, the positive relationship between visiting friends and psychological well-being appeared for only those in the pre-retirement age group (*see Figure 1*). For older adults between the ages of 65 and 74 years, psychological well-being decreased somewhat with moderate involvement in visiting friends and then raised substantially with regular involvement. On the other hand, psychological well-being increased with moderate levels of visitation for those adults 75 years and older, but then decreased slightly with regular participation.

In all other cases, the significant positive relationships between psychological well-being and participation in hobbies and crafts, visiting friends, and swimming remained even after the introduction of controls for sex, age, and marital status. Significant main effects resulting from participation in hobbies and crafts, visiting friends, and swimming as well as sex and marital status, again were present for depression, however, there were no significant interaction effects between participation in the activities and either sex or marital status. Clearly, the relationship of these factors to depression are independent of one another. Overall, the relationships between psychological well-being and depression and participation in each of the activities considered in this study were generally not moderated by the demographic variables examined here.

In order to describe the relative strength of the affect of the variables in these relationships, their deviations from the grand mean of psychological well-being and depression and their associated beta values are reported in Table 5 based on the MCA. Of the six leisure activities considered, participation in hobbies and crafts showed the strongest relationship with psychological well-being and depression. Participation in hobbies and crafts (Beta = .21), visiting friends (Beta = .13) and swimming (Beta = .11) were the three strongest predictors of psychological well-being. Sex (Beta=.16), participation in hobbies and crafts (Beta=.14), and marital status (Beta=.12) showed the strongest relationships with levels of depressive symptoms. It would appear that participation levels in selected activities are more closely linked to psychological well-being and that demographic variables are more closely associated with depression. Consequently, these results provide further evidence that psychological well-being and depression are not necessarily analogous concepts.

FIGURE 1

**Relationship Between Psychological Well-Being,
Participation in Hobbies and Crafts, and Age**

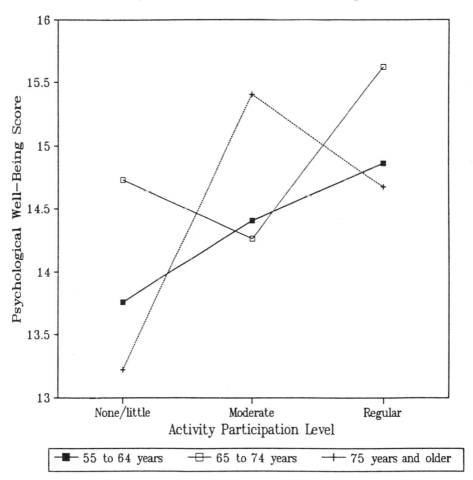

TABLE 5

Deviations from the Grand Mean and Beta Values for Moderating Affects of Variables on Psychological Well-Being and Depression

Variable	Psychological Well-Being			Depression		
Category	n	Deviation	Beta	n	Deviation	Beta
Leisure Participation						
Television viewing						
None/little	139	.17		137	-.48	
Moderate	301	.05	.04	293	.16	.04
Regular	215	-.18		211	.09	
Hobbies/crafts						
None/little	225	-.77		217	1.00	
Moderate	195	.11	.21**	191	.37	.14**
Regular	222	.68		221	-1.31	
Visiting friends						
None/little	131	-.54		127	1.42	
Moderate	369	-.05	.13**	363	-.07	.11*
Regular	150	.59		148	-1.05	
Social clubs/org.						
None/little	455	-.13		446	.13	
Moderate	78	.52	.08	78	.63	.06
Regular	116	.17		113	-.94	
Walking for exercise						
None/little	186	-.10		183	-.35	
Moderate	113	-.10	.03	107	.01	.03
Regular	348	.09		342	.18	
Swimming						
Non-participants	503	-.18	.11**	491	.36	.09*
Participants	149	.61		147	-1.21	
Demographics						
Sex						
Females	378	.02	.01	370	.97	.16**
Males	278	-.03		274	-1.30	
Age Group						
55 to 64 years	349	-.13		338	.25	
65 to 74 years	223	.15	.05	222	-.22	.04
75 years or older	84	.13		84	-.44	
Marital Status						
Married	462	.12		451	-.56	
Widowed	126	-.11	.08	125	1.02	.12**
Single/Div./Sep.	68	-.61		68	1.81	

* significant difference between groups at 0.05 level
** significant difference between groups at 0.01 level

The Relationship Between Well-Being and Leisure Diversity

Pearson correlation coefficients were used to assess whether or not there were significant relationships between psychological well-being and depressive symptoms and leisure diversity. The results suggest that leisure diversity has a significant, positive correlation with psychological well-being ($r = .1993$, $p < .001$) and a significant negative correlation with depression ($r = -.1661$, $p < .001$). When these relationships were examined for each of the different groups based on sex, age, and marital status, they remained consistently significant. Of note, the relationship between psychological well-being and leisure repertoire was especially strong for older adults over the age of 75 years ($r = .3015$, $p < .001$).

Apparently, a greater repertoire of leisure pursuits from which to draw may be related to higher levels of psychological well-being and less frequent occurrences of depression among older adults. These results are consistent with the findings of other researchers who have examined the relationship between life satisfaction and the leisure diversity. For example, Zuzanek and Box (1988, p. 178) concluded: "In general, it appears that the greater the number of leisure activities older adults engage in, and the greater their participation in structured leisure pursuits, the happier they are."

Discussion and Conclusions

The assumption that leisure activity participation is positively related to psychological well-being and negatively related to depression received some support by the results generated in this study. The findings, however, suggest that certain activities are more strongly related to psychological well-being and lower levels of depression than are others. Higher participation rates in selected passive (hobbies and crafts), social (visiting friends), and physical (swimming) activities appeared to be significantly related to higher psychological well-being and lower depression. Interestingly, the effects of participation were most pronounced for a passive activity (crafts and hobbies) rather than for a physically active or social pursuit which is somewhat of a departure from previous findings (Brown, Frankel, & Fennell, 1991; Peppers, 1976; Ragheb & Griffith, 1982; Zuzanek & Box, 1988). Zuzanek and Box (1988), for example, found that the correlations between the life satisfaction of older adults and participation in most leisure activities were strong with the exception of participation in hobbies. Furthermore, studies that have focused on the psychological well-being/leisure activity participation relationships have found few if any significant relationships for adults 65 years of age and older (Brown, Frankel, & Fennell, 1991).

The significant relationships between participation in hobbies and crafts and psychological well-being and depression are especially important when one considers that the rate of participation in hobbies and crafts increases substantially after retirement in comparison with other activities. Zuzanek and Box (1988) found in 1981 that older adults spent an average of 5.9 hours per week on hobbies after retirement compared to 1.8 hours before retirement – an increase of more than three times the duration. On the other hand, the amount of time spent in social leisure and physically active leisure was only 44 % and 20 % higher respectively among older adults than among their younger counterparts. Although older adults spend a greater proportion of their time in more home-centred and passive activities, these activities are frequently ignored in assessments of well-being. Future research should examine the relationship between psychological well-being and depression and other home-based activities like hobbies and crafts.

With an emphasis on physical and social well-being in much of the previous research, little attention has been given to the importance of personal outcomes linked to regular participation in specific leisure activities. Considering Tinsley and Tinsley's (1986) model of the causal effects of the leisure experience, more passive leisure pursuits may satisfy more personal needs – the needs for personal achievement, self-expression, self-fulfilment, and recognition – and in turn, contribute to higher psychological well-being and life satisfaction. In their attempt to classify leisure activities by psychological benefits, Tinsley and his associates (Tinsley, Teaff, Colbs, & Kaufman, 1985; Tinsley, Colbs, Teaff, & Kaufman, 1987) found that participation in hobbies and crafts may provide what they called "expressive solitude" benefits for older adults. In their studies, activities such as knitting, crocheting and woodworking provided the opportunity for older adults to express themselves creatively through their talents, to undertake novel activities, and to receive rewards and recognition for their achievements. Participation in more passive activities such as hobbies and crafts may also be linked to one's self-esteem by providing older adults with a sense of accomplishment and purpose. Aging is often associated with loss, especially the loss of work roles and the sense of purpose identified with those roles, and depression and low psychological well-being are typical reactions to the losses associated with the psychological aging process (Garrigan, 1986). Thus, involvement in activities that promote creativity, self-expression, and a sense of accomplishment may be most strongly related to the re-establishment of a sense of purpose and/or self-worth.

The potential psychological benefits that older adults derive from participation in specific leisure activities has been largely ignored and should be explored further. Furthermore, it may be the inherent qualities of specific leisure activities and the meanings associated with them rather than the activities themselves that are most strongly related to psychological well-being and emotional health (Smale & Dupuis, 1993). In other words, it may not simply be hobbies and crafts which are related to well-being, but rather the opportunity they provide for freedom of choice, self-expression, and personal fulfilment.

Evidence from this study generally supports and expands upon the findings of McTeer and Curtis (1990). They suggested that the relationship between psychological well-being and physical activity participation is largely a direct relationship. Overall, it appears here that the direct relationship is also true for certain social and passive activities. Only one interaction effect emerged, and in that instance, age appeared to significantly moderate the relationship between psychological well-being and visiting friends. Neither age, sex, nor marital status played a role in determining the outcomes associated with most forms of passive, social, and physically active pursuits even though, independently, both sex and marital status were significantly related to depression. Nonetheless, this study only examined the role that three demographic factors may play in the well-being/activity participation relationship. Other factors such as income, education, health status, race, and place of residence may prove to be more important than the three examined in this study. Furthermore, many of the circumstances of aging such as social isolation, economic deprivation, chronic ill health, and the loss of family members and friends can restrict one's opportunity for activity involvement and thus overall happiness (Stones & Kozma, 1989). An examination of the mediating effects of these constraints to leisure that are experienced by older adults may provide greater insights into the relationship between psychological well-being and depression and leisure activity participation.

Much of the literature has tended to regard the relationship between leisure activity participation and psychological well-being and depression as unidirectional and linear. Leisure participation has typically been treated as a contributing factor to changes in psychological states with increases in participation leading to higher levels of well-being and lower levels of depression. However, the nature of these relationships and their direction are likely much more complex. Indeed, a more plausible explanation is that the relationship between leisure participation and psychological well-being is a reciprocal one. For example, higher levels of psychological well-being may lead individuals to increase their participation in meaningful activities that contribute, in return, to the maintenance or perhaps even enhancement of their psychological state. Consequently, the effects of other life circumstances, such as social context, may ultimately serve to moderate this positive reciprocal relationship by creating opportunities for it to occur or presenting barriers to its realisation.

Finally, although the results from this study suggest that participation in certain activities is more strongly related to psychological well-being and depression than others, the study did not investigate the relationship between well-being and individual leisure lifestyles. Are certain combinations of activities more strongly related to psychological well-being more so than other combinations? The evidence demonstrates that the more activities in which older adults are involved is closely associated with higher psychological well-being and the lower levels of depression. However, it is unclear whether a leisure lifestyle based on several activities of different forms (e.g., combining passive, social, and physical) or one based on several activities of the same form (e.g., all activities of a passive nature) are more or less strongly related to the psychological well-being of older adults. Investigations into the relationship between well-being and differing leisure lifestyles may prove useful and informative.

References

ANDREWS, F.M. & MCKENNELL, A.C. (1980). Measures of self-reported well-being: Their affective, cognitive, and other components. *Social Indicators Research, 8,* 127-155.

BENNETT, J., CARMACK, M.A., & GARDNER, V.J. (1982). The effect of a program of physical exercise on depression in older adults. *Physical Educator, 39,* 21-24.

BILD, B.K. & HAVIGHURST, R.J. (1976). Life satisfaction. *The Gerontologist, 16,* 70-75.

BOWLING, A. (1991). *Measuring health: A review of quality of life measurement scales.* Philadelphia, PA: Milton Keynes.

BRADBURN, N.M. (1969). *The structure of psychological well-being.* Chicago: Aldine.

BROWN, B.A., FRANKEL, B.G., & FENNELL, M. (1991). Happiness through leisure: The impact of type of leisure activity, age, gender and leisure satisfaction on psychological well-being. *Journal of Applied Recreation Research, 16,* 367-391.

BUSSE, E.W. & PFEIFFER, E. (1973). *Mental illness in later life.* Washington, DC: American Psychiatric Association.

CAMPBELL, A., CONVERSE, P.E., & RODGERS, W.L. (1976). *The quality of American life: Perceptions, evaluations, and satisfaction.* New York, NY: Russell Sage Foundation.

ELWELL, F. & MALTBIE-CRANNELL, A.D. (1981). The impact of role loss upon coping resources and life satisfaction of the elderly. *Journal of Gerontology, 36,* 223-232.

EMERY, C.F. & GATZ, M. (1990). Psychological and cognitive effects of an exercise program for community-residing older adults. *The Gerontologist, 30,* 184-188.

ESSEX, M. & NAM, S. (1987). Marital status and loneliness among older women: The differential importance of close family and friends. *Journal of Marriage and the Family, 48,* 93-106.

GARRIGAN, S.S. (1986). Who did you used to be? The psychological process of aging's impact on institutionalization: Implications for activities. *In* P.M. Foster (Éd.), *Therapeutic activities with the impaired elderly* (pp. 75-78). New York: The Haworth Press.

GEORGE, L.K. (1978). The impact of personality and social status factors upon levels of activity and psychological well-being. *Journal of Gerontology, 33,* 840-847.

GEORGE, L.K. (1989). Stress, social support, and depression over the life-course. *In* K.S. Markides & C.L. Cooper (Éds.), *Aging, stress and health* (pp. 241-267). Chichester: John Wiley and Sons.

GEORGE, L K. & BEARON, L.B. (1980). *Quality of life in older persons: Meaning and measurement.* New York: Human Sciences Press.

GORDON, M. (1987). *Manual of Nursing Diagnosis: 1986-1987.* New York, NY: McGraw-Hill.

KANE, R.A., OUSLANDER, J., & ABRASS, I. (1984). *Essentials of clinical geriatrics.* New York: McGraw-Hill.

KELLY, J.R. & ROSS, J. (1989). Later-life leisure: Beginning a new agenda. *Leisure Sciences, 11,* 47-59.

KELLY, J.R., STEINKAMP, M., & KELLY, J. (1987). Later-life satisfaction: Does leisure contribute? *Leisure Sciences, 9,* 189:200.

KOZMA, A., STONES, M.J., & MCNEIL, J.K. (1991). *Psychological well-being in later life.* Toronto, Canada: Butterworths Canada Ltd.

LARSON, R., MANNELL, R., & ZUZANEK, J. (1986). Daily well-being of older adults with friends and family. *Psychology and Aging, 1,* 117-126.

LARSON, R., ZUZANEK, J., & MANNELL, R. (1985). Being alone versus being with people: Disengagement in the daily experience of older adults. *Journal of Gerontology, 40,* 375-381.

LAWTON, M.P. (1972). The dimensions of morale. *In* D. Kent *et al.* (Éds.), *Research, planning and action for the elderly.* New York, NY: Behavioral Publications.

LEE, G.R. & ISHII-KUNTZ, M. (1987). Social interaction, loneliness, and emotional well-being among the elderly. *Research on Aging, 9,* 459-482.

LEVITT, E.E., LUBIN, B., & BROOKS, J.M. (1983). *Depression: Concepts, controversies, and some new facts* (2nd edition). Hillsdale, New Jersey: Lawrence Erlbaum Associates, Publishers.

LOMRANZ, J., BERGMAN, S., EYAL, N., & SHMOTKIN, D. (1988) Indoor and outdoor activities of aged women and men as related to depression and well-being. *International Journal of Aging and Human Development, 26,* 303-314.

LOPATA, H.Z., HEINEMANN, G., & BAUM, J. (1982). Loneliness: Antecedents and coping strategies in the lives of widows. *In* L.A. Peplau & D. Perlman (Éds.), *Loneliness: A sourcebook of current theory, research and therapy* (pp. 310-326). New York: John Wiley and Sons.

MACRAE, H. (1990). Older women and identity maintenance in later life. *Canadian Journal on Aging, 9,* 248-267.

MCKENNELL, A.C. (1978). Cognition and affect in perceptions of well-being. *Social Indicators Research, 5,* 389-426.

MCKENNELL, A.C. & ANDREWS, F.M. (1980). Models of cognition and affect in perceptions of well-being. *Social Indicators Research, 8,* 257-298.

MCPHERSON, B.D. (1990). *Aging as a social process: An introduction to individual and population aging,* 2nd Edition. Toronto: Butterworth.

MCTEER, W. & CURTIS, J.E. (1990). Physical activity and psychological well-being: Testing alternative sociological interpretations. *Sociology of Sport Journal, 7,* 329-346.

MORGAN, K., DALLOSSO, H., BASSEY, E.J., EBRAHIM, S., FENTEM, P.H., & ARIE, T.H.D. (1991). Customary physical activity, psychological well-being and successful ageing. *Ageing and Society, 11,* 399-415.

MORGAN, L.A. (1976). A re-examination of widowhood and morale. *Journal of Gerontology, 31*, 687-695.

MORIWAKI, S.Y. (1974). The Affect Balance Scale: A validity study with aged samples. *Journal of Gerontology, 29*, 73-78.

MULLINS, L.C. & MUSHEL, M. (1992). The existence and emotional closeness of relationships with children, friends, and spouses: The effect on loneliness among older persons. *Research on Aging, 14*, 448-470.

OKUN, M.A., STOCK, W.A., HARING, M.J., & WITTER, R.A. (1984). The social activity/subjective well-being relation: A quantitative synthesis. *Research on Aging, 6*, 45-65.

PALMORE, E. & KIVETT, V. (1977). Change in life satisfaction: A longitudinal study of persons aged 46-70. *Journal of Gerontology, 32*, 311-316.

PARKER, G. (1978). *The bonds of depression.* Sydney, Australia: Angus and Robertson.

PEPPERS, L.G. (1976). Patterns of leisure and adjustment to retirement. *The Gerontologist, 16*, 441-446.

PEARLIN, L.I. & JOHNSON, J.S. (1981). Marital status, life-strains and depression. *In* P.J. Stein (Éd.), *Single-Life: Unmarried adults in social context* (pp. 165-178). New York: St. Martin's Press.

RADLOFF, L.S. & LOCKE, B.Z. (1986). The Community Mental Health Assessment Survey and CES-D Scale. *In* M.M. Weissman, J.K. Myers, & C.E. Ross (Éds.), *Community surveys of psychiatric disorders* (pp. 177-189). New Brunswick, NJ: Rutgers University Press.

RAGHEB, M. (1993). Leisure and perceived wellness: A field investigation. *Leisure Sciences, 15*, 13-24.

RAGHEB, M. & GRIFFITH, C.A. (1982). The contribution of leisure participation and leisure satisfaction to life satisfaction of older persons. *Journal of Leisure Research, 14*, 295-305.

RIDDICK, C.C. (1985a). Life satisfaction for older female homemakers, retirees, and workers. *Research on Aging, 7*, 383-393.

RIDDICK, C.C. (1985b). Life satisfaction determinants of older males and females. *Leisure Sciences, 7*, 47-63.

RIDDICK, C.C. & DANIEL, S.N. (1984). The relative contribution of leisure activities and other factors to the mental health of older women. *Journal of Leisure Research, 16*, 136-148.

RUSSELL, R.V. (1987). The importance of recreation satisfaction and activity participation to the life satisfaction of age-segregated retirees. *Journal of Leisure Research, 19*, 273-283.

SAUER, W. (1977). Morale of the urban aged: A regression analysis by race. *Journal of Gerontology, 32*, 600-608.

SMALE, B.J.A. & DUPUIS, S L. (1993). The relationship between leisure activity participation and psychological well-being across the lifespan. *Journal of Applied Recreation Research, 18*, 281-300.

SNEEGAS, J.J. (1986). Components of life satisfaction in middle and later life adults: Perceived social competence, leisure participation, and leisure satisfaction. *Journal of Leisure Research, 18*, 248-258.

STEINKAMP, M.W. & KELLY, J.R. (1987). Social integration, leisure activity and life satisfaction in older adults: Activity theory revisited. *International Journal of Aging and Human Development, 25*, 293-307.

STEPHENS, T. & CRAIG, C.L. (1990). *The Well-Being of Canadians: Highlights of the 1988 Campbell's Survey.* Ottawa, Canada: Canadian Fitness and Lifestyle Research Institute.

STONES, M.J. & KOZMA, A. (1989). Happiness and activities in later life: A propensity formulation. *Canadian Psychology, 30*, 526-537.

STOUDEMIRE, A. & BLAZER, D.G. (1985). Depression in the elderly. *In* E.E. Beckham & W.R. Leber (Éds.), *Handbook of depression: Treatment, assessment, and research* (pp. 556-586). Homewood, IL: The Dorsey Press.

STULL, D.E. (1987). Conceptualization and measurement of well-being: Implications for policy evaluation. *In* E.F. Borgatta & R.J.F. Montgomery (Éds.), *Critical issues in aging policy* (pp. 55-90). Newbury Park, CA: Sage Publications.

TINSLEY, H.E.A., COLBS, S L., TEAFF, J.D., & KAUFMAN, N. (1987). The relationship of age, gender, health and economic status to the psychological benefits older persons report from participation in leisure activities. *Leisure Sciences, 9*, 53-65.

TINSLEY, H.E.A. & TINSLEY, D.J. (1986). A theory of the attributes, benefits, and causes of leisure experience. *Leisure Sciences, 8*, 1-45.

TINSLEY, H.E.A., TEAFF, J.D., COLBS, S.L., & KAUFMAN, N. (1985). A system of classifying leisure activities in terms of the psychological benefits of participation reported by older person. *Journal of Gerontology, 40*, 172-178.

WEINSTEIN, W.S. & KHANNA, P. (1986). *Depression in the elderly.* New York: Philosophical Library.

WILLIAMSON, J. (1974). Depression. *In* W. Anderson & T. Judge (Éds.), *Geriatric medicine* (pp. 67-75). New York: Academic Press.

WINOKUR, G. (1981). *Depression: The facts.* Oxford: Oxford University Press

WOOD, V., WYLIE, M.L., & SHEAFOR, B. (1969). An analysis of a short self-report measure of life satisfaction: Correlation with rater judgments. *Journal of Gerontology, 24*, 465-469.

ZIMMER, H. & FOY, J.L. (1959). A conceptual framework for the study of depressive reactions. *Neuropsychiatry, 5*, 129-152.

ZUZANEK J. & BOX, S.J. (1988). Life course and the daily lives of older adults in Canada. *In* K. Altergott (Éd.), *Daily life in later life* (pp. 147-185). London: Sage Publications.

Sherry L. DUPUIS et Bryan J.A. SMALE
Analyse de la relation entre le bien-être psychologique, la dépression et la participation aux activités de loisir chez les personnes âgées

RÉSUMÉ

Les recherches publiées à ce jour permettent de penser que la participation au loisir se rattache positivement au bien-être physique et à la satisfaction générale des individus par rapport à la vie ; elles ont cependant négligé sa relation au bien-être psychologique et à la dépression. Pourtant, les personnes âgées risquent davantage de voir diminuer leur bien-être psychologique en raison des pertes généralement reliées au vieillissement. Les auteurs ont donc choisi d'analyser les relations entre la participation aux activités de loisir d'une part et le bien-être psychologique et la dépression d'autre part chez les personnes âgées. La participation à des activités de loisir à caractère passif (télévision et passe-temps et bricolage), social (visites à des amis et participation à des clubs et organisations sociaux), et physique (marche d'exercice et natation) a été analysée relativement à ses effets sur le bien-être psychologique et la dépression des personnes de plus de 55 ans. Ces relations ont été également analysées par rapport au sexe, à l'âge et à l'état matrimonial afin de déterminer le rôle de ces facteurs dans la variation des relations. Les résultats indiquent que la participation à des passe-temps et à du bricolage ainsi que les visites à des amis sont reliées positivement à un plus grand bien-être psychologique et à des degrés inférieurs de symptômes dépressifs chez tous les sujets, peu importe le sexe, l'âge et l'état matrimonial. Il semble également qu'une plus grande variété d'activités de loisir soit associée à un plus grand bien-être psychologique et à des symptômes moins prononcés de dépression. Dans l'ensemble, les résultats permettent de penser que les activités de loisir qui fournissent le plus d'occasions de faire des choix, de s'exprimer et de créer sont celles qui sont le plus susceptibles d'améliorer le bien-être psychologique et de diminuer la dépression chez les personnes âgées.

Sherry L. DUPUIS and Bryan J.A. SMALE
An Examination of the Relationship Between Psychological Well-Being and Depression and Leisure Activity Participation Among Older Adults

ABSTRACT

Previous research has suggested that leisure participation is positively related to an individual's physical well-being and overall life satisfaction, but has generally neglected its relationship to psychological well-being and depression. Older adults are most susceptible to declines in these psychological states because of the losses typically associated with the aging process. Therefore, in this paper, the relationships between leisure activity participation and psychological well-being and depression are examined for older adults. Participation in passive leisure activities (television viewing and hobbies and crafts), social leisure activities (visiting friends and participation in social clubs and organisations), and physically active pursuits (walking for exercise and swimming) was assessed for its affect on both the psychological well-being and depression of individuals over the age of 55. These relationships are further examined within the context of sex, age, and marital status to determine the role these factors may play in moderating the relationships. The results indicated that participation in hobbies and crafts and visiting friends was positively related to greater psychological well-being and to lower levels of depressive symptoms among all older adults regardless of sex, age, and marital status. A greater diversity of leisure activities also appeared to be associated with higher psychological well-being and lower depressive symptoms. Overall, the findings suggest that leisure activities with the qualities best able to provide opportunities for freedom of choice, self-expression, and creativity are most likely to bring about higher psychological well-being and lower depression among older adults.

Sherry L. DUPUIS y Bryan J.A. SMALE
Análisis de la relación entre el bienestar psicológico, la depresión
y la participación a las actividades recreativas en las personas ancianas.

RESUMEN

Las investigaciones publicadas hasta hoy en día permiten de pensar que la participación a las actividades de diversión se ligan positivamente al bienestar físico y a la satisfacción general de los individuos con relación a la vida; sin embargo, éstas descuidaron su relación con el bienestar psicológico y la depresión. Por lo tanto, las personas ancianas son más propensas a disminuir su bienestar psicológico a causa de las pérdidas generalmente ligadas al envejecimiento. Los autores escogieron pues, de analizar las relaciones entre la participación a las actividades de recreo por una parte, y el bienestar psicológico y la depresión, por otra; entre las personas ancianas. La participación a las actividades de diversión con carácter pasivo (televisión, pasatiempos y bricolages), social (visitas a amigos y participación a los clubes y organizaciones sociales), y físico (caminata y natación) fue analizada con respecto a sus efectos sobre el bienestar psicológico y la depresión, en las personas de más de 55 años. Estas relaciones fueron también evaluadas con referancia al sexo, a la edad y al estado matrimonial, afín de determinar el papel de estos factores en la variación de las relaciones. Los resultados indican que la participación en pasatiempos y en el bricolage, así como las visitas a los amigos, están ligadas positivamente a un mayor bienestar psicológico y a los grados inferiores de síntomas depresivos entre todos los sujetos, poco importa el sexo, la edad y el estado matrimonial. Parece ser, igualmente, que una gran variedad de actividades de diversión esté asociada a un mayor bienestar psicológico y a síntomas menos marcados de depresión. En conjunto, los resultados permiten de pensar que las actividades de diversión que proporcionan más ocasiones de hacer elecciones, de exprimirse y de crear, son las más susceptibles de mejorar el bienestar psicológico y de disminuir la depresión entre las personas mayores.

L'ACTIVITÉ, L'AUTONOMIE ET LE BIEN-ÊTRE PSYCHOLOGIQUE DES PERSONNES ÂGÉES

Jacques ROUSSEAU
Marie-Claude DENIS
Micheline DUBÉ
Micheline BEAUCHESNE

Département de psychologie
Université du Québec à Trois-Rivières
Québec, Canada

Problématique

Le vieillissement de la population pose de multiples défis à notre société ; la manière d'aborder cette question influe cependant sur le type d'intervention privilégié. Ainsi, il n'est pas rare de retrouver une vision pessimiste de ce phénomène : l'accent est mis sur la perte d'autonomie, les problèmes de santé physique et mentale, les programmes et les services à instaurer, bref sur l'inadaptation qui semble accompagner inévitablement la vieillesse. On s'intéresse moins fréquemment aux aspects dynamiques de ce processus, à la qualité de la vie et aux facteurs qui contribuent au développement et au bonheur des personnes âgées.

La présente recherche est axée sur la santé plutôt que la maladie ; elle cherche à décrire et à analyser certains facteurs reliés à un vieillissement « réussi ». Il s'agit d'une approche développementale, et non déficitaire, de la vieillesse. Les contraintes inhérentes à cet âge (santé, conditions de vie, veuvage) ne sont pas présentées comme entraînant une baisse irrémédiable de la qualité de vie ; l'accent porte plutôt sur un ensemble d'autres facteurs personnels, sociaux et environnementaux capables d'assurer un maintien ou une croissance du bien-être psychologique.

Loisir et société / Society and Leisure
Volume 18, numéro 1, printemps 1995, pp. 93-122 • © Presses de l'Université du Québec

Cette recherche tente particulièrement de relier le bien-être psychologique à l'activité chez la personne âgée. À cette fin sont tout d'abord délimités les concepts de bien-être psychologique et d'activité, qui déborde celui de loisir ; certaines variables personnelles et environnementales, notamment l'autonomie psychologique, les événements stressants, la santé et l'habitat, sont ensuite introduites dans un modèle plus général ; finalement, les résultats sont présentés et discutés.

Le bien-être psychologique

Le bien-être psychologique a souvent été cerné par deux concepts considérés comme synonymes : la qualité de vie subjective et la satisfaction de vivre. La qualité de vie constitue, selon Okun et Stock (1987), un « concept parapluie » désignant, sur un continuum allant du négatif au positif, les réactions des individus à leurs expériences de vie. Il s'agit d'une réaction ou d'une réponse personnelle susceptible d'être évaluée uniquement par le recours aux représentations individuelles, car les critères d'une « bonne » qualité de vie sont propres à chacun. Lawton (1983) fait remarquer que la qualité de vie peut être évaluée soit de façon globale, soit à l'intérieur de domaines de vie précis comme le travail, la santé ou les loisirs. Cutler (1979) distingue ainsi plus de dix « domaines » particuliers : maison, quartier, travail, organisations, mariage, famille, amis, santé, revenu, etc. L'autre concept associé, celui de la satisfaction de vivre, comporte également une composante cognitive : il renvoie à l'évaluation faite par l'individu de sa vie, de lui-même et de son environnement (Neugarten, Havigurst et Tobin, 1961).

Le concept de bien-être psychologique est toutefois plus large que ces deux concepts associés, puisqu'il met l'accent non seulement sur la dimension cognitive ou évaluative, mais également sur l'aspect affectif découlant de cette évaluation des conditions et des expériences de vie. Bradburn (1969) a beaucoup contribué à définir cet aspect du bien-être. Il propose une vision plus affective et plus émotionnelle que celle de Lawton. Pour lui, le bien-être psychologique est passablement indépendant des conditions de vie ou de l'environnement ; il renvoie à des dimensions plus intérieures telles que le sentiment de compétence, l'estime de soi, les relations affectives et, plus généralement, l'optimisme et le bonheur. Ce dernier s'évalue par la prépondérance des affects positifs sur les affects négatifs.

Certains chercheurs prétendent qu'il est possible et utile de distinguer ces deux composantes ou dimensions du bien-être psychologique, c'est-à-dire l'affect (positif et négatif) et la cognition (Andrews et McKennell, 1980 ; Stock, Okun et Benin, 1986 ; Warr, Barter et Brownbridge, 1983). Plusieurs autres demeurent cependant ambigus sur la question de savoir si ces dimensions sont indépendantes, interreliées ou totalement unifiées. Par exemple, Stock *et al.*

(1986) proposent que le concept de bien-être subjectif soit intégré à une théorie cognitive des émotions, impliquant par le fait même que les deux composantes sont indissociables. Pour découvrir comment et pourquoi les individus en arrivent à évaluer leur vie d'une manière positive, il serait donc essentiel de considérer à la fois leurs jugements cognitifs et leurs réactions affectives. Appuyant cette idée, Kosma et Stones (1978), Georges (1981) et Horley (1984) suggèrent de définir le bien-être subjectif comme un métaconcept large et abstrait, opérationalisé par des indicateurs concrets comme la satisfaction de vivre, le bonheur ou le moral.

La notion de bien-être psychologique se construit donc autour de l'évaluation de la vie personnelle, présente ou passée, de la satisfaction par rapport à soi, du sentiment de compétence et du bonheur.

> *Une personne sera considérée au pôle positif du bien-être dans la mesure où elle :* a) *prend plaisir dans la routine d'activités quotidiennes qui constitue chacune de ses journées ;* b) *regarde sa vie comme pleine de sens et accepte résolument ce que sa vie a été ;* c) *ressent qu'elle a réussi dans l'accomplissement de ses buts principaux ;* d) *a une image positive d'elle-même ;* e) *conserve une humeur joyeuse et une attitude optimiste* (Neugarten *et al.*, 1961, p. 137).

Les corrélats du bien-être psychologique

Les déterminants du bien-être le plus souvent signalés dans les recherches en gérontologie sont l'âge, le sexe, l'état civil, l'éducation, le statut socio-économique, la santé, le revenu, l'environnement résidentiel, le milieu (rural ou urbain), les événements stressants, la compétence personnelle, l'estime de soi, le lieu de contrôle et la participation à des activités physiques et sociales (Diener, 1984 ; Kosma et Stones, 1978 ; Kosma, Stones et McNeil, 1991 ; Larson, 1978). La présente recherche s'intéresse particulièrement à l'activité comme prédicteur du bien-être.

Activités, participation sociale et loisirs des personnes âgées

L'activité constitue un facteur ambigu dans une société où les rôles valorisés sont ceux de travailleur et d'entrepreneur, et où le statut de la personne âgée semble dépourvu de fonction sociale significative. Les premières recherches psychosociales en gérontologie s'inscrivent d'ailleurs dans cette problématique de l'opposition entre l'activité et le désengagement inévitable sur le plan social. Dès le début des années 60, Cummins et Henry (1961), face aux transformations de la société moderne, prétendent qu'un vieillissement réussi implique un désengagement des rôles sociaux et une diminution des activités. Ce retrait progressif entraîne un déplacement de l'activité de l'extérieur vers l'intérieur (Hochschild, 1975). Selon Hétu (1988), les relations qui se maintiennent sont plus expressives qu'instrumentales ou fonctionnelles : la personne désengagée s'orienterait vers des activités agréables pour elle, ici et maintenant, plutôt que vers des activités susceptibles de lui rapporter ultérieurement.

Un important courant en gérontologie a cependant démontré que le moral et la satisfaction sont plutôt liés à la conservation des rôles sociaux et même à l'adoption de nouveaux rôles (Neugarten *et al.*, 1961). Cette théorie de l'activité soutient que les personnes âgées doivent demeurer actives et engagées socialement tout au long de la vie, et que la réussite du vieillissement est proportionnelle à la quantité d'activités auxquelles elles s'adonnent. Ainsi, Lemon, Bengtson et Peterson (1972) indiquent que ces personnes tentent de trouver des substituts aux rôles sociaux perdus ou volontairement abandonnés, un de ces substituts pouvant être le loisir. En ce sens, la satisfaction de vivre serait fonction de l'engagement et de la participation à la vie sociale.

En propageant l'idée selon laquelle une implication active est associée au bonheur, la théorie de l'activité a joué un rôle essentiel en gérontologie (Diener, 1984 ; Russel, 1990 ; Seneegas, 1987). Elle jouit encore d'une grande popularité, et est à l'origine des programmes visant à maintenir les personnes âgées le plus actives possible. Cependant, des chercheurs et des intervenants notent que si l'on force un sujet à participer à des activités non significatives à ses yeux, les conséquences sur le plan psychologique risquent de ne pas se révéler positives, bien au contraire (Hétu, 1988 ; Delisle, 1992). D'après Zay (1980), ce n'est pas tant l'activité qui serait garante du succès du vieillissement, mais la possibilité de rester actif si l'on en ressent le désir. De même, Roff et Atherton (1989) indiquent que l'activité en soi n'assure pas une vieillesse réussie, mais l'activité librement choisie et se déroulant dans un environnement social positif.

On peut trouver la réconciliation de ces deux conceptions dans la théorie du « noyau d'occupation » développée par J.R. Kelly. Selon cet auteur, l'identité sociale et l'estime de soi sont fonction des relations qu'entretient l'individu avec autrui. Son modèle stipule que la majorité des adultes possèdent un noyau stable d'activités formelles et informelles qui demeure le même tout au long des années et qui se révèle d'une importance capitale, car il est le reflet de leur mode de vie et de leur personnalité. Certes, à mesure que les gens vieillissent, certaines activités sont abandonnées tandis que de nouvelles se greffent à ce noyau au rythme des changements physiques et psychologiques. Les styles et les contextes d'engagement peuvent ainsi changer à mesure que l'identité sociale et personnelle se modifie au cours de l'existence. Il en va de même des rôles de loisir qui, selon Kelly, constituent un contexte d'interaction sociale et une façon d'exprimer et de développer l'identité personnelle (Delisle, 1992 ; Kelly, 1982 ; Kelly et Ross, 1989 ; Kelly et Steinkamp, 1986). Kelly affirme que cet espace de liberté permet à l'individu d'exercer des activités par lesquelles il s'exprime et se reconnaît, donc des activités significatives pour lui.

Typologies des activités

Le manque d'uniformité dans la façon de définir et de mesurer le concept d'activité diminue la comparabilité des résultats des différentes recherches et rend les liens entre l'activité et le bien-être psychologique difficiles à clarifier (McNeil, Stones et Kosma, 1986). Pour préciser et opérationaliser ce concept, il importe d'établir des distinctions entre les divers types d'activités de façon à évaluer leur contribution respective au bien-être psychologique. Ainsi, le fait de distinguer les *activités formelles* (participation à des organisations et associations) des *activités informelles* (interaction avec des amis ou des parents) a permis de constater que ces dernières sont les plus clairement associées au bien-être psychologique (Edwards et Klemmack, 1973 ; Longino et Kart, 1982). Une autre distinction importante porte sur le degré de contrainte : activités *obligatoires* (liées au travail ou à l'entretien) ou *libres* (liées au loisir). On constate que ces dernières contribuent davantage au bien-être psychologique (Larson, 1978 ; Mancini et Orthner, 1980 ; Russell, 1987). Ainsi, Hickson, Housley et Boyle (1988) ont vérifié le fait que les activités volontaires ont des effets significativement différents de celles qui sont imposées sur le bien-être psychologique des personnes âgées.

Par ailleurs, Tinsley, Colbs, Teaff et Kaufman (1985) remarquent que la classification des activités s'appuie souvent sur des bases théoriques plutôt qu'empiriques. On trouve ainsi une multitude d'autres classifications, telles la dichotomie actif-passif et les catégorisations par type de loisir (physique, artistique, pratique, intellectuel, sociaux (*cf.* Dumazedier, 1974). De plus, les catégories diffèrent souvent d'un chercheur à l'autre (Kelly et Ross 1989 ; Lemon *et al.*, 1972 ; Palmore, 1968 ; Pronovost, 1988). Nystrom (1974) et Tinsley *et al.* (1985), par exemple, ont classifié les activités en fonction des besoins que chacune d'elles satisfait (avoir des contacts, rendre service, passer le temps, être en forme, s'amuser, se développer, etc.). Ces différents travaux ont contribué à montrer l'importance de faire appel aux significations propres que revêtent les différentes activités pour les personnes elles-mêmes. Une activité considérée par l'une comme libre ou un loisir peut être vue par l'autre comme obligatoire, tout comme une activité peut permettre de satisfaire des besoins différents chez deux personnes. Ainsi, la quantité d'activités ne semble pas aussi importante que leur signification pour l'individu (Russell, 1987 ; Ragheb et Griffith, 1982). Selon Laforest (1989), pour échapper à l'ennui et à la solitude, les vieillards n'ont pas seulement besoin d'activités, mais d'activités significatives ; la stimulation ne vient donc pas des activités en elles-mêmes, mais du sens qu'elles prennent à leurs yeux.

Aspects qualitatifs de l'activité

Zay (1985) montre qu'il ne suffit pas d'être ou de se tenir occupé, puisque la qualité de l'activité est plus importante que sa fréquence ou que le nombre total des activités pratiquées. Celles-ci devraient comporter, selon lui, un certain défi et être suffisamment complexes pour meubler utilement le temps libre. Elles n'ont pas à être obligatoirement utiles ou nécessaires, et il est important de considérer le plaisir qu'elles procurent et la signification que chaque personne leur accorde. Le sujet qui s'adonne régulièrement à des activités sociales significatives pour lui peut faire face à la perte des rôles majeurs plus facilement que celui qui est privé de telles activités (Hétu, 1988). Lawton ajoute que la signification des activités n'est pas nécessairement rattachée à une grande dépense d'énergie, mais surtout au contexte dans lequel elles se situent et aux caractéristiques personnelles de l'individu (Delisle, 1992).

Trois dimensions qualitatives semblent particulièrement importantes : la motivation, la compétence et le plaisir retiré de la participation. La première, et la plus importante, se rapporte au sentiment de contrôle et à l'autonomie éprouvé par la personne dans l'accomplissement de ses activités (Deci et Ryan, 1985 ; Vallerand et O'Connors, 1991). Plusieurs études permettent de conclure que la liberté perçue et la motivation intrinsèque constituent des dimensions subjectives critiques pour l'atteinte de la satisfaction de vivre et du bien-être, alors qu'une motivation extrinsèque peut comporter des effets néfastes. Le sentiment d'autonomie ou d'obligation, la résignation ou la liberté de choix semblent donc être des dimensions tout aussi essentielles que le fait d'être actif ou inactif et d'accomplir beaucoup ou peu d'activités.

Selon Deci et Ryan (1985), la personne motivée de façon intrinsèque démontre une meilleure adaptation psychologique et physique. Le contexte dans lequel elle évolue semble aussi agir sur sa motivation : plus celui-ci offre des possibilités d'autonomie, plus elle est motivée de façon autodéterminée. La motivation intrinsèque est issue des besoins de compétence et d'autodétermination. Les événements, activités et situations qui font naître des sentiments de compétence chez la personne augmentent sa motivation intrinsèque (Vallerand et O'Connors, 1989), et ils ont un impact sur diverses variables telles la créativité, la concentration et les émotions positives ressenties au cours de la réalisation de la tâche.

La deuxième dimension consiste dans le sentiment de compétence, c'est-à-dire le jugement que la personne porte sur son habileté à accomplir des activités. Plusieurs auteurs (Lawton, 1985 ; Mancini et Othner, 1982) soutiennent que la compétence perçue représente une caractéristique particulièrement importante des activités de loisirs ; Atchley (1977) avance même qu'elle constitue la source majeure d'affirmation de la valeur des personnes âgées.

Il est important que les activités pratiquées correspondent au niveau d'habileté de la personne. Une trop grande facilité provoque l'ennui, et l'inverse fait naître l'anxiété. Csikszentmihalyi et Greaf (1980) rapportent qu'on observe un plus haut niveau de compétence dans une activité librement choisie que dans une activité obligatoire. L'habileté sociale des individus dans leur participation aux activités peut dépendre de la perception de leur efficacité personnelle (Seneegas, 1986). De leur côté, Thornton, Ryckman, Robins, Donolli et Bissen (1987) établissent un lien entre la perception de l'habileté et l'investissement dans les activités physiques. Les recherches effectuées par Nichols (1984) et Duda (1987) indiquent que la maîtrise des objectifs dans le domaine des exercices physiques devrait augmenter l'intérêt intrinsèque pour l'activité ainsi que prolonger la participation pendant l'exercice.

L'environnement joue aussi un rôle important dans la compétence perçue des aînés dans leurs activités. La recherche de Romaniuk, Hoyer et Romaniuk (1977) révèle que l'habilité des personnes âgées dépend partiellement des renforcements procurés par leur environnement social et physique. Selon le modèle d'adaptation au vieillissement de Lawton, une augmentation de la qualité environnementale favorise le sentiment de compétence. Kuypers et Bengtson (1973) affirment également qu'une performance fructueuse dans les rôles sociaux peut apporter à l'individu des informations à propos de sa compétence et contrer une éventuelle atrophie de ses habiletés.

Enfin, la troisième dimension, appelée satisfaction ou plaisir, se définit comme le fait de trouver agréable une activité et d'en retirer de la joie ou du contentement. La dimension affective est, bien sûr, fondamentale ici. Gordon et Gaith (1976) définissent le plaisir comme un aspect « expressif » ou gratuit du comportement ou de l'activité de loisir. Selon eux, certains plaisirs découlent cependant de la performance dans l'activité et sont reliés à un but, donc à la motivation. Le plaisir serait donc partiellement assimilable à l'autonomie. De même, Csikszentmihalyi (1975) soutient que le plaisir dérive du sentiment de compétence. Nous formulons cependant l'hypothèse que la dimension du plaisir se distingue à la fois de la compétence et de l'autonomie, et qu'elle constitue une dimension spécifique de l'activité. On peut, en effet, trouver agréables certaines activités, même si la motivation est extrinsèque ou le sentiment de compétence, limité. Les activités très populaires telles que l'écoute de la radio ou de la télévision en sont des exemples.

Les variables personnelles et environnementales

Outre le rôle de l'activité, la présente recherche examine plusieurs variables personnelles ou environnementales susceptibles d'être reliées au bien-être psychologique : les variables personnelles sont l'âge et le sexe, la santé et le revenu perçu, la résignation acquise et l'autonomie psychologique ; les variables environnementales sont l'habitat, le réseau social et les événements stressants.

Les variables personnelles

Le bien-être psychologique et l'activité semblent décroître avec l'âge, mais cette baisse serait plutôt liée à la diminution de la santé, du revenu ou du réseau social. Lorsque ces variables sont contrôlées, on n'observe plus d'effet spécifiquement relié à l'âge (Larson, 1978). La plupart des recherches n'ont découvert aucune influence de la variable sexe sur le bien-être (Bond, 1982).

Parmi tous les éléments composant la situation de vie d'une personne, la santé est un des plus fortement reliés au bien-être psychologique et aux activités sociales (McNeil et al., 1986). Les gens malades ou handicapés physiquement sont moins enclins à exprimer un contentement face à la vie, et ce, peu importe la manière dont la santé est évaluée, par le biais d'une évaluation subjective ou d'une mesure objective (Kosma et al., 1991).

Il en va de même pour le revenu. Plusieurs études ont établi que les personnes âgées dont le statut socio-économique est inférieur tendent également à présenter un faible bien-être psychologique (Mullis, 1992). Cette association se maintient lorsque les variables santé, emploi ou état civil sont contrôlées. Il faut noter que le statut socio-économique se présente comme une variable multidimensionnelle, obtenue par pondération du revenu, de l'occupation et de l'éducation. Le revenu semble être la variable prépondérante ; la corrélation entre le bien-être psychologique et l'éducation est plus faible quand des contrôles statistiques sont introduits (Krause, 1991). Des études indiquent que l'association entre le revenu et le bien-être psychologique ne se vérifie que sous sa forme négative, c'est-à-dire qu'on observe une relation entre le revenu inférieur et un faible niveau de bien-être psychologique (Palmore et Luikart, 1972). Enfin, si plusieurs autres études démontrent que le revenu objectif est relié au bien-être subjectif, la satisfaction face au revenu semble également constituer un bon indicateur du bonheur (Campbell et al., 1976 ; Rousseau et Dubé, 1991).

Parmi les caractéristiques personnelles retenues dans cette recherche, l'autonomie psychologique et sa contrepartie négative, la résignation, occupent une place centrale, place qui découle de la réflexion précédente sur les concepts de bien-être psychologique et d'activité. Selon plusieurs auteurs, dont Ellenberger (1987), Hageman et Tobin (1988), Moody (1988) et Saup (1987), l'aspect fondamental de l'autonomie psychologique des personnes âgées est la notion de contrôle, c'est-à-dire la volonté d'exercer son pouvoir de décider et d'agir selon ses propres règles et ses valeurs. Lebeau, Sicotte, Tilquin et Tremblay (1980) définissent l'autonomie comme «le pouvoir d'agir (comportemental) ou de ne pas agir, donc de choisir». La perte ou le manque de contrôle peut comporter un effet négatif sur la satisfaction de vie, l'estime de soi et l'engagement dans des activités (Rakowski et Cryan, 1990).

La définition de l'autonomie est généralement établie en fonction des décisions et des actions, mais la plupart des auteurs tiennent compte de la dynamique interne de l'individu. Collopy *et al.* (1990) décrivent le caractère de l'individu par rapport à l'authenticité ou à la non-authenticité. Lebeau *et al.* (1980) parlent de la possibilité de choisir l'orientation de sa conduite selon ses propres règles, et définissent certains aspects psychosociaux de l'autonomie comme des traits de personnalité. Paré (1984) fait ressortir l'importance de la possibilité d'être soi-même, de la liberté de poser les actions habituelles qui assurent le maintien de la personnalité et de ses expressions. Deci et Ryan (1987) indiquent qu'un individu doit ressentir une adhésion intérieure à ses choix. Ainsi, l'autonomie psychologique repose sur le contrôle exercé par la personne à partir de sa dynamique propre, c'est-à-dire en fonction de la perception de soi, des sentiments et de la motivation.

Un deuxième aspect de l'autonomie consiste en la compétence. Dimensions importantes de l'autonomie, les capacités physiques, cognitives et sociales se traduisent en activités susceptibles de promouvoir et d'entretenir cette compétence.

Jameton (1988) et Ploton (1990) signalent un dernier aspect de l'autonomie : la responsabilité, c'est-à-dire le souci de tenir compte du contexte social et de l'environnement dont doit faire preuve la personne autonome. Lebeau *et al.* (1980) parlent de choisir l'orientation de sa conduite en tenant compte des règles établies socialement.

En résumé, on peut distinguer, avec Dubé et Lalande (1991), deux grandes dimensions de l'autonomie : le contrôle (pouvoir) décisionnel et le contrôle (pouvoir) comportemental. De plus, selon ces auteurs, l'autonomie psychologique signifie « le maintien de la volonté d'exercer soi-même son pouvoir de décider et son pouvoir d'agir, en tenant compte des trois facteurs, soit la dynamique de l'individu, les capacités personnelles et l'intégration sociale » (p. 12).

Certains auteurs considèrent que l'absence de contrôle ou d'autonomie entraîne des effets néfastes et conduit à une situation appelée *résignation acquise ou apprise*. Lorsque les personnes sont exposées à des événements sur lesquels elles n'exercent pas de contrôle, ou peu, des effets débilitants risquent de se produire (Abramson, Seligman et Teasdale, 1978 ; Fry, 1989). Ces effets sont de nature cognitive (difficulté à apprendre une nouvelle tâche), motivationnelle (diminution de la motivation à exécuter cette nouvelle tâche et de la persistance face à un obstacle) ou émotionnelle (dépression, découragement et baisse de l'estime de soi). La théorie de la résignation acquise est d'inspiration attributionnelle (Abramson *et al.*, 1978). Lorsque les personnes se rendent compte de la non-contingence entre leur comportement et ses conséquences, elles en cherchent les causes, et cette démarche (l'attribution) débouche sur des degrés plus ou moins forts de résignation selon le type d'attribution.

Les variables environnementales

En tant que variable, l'habitat comporte plusieurs dimensions, dont notamment la satisfaction résidentielle, la satisfaction du quartier et l'enracinement, c'est-à-dire la durée de vie au même endroit. Les personnes âgées accordent une grande importance au facteur résidentiel, peut-être parce qu'elles sont moins engagées dans des activités de travail hors de leur logement.

La résidence et la satisfaction résidentielle ont fait l'objet de nombreuses recherches en gérontologie (Altman, Lawton et Wohlwill, 1984). Carp et Christensen (1986) établissent un lien entre certaines caractéristiques objectives (sécurité, propreté, calme, intimité, proximité des services) et la satisfaction résidentielle des personnes âgées. Golant (1986) fait cependant remarquer que celle-ci ne repose pas uniquement sur la qualité objective du logement, mais également sur des facteurs personnels tels que la perception de contrôle, l'état civil, la richesse, la santé, les activités, etc.

La satisfaction vis-à-vis du quartier a également été étudiée par rapport à la qualité de vie et au bien-être psychologique. Plusieurs variables peuvent être considérées ici : la proximité des amis et de la famille, l'homogénéité des résidants, le bruit, la propreté, la sécurité, l'accessibilité et l'abondance des services, la richesse du quartier, etc. Rousseau et Dubé (1991) considèrent également l'enracinement, c'est-à-dire la durée de vie au même endroit. Ce facteur est significativement corrélé à la satisfaction.

La présence d'un réseau social constitue un des meilleurs prédicteurs du bien-être psychologique. Cohen et Wills (1985) ainsi que Barrera (1988) montrent que le réseau social contribue au bien-être soit directement, en répondant aux besoins d'estime de soi et d'affiliation, soit indirectement, en procurant un soutien instrumental et émotionnel qui permet d'atténuer les effets négatifs du stress et des événements stressants de la vie.

Enfin, certaines recherches font ressortir le lien négatif entre le stress et le bien-être psychologique (Markides et Cooper, 1989). La conception du stress est généralement objective (situation, événement), plutôt que subjective (sentiment d'être stressé), car elle ressemble trop au concept de bien-être ou de santé mentale. Cependant, certaines études tiennent compte de l'évaluation ou de la pondération accordée par la personne aux situations potentiellement stressantes. Elles distinguent plusieurs types de stress : les embêtements quotidiens, les événements de la vie et les stresseurs chroniques. Les premiers regroupent les petits agacements rencontrés dans le cours des activités quotidiennes ; les deuxièmes consistent dans les situations plus importantes, moins fréquentes, mais ayant plus de conséquences à plus long terme (deuil, naissance, promotion ou licenciement) ; les troisièmes ne sont pas envisagés dans la présente recherche, car, chez les personnes âgées, il s'agit surtout de problèmes de santé, et cette variable est traitée de façon séparée. Des études indiquent que les embêtements quotidiens exercent une influence considérable sur le bien-être (Landreville et Vézina, 1992); les événements de la vie semblent cependant comporter un impact à plus long terme (Kosma *et al.*, 1991). Dans la présente recherche, le stress est opérationalisé par une mesure des événements de la vie.

Modèle d'analyse

Nous nous intéressons ici au rôle de l'activité dans le maintien du bien-être psychologique des personnes âgées, activité définie sur les plans quantitatif (fréquence) et qualitatif (compétence, motivation et plaisir). La recension des écrits a permis de distinguer plusieurs variables reliées à la fois au bien-être et à l'activité, en particulier les variables personnelles (âge, santé, revenu, résignation, autonomie psychologique) et les variables environnementales (événements stressants, logement, quartier, enracinement).

FIGURE 1

**Modèle illustrant les liens hypothétiques
entre les variables de la recherche**

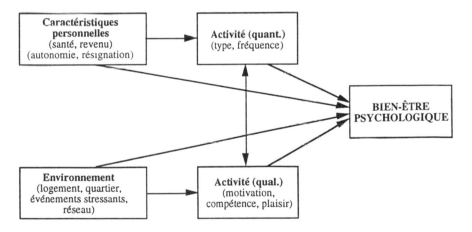

On peut donc faire l'hypothèse que l'activité non seulement contribue directement au bien-être psychologique, mais joue un rôle de « médiation » (effet atténuateur ou indirect) par rapport aux variables personnelles et environnementales. Ainsi, la santé, le statut socio-économique et l'habitat constituent à la fois des prédicteurs importants du bien-être psychologique et des déterminants de l'aménagement du temps chez les personnes âgées (Cutler, 1973; Markides et Martin, 1979). Certains chercheurs ont ainsi été amenés à élaborer des modèles permettant de vérifier les effets directs et indirects de ces variables sur le bien-être psychologique (Markides et Martin, 1979 ; Russell, 1990). Riddick (1985) montre que lorsqu'on relie les variables activités, santé et revenu, les activités constituent le meilleur prédicteur de la satisfaction de vivre, et que les problèmes de revenu et de santé influent sur la satisfaction de vivre par l'intermédiaire de la variable « activité de loisir ».

Le modèle de mise en relation des variables présenté dans la figure 1 s'inspire de Lawton (1983) et de Stones et Kosma (1987) ; il permet d'évaluer les effets directs et indirects de l'activité sur le bien-être.

Le type de recherche adopté est corrélationnel : le bien-être psychologique constitue la variable dépendante ou critère ; les caractéristiques personnelles (âge, santé, revenu, résignation, autonomie) et les facteurs environnementaux (habitat, réseau et événements stressants) constituent les variables prédictives ; l'activité (dans ses dimensions quantitative et qualitative) constitue la variable intermédiaire, à la fois prédictive du bien-être et dépendante des caractéristiques personnelles et de l'environnement.

Méthode

Le déroulement de la recherche (recrutement des participants et des inter-viewers) ainsi que les instruments utilisés lors de la collecte des données sont présentés ci-dessous.

Recrutement des participants

Les participants à cette recherche sont 180 personnes âgées (c'est-à-dire ayant plus de 65 ans et retirées du marché du travail depuis au moins 3 ans), répar-ties également entre les hommes et les femmes. Ces personnes âgées étaient rencontrées individuellement dans leur milieu de vie en une seule entrevue d'une durée moyenne d'une heure et demie.

Mesure du bien-être psychologique

La notion de bien-être psychologique a été définie comme l'évaluation qu'un individu fait de sa vie présente ou passée, la satisfaction par rapport à lui-même, le sentiment de compétence et le bonheur. Mais quelles dimensions plus pré-cises peut comporter ce concept de satisfaction générale ? Neugarten *et al.* (1961) distinguent cinq dimensions, déjà signalées, très fréquemment utilisées dans les recherches sur le bien-être subjectif (ou satisfaction de vivre) auprès des personnes âgées. Ces dimensions du bien-être psychologique sont opéra-tionalisées de la façon suivante :

   – Les *activités quotidiennes* sont mesurées par la satisfaction à l'égard des activités quotidiennes non spécifiques ;

- Le *sens de la vie* est mesuré par l'attitude envers la situation de vie actuelle et le sentiment que la vie sert à quelque chose ;

- Les *buts* sont mesurés par la satisfaction à l'égard de la présente étape de développement, par comparaison avec les étapes précédentes de la vie ;

- L'*humeur* est mesurée par l'affect général, la joie ou la peine, l'optimisme ou le pessimisme en rapport avec sa situation de vie, son environnement ou son milieu social ;

- Le *concept de soi* est mesuré par la considération personnelle et l'estime de soi.

L'*Échelle de satisfaction de vivre* (*Life Satisfaction in the Elderly Scale*) de Salamon et Conte (1982) a été retenue pour cette recherche, car elle constitue un instrument approprié pour mesurer le bien-être psychologique des personnes âgées. Elle reprend les cinq catégories des *Échelles de satisfaction de vivre* de Neugarten *et al.* (1961) et ajoute trois items originaux : les dimensions « santé », « sécurité financière » et « contacts sociaux ». Une étude québécoise utilisant cet instrument (Rousseau et Dubé, 1991), fait ressortir des corrélations entre les sous-échelles et l'échelle de bien être total plus faibles pour ces trois variables « exogènes », fournissant une justification pour ne pas les inclure dans le concept de bien-être psychologique proprement dit. Il y a donc lieu de distinguer le construit de bien-être psychologique (mesuré par les cinq sous-échelles de satisfaction de vivre empruntées à Neugarten), et celui de bien-être subjectif ou bien-être global (mesuré par la somme des huit échelles).

L'instrument de mesure du bien-être retenu ici comporte donc 25 questions regroupées en cinq sous-échelles. L'intérêt de cette échelle provient du fait que les items s'évaluent non pas de façon dichotomique (oui ou non), mais selon une gradation à cinq niveaux (échelle de type Likert). Elle permet une plus grande variabilité (vingt points par échelle, cent pour l'échelle totale) et suffisamment d'options de réponses pour l'expression de nuances dans la satisfaction, ce que les échelles par réponses dichotomiques (par oui ou non, telle l'échelle de Neugarten *et al.*) ne permettent pas.

Comme l'*Échelle de satisfaction de vivre* de Salamon et Conte est très récente, il n'existe pas d'adaptation française de ce questionnaire. L'équipe de recherche du Laboratoire de gérontologie de l'UQTR a soumis la version anglaise à trois traducteurs, et chacun en a effectué une traduction indépendante. Plusieurs rencontres ont ensuite permis à ces traducteurs d'en arriver à un consensus. Des coefficients d'homogénéité ont été calculés, d'abord auprès d'un échantillon de 180 personnes âgées (Rousseau et Dubé, 1991), puis auprès de l'échantillon de la présente recherche (180 personnes). Pour les deux recherches, les coefficient globaux sont respectivement de 0,89 et de 0,88.

Le questionnaire des informations socio-démographiques

Le questionnaire de renseignements généraux vise d'abord à recueillir divers renseignements personnels tels l'âge, le sexe, l'état civil, le nombre d'enfants, l'instruction, le nombre de corésidants dans le logement, le milieu (rural ou urbain) et le mode de résidence.

La santé et le revenu sont évalués à partir des échelles « santé », « ressources financières » et « réseau social » de l'*Échelle de satisfaction de vivre* de Salamon et Conte (1982). De plus, deux questions spécifiques sont présentées pour mesurer les dimensions santé et revenu, encore une fois de façon subjective. Ces questions sont inspirées du questionnaire de l'*Enquête Santé Québec* (1987). Dans plusieurs recherches, les mesures subjectives s'avèrent de bons indicateurs de la santé et du revenu objectif (Golant, 1986).

Les échelles de satisfaction à l'égard du logement et du quartier constituent des adaptations des échelles de Carp et Christensen (1986) qui s'intéressent aux liens entre la qualité objective du milieu et la satisfaction par rapport à ce milieu chez les personnes âgées. Ces échelles comportent six questions chacune et les scores varient de -12 à +12. Les coefficients d'homogénéité, calculés à partir de l'échantillon total (180 sujets), sont respectivement de 0,72 pour la satisfaction par rapport au logement et de 0,80 pour la satisfaction par rapport au quartier.

La mesure de l'activité

Trois principales formes de mesure servent à estimer les caractéristiques quantitatives et qualitatives de l'activité. La première, la méthode d'observation directe, s'applique surtout en milieu institutionnel ; la seconde, la technique du budget-temps, consiste à faire noter systématiquement toutes les activités dans un journal préstructuré tenu par le sujet ; la troisième, la plus utilisée, consiste en des inventaires ou listes d'activités considérées comme typiques de la population (ici la population âgée) et soumises sous forme de questionnaires (Broderick et Glazer, 1983 ; Gregory, 1983 ; Nystrom, 1974 ; Stones et Kosma, 1986). À partir d'une liste préétablie, la personne indique la fréquence de sa participation ainsi que des informations qualitatives (satisfaction, plaisir ou sentiment de compétence éprouvé, contact sociaux, etc.). L'avantage de cette méthode est qu'elle assure l'uniformité des réponses, car ce sont toujours des mêmes activités qui sont proposées. Par contre, Sceuch (1972) et Robinson (1977) soutiennent que les activités hautement désirables peuvent être surestimées quand la personne rapporte elle-même la fréquence. Un autre problème rattaché à ces inventaires tient au fait que la classification des activités s'appuie souvent sur des bases théoriques plutôt qu'empiriques (Tinsley, Colbs, Teaff et Kaufman, 1985).

Nous avons opté pour une mesure de type «inventaire» ou liste préétablie. Or, comme aucun des inventaires existants ne semblait tout à fait satisfaisant compte tenu du type de participants et des objectifs de la recherche, il nous a fallu construire un instrument original, en nous inspirant fortement des outils disponibles. En particulier, deux instruments ont été utilisés : celui de Gregory (1983) et celui de Stones et Kosma (1986).

L'*Inventaire des activités* (*Activity Index*) de Gregory (1983), lui-même une adaptation de l'inventaire de Nystrom (1974), dresse une liste des principales activités susceptibles d'être accomplies par les personnes âgées, en excluant les activités d'entretien personnel et le travail régulier. Contrairement à Nystrom, Gregory n'utilise pas le terme de loisir, puisque celui-ci, surtout chez les aînés, semble résider dans la signification donnée à l'activité plutôt que dans un type particulier d'activité. L'inventaire comporte une liste de 23 activités (avec possibilité d'ajouter trois activités supplémentaires) regroupées en activités «actives», activités «passives» et activités «de participation». L'inventaire permet de mesurer la réalisation des diverses activités et leur fréquence (base hebdomadaire).

L'autre instrument est l'*Inventaire des activités de l'Université Memorial* (*MUNAI*), de Stones et Kosma (1986). Il comporte une liste de 37 activités, établie après des entrevues effectuées auprès de 301 personnes âgées. Il est utilisé pour compléter l'*Inventaire des activités* de Gregory (1983).

Notre modèle de relations entre variables privilégie non seulement le fait d'accomplir ou non des activités, mais le type de motivation qui est à l'origine de ces activités. Cette dimension est mesurée par l'échelle de signification de l'activité de Gregory (1983). Cette échelle accompagne l'*Inventaire des activités* et, pour chaque activité accomplie, collecte l'information sur : a) le plaisir procuré par l'activité ; b) la raison ou motivation à la source de l'activité (intrinsèque ou extrinsèque) ; c) le sentiment de compétence éprouvé en accomplissant cette activité. Nous nous intéressons également à la dimension sociale de l'activité (le fait de l'accomplir seul ou avec d'autres personnes), de même qu'à sa dimension privée ou publique (le fait de l'accomplir à l'intérieur ou à l'extérieur de la résidence).

L'inventaire final que nous avons constitué comporte 33 activités, et, pour chacune d'elles, la personne indique à l'interviewer si elle accomplit l'activité, selon quelle fréquence et avec qui. Trois questions portent ensuite sur la signification de cette activité, soit la compétence, la source de la motivation (interne ou externe) et la satisfaction ou plaisir ressenti lors de l'activité.

Validité et fidélité de l'Inventaire des activités

Afin de pouvoir disposer d'une typologie des activités reposant sur des bases empiriques, une analyse factorielle a été effectuée sur les données de l'inventaire des activités (les 33 activités originales). Onze activités ont été retirées de l'instrument; six l'ont été parce que leur fréquence d'accomplissement était trop faible ou trop forte (moins de 10 % ou plus de 90 %), ce qui les rendait moins intéressantes, car non discriminantes. Ainsi les activités très fréquemment accomplies, comme regarder la télévision ou lire les journaux, ont été éliminées. L'objectif de notre recherche n'était pas, en effet, de connaître et de décrire l'utilisation du temps par les personnes âgées, mais de découvrir quelles activités contribuent à discriminer ces personnes sur des échelles de bien-être psychologique, d'autonomie et de résignation. Cinq autres activités ont été abandonnées parce que leur corrélation avec l'échelle totale, ou avec l'une des sous-échelles, était trop faible (ces activités étaient « passives », comme se bercer ou méditer).

L'analyse factorielle a fait ressortir quatre facteurs servant à distinguer et à nommer les quatre sous-échelles suivantes :

- *Les activités sociales.* Avec un coefficient d'homogénéité de 0,68, cette échelle comprend les 9 activités suivantes : faire du bénévolat, visiter quelqu'un, faire partie d'une association, aller à l'église, jouer aux cartes, marcher et faire de l'activité physique à l'extérieur, s'occuper d'amis ou de parents malades et aller à des spectacles, des concerts ou au cinéma.

- *Les activités instrumentales.* Avec un coefficient d'homogénéité de 0,63, cette échelle comprend les 4 activités suivantes : faire des travaux ménagers, faire du magasinage, aller chez le coiffeur et parler au téléphone.

- *Les activités expressives.* Avec un coefficient d'homogénéité est de 0,58, cette échelle comprend les 6 activités suivantes : faire de la musique, écouter de la musique, écrire, faire de la peinture, méditer et faire des mots croisés, des casse-tête ou d'autres passe-temps semblables.

- *Les activités de hobby-loisir.* Avec un coefficient d'homogénéité de 0,50, cette échelle comprend les 3 activités suivantes : s'occuper des plantes intérieures ou extérieures, faire du bricolage et faire des voyages.

Le coefficient d'homogénéité de l'inventaire total est de 0,58. Les coefficients ne sont pas tous très élevés, mais on peut les considérer comme suffisants dans ce genre d'inventaire, compte tenu du fait que la notion même d'activité peut prêter à confusion chez les personnes âgées, en particulier parce qu'il est difficile de distinguer le loisir des autres activités quotidiennes. De plus, rappelons que la plupart des classifications disponibles sont établies à partir d'une base théorique, et que cette recherche constitue une tentative pour classer les activités empiriquement et disposer d'une typologie valide.

La résignation apprise et l'autonomie psychologique

Le *Questionnaire de résignation acquise* est la traduction et l'adaptation de l'instrument de Thornton (1982) ; cette adaptation présente des qualités psychométriques satisfaisantes. La mesure révèle un coefficient de consistance interne de 0,87 ; la sous-échelle « désir de contrôle » affiche un coefficient de 0,64 et l'échelle « estime de soi », de 0,72.

Le *Questionnaire d'autonomie psychologique* (*QAP*), (Dubé et Lamy, 1990) a été développé en tenant compte des deux dimensions théoriques de l'autonomie : le contrôle décisionnel et le contrôle comportemental. Chaque dimension comporte trois facteurs : la dynamique de l'individu, ses capacités et l'intégration sociale.

Les tests de fidélité effectués sur les items du questionnaire d'autonomie psychologique montrent une excellent consistance interne (Dubé et Lamy, 1990). L'échelle d'autonomie totale obtient un coefficient Alpha de Cronbach de 0,89, et les différentes sous-échelles obtiennent des coefficients variant de 0,60 à 0,85. De plus, une analyse factorielle révèle que tous les items concourent bien à mesurer l'autonomie psychologique puisqu'ils obtiennent une corrélation variant de 0,62 à 0,45 avec un premier facteur qui explique 27 % de la variance.

Mesure des événements stressants de la vie

Le *Répertoire des événements de vie* utilisé dans cette recherche est une traduction et une adaptation du *Geriatric Scale of Recent Life Events* de Kiyak, Liang et Kahana (1976). Cet instrument énumère 56 événements ou situations stressantes auxquels les personnes âgées sont susceptibles de faire face. Le temps de référence choisi est de douze mois (un an). On y retrouve des événements comme le décès d'un membre de la famille, la perte du permis de conduire, le mariage d'un enfant ou un changement de résidence. L'examen des données de la recherche a permis de réduire à 42 le nombre d'événements, car 14 situations n'avaient été rencontrées par aucun des participants. Le coefficient d'homogénéité du Répertoire est de 0,52. Cette faiblesse relative s'explique par le fait que les événements sont assez disparates et que l'instrument comporte à la fois des situations positives et négatives.

Résultats

La section suivante présente les principales caractéristiques des participants, puis examine le lien entre l'activité et le bien-être psychologique, conformément à l'hypothèse apparaissant dans le modèle de mise en relation des variables. Deux analyses complémentaires vérifient ensuite l'effet du sexe et de l'âge (« âgés » ou « très âgés ») sur les principales variables de la recherche.

Caractéristiques des participants

Cent quatre-vingts sujets ont utilisé l'ensemble des instruments de collecte d'information. Leur âge varie de 65 à 93 ans, avec une moyenne de 72 ans et 4 mois. Les participants de moins de 75 ans, qualifiés d'*âgés,* sont au nombre de 127 (70 %), et ceux qui ont plus de 75 ans, qualifiés de *très âgés,* sont au nombre de 53 (30 %). Les répondants se répartissent également entre hommes (90 sujets) et femmes (90 sujets). Les participants sont originaires du milieu urbain dans une proportion de 64,5 %.

Les personnes âgées qui ont été rencontrées habitent au même endroit depuis une longue période de temps, soit 23,5 ans en moyenne, avec des écarts allant de quelques mois à 82 ans. L'état civil se répartit de la façon suivante : 111 personnes vivent en couple (61 %), 59 sont veuves ou veufs (33 %), 9 sont célibataires (5 %) et une est séparée. Dans l'année précédant la recherche, ces personnes avaient vécu en moyenne 5,5 événements stressants (*é.t.* =3,02), le minimum étant 1 et le maximum, 17.

L'activité et le bien-être psychologique

Le modèle de mise en relation des variables présente les principales variables potentiellement reliées au bien-être psychologique des personnes âgées. Pour vérifier l'adéquation de ce modèle, une régression multiple examine quinze variables, soit les huit variables personnelles et environnementales, et, bien sûr, l'activité, tant dans ses dimensions quantitatives (fréquence des quatre types d'activités) que qualitatives (motivation, plaisir et compétence).

Le tableau 1 indique que les variables personnelles et environnementales jouent un rôle important, puisque 7 d'entre elles sont corrélées significativement au bien-être : l'autonomie, la résignation (corrélation négative), la santé, le revenu, les événements stressants (corrélation négative), le réseau social et la satisfaction à l'égard du quartier de résidence.

En ce qui concerne l'activité, seule la fréquence des activités sociales apparaît comme un déterminant significatif du bien-être. Il faut cependant rappeler que cette sous-échelle de l'*Inventaire des activités* est importante puisqu'elle regroupe près de la moitié des activités et qu'elle affiche le meilleur coefficient d'homogénéité.

TABLEAU 1

**Régression multiple des douze variables principales
influant sur le bien-être psychologique (N=180)**

Variables	Beta	t	p
Santé	,15	2,5	<,05
Événements stressants	-,17	3,2	<,05
Revenu	,11	2,0	<,05
Réseau social	,22	3,8	<,001
Satisfaction à l'égard du logement	,04	0,8	N.S.
Satisfaction à l'égard du quartier	,11	1,9	<,05
Résignation	-,29	4,9	<,001
Autonomie psychologique	,21	3,4	<,001
Activités sociales	,13	2,1	<,05
Activités instrumentales	,03	0,5	N.S.
Activités expressives	,07	1,3	N.S.
Hobby-loisirs	,07	1,4	N.S.
Motivation dans l'activité	,05	0,7	N.S.
Plaisir dans l'activité	,09	1,3	N.S.
Compétence dans l'activité	,02	1,4	N.S.

$R = ,78$ $R2 = ,60$ $F = 16,5$ $p < ,001$

Les variables qui démontrent le lien le plus fort avec le bien-être sont la résignation (β=-0,29) et sa contrepartie positive, l'autonomie psychologique (β=0,21). Nous n'avions pas prévu une telle importance du facteur psychologique, ni le fait que les dimensions qualitatives de l'activité, en particulier la compétence et la motivation, n'afficheraient que des corrélations très faibles avec le bien-être des personnes âgées.

Ces résultats, non conformes au modèle de départ, nous ont conduits à réexaminer les relations entre les variables à l'étude et à nous interroger sur le rôle central de l'autonomie psychologique. Nous avons donc fait l'hypothèse que c'est plutôt cette variable qui servirait de modérateur ou de catalyseur, non seulement par rapport aux variables personnelles ou environnementales (santé, stress et participation sociale), mais surtout par rapport aux activités plus individuelles telles que les activités expressives ou instrumentales. Il s'agissait donc d'examiner cette fonction potentielle de l'autonomie. Pour ce faire, une nouvelle régression des principales variables a été effectuée, mais, cette fois, par rapport à l'autonomie psychologique (pour cette analyse, la dimension positive a été préférée à la dimension négative, c'est-à-dire la résignation apprise).

TABLEAU 2

**Régression multiple des treize variables
reliées à l'autonomie psychologique (N=180)**

Variables	Beta	t	p
Santé	,21	2,9	p<01
Réseau social	,24	3,4	p<01
Événements stressants	,03	0,5	N.S.
Satisfaction à l'égard du quartier	,15	2,0	p<05
Satisfaction à l'égard du logement	,06	0,8	N.S.
Revenu	,07	0,9	N.S.
Activité sociale	,03	0,4	N.S.
Activité instrumentale	-,14	2,0	p<05
Activité expressive	,14	1,9	p<05
Hobby-loisirs	-,05	0,7	N.S.
Motivation dans l'activité	,27	2,8	p<01
Plaisir dans l'activité	,10	1,3	p<01
Compétence dans l'activité	,24	2,4	N.S.

$R = ,56$ $R^2 = ,32$ $F = 6,0$ $p<001$

Le tableau 2 est révélateur de cette fonction centrale de l'autonomie. On constate que les activités expressives, de même que la motivation et le plaisir qui les accompagnent, sont reliés à l'autonomie psychologique, laquelle, nous l'avons vu plus haut, est un des principaux prédicteurs de la satisfaction de vivre. Ces activités ne sont favorables à la santé mentale que si la personne âgée possède du pouvoir décisionnel et du contrôle comportemental. Quant aux activités instrumentales, ou activités d'entretien, elles entrent en relation négative avec l'autonomie. Leur caractère obligatoire ou contraignant semble empêcher les personnes âgées d'y exercer du contrôle, d'y appliquer leurs propres règles et d'y investir leurs valeurs propres.

Modèle corrigé de relations entre les variables

Le modèle de mise en relation des variables présenté en hypothèse regroupait les variables reliées au bien-être psychologique en trois blocs: les variables personnelles (âge, santé, revenu, résignation et autonomie), les variables environnementales (stress, réseau, logement et quartier) et les variables d'activité (fréquence et dimensions qualitatives). Les régressions présentées dans les deux tableaux précédents ont révélé le rôle important de la résignation et de l'autonomie psychologique, d'une part, comme déterminant du bien-être et, d'autre part, comme variable significativement reliée à l'activité expressive et aux dimensions de motivation et de plaisir dans les activités.

Ces résultats nous ont conduits à modifier le modèle de mise en relation de la façon suivante. D'abord, cinq variables prédictives ont été conservées à cause de leur corrélation élevée avec le bien-être : la santé, le revenu, les événements stressants, la satisfaction à l'égard du réseau social, la satisfaction à l'égard du quartier de résidence et la fréquence des activités sociales. Puis les variables d'autonomie (et de résignation) ont été ajoutées comme variables intermédiaires, reliées d'une part à trois dimensions de l'activité : la fréquence des activités expressives, la motivation et le plaisir dans l'activité et, d'autre part, au bien-être psychologique dont elles sont d'importants prédicteurs. La figure suivante (figure 2) illustre ces corrélations.

FIGURE 2

Modèle révisé de mise en relation des variables

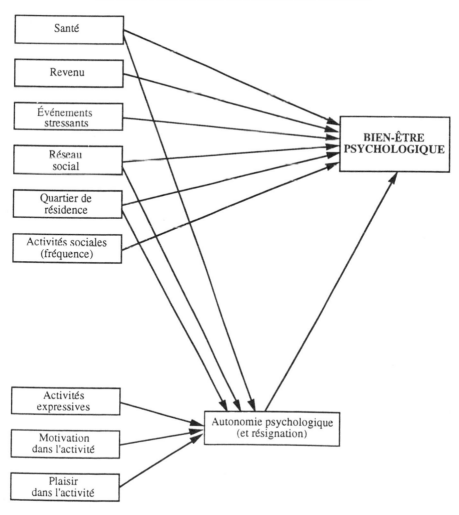

Analyses complémentaires : différences liées au sexe et à l'âge

Une série d'analyses ont été effectuées afin de déceler les différences significatives entre les hommes et les femmes pour toutes les variables de cette recherche. Le sexe s'avère être un facteur déterminant pour six variables : la santé perçue ($F=6,9$, $p<0,01$), la résignation ($F=5,0$, $p<0,05$), la participation aux activités instrumentales ($F=31,8$, $p<0,001$), la participation aux activités expressives ($F=5,2$, $p<0,05$), le nombre total d'activités ($F=3,7$, $p<0,05$) et le plaisir dans les activités ($F=4,5$, $p<0,05$). Pour toutes ces variables, les femmes obtiennent des scores significativement plus élevés que les hommes, à l'exception de l'évaluation de la santé, où ces derniers estiment être en meilleure santé.

De plus, à partir de la distinction entre les *âgés* (65 à 75 ans) et les *très âgés* (plus de 75 ans), des analyses ont vérifié l'effet de la catégorie d'âge sur toutes les variables de la recherche. Cinq facteurs se révèlent être significativement reliés à l'âge et, pour chacun d'eux, les *âgés,* (donc les participants plus jeunes), obtiennent des scores plus élevés que les *très âgés*. Ces variables sont le revenu perçu ($F=19,2$, $p<0,001$), le nombre total d'activités ($F=4,0$, $p<0,05$), le nombre d'activités accomplies avec d'autres ($F=9,8$, $p<0,01$), la participation aux activités sociales ($F=19,5$, $p<0,001$) et la participation aux activités « hobby-loisir » ($F=9,1$, $p<0,01$).

Discussion des résultats et conclusion

Cette recherche a tenté de déterminer quels facteurs peuvent contribuer au bien-être psychologique des personnes âgées autonomes. L'hypothèse principale prévoyait que l'activité, tant dans son aspect quantitatif que qualitatif, constituerait une variable importante, au point même d'atténuer les effets négatifs reliés au stress, à la maladie, au faible revenu et au réseau social insuffisant. ; les résultats révèlent cependant qu'elle joue un rôle plus modéré. Ce sont plutôt les attitudes de résignation apprise et d'autonomie psychologique qui apparaissent comme des variables clés expliquant les variations du bien-être psychologique. Et parce que ces variables sont reliées à la fois à des facteurs plus externes tels que les conditions d'habitat, et aux activités instrumentales ou expressives, de même qu'à la motivation ou au plaisir retiré de l'accomplissement des activités, on peut présumer que l'autonomie sert en quelque sorte d'intermédiaire entre ces variables et le bien-être psychologique (sans que l'on puisse toujours fixer le sens de ces corrélations).

Notre modèle révisé de mise en relation des variables indique clairement que la plupart des caractéristiques des activités ne sont pas en relation directe avec la satisfaction de vivre des personnes âgées. Cette constatation vient nuancer les résultats de plusieurs recherches citées précédemment selon lesquels la pratique d'activités (de loisir en particulier) entraîne un état de bien-être élevé. Notre recherche démontre que seule la pratique fréquente d'activités sociales contribue directement au bien-être, conformément aux observations d'autres chercheurs (Russel, 1990; Seneegas, 1987).

Outre les variables de santé, de stress, de revenu, d'habitat et de réseau social, déjà bien cernées dans les études antérieures (Kosma *et al.*, 1991), la présente recherche fait ressortir un facteur original dont la pondération l'emporte sur tous les autres : l'*autonomie psychologique* (ou de sa contrepartie négative, la *résignation*). Non seulement l'autonomie contribue-t-elle directement au bien-être, mais elle devient un élément qui médiatise l'effet de la participation à certaines activités, en particulier les activités expressives.

Conformément aux résultats des travaux de Vallerand (1990), il ressort de la présente étude que c'est la source de la motivation qui serait d'abord déterminante. Plus la source de cette motivation à réaliser l'activité est intrinsèque ou autodéterminée, c'est-à-dire plus l'individu s'y engage de son propre gré, plus cette activité lui permet d'exercer son pouvoir de décider et d'agir, et contribue ainsi à favoriser son bien-être. Cette relation s'observe tant chez les hommes que les femmes et tant chez les âgés (de 65 à 75 ans) que chez les très âgés (plus de 75 ans). Il en va de même pour la dimension « plaisir à accomplir les activités », qui affiche une relation significative positive avec l'autonomie. Pour cette variable, les femmes âgées manifestent, globalement, plus de plaisir aux activités que les hommes.

La place centrale occupée par la motivation nous aide à interpréter le fait que la fréquence des activités expressives (écriture, musique, jeux créatifs) présente une relation significative avec l'autonomie psychologique, c'est-à-dire avec le pouvoir de décider et la perception de compétence et de contrôle. Cette relation est fort intéressante et peut être comprise de deux façons : d'une part, la participation à ce type d'activités exige un niveau préalable d'autonomie élevé et le dépassement de la résignation ou du sentiment d'incompétence qu'on retrouve parfois chez les personnes âgées qui voient décliner leurs habiletés et leurs ressources ; d'autre part, la seule implication dans des activités expressives, qui sont pourtant des activités plutôt solitaires, serait de nature à augmenter le sentiment de contrôle sur sa propre vie et sur son environnement.

La fréquence des activités instrumentales, par contre, apparaît en relation négative avec l'autonomie. Les personnes âgées considèrent probablement ces activités comme trop contraignantes ou extrodéterminées et, par conséquent, non propices aux choix et aux actions personnalisées, conformément aux conclusions de Hickson *et al.* (1988).

La présente recherche pourra se révéler utile à deux égards : d'abord, elle fournira aux chercheurs un instrument de mesure de l'activité chez les personnes âgées – cet instrument, qui devra être validé auprès d'une population plus vaste, a néanmoins permis d'établir une typologie des activités reposant sur une base empirique –; ensuite, elle pourra apprendre aux intervenants que les activités peuvent contribuer à la satisfaction de vivre seulement si la personne conserve une attitude d'autonomie et ne laisse pas s'installer la résignation. Ces spécialistes tenteront donc d'offrir et de favoriser des activités qui découlent d'un libre choix et qui permettent à cette clientèle de développer la confiance en ses capacités et en ses habiletés propres.

Références

ABRAMSON, L.Y., SELIGMAN, M.E.P. et TEASDALE, J.D. (1978). Learned helplessness in humans : Critique and reformulation. *Journal of Abnormal Psychology, 87,* 49-74.

ALTMAN, I., LAWTON, M.P. et WOHLWILL, J.F. (1984). *Elderly People and the Environment,* New-York : Plenum Press.

ANDREWS, F.M. et WITHEY, S.B. (1976). *Social Indicators of Well-being : America's Perception of Life Quality.* New York : Plenum Press.

ANDREWS, F.M. et McKENNELL, A.C. (1980). Measures of self-reported well-being : Their affective, cognitive and other components. *Social Indicators Research, 8,* 127-155.

ATCHLEY, R.C. (1971). Retirement and leisure participation : Continuity or crisis? *The Gerontologist, 11,* 13-17.

BARRERA, M. Jr. (1988). Models of social support and life stress : beyond the buffering hypothesis. *In* L.H. Cohen (Éd.), *Life Events and Psychological Functionning.* Beverly Hills : Sage Publications

BOND, J.B. (1982). Volonteerism and life satisfaction among older adults. *Canadian Counselor, 16*(3), 168-172.

BRADBURN, N.M. (1969). *The Structure of Psychological Well-being.* Chicago : Aldine.

BRODERICK, T. et GLAZER, B. (1983). Leisure participation and the retirement process. *The American Journal of Occupational Therapy, 37,* 15-22.

CARP, F.M. et CHRISTENSEN, D.L. (1986). Technical environmental assessment predictors of residential satisfaction. *Research on Aging, 8,* 269-287.

COHEN, S. et WILLS, T.A. (1985). Stress, social support and the buffering hypothesis. *Psychological Bulletin, 98*(2), 310-357.

CONTE, V.A. et SALAMON, M.J. (1982). An objective approach to the measurement and use of life satisfaction with older persons. *Measurement and Evaluation in Guidance, 15,* 194-200.

CUMMING, E. et HENRY, W.E. (1961). *Growing Old and the Process of Disengagement.* New York : Basic Books.

CSIKSZENTMIHALYI, M. (1975). *Beyond Boredom and Anxiety.* San Francisco : Jossey-Bass.

CSIKSZENTMIHALYI, M. et GRAEF, R. (1980). The experience of freedom in daily life. *American Journal of Community Psychology, 8,* 401-414.

CUTLER, N.E. (1979). Age variations in the dimensionality of life satisfaction. *Journal of Gerontology, 34,* 573-578.

DECI, E.L. et RYAN, R.M. (1987). The support of autonomy and the control of behavior. *Journal of Personality and Social Psychology, 53,* 1024-1037.

DELISLE, M.A. (1992). *Un âge à dorer.* Québec : La Liberté inc.

DELISLE, M.A. (1982). Loisir et structuration du temps chez les personnes âgées. *Loisir et société, 5*(2), 387-413.

DELISLE, M.A. (1987). *La république du silence: solitude et vieillissement.* Coll. Rapports de recherche n° 25, Québec : Laboratoire de recherches sociologiques de l'Université Laval.

DIENER, E. (1984). Subjective well-being. *Psychological Bulletin, 95,* 542-575.

DUBÉ, M. et LALANDE, G. (1991). *Le maintien et le développement de l'autonomie des personnes âgées et très âgées : Étude des facteurs psychologiques associés, recommandations et projets d'intervention.* Rapport au Ministère de la Santé et des Services sociaux du Québec et au C.R.S.S.S.04.

DUBÉ, M. et LAMY, L. (1990). *L'autonomie psychologique des personnes âgées.* Communication au quatrième congrès international francophone de gérontologie, Montréal.

DUDA, J.L. (1987). Toward a developmental theory of children's motivation in sport. *Journal of Sport Psychology, 9,* 130-145.

DUMAZEDIER, J. (1974). *Sociologie empirique du loisir.* Paris : Éd. du Seuil.

EDWARDS, N.J. et KLEMMACK, D.L. (1973). Correlates of life satisfaction: A re-examination. *Journal of Gerontology, 28,* 497-502.

ELLENBERGER, H.F. (1987). Regards sur les institutions pour vieillards et malades chroniques. *L'union médicale du Canada, 116,* 125-135.

FRY, P.S. (1989). *Psychological Perspectives of Helplessness and Control in the Elderly.* North Holland : Elsevier science publisher

GEORGES, L.K. (1981). Subjective well-being : Conceptual and methodological issues. *In* C.F. Eisdorfer (Éd.), *Annual Review of Gerontology and Geriatrics.* New York : Springer.

GOLANT, S.M. (1986). The influence of experienced residential environment on old people's life satisfaction. *Journal of Housing for the Elderly, 3,* 23-49.

GORDON, C. et GAITZ, C.M. (1976). Leisure and mental health late in the life cycle. *Psychiatric Annals, 2,* 38-68.

GORDON, C., GAITZ, C.M. et SCOTT, J. (1986). Leisure and lives : Personal expressivity across the lifespan. *In* R.H. Binstock et E. Shanas (Éds.), *Handbook of aging and the social sciences,* (pp. 310-341). New York : Van Nostrand Reinhold.

GREGORY, M.D. (1983). Occupational behavior and life satisfaction among retirees. *The American Journal of Occupational Therapy, 37,* 548-553.

HAGEMAN, C. et TOBIN, S. (1988). Enhancing the autonomy of mentally impaired nursing home residents. *The Gerontologist, 28,* 71-75.

HÉTU, J.L. (1988). *Psychologie du vieillissement.* Montréal : Édition du Méridien.

HICKSON, J., HOUSLEY, W.F. et BOYLE, C. (1988). The relationship of locus of control, age and sex to life satisfaction and death anxiety in older persons. *International Journal of Aging and Human Development, 26,* 191-199.

HOCHSCHILD A. (1975). Disengagement theory : A critical and proposal. *American Sociological Review, 40,* 553-569.

HORLEY, J. (1984). Life satisfaction, happiness and morale : Two problems with the use of subjective well-being indicators. *The Gerontologist, 24,* 142-127.

JAMETON, A. (1988). In the borderlands of anatomy : Responsibility in long term care facilities. *The Gerontologist, 28,* 18-23.

KELLER, M.J. (1983). *The Relationships between Leisure and Life Satisfaction among Older Women.* Paper presented at the meeting of the National Recreation and Park Association, Kansas City, MO.

KELLY, J.R. (1982). Leisure in later life : roles and identities. *In* N.J. Osgood (Éd.), *Life after Work : Retirement, Leisure, Recreation and the Elderly.* New York : Praeger Press.

KELLY, J.R. (1990). Leisure and aging : A second agenda. *Loisir et société/Society and Leisure, 13*(1), 145-167.

KELLY, J.R. et ROSS, J.E. (1989). Later-life leisure : Beginning a new agenda. *Leisure Science, 11,* 47-59.

KELLY, J.R., STEINKAMP, M.W. et KELLY, J. R. (1986). Later life leisure : How they play in peoria. *The Gerontologist, 26*(5), 531-537.

KIYAK, A., LIANG, J. et KAHANA, E. (1976). *A Methodological Inquiry into the Schedule of Recent Life Events.* Paper presented to the Meetings of APA, Washington, August.

KOSMA, A. et STONES, M. (1978). Some research issues and findings in the assessment of well-being in the elderly. *Canadian Psychology Review, 9,* 241-249.

KOSMA, A., STONES, M.J. et MCNEIL, J.K. (1991). *Psychological Well-being in later life.* Toronto : Butterworths.

KRAUSE, N. (1991). Stress ans isolation from close ties in later life. *Journal of Gerontology, 46,* 183-194.

KUYPERS, J.A. et BENGTSON, V.L. (1973). Social breakdown and competence : A model of normal aging. *Human Development, 16,* 181-201.

LAFOREST, J. (1989). *Introduction à la gérontologie : croissance et déclin.* Hurtibise, H.M.H.

LANDREVILLE, P. et VÉZINA, J. (1992). A comparison between daily hassles and major life events as correlate of well-being in older adults. *Canadian Journal of Aging, 11*(2), 137-149.

LARSON, R. (1978). Thirty years of research on the subjective well-being in older adults. *The Gerontologist, 33,*

LAWTON, M.P. (1985). Activities and leisure. *Annual Review of Gerontology, 5,* 127-164.

LAWTON, M.P. (1983). Environment and other determinants of well-being in older adults. *The Gerontologist, 23,* 349-357.

LEBEAU, A., SICOTTE, C., TILQUIN, C. et TREMBLAY, L. (1980). Le concept d'autonomie. *Santé mentale au Québec, 5,* 71-89.

LEMON, B.W., BENGTSON, V.L. et PETERSON, J.A. (1972). An exploration of the activity theory of aging: Activity types and life satisfaction among in-movers to a retirement community. *Journal of Gerontology, 27*, 511-523.

LONGINO, C. et KART, C. (1982). Explicating activity theory: A formal replication. *Journal of Gerontology, 37*, 713-722.

MANCINI, J.A. et ORTHNER, D.K. (1980). Situational influences of leisure satisfaction and morale in old age. *Journal of American Geriatrics Society, 28*, 466-471.

MARKIDES, K.S. et MARTIN, H.W. (1979). A causal model of life satisfaction among the elderly. *Journal of Gerontology, 34*, 86-93.

MARKIDES, K.S. et COOPER, C.L. (1989). *Aging, Stress and Health.* Chichester: John Wiley et Son.

MCNEIL, J.K., STONES, M.J. et KOSMA, A. (1986). Subjective well-being in later life: Issues concerning measurement and prediction. *Social Indicators Research, 18*, 35-70.

MOODY, H.R. (1988). From informed consent to negociated consent. *The Gerontologist, 28*(suppl.), 64-70.

MULLIS, R.J. (1992). Measures of economic well-being as predictors of psychological well-being. *Social Indicators Research, 26*, 119-135

NEUGARTEN, B.L. (1980). A developmental view of adult personnality. *In* Birren (Éd.), *Relations of Developmentand Aging* (pp. 176-208), New York: Arno Press.

NEUGARTEN, B.L., HAVIGHURST, R.J. et TOBIN, S.S. (1961). *The measurement of life satisfaction. Journal of Gerontology, 16*, 134-143.

NEUGARTEN, B. L., HAVIGURST, R.J. et TOBIN, S.S. (1968). Personnality and patterns of aging. *In* Neugarten (Éd.), *Middle Age and Aging*, (pp. 173-177), Illinois : U. of Chicago.

NICHOLS, J. (1984). Conceptions of ability and achievement motivation. *In* R. Ames et C. Ames (Éds.), *Research on Motivation in Education: Student Motivation, 1*, (pp. 39-73), New York: Academic Press.

NYSTROM, E. (1974). Activity pattern and leisure concepts among the elderly. *The American Journal of Occupational Therapy, 28*, 337-345.

OKUN, M.A. et STOCK, W.A. (1987). The construct validity of subjective well-being measures: An assessment via quantitative synthetis. *Journal of Community Psychology, 5*, 481-492.

OKUN, M.A. STOCK, W.A., HARING, M.J. et WITTER, R.A. (1984). The social activity/well-being relation. *Research on Aging, 6*, 45-65.

PALMORE, E. (1970). *Normal Aging.* Durham, N.C.: Duke University Press.

PALMORE, E. et LUICKART, C. (1972). Health and social factors related to life satisfaction. *Journal of Health and Social Behavior, 13*, 68-80.

PARÉ, S. (1984). Qualité de vie de la personne âgée autonome. *Le Gérontophile, 2*, 8-10.

PLOTON, L. (1990). La personne âgée: son accompagnement médical et psychologique et la question de démence. *Chronique sociale*, 128-137, Lyon.

PRONOVOST, G. (1988). Le budget-temps des Québécois. *Recherches sociographiques, XXIX*, 1, 23-43.

RAGHEB, M.G. et GRIFFITH, C.A. (1982). The contribution of leisure participation and leisure satisfaction to life satisfaction of older persons. *Journal of Leisure Research, 14*, 295-306.

RAKOWSKI, W. et CRYAN, C. (1990). Associations among health perceptions and health status within three age groups. *Journal of Aging and Health, 2,* 58-80.

RIDDICK, C.C. (1985). Life satisfaction determinants of older males and females. *Leisure Sciences, 7,* 47-63.

ROFF, L.L. et ATHERTON, C.R. (1989). *Promoting Successful Aging.* Chicago : Nelson-Hall.

ROMANIUK, M., HOYER, F.W. et ROMANIUK, J.G. (1977). *Helpless Self-attitudes of the Elderly : The Effect of Patronizing Statements.* Read before the annual meeting of the Gerotonlogical Society, San Francisco.

ROUSSEAU, J. et DUBÉ, M. (1991). *Étude du réseau de support social, du système de croyance et du milieu de vie comme déterminants du bien-être psychologique chez les personnes âgées.* Rapport de recherche au C.Q.R.S., Université du Québec à Trois-Rivières.

RUSSELL, R.V. (1990). Recreation and quality of life in old age : A causal analysis. *The Journal of Applied Psychology, 9,* 77-90.

SALAMON, M.J. et CONTE, V.A. (1982). An objective approach to the measurement and use of life satisfaction with older persons. *Measurement and Evaluation in Guidance, 15,* 194-200.

SALAMON, M.J. et CONTE, V.A. (1981). *The Salamon-Conte Life Satisfaction in the Elderly Scale.* Communication présentée à la 4ᵉ rencontre annuelle de la Gerontological Society of America, Toronto, Ontario.

SAUP, W. (1987). Lack of autonomy in old age homes : A stress and coping study. *Journal of Housing for the Elderly, 4,* 21-36.

SENEEGAS, J.J. (1986). Components of life satisfaction in middle and later life adults : Perceived social competence, leisure participation, and leisure satisfaction. *Journal of Leisure Research, 18*(4), 248-258.

STOCK, W.A., OKUN, M.A. et BENIN, M. (1986). Structure of subjective well-being among the elderly. *Psychology and Aging, 1,* 91-102.

STONES, M.J. et KOSMA, A. (1986). Happiness and activities as propensities. *Journal of Gerontology, 41,* 85-90.

STONES, M.J. et KOSMA, A. (1987). Happiness and activities in later life : A propensy formulation. *Psychologie canadienne, 30,* 526-537.

THORNTON, B., RYCKMAN, R.M., ROBINS, M.A., DONOLLI, J. et BISEN, G. (1987). Relationship between perceived physically ability and indices of actual physical fitness. *Journal of Sports Psychology, 9,* 295-300.

TINSLEY, H.E.A., COLBS, S.L., TEAFF, J.D. et KAUFMAN, N.A (1987). System of classifying leisure activities in terms of the psychological benefits of participation reported by older persons. *Journal of Gerontology, 40,* 172-178.

VALLERAND, R.J. (1990). *Motivation chez les personnes âgées : conséquences pour la santé physique et mentale.* Rapport au C.Q.R.S., Université du Québec à Montréal.

VALLERAND, R.J. et O'CONNORS, B.P. (1991). Construction et validation de l'*Échelle de motivation des personnes âgées (EMPA). Journal international de Psychologie, 26,* 219-240.

VALLERAND, R.J. et O'CONNORS, B.P. (1989). Motivation in the elderly : A theoritical framework and some promising findings. *Psychologie Canadienne, 30,* 538-550.

WARR, P., BARTER, J. et BROWNBRIDGE, G. (1983). On the independence of the negative and positive affect. *Journal of Personality and Social Psychology, 44,* 644-651.

ZAY, N. (1980). *Adaptabilité et vieillissement.* IXe conférence internationale de gérontologie sociale. Centre International de Gérontologie Sociale.

———————

Jacques ROUSSEAU, Marie-Claude DENIS, Micheline DUBÉ
et Micheline BEAUCHESNE
L'activité, l'autonomie et le bien-être psychologique des personnes âgées

RÉSUMÉ

Cette recherche explore les relations entre le bien-être psychologique des personnes âgées et un ensemble de dimensions se rapportant aux activités, aux caractéristiques personnelles et au milieu de vie. On y examine plus particulièrement la fréquence et le type d'activités ainsi que l'autonomie ou le contrôle perçu dans l'accomplissement de ces activités. Cent quatre-vingt-deux personnes âgées ($M = 72,4$ ans) ont été rencontrées individuellement à leur domicile. Outre le bien-être et l'activité, l'étude comporte des mesures de l'autonomie psychologique, des événements stressants, de la résignation apprise ainsi que des échelles de satisfaction touchant la santé, le revenu, le logement et le quartier. Les résultats révèlent que si l'activité sociale joue un rôle important, la résignation apprise et l'autonomie psychologique apparaissent cependant comme des variables clés. Ces attitudes modulent les effets des activités quotidiennes et ceux des facteurs personnels et environnementaux (santé et conditions d'habitat). Les données de cette étude devraient permettre d'orienter les programmes d'intervention auprès des personnes âgées en vue de favoriser le développement d'attitudes d'autonomie et d'activités autodéterminées.

———————

Jacques ROUSSEAU, Marie-Claude DENIS, Micheline DUBÉ
and Micheiine BEAUCHESNE
Activity, Autonomy and Psychological Well-Being of the Elderly

ABSTRACT

This study examines the relations between the psychological well-being of the elderly and a set of dimensions relating to activities, personal characteristics and living environment. More specifically, the frequency and type of activities are examined as well as perceived autonomy or control in carrying out these activities. One hundred eighty-two elderly subjects (M = 72.4) were met individually in their home. In addition to well-being and activity, the study includes measures of psychological autonomy, stressful events and learned resignation, as well as satisfaction scales relating to health, income, dwelling and residence area. The results show that while social activity plays an important role, learned resignation and psychological autonomy appear to be key variables. These attitudes moderate both the effects of daily activities and of personal and environmental factors (health and living conditions). The findings of the study should serve as a valuable aid in designing intervention programs for the elderly aimed at promoting the development of attitudes of autonomy and self-determined activities.

Jacques ROUSSEAU, Marie-Claude DENIS, Micheline DUBÉ
y Micheline BEAUCHESNE
La actividad, autonomía y bienestar psicológico de las personas ancianas.

RESUMEN

Esta investigación explora las relaciones entre el bienestar psicológico de las personas ancianas y un conjunto de dimensiones relativas a las actividades, a las características personales y al medio de vida. La frecuencia y el tipo de actividades, así que la autonomía o el control observado en la realización de sus actividades, son particularmente examinados. Ciento ochenta y dos personas mayores (con una media de 72.4 años) fueron visitadas individualmente en su domicilio. Además del bienestar y la actividad, el estudio incluye medidas sobre la autonomía psicológica, hechos que ocasionan tensión, la resignación adquirida, así que las escalas de satisfacción en cuanto a la salud, el ingreso, la vivienda y la vecindad. Los resultados revelan que si la actividad social juega un papel importante, las actitudes de resignación adquirida y la autonomía psicológica aparecen sin embargo como variables claves, éstas modulan los efectos de las actividades cotidianas y de los factores personales y del medio ambiente (salud y condiciones de hábitat). Estos datos deberán permitir de orientar los programas de intervención de las personas ancianas en vista de favorecer el desarrollo de actitudes de autonomía y de actividades auto-determinadas.

Partie II / *Part II*

Loisir, comportements à risque et santé

Leisure, at-risk Behaviors and Health

Alcohol Consumption and Leisure Participation

Cynthia P. CARRUTHERS
James A. BUSSER

Department of Sport and Leisure Studies
University of Nevada,
Las Vegas, United States

Introduction

Healthy and rewarding recreation participation is often espoused as an alternative to alcohol consumption (Corwin, 1991 ; Kraus, 1990). Paradoxically, alcohol consumption usually occurs in a leisure context (Simpura, 1985), and is often considered a recreational behavior (Bammel & Burris-Bammel, 1992). Although the relationship between alcohol consumption and leisure would seem to be of apparent interest to those who study leisure behavior or provide leisure services, the relationship has been only sporadically investigated.

Social Learning Theory

Drinking behaviors have been examined from a variety of disciplinary perspectives, including personality, biological, life course development, sociological, and cognitive styles (Schall, Kemeny, & Maltzman, 1992). Much current research is using a social learning approach which assumes an interaction between the individual and the environment (reciprocal determinism) (Institute of Medicine, 1992). Social learning theory considers the life stage of the individual, biobehavioral factors, and cultural influences that shape drinking behavior. However, the main focus is on the learned acquisition and maintenance of drinking behaviors (Institute of Medicine, 1992). According to social learning theory, the expectancies that one holds regarding the effects of alcohol shape drinking behavior (Brown, Christiansen, & Goldman, 1987). In addition, drinking behavior is very much influenced by the social context in which one is involved (Institute of Medicine, 1989).

Loisir et société / *Society and Leisure*
Volume 18, numéro 1, printemps 1995, pp. 125-142 • © Presses de l'Université du Québec

Social contexts can encourage drinking, discourage drinking or be neutral in their effect on drinking (Orcutt, 1991). Contexts often have social norms which will determine if it is acceptable to drink or even encourage drinking behavior (Schall, Kemeny, & Mattzman, 1992). The drinking behaviors and attitudes of those with whom individuals associate and the context in which those associations occur provide partial explanation for variability in drinking behaviors (Schall, Kemeny, & Mattzman, 1992). In addition, frequent drinking might be viewed differently within one's social system than drinking large quantities (intoxication). For example, some social systems may condone frequent drinking, yet frown upon drinking large quantities (Kinney & Leaton, 1991).

Individuals may also gravitate towards contexts that accept or encourage drinking (Kinney & Leaton, 1991). According to Fingarette (1988), heavy drinkers "tend to seek out people and situations that evoke and stimulate drinking – choices reinforced by various socially acceptable settings, rituals, and justifications for drinking" (p. 102). In addition, heavier drinkers expect drinking to have a more positive effect on their leisure experiences than lighter drinkers (Carruthers, 1993). In essence, heavier drinkers might not only be more engaged in certain types of situations in which drinking is acceptable, but they also expect drinking to enhance their involvement in those situations. Again, there is a reciprocal determinism through which the environment influences the behaviors of the individual while the individuals bring expectations and behaviors to bear on the environment.

Leisure Contexts and Alcohol Consumption

Little research has been conducted directly related to drinking practices and leisure activity participation. The studies that do exist have focused on specific populations and narrow ranges of activities. Additionally, there have been some inconsistencies in the findings of the studies.

General Population Studies

Studies of individuals from the general population indicate some patterns of relationships between drinking and leisure. Cahalan, Cisin, and Crossley (1969) included items related to frequency of leisure participation in seven activities as part of the "warm-up" questions in their extensive national study of alcohol practices. They reported that heavy drinkers were less likely to be involved in church activities, participate in hobbies, and read; however, a higher proportion of heavy drinkers were involved in social activities, such as going out for entertainment and visiting with friends, and television viewing. They recommended that further research using a broader range of leisure activities be conducted.

In an investigation of alcohol consumption and leisure participation among the ageing, Johnson (1974) reported that frequency of drinking was associated with a more active lifestyle, including such things as shopping, reading, playing card games, and social and cultural involvement. In a study of adults in the general population, Young and Kronus (1977) found that participation in outdoor recreation and frequency of alcohol consumption were positively related. Perdue and Rainwater's (1984) study of adolescents concluded that as frequency of recreation participation increases, alcohol consumption in conjunction with these activities also increases. Finally, in a study of college students, Iso-Ahola and Hayllar (1992) reported that level of home-based leisure participation, organized leisure participation, and participation in informal leisure activities were all related positively to the amount of alcohol consumed by subjects per occasion (quantity). Some of these studies measured alcohol consumption by frequency, some measured quantity, and some used a categorization system that used both quantity and frequency.

Problem Drinking

Some research using general population samples have investigated the relationship between drinking styles and problem drinking. Kilty, Leung, and Cheung (1987) reported a negative relationship between participation in convivial drinking (which included drinking at a party in someone's home, drinking at the beach), lifestyle drinking (such as having a drink at lunch with a friend), and problem drinking (which included loss of control, blackouts, and drunken driving). Similarly, Glynn, Lo Castro, Hermos and Bosse (1983) reported that spending time with friends and in social settings (not including bars) was associated with non problematic drinking; however, participation in what the authors referred to as "masculine activities," such as going to sporting events and bars was associated with problem drinking (which included drunken driving and drinking which affected health and family relationships negatively).

The leisure of alcoholics and substance abusers have been the focus of a number of investigations in the field. Sessoms and Oakley (1969) found that clinical alcoholics tended to be more passive in their leisure involvement than the general population, and that fewer alcoholics participate in outdoor recreation, sport, cultural activities, hobbies or community organizations. Similarly, Selzer (1977) found that clinical alcoholics participated in leisure activities less frequently than non alcoholics.

Studies of at-risk or substance abusing youth reveal a very different relationship between drinking and leisure participation than with alcoholic adults. In a comparison of youth in treatment for substance abuse with a control group, Iso-Ahola and Crowley (1991) reported that substance abusers participated more frequently in leisure in general, especially physical leisure activities. In a study of high-risk youth, Caldwell and Smith (1992) found that participation in sport activity outside of the home and the number of nights per week that the youth went out for fun were both related to having had five or more drinks in a row in the last two weeks.

This review of the literature would suggest that, with the exception of alcoholics or individuals who had experienced significant problems as a result of their drinking, there is a positive correlational relationship between drinking and leisure participation. Although there has been some investigation of the relationship between leisure activity patterns and drinking for non clinical adolescents and college students, there is an absence in the literature of a comprehensive investigation of the leisure activity and alcohol consumption patterns of adults in the general population.

Gender and Age

When investigating any relationship between alcohol consumption and leisure, gender and age must be considered because of their effects on both drinking and leisure practices. Men drink significantly more than women (Hunter, 1982; NIAAA, 1984); younger adults drink significantly more than older adults (Neff & Husaini, 1982; NIAAA, 1984); and older drinkers drink more frequently but less heavily than younger drinkers (Martin & Casswell, 1987; Vogel-Sprott, 1974).

Gordon, Gaitz, and Scott (1976) reported that leisure patterns differed between men and women with men more involved in intense activities outside of the home, such as drinking, sports or exercise, outdoor activities, spectator sports, and memberships in organizations. Women participated more frequently in individual and home-based activities such as television viewing, home decorating, cooking, relaxation and solitude. Kelly (1982) indicated similar findings; however, he emphasized that large differences in male and female activity participation occur in very select areas such as team sports, golf, hunting and fishing, and window shopping. Henderson, Bialeschki, Shaw, and Freysinger (1989) reported that while women still participate less frequently than men in competitive sport and some outdoor activities, they tend to be more involved in volunteer and educational activities, as well as home based leisure. Kelly (1989) reported that leisure participation is influenced by ageing with decreases in participation in outdoor recreation, travel, and exercise and sport.

Although the literature suggests that relationships exist between drinking and leisure behaviors, no study to date has looked at a broad spectrum of leisure activities and their relationship to frequency and quantity of drinking while controlling for gender and age. The purpose of this study was to examine whether leisure activity participation differs in the general adult population on the basis of frequency of alcohol consumption or quantity of alcohol typically consumed per drinking occasion.

Methods

Subjects

A simple random sample of one thousand and six households was drawn from the telephone directory of a large south-western city in the United States. Individuals answering the telephone who were over 21 years old were asked to complete a telephone interview related to their leisure. Forty seven percent of the sample (470 individuals) agreed to participate in the telephone interview. The telephone interview addressed the frequency of the subjects' participation in 31 leisure activities. The subjects were asked also how often they drank alcoholic beverages, and the quantity they typically consumed per drinking occasion, as well as demographic information.

Independent Variables

Age, gender, frequency of alcohol consumption, and quantity of alcohol consumption were the independent variables for this study. Measures of the subjects' frequency of alcohol consumption was obtained through the question: "How often do you drink alcoholic beverages?" The frequency response categories included: Never, once a month or less, 2-3 times a month, 1-2 times a week, 3-4 times a week, 5-6 times a week, and daily. Measures of quantity were obtained through the question: "How many drinks do you usually have when you do drink?" There were six quantity response categories, ranging from 1 drink to 6 or more drinks.

Dependent Variables

Participation in 31 leisure activities representing 6 leisure factors were the dependent variables. The leisure activity inventory was developed originally by Kelly, evolved through a series of studies (Kelly, 1975, 1978, 1986), and consisted of 28 leisure activities. Three leisure activities were added to supplement Kelly's inventory. In response to each item, subjects indicated their frequency of activity participation by specifying: "A lot, Sometimes, Seldom, Never".

Results

Sample Characteristics

Analysis of the demographic data for the initial sample ($n=470$) indicated: 43 % were male; 22 % were between 21-29 years old; 27 % were between 30-39 years old; 22 % were between 40-49 years old; 29 % were 50 years old or older; over 65 % had some college education; 53 % had household gross incomes of \$30,000 or more; approximately one-half were married; and 58 % did not have children living at home. The six categories of drinking frequency were collapsed into four categories so that there was an adequate number of cases in each cell for analysis. Fifty three percent of the sample drank less than once a month; 31 % drank between 2-3 times a month and 1-2 times a week; 9 % drank 3-6 times a week; and 7 % drank daily. Categories were also created for quantity of drinking per occasion. Seventy seven percent of the subjects consumed 3 drinks or less per occasion; 16 % consumed 4-5 drinks per occasion; and 7 % consumed more than five drinks per occasion.

Analyses

A principal components analysis with orthogonal rotation to the varimax criteria was used to reduce the 31 leisure activities to six factors: community social, outdoor, family and home entertainment, community organizations, domestic, and fitness. The six factor solution accounted for 41.3 % of the variance in leisure participation scores. No items with less than a .30 factor loading were included in the analysis. The internal consistency of the overall leisure participation inventory and each of the factors were calculated using Cronbach's alpha. The reliability coefficients, or Cronbach's alpha values, are respectively: overall scale (.76), community social (.63), outdoor (.72), family and home entertainment (.62), community organizations (.48), domestic (.41), and fitness (.43). The low reliability of some of the factors may be partially explained by the limited number of items in each of those factors: community organizations (3 items), domestic (5 items), fitness (3 items). Examples of activities in the six factors included: community social (socializing with friends, eating out, travelling), outdoor (fishing, boating, camping), family social and home entertainment (talking with others at your home, doing fun things with family, family outings such as picnics), community organizations (community clubs, performing arts groups, religious activities), domestic (gardening, cooking for fun), and fitness (exercise, sports).

Two MANOVA analyses were used to investigate the relationship between drinking levels and leisure participation. The first analysis used frequency of drinking per month, gender and age as the independent variables. The four levels of frequency were: less than once a month; 2-3 times a month or 1-2 times a week; 3-6 times a week; and daily. Daily drinking is often isolated as a separate category in alcohol studies (Lemmens & Knibbe, 1992). The second MANOVA analysis used quantity of alcohol consumed per occasion, together with gender and age, as the independent variables. The three levels of quantity were: 2 drinks or less, 3-4 drinks, and 5 drinks or more. Gender and age were included in the analyses primarily to identify any interaction effects. The dependent variables for both of the analyses were the six factors of leisure activity participation.

MANOVA results for frequency of drinking per month, gender and age were significant (p<.001). The results of the MANOVA analysis are displayed in Table 1. The univariate F-test for frequency of drinking per month indicated significant differences in means for community social leisure participation (p<.001), and outdoor participation (*p*<.006). The results of the univariate F-test is displayed in Table 1. Post-hoc Scheffe tests were used to determine more specifically how participation in community social activities and outdoor activities was related to frequency of drinking. The Scheffe tests indicated that subjects who drink between 3-6 times a week participated more frequently in community social activities than subjects who drink less than once a month or those who drink daily (p<.05). In addition, subjects who drink either 2-3 times a month or 1-2 times a week participated more frequently in community social activities than subjects who drink less than once per month (p<.05). The results also indicated that subjects who drink 3-6 times a week participated more frequently in outdoor activities than subjects who drink less than once a month (p<.05).

The MANOVA results for both gender (p<.001) and age (*p*<.001) were also significant, however, there were no interaction effects. See Table 1 for the multivariate and univariate tests for gender and age. The univariate F-test for gender indicated that significant differences existed for family/home entertainment and fitness. An inspection of the mean scores for gender indicated that females participated more frequently in family and home entertainment activities, and less frequently in fitness than men. The univariate F-tests for age groups indicated differences in frequency of participation in community social, outdoor, and family/home entertainment, and fitness activities. The Post-hoc Scheffe test revealed that those 35 or younger participated more frequently in community social activities than either those between 35-50, or over 50 years old (p<.05). Individuals over 50 years old participated less frequently in outdoor activities than either those between 35-50, or age 35 or younger (p<.05). Individuals 35 years old or younger participated more frequently in family and home entertainment activities than those over 50 years old (p<.05). Individuals over 50 years old participated less frequently in fitness activities than either those 36-50 or those 35 or younger (p<.05). Those individuals 36-50 years old participated less frequently in fitness than those 35 years old or younger (p<.05). Means and standard deviations for each of the significant variables in the univariate analyses are presented in Tables 2, 3 and 4.

TABLE 1

A Summary of MANOVA Analysis with Drinking Frequency, Gender and Age by Types of Leisure Activity Participation

Effect	Wilk's	F	Hyp. df	Error df	p
Drinking Frequency	.875	3.343	18	1247	.000
Gender	.940	4.667	6	441	.000
Age	.914	3.355	12	882	.000

Univariate F-Test for Drinking Frequency with 3,446 df

Variable	Hypoth. SS	Error SS	Hypoth MS	Error MS	F	p
Community Social	6.933	103.817	2.311	2.311	9.927	.000
Outdoor	8.204	291.368	2.734	.653	4.186	.006
Family/Home Entertainment	.553	123.653	.185	.277	.665	.573
Community Organizations	3.490	262.670	1.164	.589	1.976	.117
Domestic	.453	234.554	.151	.526	.287	.835
Fitness	2.010	240.214	.670	.539	1.243	.293

Univariate F-Test for Gender with 1,446 df

Variable	Hypoth. SS	Error SS	Hypoth MS	Error MS	F	p
Community Social	.065	103.817	.065	.233	.277	.599
Outdoor	.569	291.368	.569	.653	.871	.351
Family/Home Entertainment	3.821	123.653	3.821	.277	13.783	.000
Community Organizations	1.990	262.640	1.991	.589	3.380	.067
Domestic	.809	234.554	.809	.526	1.538	.215
Fitness	3.490	240.214	3.490	.539	6.479	.011

Univariate F-Test for Age with 2,446 df

Variable	Hypoth. SS	Error SS	Hypoth MS	Error MS	F	p
Community Social	5.010	103.817	2.505	.233	10.762	.000
Outdoor	6.869	291.368	3.434	.653	5.257	.006
Family/Home Entertainment	2.201	123.653	1.100	.277	3.969	.020
Community Organizations	.049	262.639	.024	.589	.041	.959
Domestic	2.332	234.554	1.166	.526	2.217	.110
Fitness	6.318	240.214	3.160	.539	5.865	.003

TABLE 3

A Summary of Univariate Analyses for the Gender Effect on Leisure Activity Participation Variables

	Gender					
	Male		Female			
Variable	M	S	M	S	F (1,483df)	p
Family/Home Entertainment	2.653	.521	2.901	.532	13.783	.000
Fitness	2.571	.770	2.328	.756	6.479	.011

Two partial correlation analyses were used to examine the relationships between how often subjects reported drinking each month, the amount they drink on each drinking occasion, and frequency of participation in each of the six types of activities. One partial correlation analysis included daily drinkers ; the other excluded daily drinkers. Age and gender were controlled in the analyses. The results of both analyses indicated significant relationships, however, the relationships differed on whether or not daily drinkers were included in the analysis. Whether daily drinkers are included or excluded from the partial correlation analyses, there is a significant positive relationship between participation in community social activities and frequency of drinking ; however, the correlation is much stronger when the daily drinkers are removed from the analyses. Whether daily drinkers are included or excluded from the partial correlation analyses, there is a significant positive relationship between participation in outdoor recreation and frequency of drinking and a consistent negative relationship between participation in community organizations and frequency of drinking. The two partial correlation analyses are presented in Tables 5 and 6.

TABLE 2
A Summary of Univariate Analyses for the Drinking Frequency Effect on Leisure Activity Participation Variables

	Drinking Frequency*									
	Level 1		Level 2		Level 3		Level 4		F (3,497df)	p
Variable	M	S	M	S	M	S	M	S		
Community Social	2.559	.516	2.773	.448	2.921	.470	2.564	.536	9.927	.000
Outdoor	1.679	.789	1.715	.810	2.078	1.005	1.902	.904	4.186	.006

* Drinking Frequency
Level 1 = once a month or less
Level 2 = 2-3 times per month / 1-2 times per week
Level 3 = 3-6 times per week
Level 4 = daily drinking

TABLE 4
A Summary of Univariate Analyses for the Age Effect on Leisure Activity Participation Variables

	Age in Years							
	≤35		36-50		50+		F (2,479df)	p
Variable	M	S	M	S	M	S		
Community Social	2.813	.448	2.605	.522	2.546	.512	10.762	.000
Outdoor	1.949	.884	1.756	.803	1.483	.730	5.257	.006
Family/Home Entertainment	2.887	.488	2.799	.553	2.695	.573	3.969	.020
Fitness	2.691	6.845	2.471	.740	2.093	.780	5.865	.003

TABLE 5

**Partial Correlations for all Subjects
between Quantity of Alcohol Consumed per Occasion,
Frequency of Drinking per Month and Leisure Activity Participation**

Leisure Activities	Correlation with Quantity	Correlation with Frequency
Community Social	-.15**	.12**
Outdoor	-.02	.15**
Family/Home	-.08*	.02
Comunity Organizations	.13**	-.09*
Domestic	-.09*	.03
Fitness	-.05	-.04

*p<.05   **p<.01

TABLE 6

**Partial Correlations without Daily Drinkers
between Quantity of Alcohol Consumed per Occasion,
Frequency of Drinking per Month and Leisure Activity Participation**

Leisure Activities	Correlation with Quantity	Correlation with Frequency
Community Social	.13**	.26**
Outdoor	.08	.16**
Family/Home	-.02	.04
Comunity Organizations	-.18**	-.11**
Domestic	-.05	.03
Fitness	-.08*	.03

*p<.05   **p<.01

Two correlations reversed their directions of relationship significantly on the basis of whether or not daily drinkers were in the analyses. When daily drinkers are left in the analysis, alcohol quantity is negatively related to participation in community social activities; when daily drinkers are not in the analysis, there is a significant positive relationship. When daily drinkers are left in the analysis, alcohol quantity is positively related to participation in community organization activities (which include church activities). When daily drinkers are taken out of the analysis, greater quantity of drinking is associated negatively with participation in community organization activities. When daily drinkers are included, quantity of drinking is associated with less participation in family and domestic leisure activities. When daily drinkers are not included in the analyses, greater quantity of drinking is associated with less participation in fitness activities.

MANOVA results for quantity of drinking per occasion were non significant, although trends in the data suggested that some relationships might exist between quantity of drinking per occasion and outdoor, fitness, and domestic leisure participation.

Discussion

The results of this study indicate that some relationships exist between drinking practices and leisure participation patterns. More specifically, the frequency of drinking versus the quantity of drinking are differentially related to leisure participation. People who drink more frequently are more involved in community social situations, such as eating out, socializing with friends, travelling and going to concerts. This relationship does not hold true for individuals who drink daily. Daily drinking does not appear to be associated with frequent participation in community social activities. There are a number of potential explanations for this absence of relationship. First, daily drinking may be a ritualistic activity that is woven into the individuals' daily lifestyle, such as the cocktail or beer consumed at the end of the day. Second, for some individuals daily drinking may signify alcohol dependence. When individuals are alcohol dependent, they often drink to maintain a state of physiological comfort (Kinney & Leaton, 1991). This dependent type of drinking may at times occur in community social situations, but is just as likely to occur in the context of one's home.

In addition, drinkers who consume alcohol frequently, but not daily, are more likely to participate in outdoor activities, such as boating and camping than very infrequent drinkers. This finding is consistent with previous research (Young & Kronus, 1977), and suggests that drinking is at least condoned in outdoor leisure contexts, if not actually encouraged. Frequency of drinking and participation in community organization activities were consistently negatively associated. These findings would suggest that community organization contexts (including religious activities) do not encourage frequent alcohol use.

The relationships between quantity of drinking and leisure participation patterns were weaker, less consistent, and changed depending on the inclusion or exclusion of daily drinkers. For example, quantity of drinking was associated with more community social involvement, unless daily drinkers were included. Daily, heavier drinking was negatively associated with community social involvement. Daily, heavy drinking is also associated with problem drinking (Glynn et al., 1983). Therefore, this study would lend some support to previous findings that convivial, lifestyle drinking (outside of a bar setting) even when done frequently is not associated with severe, problem drinking (Kilty et al., 1987).

The relationship between quantity of drinking and participation in community leisure organizations is less consistent and difficult to explain. When daily drinkers are removed from the analysis, the anticipated relationship that quantity of drinking was negatively associated with community organization activities holds. However, when daily drinkers were included there was a positive relationship between community organization activity and quantity of drinking which suggests that daily, heavier drinkers are involved in community organization activities. One aspect of the explanation may be that community organization contexts may minimize frequency of drinking (that is not heavy) and quantity of drinking (that is not daily) because these types of drinking do not represent necessarily problem drinking which may be beyond the control of the individual. However, further research is needed to explain the counterintuitive finding that heavy, daily drinking may be somehow related to involvement in community organization activity.

Previous research has suggested that heavy, binge drinking (Caldwell & Smith, 1992; Iso-Ahola & Hayllar 1992) and frequency of drinking (Young & Kronus, 1977) are intertwined with leisure for some youth and young adults. However, problem drinking in adults is not associated with high levels of leisure participation (Glynn et al., 1983; Kilty et al., 1987), nor is alcoholism (Selzer, 1977). The results of this study suggest that frequency of drinking is associated with leisure participation, unless the drinking occurs daily. Daily drinking can be fairly innocuous as in the individual who drinks one glass of wine a day. However, daily heavy drinking may be indicative of a problem (Glynn et al., 1983). The development of problem drinking may lay the foundation for the transition away from community social leisure participation, as well as family and home entertainment and domestic activities. Determining if a transition from a previously active to an inactive lifestyle parallels the evolution of problem drinking could be a promising research focus.

According to social learning theory, cognition, behavior and environmental attributes all interact as determinants of each other (reciprocal determinism) (Bandura, 1986). Bandura (1986) proposed that upon entering situations, individuals make judgments about the attributes of a situation and the behaviors required to produce positive outcomes in that situation. Using the example of leisure, individuals may associate leisure situations with enjoyment, sense of separation, spontaneity, adventure, relaxation, and the lack of self-evaluation (Gunter, 1987; Shaw, 1985). The media presents alcohol as an easy means to create enjoyable experiences. For example, the enticement that consuming a certain beer will make a night that is "kind of special" even more memorable and the image of parched hikers who pop a beer tab and a party unfolds are common in the media. These positive associations presented by society between drinking and leisure participation may be internalized. Research indicates that children who have never had a drink have already formed alcohol expectancies (Kraus, Smith, & Ratner, 1994), and that positive expectancies are associated with heavier drinking among adolescents (Webb, Baer, Francis, & Caid, 1993). Recent research (Carruthers, 1993) related directly to alcohol expectancies associated with leisure reported that adult drinkers do have the expectation that drinking will enhance their recreation and social leisure experiences, and that heavier drinkers have stronger expectations of these positive effects. The relationship then between drinking frequency and community social and outdoor recreation participation may be partially explained by the anticipated outcomes of drinking on these leisure situations.

From a reciprocal determinism perspective, the results of this study would suggest also that community social and outdoor environments may reinforce drinking behaviors. In a review of the sociological perspectives of alcohol use, Bacon (1991) suggested that drinking behaviors are most commonly acted out at particular places and at particular times. Generally, solitary drinking, morning drinking and drinking during the work day are considered unacceptable, while drinking is often sanctioned and reinforced within "recreational gatherings" (Bacon, 1991). Future research should examine the elements of certain leisure experiences that either discourage or encourage drinking behaviors.

This study had a number of limitations that should be considered. Some of the correlations, while significant, were very small. In addition, the proportion of drinkers at the heavier end of the drinking continuum is small, and heavy, daily drinkers smaller still. Lastly, a telephone interview was used to collect data. While the reliability of self reports of drinking behavior have been questioned (Helzer, 1987), other authors have reported fairly strong reliability in self-reports of alcohol consumption (O'Malley, Bachman and Johnson, 1983).

References

BACON, S. (1991). Sociology and the problems of alcohol: Foundations for a sociologic study of drinking behavior. In P.M. Roman (Ed.), *Alcohol: The development of sociological perspectives on use and abuse* (pp. 19-58). New Brunswick, NJ: Rutgers Center of Alcohol Studies, Publications Division.

BAMMEL, G. & BURRIS-BAMMEL, L.L. (1992). *Leisure and human behavior* (2nd ed.). Dubuque, IA: Wm. C. Brown.

BANDURA, A. (1986). *Social foundations of thought and action.* Englewood Cliffs, NJ: Prentice-Hall.

BROWN, S., CHRISTIANSEN, B., & GOLDMAN, M. (1987). The alcohol expectancy questionnaire: An instrument for the assessment of adolescent and adult alcohol expectancies. *Journal of Studies on Alcohol, 48,* 483-491.

CAHALAN, D., CISIN, I., & CROSSLEY, H. (1969). *American drinking practices.* New Haven, CN: College and University Press.

CALDWELL, L. & SMITH, E. (1992, July). *Leisure and high risk youth.* Paper presented at the International Conference on Leisure and Mental Health. Salt Lake City, UT.

CARRUTHERS, C. (1993). Leisure and alcohol expectancies. *Journal of Leisure Research, 25*(3), 229-244.

CORWIN, M. (1991). Exercising the right choice. *Parks and Recreation, 26*(3), 36-40.

CRITCHLOW-LEIGH, B. (1987). Beliefs about the effects of alcohol on self and others. *Journal of Studies on Alcohol, 48*(5), 467-475.

ENGS, R. & HANSON, D. (1985). The drinking patterns and drinking problems of college students. *Journal of Alcohol and Drug Education, 31*(1), 65-83.

FINGARETTE, H. (1988). *Heavy drinking: The myth of alcoholism as a disease.* Berkeley, CA: University of California Press.

GLYNN, R., LO CASTRO, J., HERMOS, J., & BOSSE, R. (1983). Social contexts and motives for drinking in men. *Journal of Studies on Alcohol, 44*(6), 1011-1025.

GORDON, C., GAITZ, C., & SCOTT, J. (1976). Leisure and lives: Personal expressivity across the life span. *In* R. Binstock & E. Shanas (Eds.), H*andbook of aging and the social sciences* (pp. 310-340). New York: Van Nostrand Reinhold.

GUNTER, B.G. (1987). The leisure experience: Selected properties. *Journal of Leisure Research, 19*(2), 115-130.

HENDERSON, K., BIALESCHKI, M.D., SHAW, S., & FREYSINGER, V. (1989). *A leisure of one's own: A feminist perspective on women's leisure.* State College, PA: Venture.

HUNTER, P., HANNON, R., & MARCHI, D. (1982). Alcohol consumption in natural settings as a function of sex, age and income level. *Journal of Studies on Alcohol, 43*(3), 387-392.

KELLY, J.R. (1989). Later-life leisure: Beginning a new agenda. *Leisure Sciences, 11*, 47-59.

KELLY, J.R. (1987). *Freedom to be: A new sociology of leisure.* New York: MacMillan.

KELLY, J.R. (1982). *Leisure.* Englewood Cliffs, NJ: Prentice-Hall.

KELLY, J.R. (1978). Family leisure in three communities. *Journal of Leisure Research, 10*, 47-60.

KILTY, K., LEUNG, P., & MONIT CHEUNG, K. (1987). Drinking styles and drinking problems. *The International Journal of the Addictions, 22*(5). 389-412.

KINNEY, J. & LEATON, G. (1991). *Loosening the grip: A handbook of alcohol information* (4th ed.). St. Louis, MO: Mosby Year Book.

KRAUS, R. (1990). *Recreation and leisure in modern society* (4th ed.). United States: Harper Collins.

KRAUS, D., SMITH, G., & RATNER, H. (1994). Modifying alcohol-related expectancies in grade-school children. *Journal of Studies on Alcohol, 55*, 535-542.

INSTITUTE OF MEDICINE (1992). Prevention and treatment of alcohol-related problems: Research opportunities. *Journal of Studies on Alcohol, 53*(1), 5-16.

INSTITUTE OF MEDICINE (1989). *Prevention and treatment of alcohol problems: Research opportunities.* Washington, D.C.: National Academy Press.

ISO-AHOLA, S. & CROWLEY, E. (1991). Adolescent substance abuse and leisure boredom. *Journal of Leisure Research, 23*(3), 260-271.

ISO-AHOLA, S. & HAYLLAR, B. (1992). *Leisure, drug use, and life satisfaction.* Paper presented at the International conference on Leisure and Mental Health, Salt Lake City, UT.

LEMMENS, P., TAN, E., & KNIBBE, R. (1992). Measuring quantity and frequency of drinking in a general population survey: A comparison of five indices. *Journal of Studies on Alcohol, 53*, 476-486.

MARTIN, C. & CASSWELL, S. (1987). Types of male drinkers: A multivariate study. *Journal of Studies on Alcohol, 48*(2), 109-118.

NATIONAL INSTITUTE ON ALCOHOL ABUSE AND ALCOHOLISM (1984). Special focus: The fifth special report to the U.S. Congress on alcohol and health. *Alcohol Health and Research World, 9*(1).

NEFF, J. & HUSAINI, B. (1982). Life events, drinking patterns and depressive symptomatology: The stress-buffering role of alcohol consumption. *Journal of Studies on Alcohol, 43*(3), 301-318.

ORCUTT, J. (1991). Beyond the "exotic and pathologic": Alcohol problems, norm qualities, and sociological theories of deviance. *In* P. Roman (Ed.), A*lcohol: The development of sociological perspectives on use and abuse* (pp. 145-173). New Brunswick, NJ: Rutgers Center of Alcohol Studies.

PERDUE, R.R. & RAINWATER, A. (1984). Adolescent recreation and alcohol consumption. *Therapeutic Recreation Journal, 18*(2), 41-51.

SCHALL, M., KEMENY, A., & MALTZMAN, I. (1992). Factors associated with alcohol use in university students. *Journal of Studies on Alcohol, 53*(2), 122-136.

SELZER, M.L. (1977). Treatment-related factors in alcoholic populations. *Alcohol Health and the Research World, 1*(3), 23-27.

SESSOMS, H.D. & OAKLEY, S.R. (1969). Recreation, leisure and the alcoholic. *Journal of Leisure Research, 1*(1), 21-31.

SHAW, S. (1985). The meaning of leisure in everyday life. *Leisure Sciences, 7*(1), 1-23.

SIMPURA, J. (1985). Drinking: An ignored leisure activity. *Journal of Leisure Research, 17*(3), 200-211.

SOBELL, L.C., CUNNINGHAM, J.A., SOBELL, M.B., & TONEATTO, T. (1993). A life-span perspective on natural recovery (self change) from alcohol problems. *In* J.S. Baer, G.A. Marlatt, & R.J. McMahon (Eds.), *Addictive behaviors across the life span: Prevention, treatment, and policy issues*, (pp. 34-66). Newbury Park, CA: Sage.

TUCHFIELD, B.S., LIPTON, W L., & LILE, E.A. (1983). Social involvement and the resolution of alcoholism. *Journal of Drug Issues, 13*(3), 323-332.

VOGEL-SPROTT, M. (1974). Defining light and heavy social drinking: Research implications and hypothesis. *Quarterly Journal Studies on Alcohol, 35*, 1388-1392.

WEBB, J., BAER, P., FRANCIS, D., & CAID, C. (1993). Relationship among social and intrapersonal risk, alcohol expectancies, and alcohol usage among early adolescents. *Addictive Behaviors, 18*(2), 127-134.

YOUNG, R. & KRONUS, S. (1977). Drinking behavior and its relationship to outdoor recreation participation. *Journal of Leisure Research, 9*(3), 165-173.

Cynthia P. CARRUTHERS et James A. BUSSER
Consommation d'alcool et participation au loisir

RÉSUMÉ

On recommande souvent la participation à des activités de loisir saines et valorisantes en contrepartie de la consommation et de l'abus d'alcool. Pourtant, les personnes qui boivent le font généralement en dehors des heures de travail et souhaitent y trouver la détente et le plaisir. À ce jour, peu de recherches ont porté sur le lien entre la consommation d'alcool et la participation au loisir. La présente recherche s'est précisément penchée sur cette question en ciblant les adultes de la population générale. Des entrevues téléphoniques ont permis de déterminer la fréquence de participation des sujets à diverses activités de loisir ainsi que la fréquence et la quantité d'alcool consommé par mois. Les analyses MANOVA ont révélé que la fréquence de consommation mensuelle se rattache à une plus grande participation à des activités sociales communautaires et de plein air. Des analyses de corrélation partielle ont montré que certaines relations entre la consommation d'alcool et la participation au loisir varient de manière significative en fonction de l'inclusion ou non des buveurs quotidiens dans les analyses. La présentation des résultats est suivie d'une discussion des répercussions de cette étude sur la pratique et la recherche à venir.

Cynthia P. CARRUTHERS and James A. BUSSER
Alcohol Consumption and Leisure Participation

ABSTRACT

Healthy and rewarding recreation participation is often proposed as an alternative to alcohol use and abuse. Yet, alcohol consumption usually occurs in one's non-work time and drinkers anticipate that alcohol consumption will contribute to their relaxation and enjoyment. Little research has investigated the link between alcohol consumption and leisure participation. This study investigated the relationship between alcohol consumption and leisure participation patterns in adults in the general population. Telephone interviews were used to determine subjects' frequency of participation in various leisure activities, frequency of drinking per month, and quantity of alcohol consumed per month. MANOVA analyses indicated that frequency of drinking per month is associated with greater participation in community social and outdoor activities. Partial correlation analyses indicated that some relationships between drinking and leisure participation varied significantly on the basis of whether or not daily drinkers were included in the analyses. Implications for practice and further research are discussed.

Cynthia P. CARRUTHERS y James A. BUSSER
Consumo de alcohol y participación en las actividades de diversión

RESUMEN

Se recomienda muy a menudo de participar en actividades de diversión sanas y valorizadoras, como una alternativa al consumo y abuso del alcohol. Por lo tanto, las personas que consumen alcohol lo hacen generalmente fuera de las horas de trabajo como para encontrar reposo y placer. Hasta hoy en día se han realizado pocas investigaciones que traten sobre el vínculo que existe entre el consumo del alcohol y la participación a las actividades de diversión. Este estudio examina precisamente este sujeto tomando como patrón los adultos de la población en general. Se realizaron entrevistas telefónicas que permitieron determinar, para cada sujeto, la frecuencia de participación a diversas actividades de recreo así que la frecuencia y la cantidad de alcohol consumida por mes. Los análisis MANOVA revelaron que la frecuencia de consumo mensual está ligada a una amplia participación a las actividades sociales comunitarias y al aire libre. Análisis de correlación parcial mostraron que ciertas relaciones entre el consumo del alcohol y la participación a las actividades de recreo varían de manera significativa en función de la inclusión o no de los bebedores cotidianos dentro de los análisis. Los resultados son seguidos de una discusión de las repercusiones de este estudio sobre la práctica y la investigación en el futuro.

HEALTH BEHAVIORS
OF LEISURE ALIENATED YOUTH

Linda L. CALDWELL

School of Hotel, Restaurant and recreation Management
The Pensylvania State University
Pensylvania , United States

Edward A. SMITH

Department of Health Promotion and Behavior
University of Georgia
Georgia, United States

The increased research activity on understanding adolescents and leisure over the past decade has addressed an area that had been previously neglected. A parallel neglect had occurred in research on adolescents in general, and was followed by a similar increase in research activity as noted by Petersen (1993), who commented : "There has been an explosion of research in adolescence over the past 20 years, especially in the last decade" (p. 1). It is no surprise that adolescent research in general, and specific to leisure, has seen this increase in activity. Adolescent lives and problems seem to be an ever increasing social concern of Western culture, indicated in part by the prominence of political interest and media attention.

Many adolescent problems center around health-related concerns such as suicide, depression, sexual activity (and unwanted pregnancy), alcohol use, and so on. Despite increased attention to these problem behaviors of adolescents and the associated challenges which accompany the transition from childhood to adult status, many researchers agree that adolescence is not by definition a time of "storm and stress" (Offer & Offer, 1975 ; Petersen, 1988, 1993 ; Rutter, 1980). This transitional period is, however, a critical time in the establishment of a life course, including the establishment and reinforcement of healthy behaviors. Unfortunately, there appears to be a growing number of youth who engage daily in risky behaviors which compromise healthy development (e.g, Benson, 1990 ; Carnegie Council on Adolescent Development, 1992 ; Vanderschmidt, Lang, Knight-Williams, & Vanderschmidt, 1993).

Proportionately at a national level, youth at-risk constitute a growing population (Dryfoos, 1990). Due to social and economic conditions, in some areas entire neighborhoods can be classified as at-risk. Even in middle and upper income communities, however, a large number of youth engage in health compromising behaviors. While some of the factors which place youth in an at-risk status are overcome as youth mature and become less susceptible to peer pressure, other factors become compounded with age. As a result, some high risk problems, such as smoking, bulimia, and depression, may not disappear over time without structured interventions (e.g., Petersen, 1993).

Although leisure and adolescence, adolescence in general, and adolescent health compromising behaviors have been studied individually from disciplinary perspectives, it still remains a critical need to understand adolescents and adolescent problem behavior from inter- or multidisciplinary perspectives. These perspectives should include the everyday life contexts and structures that are central to adolescent life (e.g., Petersen, 1993). In the present study that everyday context is leisure time.

The purpose of our study was to explore the relationship of youth who appeared alienated in their leisure to health compromising, or at-risk, behaviors. There is fairly clear evidence that youth who engage in one health compromising behavior (e.g., alcohol consumption) are also predisposed to other at-risk behaviors or states (Jessor & Jessor, 1977). Therefore, rather than single out one or two at-risk health behaviors, a number of at-risk behaviors and states were considered. These included smoking, heavy alcohol use, vomiting on purpose, depression, and attempting suicide. We were also interested in objective leisure behavior (e.g., participation in clubs and organization, sports teams both in and outside of school, and going out in the evening for fun and recreation). Additionally, we measured adolescents' perceptions of their leisure (free) time as being boring and their degree of intentional deviance with respect to use of their leisure time.

Related Literature

There are no other studies which have examined the relationship of leisure experience and participation with the extended constellation of at-risk behaviors of interest to this investigation. Other researchers have, however, reported findings that are linked to this study. Boredom proneness (Farmer & Sundberg, 1986) was reported to covary significantly with alienation in a sample of college students (Tolor, 1989). Drug use, although not reported here, has been hypothesized to be a means of adolescent communication, expressing opposition to the norms and values of society (Jessor, 1986). Alcohol use has been linked with suicidal ideation and attempts, as well as with participation in high risk recreational activities (Windle, Miller-Tutzauer, & Domenico, 1992). Using leisure time as a context, Iso-Ahola and Crowley (1991) concluded that adolescent substance abusers undergoing clinical treatment were more likely to experience leisure time as boring than non-substance abusers.

Although often thought as a panacea for social problems, and despite much evidence reflecting the benefits of leisure (Driver, Peterson, & Brown, 1991), leisure has undergone some critical scrutiny which has indicated that not all leisure is positive (Iso-Ahola & Weissinger, 1987; Lee, Dattilo, & Howard, 1994). Research on leisure and adolescents has also provided evidence to suggest the same conclusion (Caldwell & Smith, 1994). One of the variables currently associated with a negative leisure experience has been boredom (e.g., Iso-Ahola & Weissinger, 1987; Smith & Caldwell, 1989), and there is some evidence that the experience of boredom during free time is associated with health compromising behaviors (Caldwell & Smith, 1994; Smith & Caldwell, 1989).

The growing literature on boredom in general, as well as on boredom of adolescents, reflects that it is a complex and multidimensional construct. There appear to be cognitive (e.g., attentional capacity, Hamilton, 1983), psychological (see Larson & Richards (1991) for a brief review), and social construction (e.g., Tolor, 1989; Wasson, 1981) models of boredom which have relevance to adolescent lives. Some recent studies have been constructed such that one model of boredom was compared for explanatory power with another model of boredom (e.g., Larson & Richards, 1991; Orcutt, 1985). For example, in their comparative study of boredom in school as a psychological construct vs. a result of social construction, Larson and Richards (1991) concluded tentatively that boredom is related to individual dispositions. They were unable, however, to identify the antecedent variables which precipitated feelings of boredom.

Larson and Richards (1991) also found some support for the notion that adolescents experience boredom in reaction to adult authority or social controls. Other conceptualizations of adolescent boredom include feelings of frustration and anger (Robinson, 1975; Tolor, 1989), deviance at school (Fogelman, 1976; Wasson, 1981) as well as boredom as a reaction to social control (Shaw, Caldwell, & Kleiber, 1994). These studies present a view of boredom as stemming from a "resistance model" (Larson & Richards, 1991) and suggest that adolescents adopt a posture of boredom purposely as a stance of alienation and rejection of adult structure.

Upon reflection of the above findings, coupled with the notion of the instrumental nature of leisure among adolescents (e.g., Larson & Kleiber, 1991), we wanted to see if some adolescents actually used their leisure time as a means of defiance against or rejection of adult structure. While the literature reflects a suggestion that some leisure may in fact be construed as unhealthy or problematic, with the exception of Stebbins's (1988) examination of deviance, there is no discussion or study of leisure actively being used as a time or opportunity for deviance. The instrumental use of leisure participation to gain positive rewards from leisure has been explored (Larson & Kleiber, 1991), but their work implies that outcomes of leisure are positive.

In this study, we predicted that those youth who used leisure as a time to reject adult control would also be those youth who were bored in their leisure time. It also seemed important to this study to gain objective data regarding leisure participation in order to compare it to boredom in leisure time and leisure time used to reject adult structure. Gender differences were examined because past evidence suggested that males and females not only perceive and experience leisure time differently (e.g., Caldwell & Smith, 1994; Shaw, Kleiber, & Caldwell, 1994), but also because males and females differ on incidences of health compromising behaviors (e.g., Gore, Aseltine, & Colten, 1993; Windle, Miller-Tutzauer, & Domenico, 1992).

Methods

Sample and Procedures

Data from a self-administered questionnaire were collected in the spring of 1994 from students in four high schools in a county located in south eastern United States. Parents had been previously notified of the survey and were given the option of refusing their child's participation. On the day of administration, the adolescents were given the same option. There were a total of 159 refusals (12 parents, 147 students). Of the remaining 2,862 participants, 106 surveys were omitted because the participants indicated use of a bogus drug, thus calling into question the veracity of their answers. The remaining 2,756 surveys represent 91.2% of the students present the day of administration.

Measures

The closed-ended questionnaire included standardized items from the Centers for Disease Control *Youth Risk Behavior Survey* (*YRBS*), (Kolbe, Kann, & Collins, 1993), the Search Institute's *Profiles of Student Life* (Benson, 1992), the boredom in leisure component of the *Leisure Experience Battery for Adolescent* (*LEBA*) (Caldwell, Smith, & Weissinger, 1993), and questions derived specifically for measuring adolescent's use of leisure as a reaction to or rejection of adult structure. Data were collected on five health behaviors, four leisure participation behaviors, and two aspects of *leisure alienation* as shown in Table 1. The health indices (smoking, drinking, suicide, vomiting on purpose, and depression) were all single-item variables drawn from the YRBS instrument which has been thoroughly tested for reliability and validity. The four leisure participation behaviors (participation in clubs, going out for fun, and sports involvement in and outside school) were obtained from the YRBS.

TABLE 1

**Measurement of Health, Leisure Alienation,
and Leisure Participation Variables**

Variable	Question	Coding
Regular smoker	Have you ever smoked cigarettes regularly, that is, at least one cigarette everyday for 30 days?	Yes/No
Heavy alcohol use	Think back over the LAST TWO WEEKS. How many times have you had five or more drinks in a row? (A "drink" is a glass of wine, a bottle or can of beer, a shot glass of liquor, or a mixed drink.)	None/1+ times*
Vomit on purpose	How often do you vomit (throw up) on purpose after eating?	Never/1+ times per month*
Attempt suicide	During the past 12 months, how many times did you actually attempt suicide?	0 times/1+ times*
Depressed	How often have you felt sad or depressed during the last 30 days?	All or most of the time/some, once in a while, not at all
Boredom	For me, free time just drags on and on.	Strongly agree (1) to strongly disagree (5), summed and averaged (<3.0)
	Free time is boring.	
	In my free time, I usually don't like what I am doing, but I don't know what else to do.	
Reject adult structure	My parents wouldn't approve of what I do in my free time.	Strongly agree (1) to strongly disagree (5), summed and averaged (<3.0)
	Sometimes I do things in my free time to get back at society.	
	Sometimes I do things in my free time to get back at my parents.	
Clubs/organizations	During an average week, how many hours do you spend in clubs or organizations (other than sports?	0 hours/1+ hours*
Go out for fun/ recreation	During a typical week, on how many evenings do you go out for fun and recreation?	0-2/3+*
Teams outside of school	During the past 12 months, on how many sports teams run by organizations out*side* of your school, did you play?	0/1+*
Teams in school	During the school year, have you participated in any of the following teams at your school? (A list of all school sports was provided.)	Yes/No

* dichotomized from a scale of 5 potential responses

As consistent with past use of the boredom component of the LEBA, this three item measure produced a Cronbach's alpha reliability coefficient of .75. The measure of leisure used as a rejection of adult structure, also comprised of three items, had a Cronbach's alpha reliability coefficient of .70. While neither reliability coefficient is high, given that both leisure related measures were each comprised of three items, the coefficient for each was deemed adequate.

Results

Table 2 indicates that approximately 8-9% of these high school students expressed boredom with their free time (112 females, 107 males). Almost twice as many students (232 females, 218 males) actively used leisure time to reject adult structure. While there is a significant amount of overlap between these two measures (41.1% of females who are bored reject adult structure, 58.9% of males) there remain a large number of adolescents who fit in one category of leisure alienation and not the other.

TABLE 2

**Percent Distribution of Female and Male High School Students'
Rejection of Adult Structure by Boredom**

	Females			Males		
	Yes (112)	Bored No (1243)	Total (1355)	Yes (107)	Bored No (1031)	Total (1138)
Reject adult structure – YES	41.1%	15.0%	(232)	58.9%	15.0%	(218)
Reject adult structure – NO	58.9%	85.0%	(1123)	41.1%	85.0%	(920)
Total %	100%	100%		100%	100%	

The relationship between leisure alienation and health is presented in Table 3. This table, with the data separated by gender, indicates a clear and consistent relationship between health and leisure. Both measures of leisure alienation, boredom and rejection of adult structure are consistently associated with higher rates of undesirable health behaviors. Within gender, adolescents who are bored, or who reject adult structure, are significantly more likely to: smoke cigarettes, abuse alcohol, vomit on purpose, attempt suicide, and be depressed. In many instances the participation rates in these compromising health behaviors are two or more times as high among those adolescents who express leisure alienation.

TABLE 3

**Percent Distribution of Health Behaviors
of Female and Male High School Students by Leisure Alienation**

	Leisure Alienation							
	Females				Males			
	Bored		Reject Adult Structure		Bored		Reject Adult Structure	
	Yes (112)	No (1243)	Yes (232)	No (1123)	Yes (107)	No (1031)	Yes (218)	No (920)
Health Behavior								
Regular smoker	43.8	25.9***	43.1	24.1***	43.0	29.6**	44.0	27.7***
Heavy alcohol use	25.9	15.2**	34.1	12.4***	42.1	26.0***	45.4	23.3***
Vomit on purpose	12.5	3.5***	11.2	2.8***	5.6	1.8*	5.5	1.4***
Attempt suicide	22.3	8.5***	19.8	7.6***	15.0	4.4***	13.3	3.5***
Depressed	44.6	20.7***	40.1	19.1***	27.1	11.2***	19.7	11.0***

    * Chi-square sig <.05
   ** Chi-square sig <.01
  *** Chi-square sig <.001

Within this consistent overall pattern there are gender differences in the reported rates of most of these undesirable health behaviors. These different rates, however, are generally reflective of gender norms in our society. It is important to recognize that the two constructs of leisure alienation remain significantly associated with higher rates of behavior even among behaviors that are normatively gender biased. Vomiting on purpose, for example, is a behavior indicative of potential eating disorders that is much more prominent among adolescent females than males. Table 3 indicates that males who are bored (5.6%) and males who reject adult structure (5.5%) are significantly more likely to vomit on purpose than males who are not alienated (1.8%, bored: 1.4%, rejection). Of additional interest is the fact that females who are not alienated have lower rates of this behavior (3.5%, bored; 2.8%, rejection) than the alienated males. Correspondingly, heavy alcohol use, which is usually more prominent among adolescent males, is significantly higher among alienated females (25.9%, bored; 34.1%, rejection) than among females who are not alienated (15.2%, bored; 12.4%, rejection) and is at least equal to the alcohol use of non-alienated males (26.0%, bored; 32.3%, rejection).

Table 4 indicates the rates of participation in some aspects of leisure among the adolescents in this study. Among females, those who express boredom in their leisure were significantly less likely to participate in clubs or organizations (32.1% vs. 51.9%), to go out in the evenings for fun or recreation

(27.7% vs. 38.0%) or to participate in teams at school (32.1% vs. 45.9%). Lower participation in teams at school is the only significant difference among females who reject adult structure (37.1% vs. 46.4%).

TABLE 4

**Percent Distribution of Leisure Participation
of Female and Male High School Students by Leisure Alienation**

	Leisure Alienation							
	Females				Males			
	Bored		Reject Adult Structure		Bored		Reject Adult Structure	
	Yes (112)	No (1243)	Yes (232)	No (1123)	Yes (107)	No (1031)	Yes (218)	No (920)
Leisure Participation								
Club/organisations	32.1	51.9***	45.7	51.2	44.9	39.7	44.0	39.2
Go out for fun/ recreation (3+)	27.7	38.0*	38.4	36.9	31.8	52.3***	48.6	50.8
Teams outside of school	16.1	20.8	20.3	20.4	45.8	33.9*	38.5	34.2
Teams in school	32.1	45.9**	37.1	46.4**	57.0	52.9	56.4	52.5

* Chi-square sig <.05
** Chi-square sig <.01
*** Chi-square sig <.001

Among males, Table 4 indicates that those who are bored are significantly less likely to go out in the evenings (31.8% vs. 52.3%) but are more likely to participate on teams outside of school (45.8% vs. 33.9%). There were no differences in rates of participation in clubs or organizations, or on school teams. Among males who reject adult structure, there were no differences in participation in any of the leisure activities.

Discussion

The results of this study clearly indicate a relationship between what might be termed alienated leisure and engagement in high risk health behaviors. Approximately 9% of males and 8% of females felt that their leisure time was boring, while about 17% of females and 19% of males appeared to use their leisure time to "get back at" their parents or society. Moreover, both male and female adolescents who fit into this alienated leisure category participated in higher levels of every at-risk health behavior measured than their peers. These results may shed some insight on Larson and Kleiber's (1991) finding according to which one of the five most common leisure pursuits of adolescents was anti-social activities.

The pattern of participation in leisure time activities was not as clear, and the pattern indicated possible gender differences. With one exception, it did not appear that adolescents who used leisure time as a means of rejecting adult structure were any more likely than their peers to participate, or not participate, in so-called normative activities such as clubs and organizations, sports in and outside of school, and going out in the evening for fun and recreation. The exception was females; those females indicating that they used their leisure time to reject adult structure participated less in school sponsored sports teams than did their peers. This finding is generally in alignment with the findings regarding boredom. This study would suggest, however, that this pattern may be more true for a small group of at-risk adolescents.

Females who were bored in their leisure were less likely to participate in 3 of the 4 leisure activities studied; among males, only going out in the evening was lower among those who were bored. Interestingly, participation on teams outside of school was the only leisure activity not related to boredom among females. This lack of relationship, combined with the result that males who are bored are more likely to participate on non-school teams, suggests that this form of recreation may not serve to reduce boredom among high school students.

These findings are not totally consistent with other research which has explored the relationship between adolescent boredom in leisure, frequency of participation in leisure time activities, and participation in at-risk health behaviors (Caldwell & Smith, 1994; Iso-Ahola & Crowley, 1991). Iso-Ahola and Crowley (1991) found that adolescent substance abusers undergoing treatment were more likely than non-substance abusers to feel their leisure time was boring. Concomitantly, they also found a paradoxical effect in that subs-tance abusers, while more bored, were more active in their total leisure, including physical recreation activities.

In another investigation which focused solely on 8th graders who were in a program for youth considered at-risk, Caldwell and Smith (1994) found that going out in the evening for fun five or more times a week was consistently associated with both perceptions of leisure as boring and high levels of alcohol consumption. In addition, playing sports outside of school was associated with high levels of alcohol consumption. Thus, it is still not clear whether active participation in sports and clubs/organizations, as well as evening recreational activities, produces or mitigates boredom. It should be noted, however, that both of the studies referred to above involved youth who had already been identified as high-risk and thus may not be representative of youth in general.

What do these findings tell us about leisure time experience and behavior of adolescents and its relationship with participating in at-risk health behaviors? For the majority of adolescents, it appears that leisure time is a relatively positive experience in terms of not being bored and not actively using the time to participate in anti-social behaviors. For a small but probably practically significant proportion of adolescents, however, leisure time is perceived as boring or represents an opportunity to get back at society and parents. Furthermore, this group of adolescents is more likely to be involved in a variety of health compromising, if not life threatening, behaviors which may persist into adulthood (Petersen, 1993). Since it may be presumed that a majority of these health compromising behaviors occur during free time, the significance of the leisure context is critical. One should keep in mind that about 41% of leisure time bored females and 59% of males also used leisure to reject adult structure, representing a truly leisure alienated group.

A number of questions are raised from this study. One concern, identified in other studies (e.g., Caldwell & Smith, 1989; Iso-Ahola & Crowley, 1991) relates to causal order. Does feeling bored in leisure cause an adolescent to do things to reject adult structure, or to engage in health compromising behaviors, or is it the other way around? A second set of questions relates to adolescent participation in at-risk behaviors. Are the health risk behaviors a form of adolescent rebellion? For example, do adolescents specifically participate in at-risk behaviors such as alcohol consumption, suicidal ideation/attempts, and eating disorders as an attempt to get back at society or their parents? Can we even assume that the at-risk behaviors occur in leisure time? Are these at-risk behaviors perceived as leisure? There is some evidence and speculation to suggest that adolescent participation in deviant or negative leisure behaviors is a function of a lack of optimal arousal (Hamilton, 1983; Kleiber & Rickards, 1985; Iso-Ahola & Crowley, 1991). Based on that, one might ask, what specific function do health risk behaviors serve in increasing optimal arousal in the leisure time of these adolescents?

Further research is needed to answer the above questions, as well as others. Certainly the findings from this study call into question the notion that leisure is a panacea for social and/or health related problems. The challenge is to determine how leisure can be a positive, instrumental, transitional force in the lives of adolescents, especially those who are troubled or at risk.

References

BENSON, P.L. (1990). *The troubled journey: A portrait of 6th-12th grade youth.* Search Institute, Minneapolis, MN: Lutheran Brotherhood.

CALDWELL, L.L., SMITH, E.A., & WEISSINGER, E. (1992). Development of a leisure experience battery for adolescents: Parsimony, stability, and reliability. *Journal of Leisure Research, 24,* 361-376.

CALDWELL, L.L., & SMITH, E.A. (1994). Leisure and mental health of high risk adolescents. *In* D.M. Compton and S.E. Iso-Ahola (Éds.), *Leisure and Mental Health, Vol. 1,* (pp. 330-345).

CARNEGIE COUNCIL ON ADOLESCENT DEVELOPMENT. (1992). *A matter of time: Risk and opportunity in the nonschool hours.* Carnegie Corporation of New York.

DRIVER, B.L., BROWN, P.J., & PETERSON, G.L. (1991). *Benefits of leisure.* State College, PA: Venture Publishing.

DRYFOOS, J.G. (1990). *Adolescents at risk: Prevalence and prevention.* New York: Oxford University Press.

FARMER, R., & SUNDBERG, N.D. (1986). Boredom proneness – the development and correlates of a new scale. *Journal of Personality Assessment, 50,* 4-17.

FOGELMAN, K. (1976). Bored eleven-year olds. *British Journal of Social Work, 6,* 201-211.

GORE, S., ASELTINE, R.H., & COLTEN, M.E. (1993). Gender, social-relational involvement, and depression. *Journal of Research on Adolescence, 3,* 101-126.

HAMILTON, J.A. (1983). Development of interest and enjoyment in adolescence. Part II: Boredom and psychopathology. *Journal of Youth and Adolescence, 12,* 363-372.

ISO-AHOLA, S.E., & WEISSINGER, E. (1987). Leisure and boredom. *Journal of Social and Clinical Psychology, 5,* 356-364.

ISO-AHOLA, S.E., & CROWLEY, E.D. (1991). Adolescent substance abuse and leisure boredom. *Journal of Leisure Research, 23,* 260-271.

JESSOR, R., & JESSOR, S.L. (1977). *Problem behavior and psychosocial development: A longitudinal study of youth.* Orlando: Academic Press.

JESSOR, R. (1986). Adolescent problem drinking: Psychological aspects and development outcomes. *In* R.K. Silbereisen *et al.* (Éds.), (pp. 241-264), *Development as Action in Context.* Heidelberg, Berlin: Springer-Verlag.

KLEIBER, D.A., & RICKARDS, M. (1985). Leisure and recreation in adolescence: Limitations and potential. *In* M.B. Wade (Ed.), *Constraints on Leisure* (pp. 289-317). Springfield, IL: Charles C. Thomas.

KOLBE, L.J., KANN, L., & COLLINS, J.L. (1993). Overview of the youth at risk behavior surveillance system. *Public Health Reports, 108,* 2-10.

LARSON, R., & KLEIBER, D.A. (1991). Free time activities as factors in adolescent adjustment. *In* P. Tolan & B. Cohler (Eds), *Handbook of Clinical Research and Practice with Adolescents.* New York: Wiley.

LARSON, R.W., & RICHARDS, M.H. (1991). Boredom in the middle school years: Blaming schools versus blaming students. *American Journal of Education,* August, 418-443.

LEE, Y., DATTILO, J., & HOWARD, D. (1994). The complex and dynamic nature of leisure experience. *Journal of Leisure Research, 26*, 195-211.

OFFER, D., & OFFER, J.B. (1975). *From teenage to young manhood: A psychological study.* New York: Basic Books.

ORCUTT, J.D. (1985). Contrasting effects of two kinds of boredom on alcohol use. *Journal of Drug Issues, 14*, 161-173.

PETERSEN, A.C. (1988). Adolescent development. *Annual Review of Psychology, 39*, 583-607.

PETERSEN, A.C. (1993). Creating adolescents: The role of context and process in developmental trajectories. *Journal of Research on Adolescence, 3*, 1-18.

ROBINSON, W.P. (1975). Boredom at school. *British Journal of Educational Psychology, 76*, 141-152.

RUTTER, M. (1980). *Changing youth in a changing society: Patterns of adolescent development and disorder.* Cambridge, MA: Harvard University Press.

SHAW, S.M., KLEIBER, D.A., & CALDWELL, L.L. (1994). *Leisure and adolescent development: An examination of the relationship between leisure and identity formation for male and female adolescents.* Unpublished manuscript.

SHAW, S.M., CALDWELL, L.L., & KLEIBER, D.A. (1994). *Time use and free time activities during adolescence: Boredom, stress, and social control.* Unpublished manuscript.

SMITH, E.A., & CALDWELL, L.L. (1989). The perceived quality of leisure experiences among smoking and nonsmoking adolescents. *Journal of Early Adolescence, 9*, 153-162.

STEBBINS, R.A. (1988). *Deviance: Tolerable differences.* Toronto: McGraw-Hill Ryerson.

TOLOR, A. (1989). Boredom as related to alienation, assertiveness, internal-external expectancy, and sleep patterns. *Journal of Clinical Psychology, 45*, 260-265.

VANDERSCHMIDT, H.F., LANG, J.M., & KNIGHT-WILLIAMS, V., & VANDERSCHMIDT, G.F. (1993). Risks among inner-city young teens: The prevalence of sexual activity, violence, drugs, and smoking. *Society for Adolescent Medicine, 14*, 282-288.

WASSON, A.S. (1981). Susceptibility to boredom and deviant behavior at school. *Psychological Reports, 48*, 901-902.

WINDLE, M., MILLER-TUTZAUER, C., & DOMENICO, D. (1992). Alcohol use, suicidal behavior, and risky activities among adolescents. *Journal of Research on Adolescents, 2*, 317-330.

Linda L. CALDWELL et Edward A. SMITH
Désaffection pour le loisir et comportements de santé des jeunes

RÉSUMÉ

Cette étude visait à examiner la relation entre la désaffection pour le loisir chez les jeunes et l'adoption de comportements nuisibles ou à risques pour leur santé. Une enquête effectuée auprès de 2 756 jeunes en 1994 a révélé qu'environ 9 % d'entre eux s'ennuyaient durant leurs temps libres et que 18 % utilisaient ceux-ci pour se venger de la société ou de leurs parents. Comparativement à leurs pairs, ces jeunes désabusés avaient plus tendance à adopter des comportements susceptibles de nuire à leur santé : usage du tabac, usage excessif d'alcool et vomissements provoqués. Un plus grand nombre d'entre eux tendaient à être déprimés et avaient tenté de se suicider au cours des douze derniers mois. Les jeunes filles qui s'ennuyaient participaient généralement moins à des activités de loisir que les autres du même âge, alors que les jeunes garçons avaient moins tendance à sortir le soir pour s'amuser. La participation à des sports et à des clubs organisés a aussi été mesurée. Les résultats de cette étude permettent de remettre en question la conception selon laquelle la participation au loisir a des conséquences positives chez ce groupe d'adolescents qui semblent désabusés du loisir ; ils soulèvent aussi la question, plus importante, de l'origine de l'adoption de comportements nuisibles à la santé par ce type de jeunes.

Linda L. CALDWELL and Edward A. SMITH
Health Behaviors of Leisure Alienated Youth

ABSTRACT

The purpose of our study was to explore the relationship of youth who appeared alienated in their leisure to health compromising, or at-risk, behaviors. A survey of 2,756 youth in 1994 indicated that approximately 9 % were bored during leisure and 18 % used leisure as a means to get back at society or their parents. Compared to their peers, these alienated youth were more likely to engage in a number of health compromising behaviors including : smoking, heavy use of alcohol, and vomiting on purpose. They were also more likely to be depressed and to have attempted suicide in the past twelve months. Females who were bored generally participated in less leisure activities than their contemporaries while bored males were less likely to go out in the evenings for fun. Participation in organized sports and clubs was also measured. Findings from this study call into question the positive benefits derived from leisure participation for this group of adolescents who appear leisure alienated, and more importantly, raise questions about why leisure alienated youth participate in health compromising behaviors.

Linda L. CALDWELL y Edward A. SMITH
Desafición por las actividades de recreo y hábitos de salud de los jóvenes.

RESUMEN

El propósito de este estudio fue de examinar la relación entre la desafición por las actividades de recreo en los jóvenes y la adopción de hábitos nocivos o con riesgos para su salud. Una encuesta efectuada sobre 2756 jóvenes en 1994 reveló que alrededor del 9 % de ellos se aburren durante sus tiempos libres y que 18 % utilizan este tiempo como un medio para vengarse de la sociedad o de sus padres. Comparativamente a sus semejantes, estos jóvenes desilusionados tenían más tendencia a adoptar comportamientos susceptibles de dañar su salud: uso del tabaco, utilización excesiva del alcohol y vómitos provocados adrede. Un gran número de entre ellos tendían a estar deprimidos y habían intentado suicidarse en el transcurso de los últimos doce meses. Las jóvenes que se aburrían participaban generalmente menos a las actividades de recreo que las otras adolescentes de su misma edad, mientras que los jóvenes tenían menos tendencia a salir la noche para divertirse. La participación en los deportes y clubes organizados fue también evaluada. Los resultados de este estudio permiten de cuestionar la concepción según la cual la participación a las actividades de recreo tiene consecuencias positivas en este grupo de adolescentes que parecen desilusionados de dichas actividades. Los resultados obtenidos también permiten de plantear el problema más importante: el origen de la adopción de hábitos nocivos a la salud por este tipo de jóvenes.

PARTIE III / *PART III*

ACTIVITÉ PHYSIQUE : PRESSIONS SOCIALES ET INTERVENTIONS ÉTATIQUES

PHYSICAL ACTIVITY : SOCIAL PRESSURES AND GOVERNMENTAL INTERVENTIONS

BODYWORK AS A MORAL IMPERATIVE: SOME CRITICAL NOTES ON HEALTH AND FITNESS

Philip WHITE

Department of Kinesiology
McMaster University
Ontario, Canada

Kevin YOUNG

Department of Sociology
University of Calgary
Alberta, Canada

James GILLETT

Department of Sociology
McMaster University
Ontario, Canada

Introduction

Of late, the parameters around what is popularly considered healthful behaviour have expanded dramatically. Whether the definition of "healthy" is seen to include participation in regular "workouts", "safe" sex, abstaining from tobacco use, monitoring alcohol intake, using unleaded gasoline, preferring herbal or alternative medicines, eating preservative-free foods, or cutting cholesterol and other fats from our diets, it is clear that a new era of health consciousness has dawned (Labonte, 1982). Such changes in lifestyle also suggest that the idea of health has shifted from something that is viewed as the result of luck or biological inheritance to something that is largely achieved through personal volition. In other words, health has changed dramatically from being a *passive* to an *active* status (Crawford, 1984). Nowadays, we achieve or work at health, and are bombarded by messages celebrating ascetic attitudes towards health.

Loisir et société / *Society and Leisure*
Volume 18, numéro 1, printemps 1995, pp. 159-182 • © Presses de l'Université du Québec

Health educators, celebrities, employers, politicians, and popular culture more broadly constantly prevail upon us to monitor our bodies and to embark on lifestyle modifications that will enhance our "wellness" (Gillick, 1984; Vertinsky, 1985). The current emphasis on "active living," in contrast to earlier public policy initiatives that focussed on fitness, is indicative of a recent shift toward a broader health-promotion framework. It is probably accurate to say, however, that these "new" approaches still place a heavy emphasis on personal responsibility for health (O'Neill & Pederson, 1994).[1]

Contained within what has come to be called the ideology of "healthism" is a system of beliefs that defines health-promoting activities, such as involvement in some form of physical fitness program, as a *moral* obligation (Crawford, 1980). Whether it is through exercise, diet, or stress management, the avoidance of disease through personal effort has become a dominant cultural motif. Consequently, self-control, personal resolve, and deferment of gratification, all connected to traditionally bourgeois notions of "clean living," are associated with personal redemption through the demonstration of "moral character." Crucially, the ideology of healthism also tends to place responsibility for body vigilance solely on the individual, and deflects attention away from the social and cultural conditions which shape and constrain health.

In this paper we identify the contradictions that lie within popular wisdom about the generally unquestioned morality of exercise: that people *should* exercise; that people *should* control their weight (Edgley & Brissett, 1990). Arguments about the "slackers" and the slothful failing society by burdening the health care system with largely preventable illnesses are challenged by pointing to how access to knowledge and resources for becoming and staying fit are unevenly distributed throughout society. Additionally, we suggest that fitness-oriented people also suffer from illness and injury (often, ironically, as a result of fitness regimes themselves), that the financial and psycho-emotional costs of exercise-related injuries may be as disabling as the injuries themselves, and that the cost-benefit effects of exercise on the public purse have yet to be conclusively established (Vertinsky, 1985; Wagner, 1987; Young, White, & McTeer, 1994).

The academy has been influenced by popular beliefs about health. For instance, in the physical education/kinesiology profession there has been a concomitant shift in curriculum and research agendas toward health maintenance and promotion, as may be witnessed in the widespread re-labelling of departments to connote techno-rational approaches to exercise and health (Ingham, 1985; Colquhoun, 1992).[2] Indeed, many educators have begun to make the traditionally *implicit* baggage of their trade *explicit*, and present themselves as being in the business of helping people improve their physical quality of life (Harvey, 1986; Sparks, 1990). They have become modern-day evangelists leading the masses toward the good life through modification of *individual* behaviour. While this approach should not be summarily dismissed, because it is self-evident that healthy behaviour is likely beneficial, we will argue that dominant beliefs about the importance of individual responses to health deflect attention both from structural and environmental factors affecting health, and inequalities in access to health-promoting resources.

In sum, this paper provides a critique of the processes by which health and fitness have moved forward on the cultural agenda. Central to our argument is that the development and promotion of cultural beliefs around health, while often well-intended, flow from and help reproduce structures of inequality and relations of dominance. We explore this idea through a series of critical notes organized around themes of social change and social stratification : (1) an outline of how health is embodied through fitness and sport practices, and is used in the formation and display of the self as moral and virtuous ; (2) a critique of this construction of the self illustrating how it is historically specific, and how it is shaped by and in turn helps shape gender and class relations ; and (3) an examination of sport's ambiguous link with the amorphous concept of "wellness", and a reconsideration of some of the meanings of and contradictions in the contemporary health movement.

Health and the Embodied Self

In recent years, there has been an increase in popular consciousness of how health is either located within or inscribed on the surface of the body. Magazines, television shows, and newspapers are full of information about how to diet and exercise and also about how to transform the body through a variety of surgical "solutions" (Nemeth, 1984, p. 49).[3] Television "info-mercials" promising "A Better Body Fast," "Buns of Steel" and the like are symptomatic of a culture which has progressively blurred the boundaries between fitness, health, and beauty. Through actual exercise, bodywork, or through embellishment by clothes, jewelry, make-up and other forms of body art, people establish their position in a social hierarchy where health and beauty are visible units of currency. Thus the body has changed from a fixed to a malleable project which may be shaped into an actually or apparently healthy entity that is increasingly central to self-identity in a visually-oriented society (Gillett & White, 1992).

Any consideration of how popular beliefs about the body and health have become primarily individualized requires a sociological understanding of the body and self identity in contemporary culture. One approach has posited that peoples' bodily regimens are components of the notion of "lifestyle" which has become solidly entrenched in Western culture (Shilling, 1993). This conceptualization is congruent with Gidden's (1991) idea that the "self as a project" is a feature of high modernity whereby individuals seek to establish a meaningful sense of self through personal effort and control. Involvement in fitness programs, for example, provides access to discourses connecting the body with self identity. Indeed, fitness activity is one of the most important symbolic domains through which people construct and present their identities as healthy. Health is experienced subjectively as a part of a self-definition, and this self is displayed and confirmed in social interaction with others (Gillett, 1993).

Fitness programs organized around health as a goal, whether promoted by the state or the private sector, encourage people to act on their bodies in pursuit of a specific embodied cultural ideal which serves as an external sign to others of the care that has been taken to promote health. Indeed, this mode of thinking has become so self-evident that failure to be self-surveillant about health is becoming increasingly defined as deviant (Crawford, 1980). For the subjective self, the fit and healthy body is a possession to feel and display as a sign of moral and physical health. The connection that is made in discourse between fitness and well-being is one means by which health becomes a symbolic domain for the formation of the self and, more broadly, social acceptance.

The Changing Nature of Bodywork

The ascendance of health and health consciousness as a public issue did not "just happen." Rather, it can be traced to a marked shift in values since the early 1970s when health became reconceptualized and reframed ideologically as something attainable and sustainable through effort, discipline, and self-control (Rader, 1991). Subsequently, ill health has increasingly come to be associated with moral laxity, and the range of behaviours that may potentially be labelled as "unhealthy" has expanded. In this view, some people are viewed as deviant because they are unhealthy "on purpose" – they have insufficient resolve to exercise more, to quit smoking, to abstain from sex, and so forth. Remarkably, the sick are now more often blamed for being ill (Shilling, 1993). Frank (1991a) demonstrates this clearly in his reflexive study of cancer, as does Sontag (1978) in her analysis of the way in which we invoke metaphors to make sense of illnesses perceived to be life-threatening. But perhaps the most graphic example of "victim-blaming" in the connection of illness is to be seen in the ongoing AIDS crisis, and in the ultra-conservative ideologies that represent persons living with HIV/AIDS as morally disreputable and, in fact, deserving of their medical misfortunes (Crawford, 1994; Crimp, 1988).

That perceptions of health and the body are socially constructed may be further demonstrated by the changes in body ideals that have occurred over the last few decades. In contemporary Western culture, physical ideals and health ideals are congruent and emphasize both slimness and muscularity, but do so differently for men and women. For women, slimness is a culturally defined ideal although "toned" muscles, as long as they do not significantly add bulk, are also admired and valued. By contrast, for men, muscular bulk and/or delineation is highly valued, with the proviso that it should not be accompanied by visible fat.

But "preferred" shapes have become thinner over the last half-century to the extent that current ideals are widely considered both unrealistic and dangerous. This is, of course, one of the most alarming contradictions of the fitness boom, particularly given recent evidence of a positive relationship between physical activity and eating disorders (Davis, Kennedy, Pavelski, & Dionne, 1994). It now becomes obvious that biological factors determining healthy body weight and size have been overshadowed by cultural prescriptions of what is viewed as attractive and acceptable, and that these ideals only have a tenuous link to health. The increasing trend towards thinness also means that greater numbers of people come to be categorized as overweight or even obese. Such changes have also had significant effects, particularly for women, on body dissatisfaction and consequently on the prevalence of eating disorders such as anorexia nervosa, bulimia nervosa, and on exercise obsession (Bordo, 1990).

Far from being stable across time or between cultures, ideals of health and fitness tend to be context-specific and ideologically driven (Walden, 1985). During times of economic and political upheaval, of which the recessionary late 1980s and early 1990s are examples for Canadians, themes of self-control, willpower, and personal restraint move forward on the cultural agenda (Glassner, 1989 ; Stein, 1982). Contemplating reasons for our collective problems, health and the body have become metaphors for moral character and societal well being. This type of thinking is typical of those who hope to exorcize the evils of modern society by a return to an ascetic lifestyle (Carlyon, 1984). Under conditions of fiscal retrenchment, unemployment crises, and other forms of social exigency, all of which elicit a degree of panic in society, the body emerges as one of the last sites over which even disempowered individuals can maintain control (Kroker, Kroker, & Cook, 1989). However, the arena of health generates ambiguities when the struggle for meaningful control over bodies becomes distorted, such as when people undergo radical dieting or cosmetic surgery in order at least to appear healthy without adequate counselling on real and long-term health consequences. As the surface of the body becomes more culturally sensitive people become increasingly vulnerable to cynical and profit-oriented media campaigns which play on their physical and sexual insecurities.

Many of these changes, and the anxieties they produce, seem particularly germane for the current generation of young people for whom the future appears less promising than it did for their "baby boomer" parents. Put simply, if we believe economic and social indicators, this is a generation with more to be anxious about. If current projections are accurate, members of this so-called "lost generation" have a smaller chance than their parents of obtaining secure work, or being home owners, and less expectation of a bright future. For them there is, in one sense, an even greater need to devote themselves to ascetic values; hard work, self-restraint, and discipline. But as critics of youth culture have indicated, this may be much more of a short-term rather than a long-term effect of social crisis. Among other things, increasing pressures to do well educationally in a hostile economy are just as likely to precipitate among young people a return to the hedonistic joys of drug and alcohol abuse, smoking, unsafe sex, and other "unhealthy" deviances (Bibby and Posterski, 1992; Young, 1992).

Thus, health and body ideals and the practices that are available to achieve them are historically and culturally specific. Moreover, people work on their bodies in order to produce a meaningful sense of self, but as we note below, not in conditions of their own choosing. The following considers how power relations around class and gender shape and constrain the ways in which people pursue and construct health through participation in various forms of fitness management.

The Fit Body in Class Relations

The health movement largely draws its adherents from the educated middle classes. Patterns of social class influence on participation have been found repeatedly for most health-promoting behaviours. Low income and education groups typically engage less in various health habits including drinking in moderation, regular exercise, maintaining a desirable weight, eating well, abstention from tobacco use, and getting enough sleep (Schoenborn, 1986).

Research attempting to account for these disparities has varied in approach although much has been made of the supposed dispositional shortcomings of those who fail to engage in health-promotive behaviour (Goldstein, 1992). For example, psychological constructs like "self-efficacy" and "internal locus of control" have been posited as predictors of health-related behaviour even though they have also been identified as being positively correlated with measures of education and income. As Goldstein suggests:

> the use of such psychological constructs to explain the affinities of the middle-class for participation in the health movement has a tautological quality. At worst this approach is not only misleading but provides the basis for the "victim blaming" of those who do not engage in preventive health behaviour. They are seen as individuals deficient in some psychological trait and hence – at least in part – responsible for any resulting ill health (1992, p. 127).

The moral assumptions underlying this type of research and the health movement itself have identifiable origins. Expectations for individuals to impose controls upon their bodies have existed to greater or lesser degrees throughout history. From the ascetics of the Middle Ages who believed that total bodily self-denial (including living in caves, self-starvation, and self-flagellation) was the best way to serve God, the controlled body has figured as a symbol of moral rectitude and class association (Walden, 1985). However, current social practices and beliefs equating physicality with middle class morality can be traced to the Victorian doctrine of *mens sana in corpore sano* (a healthy mind in a healthy body). Originating in the British private schools, a "games cult" emerged connecting the development of moral character to participation in sport and physical activity (Mangan, 1981). Although largely unspoken, "character development" essentially implied the socialization of young males who would later become the economic, social, and political elite of Britain. According to Hargreaves:

> *body imagery, discourse, and practices figured prominently in the grand design for improvement. An upright posture with no hands in pockets, short hair, a clean well-washed body, a simple neat and tidy appearance, teetotalism, no smoking, no "self-abuse", no sex outside marriage, active participation in organized sport, frequent and regular physical exercise, fitness and good health, and above all, a "hard" body constituted the God-fearing, obedient, hard-working, respectable individual* (1987, p. 46).

Such interpretations of character excluded women and girls at this time, much as the concept of character appears to continue to exclude females in the modern era. "Gentlemanly" values instilled through athleticism included collective effort, self-denial, leadership, emotional self-restraint, and determination in the face of adversity – values that profoundly influenced the emergence of the new capitalist class that superseded an older landed aristocracy. These values fit perfectly with the socio-political values of modern capitalism. Athleticism provided a symbolic vehicle for members of the dominant class to demonstrate their self-evidently physical and moral superiority over subordinate groups – particularly women and the working class. In addition to emphasizing the "civilized" aspects of sport and physical fitness, they rejected the "uncivilized" popular recreations of the lower orders (cock-fighting, bear baiting, and the like) which were framed as evidence of a lack of personal control. In Victorian Britain, the precepts of middle-class respectability and clean living came to be imposed upon the working-class in a bid to improve "the great unwashed" whose own sporting traditions were regarded with distaste (Bailey, 1978). The encouragement of "rational recreation" (day trips, the Boy Scouts, Sunday Schools) represented a clear mission by a philanthropic segment of the middle-class to individualize responsibility for the health status of working class bodies (and, of course, their own bodies).

In terms of body weight ideals and beliefs about their connections to health status, the evidence shows variability across time and cultures. For example, Sobal and Stunkard's (1989) review of the literature on socio-economic status and obesity shows that fatness has been positively associated with social class in over 80 percent of studies of the phenomenon in developing countries. This relationship also held for Western societies until well into the twentieth century (Walden, 1985). Both of these trends have also connected rotundness with healthfulness primarily because body weight is evidence of plenty in food-scarce cultures and historical eras. In contemporary Western culture, with some exceptions for certain ethnic groups, the reverse is now generally the case. Members of the lower classes are on average heavier than members of the upper-class (Schoenborn, 1987). This shift in actual weights across classes most clearly demonstrates the effect of culture on body shape and beliefs about health status.

The change in body ideal from corpulent to thin beginning in the late nineteenth century was linked to relations between the social classes (Walden, 1985). As social historians of weight consciousness have explained, shifts in body ideals and in the attachment of moral value to thinness lie in the desire of members of the middle-class to physically mark themselves as members of the class most capable of hard work, self-denial, asceticism, and clean living. In this regard, Crawford writes that for the contemporary era : "Health has become an important means for the middle class to structure its own class identity. Conspicuous health-promotion behaviours may act as "recognition signals" for purposes of both differentiation and mutual affirmation" (1980, p. 384). Through resolve and self-denial, through diet and exercise, thinness could be achieved by those capable of "upright living".

Thus, the real champions of the ideology of healthism have been the educated middle classes. In the process through which the body and its health have become politicized, the ethos of "individualism" has become ascendant and the problems of the lower classes have been identified as personal and not rooted in structure (Ingham, 1985). Self-improvement and self-sufficiency are components of a predominantly middle-class lifestyle ideology that mystifies the structural bases of inequality. Thus the body becomes part of a power relation which contributes to acquiescence to the logic of high capitalism (Foucault, 1980).

By focusing on individual lifestyle as a major determinant of health, attention is deflected from and constrains the possibility of emancipation from class inequality. The "myopia of classic individualism" (Crawford, 1980, p. 377) creates the illusion that people are equally able to make free choices about their health – when access to resources to do so are unequally distributed by class (Tinning, 1991). As Ingham has suggested about lifestyle as an ideology :

> *If jogging is not for you, then there are other routes to fitness – routes which conveniently ignore the fact that millions of people who hover around and below the poverty line cannot afford ten-speeds, tennis racquets, and memberships at health fitness centres. And, as an active rather than passive lifestyle, it exhorts us to burn off calories while denying State dependents the food they need to survive* (1985, p. 50).

As Walden (1985) indicates, however, it would be naive to ignore the potency of agency and suggest that the project of communal health and weight consciousness has been imposed by a conspiracy of interests whose objective was the efficiency of capitalist production. Rather, the desire for greater control has come as much from those for whom social change had generated widespread feelings of insecurity. Apprehension about social upheaval has contributed to an impulse to gain stability through imposing individual control of the body.

The Fit Body in Gender Relations

As a rapidly expanding feminist literature has indicated (Coward, 1985 ; Orbach, 1978 ; Wolf, 1990), popular iconography informing the "fit" male and female body is pervaded by heavily gendered and often sexist messages. Moderation has little place here. Instead, the "cult of the perfect body" (Edgley & Brissett, 1990) shifts the emphasis away from health concerns and the acceptance of human imperfection (indeed, human averageness) towards bodily extremes, many versions of which inevitably jeopardize wellness.

For women in the late 20th century, the extremes of body symbolism often lie in obsessive exercise and eating disorders like anorexia and bulimia (Rader, 1991).[4] Although high levels of physical activity and a state of starvation would seem intuitively incompatible, they have been identified as "sister activities" (Yates, 1991). Preoccupation with one is commonly associated with obsession with the other. Sociological studies of the growing prevalence of eating disorders and obsessive exercise point to a cult of slenderness which has clear ramifications for gender politics. With cultural ideals for body weight continuing to privilege sinewy slimness,[5] more and more women feel anxious about their inability to realize "ideal" expectations of feminine beauty and fitness (Bordo, 1990). The concern women have about their weight stems in part from their bombardment with unrealistic media images, initiated in large part by the fashion and cosmetic industries, which promote and fetishize slenderness as the only desirable option for the female frame. But, for women to embrace this way of thinking about the female body leads ironically to almost inevitable feelings of inadequacy and loss of control. Eating disorders and obsessive exercise become a response directed at *regaining* control of one aspect of life that remains within reach – the body (Bordo, 1990). Thus, a woman who focuses attention on diet and exercise feels subjectively in control (by disciplining her body) when she may be, in fact, objectively participating in her own corporeal domination and potentially compromising her health.

In these respects, preoccupation with physical appearance and obsession with thinness share an ambiguous relationship with a number of health concerns (Moriarity & Moriarity, 1986). Female respondents to the 1988 Campbell's

Survey of the Well-Being of Canadians, for example, placed more importance on weight control than other reasons for participation in physical activity. This is especially noteworthy given the traditionally limited opportunities women have had to engage in many forms of physical leisure, and the current popularity of the aerobics movement.

While the women's movement has made great strides in reclaiming women's bodies from patriarchal institutions, it is unfortunate that the commodification of women's aerobics has compromised its original goal of providing an opportunity for women collectively to participate in and enjoy forms of music, dance, exercise, and sociability outside the home. Instead, the co-option of fitness by the marketplace has displaced these original goals of aerobics (witness the hundreds of "women's" exercise videos designed to be viewed in isolation at home), fetishized the sport (witness the massive sexualization of aerobics in magazines and other forms of marketing, much of it targetted to the male gaze), and have transformed a potentially emancipatory phenomenon into a possible form of body regulation and social control. As MacNeil has argued:

> *Today, aerobics does offer a high intensity option hitherto denied women,*
> *but it has not escaped the gendered preoccupation with dance aesthetics*
> *and body image. Are we only fit to be looked at? It seems so. Past and*
> *present activity options for women are limited and construed with one or*
> *more of the F motifs – Fitness, Fear of Fatness, and Fantasy and Fashion*
> (1990, p. 5).

Among men, megarexia, the obsessive quest for muscularity, represents the opposite end of the gender continuum and again is indicative of contradictions in the fitness boom. Men, faced with the gradual erosion of their power base in the public sphere, are falling back on traditional sources of masculine identification – physical power and mass. The growth in the popularity of body building (Gillett & White, 1992) and high reported rates of the use of muscle-building drugs such as anabolic steroids among male youth point to the cultural re-emphasis of muscles as symbols of masculinity (Canadian Centre for Drug-Free Sport, 1992). Confirmation for the legitimacy of men pursuing muscularity is found in contemporary film and popular culture, where physical size, power, and violence mesh to produce symbols of male omnipotence – witness Sylvester Stallone, Chuck Norris, Arnold Schwarzenegger, and others.

In assessing contradictions around the body, feminist scholars have persuasively argued that the contemporary emphasis on the body and its attendant exercise and diet disorders have coincided with significant progress made by the women's movement. With the gradual erosion of male dominance at work and in other public settings, as well as in the family, manipulation of the body to emphasize physical "difference" by gender has gained importance as a symbolic arena where male superiority is "apparently" self-evident. The manufacture and control of women's body image in a changing culture has been outlined by Walden :

> *If females were going to upset society by being more open about sexuality and more demanding of their rights, control [of women by men] could be maintained by idealizing physical features which were difficult to retain. Those who lacked these qualities in a society which stressed the importance of appearance would tend to feel deficient and inferior. Much of their potential would be dissipated fretting about shortcomings ; much of their energy would be invested trying to overcome them. Those who did conform to the ideal always would be conscious that their advantages were inexorably slipping away* (1985, p. 16).

Reversion to the body as an arena of male control, it is argued, represents one of the many forms of "backlash" against female empowerment (Faludi, 1991).

It would be easy, of course, to dismiss obsessive exercise, eating disorders, and megarexia as aberrant examples of extreme behaviours that have little relevance to the majority of the population. In terms of sheer numbers of those who might be categorized in some way as bodily disordered, this may have some face validity. On the other hand, it is also possible to argue that a large propor-tion of the population, while not at the extremes, are subject to the same cultural forces and orient their lifestyle in similar, but less excessive ways. For example, dieting is a major preoccupation of many (male *and* female) North Americans, despite its high failure rate (Dwyer, 1986). Equally, if not more alarmingly, is the fact that females especially are socialized into dieting behaviour at very young ages. Recent studies have indicated that six-year-old children have already acquired a preference for bodies that are long and lean (Feldman, Feldman, & Goodman, 1988), and that 37 percent of grade school children have already tried to lose weight (Maloney, McGuire, Daniels, & Specker, 1989). Among males, while relatively few might be regarded as obsessed with body mass, more moderate attempts to enhance body mass or to appear bigger through clothing and posture represent an identification with the masculine symbolism of body size.

Sport's Ambiguous Link with Health

> *"My life is a horrifying nightmare. It feels like there's a beast inside me, like a monster. It feels evil"* (US gymnast, Christy Henrich, speaking on her experiences with anorexia (Noden, 1994, p. 54)).

> *"I outran, outhit, outanythinged anybody...All along I was taking steroids, and I saw that they made me play better and better. I kept on because I knew I had to keep getting more size. I became very violent on the field. Off it, too"* (NFL player, Lyle Alzado, speaking on the "highs" of steroids (Alzado, 1991, p. 22)).

While much attention of late has been paid to physical activity in the broad sense in the context of human health, surely no part of our lives carries more potential for exploring what Frank (1991b) recently referred to as the "self, body, politics, violence nexus" than the specific arena of sport practices? At first glance, one might intuitively assume that sport is a practice done by and to bodies that are healthy and that sport participation is a healthy pursuit. But what of the injured body, the changing body, or the body perceived as a source of defiance and betrayal? Ironically, while popular discourses on sport tend to privilege the former view, these latter experiences are at least as common and, ultimately for all athletic bodies, are inevitably more common. Sport, then, is about active *and* inactive bodies, and about the identities developed around them by men and women in different social and historical moments.

Preoccupation with bodily extremes is nowhere more visible than in the world of sport. Among other things, the hypercompetitive and ubiquitously commodified culture of sport ushers its participants towards excess, whether it be the waif-like bodies of female Olympic gymnasts or the behemoths that are contemporary football linemen. In the struggle for profit and performance, it is essentially exaggerated, even caricatured, physical standards that result. The gendered underpinnings of this ultimately demeaning process are obvious as, indeed, are their impractical and literally incapacitating results. Both Christy Henrich and Lyle Alzado are now dead; one death (Henrich) resulted directly from an excessive desire to be thin (anorexia); the other death has not been proven to have been caused by steroids, but prior to his death Alzado's desire for body mass through steroids had left him seriously ill.

Gendered arrangements of sport and leisure sometimes constrain and repress the manner in which women and girls experience their bodies. It may be the teenage female gymnast, bulimic and weak in a sport that requires supreme strength and confidence, who is accompanied through training camp by a foam cup; the latter is at once a receptacle for vomit and the evidence of an obsessive/ dangerous "femininity". It may be her teammate, whose delayed puberty, the result of years of arduous training, is followed by amenorrhea and rapid weight gain in the de-socializing mid-teen years. It may be the middle-aged runner, whose anxieties about her changing body are fuelled by an impossible but alluring cultural ideal of feminine shape and sexuality. Or, finally, it could be the aerobics participant for whom the goal of fitness has been at least in part subsumed by a narcissistic investment in the pursuit of physical perfection – an objective that sexually objectifies and imprisons as much as it liberates.[6]

As Burstyn argues, such sports experiences are part of a patriarchal double-standard with dire consequences for women's health.[7] For example, there is a double standard when, during natural physical development, the young athletic boy welcomes his growing bulk while his female counterpart views hers with alarm. Gendered attitudes toward exercise and diet reflect this double standard and can have health-compromising effects. Like Burstyn, we understand these common sports practices and meanings in terms of the complex connections between power, discipline, and gendered identities. As Burstyn notes of athletic women : "In a very real and symbolic sense, women's power remains temporary and precarious."

Predictably, such pressures predispose females more than males to suffer from eating disorders. This is especially true of sports that require participants not only to perform well, but also to be aesthetically pleasing. Numerous cases have been documented in which athletes in such sports as gymnastics, figure skating, and even body building have been pressured by coaches to remain thin or devoid of fat. Oftentimes, these athletes are young girls whose coaches are adult men. This questionable set of sports values has recently been brought into sharp relief by the death of US gymnast Christy Henrich who died in July of 1994 after a 5-year battle with anorexia and bulimia. At the time of her death, she weighed just 61 lbs (Noden, 1994). Henrich, however, was not alone in her struggle for control over her weight. A glance at women's sport over the last two decades reveals a long list of similarly disturbing cases including : former US gymnast Cathy Rigby (12 year fight with anorexia and bulimia, twice suffered cardiac arrest as a result) ; Canadian tennis player Carling Basset-Seguso (bulimia) ; and US gymnasts Cathy Johnson and Erica Stokes (bulimia). Driven by chauvinist and profit-oriented socio-economic forces, it is clear from these cases that pressures to conform to specific body types are highly dangerous. Evidently, for female athletes who are constantly badgered to reduce body fat, exercise addiction and reckless methods of weight loss become perceived as meaningful and "normal" options despite their accompanying health risks.

Given health-compromising outcomes, data on the pervasiveness of eating disorders among female athletes are truly alarming. For instance, the American College of Sports Medicine reports that as many as 65 percent of females competing in so-called "appearance" sports (figure skating, gymnastics, synchronized swimming) and endurance sports may suffer from eating disorders, and a 1992 NCAA survey of college athletes reports that 93 percent of the programmes acknowledging eating disorders involved women's sports (Noden, 1994, p. 54). While some male athletes (such as gymnasts, boxers, and wrestlers) also use extreme methods to lose weight, importantly, there are gender differences here too. As Noden explains :

A wrestler's perception of his body is not distorted. When he is not competing, he can return to a healthy weight. That is not the case with [female] anorexics, trapped as they are behind bars they cannot see... A study conducted at Penn [State] found that while both men and women tend to be unrealistic about how others perceive their bodies, men's perceptions tended to be distorted positively, while women are more likely to be negative (1994, p. 56).

Recent work (Young, 1993 ; Young, White, & McTeer, 1994) has also led us to consider the role that sport and fitness play in the construction of dominant masculinities and men's health. By examining the centrality of forceful notions of sport in the lives of male athletes, we identified how pain, the risk of injury, and injury itself are often accepted as normal components of participation. For example, macho norms such as "taking a hit" without showing pain, playing while injured, and using one's body as both a vehicle for and site of violence were found to be sufficiently ingrained that athletes rarely question the physical risk to which they expose themselves. We have found that a generally unreflective approach to past disablement on the part of (particularly younger) male athletes is a domain feature of contemporary sport. The risks associated with violent sport go relatively unquestioned by men who have suffered debilitating, even life-threatening, injury and whose daily lives are marked by physical constraints and pain.

In sum, our reading of the literature and our own work and experiences lead us to believe that for many boys and men the sport-injury nexus is best understood as part of a masculinization process. Body mass, physical endurance, risk-taking, and various forms of body discipline including pain denial are integral features of dominance-based versions of masculinity. Learning to use the sporting body in this way implies also learning to detach oneself from it (Morgan, 1992, p. 168). As a result, sensitivity to bodily well-being and matters of preventive health in general become viewed as the jurisdiction of women and "ambiguous" men. Cultural prohibitions on self-surveillant health orientations for men outside of sport are, of course, visible in the disproportionate numbers of women found in doctors' offices, clinics, nursing, and other venues of health care provision (Hearn, 1992, p. 44). Put simply, health care interests tend to be conspicuously absent in the task orientation of men in general. In sport, this may be witnessed as a link between the gendering of injury and the gendering of men's health.

Health and Fitness Reconsidered

We have attempted to delineate some of the numerous social and political imperatives that produce, guide, and police "legitimate" versions of wellness, and which serve to undermine others. In so doing, we have attempted to demystify some taken-for-granted cornerstones of sport/fitness/health issues, and to outline some of its contradictions and unintended consequences.

The "individualistic" proposition that health is primarily determined by volitional behaviour obscures the effects of structural predictors of illness and disease and is a good example of the inadequacy of offering simple solutions for complex problems. Since body shape has become a metaphor for health and moral worth, the person who does not conform to prevailing norms for fitness can begin to perceive him/herself as deviant in their failure to pursue self-improvement. For instance, persons perceived to be overweight are told: "Just eat less and exercise more – it's simple." So those, who for reasons beyond their control, have neither the time nor the resources, nor the physical constitution to apply to health management and body sculpting (single mothers, shift workers, the poor, those with various "physical conditions") tend to be blamed for their failure to live up to their social responsibility for their own bodies (Labonte, 1982). Ironically, the strongly middle-class bias of the fitness movement is vividly exposed by the practical reality that for the working-class and other disempowered groups who often labour at physically demanding jobs, meaningful leisure is often built around liberation *from* physical effort.

Such is the current pervasiveness of healthism that individual responsibility has extended not only to concern for one's own health but also to the health achievements of others (Edgley and Brisset, 1990). The view that anyone *can* be healthy with enough effort extrapolates to the idea that everyone *should* be healthy. Thus, attribution of social responsibility to the proactive pursuit of health has spawned a self-righteous intolerance of those who are either unable or unwilling to quite literally "measure up" (Carlyon, 1984). Indeed, the social construction of the healthy self requires the co-responding construction of the unhealthy other, as is the case with popular representations of persons living with AIDS, the terminally ill, or the alcoholic, which emphasize absence of willpower (Crawford, 1994). In this way, the physical body is also a social body whose condition mirrors a broader social condition. In an era when society is commonly viewed as suffering from widespread malaise (political scandals, high divorce rates, growing incidence of violence, etc.) a key part of this metaphor is the view that the social body may be repaired by disciplinary action on the physical body (Crawford, 1984 ; Rojek, 1992).

All of this is not to deny that there is a positive relationship between exercise and health. Certain types of exercise clearly have health benefits for some people. Our concern is to indicate that this relationship is neither equally available nor without costs. The taken-for-granted assumption that physical activity is a major contribution to health is seldom, if ever, challenged. For example, the common assumption that body type is connected in a simple way with health, i.e., that slim and muscular people are assumed to be healthier than other less culturally valued body types, oversimplifies a much more complex reality. It is possible, for example, to be heavy and healthy (Ritenbaugh, 1982) and to be healthy without rigorous exercise (Nichter & Nichter, 1991). Further complicating the "body-image-equals-health" stereotype is the fact that intense exercise clearly has its own associated and often overlooked disadvantages including high injury rates and body image disorders (Edgley & Brissett, 1990 ; Young, White, & McTeer, 1994).

Nor have we meant to argue – deterministically – that the effects of sports involvement are always negative or that sport necessarily leads to eating disorders. As we have seen, while there is considerable evidence that the sexist form in which sport is currently structured leaves the door open for eating disorders to emerge,[8] it is also evident that many women enjoy an enhanced subjectivity through participation in sport and physical activities not available to previous generations. In this respect, sport and fitness activity may be a precipitant of and vehicle for the development of both wellness and unwellness.

Thus, where the relationship between sport and health is concerned, we want to emphasize, following Gruneau (1983) and other cultural theorists, that the meanings and effects of sport and fitness activity in different contexts and conditions may embody both imprisoning and emancipatory (in this case unhealthy and healthy) capacities simultaneously. These contradictory possibilities exist because sport and physical activity represent contested terrain over which there are struggles to determine the form they should take and who should play, the meanings of those activities and, of course, to determine legitimate ways of using and understanding the body. Health is inescapably implicated in this process.

While we have criticized the negative effects of current sports structures on health, we want to emphasize that this relationship nevertheless remains rich in potential. We agree with Hall (1984) and more recently Whitson that:

> it has been an all too common mistake on the left to see the com-
> modification of leisure (and I would add fitness) as entirely manipulative,
> as if the consumers of leisure goods and experiences were passive dupes
> (Whitson, 1991, p. 15).

Examples of the fact that pleasure and health are enjoyed through sport are not difficult to find. For many men, of course, engaging with their athletic bodies – to wrestle, to forecheck, to play "line" – is both experientially and symbolically significant.

But such hegemonic modes of masculine body expression are no longer universal. Counter-hegemonic challenges to the hyper-masculine body and masculinist physical culture not only exist but are precipitating resistant forms which resonate for thousands of participants. Across Canada, for instance, young hockey players, unimpressed by their toothless professional counterparts, are finding new non-contact versions of their favoured pastime both empowering in the pursuit and emancipatory in the avoidance of injury (Grigel, 1989). Elsewhere, gay men continue to resist the compulsory heterosexuality of modern sports organizations and strategically carve out new spaces both within and outside the mainstream (Pronger, 1990), while men of colour chip away at the racist foundations of sports apartheid as they construct broader opportunities for participation (Davis, 1990).

Of course, female athletic bodies may also be resistant, not only against patriarchy but also against homophobia and heterosexism. Female aerobicizers, rugby and hockey players, and bodybuilders speak of being re-socialized into new and more potent selves by their active bodies (Young and White, 1995). If naturalizing masculinity and restraining femininity have been the cornerstones of patriarchal sport, then we find in these alternative athletic sites new forms of empowerment for women. Crucially, they precipitate bolder discourses and "ways of seeing" (Berger, 1972) which link female bodies to more assured selves, and may ultimately help reconstitute women's physical, social, and political lives.

In closing, we endorse the equitable provision of opportunities to pursue health and fitness for all regardless of social background, but challenge some of the orthodoxies surrounding current social pressures to follow ascetic lifestyles. These orthodoxies tend to result in victim-blaming approaches to body image, illness, and health, and have re-energized the view that individuals, not institutions, are solely responsible for their health. As we have suggested, there are many structural factors which account for why some people are less attentive to health issues than others – even though they may seem irrational to the middle-class moralizer. The conservative values that are woven into a health ethic are tilted unevenly toward middle-class experiences and obfuscate the limited opportunities for large sections of the population to work at their health. Thus, attention is diverted away from structural factors such as mass unemployment, chronic poverty, and dangerous work conditions[9] which compromise the health of many and render bourgeois notions of health and fitness (becoming vegetarian, giving up cigarettes, joining a health club) either materially unachievable or culturally unappealing.

It has been our goal to show that a relationship popularly believed to be simple – that exercise leads to fitness which leads to health – is, in fact, complex, multi-faceted, and deeply political. Clearly, while people do have some responsibility for their own health, choices and opportunities around fitness are neither equally available nor meaningful to all people. We have also attempted to emphasize that an adequate etiology of either illness or health requires an examination of both biomedical and sociocultural factors. Such an approach is not only useful in understanding the place of cancer, AIDS, anorexia, obesity, athleticism, muscularity, slimness, slothfulness, and a range of other bodily states and predicaments, but also goes some way in uncovering the ascetic agendas of, and contradictions in, the contemporary health movement.

Notes

1. In Canada, this individualized perspective on health promotion has been reflected in public policy documents written by Federal Ministers of National Health and Welfare in both 1974 (Marc Lalonde) and 1986 (Jake Epp), although in the latter document greater attention was paid to balance between social policy and personal lifestyle.

2. Within the last few years, McMaster University and the University of Waterloo have made name changes from, respectively, Department of Physical Education and Faculty of Human Kinetics and Leisure Studies to Department of Kinesiology and Faculty of Applied Health Studies.

3. A recent report on body obsessions appearing in Canada's national news magazine (*Macleans*, May 2, 1994, pp. 44-50) described a sample of body re-shaping techniques made available by a burgeoning plastic surgery industry. Interestingly, these procedures centered on both the removal of fat from body parts like the thighs (medical thigh dermolipectomy), buttocks (buttock dermolipectomy), stomach (abdominoplasty), and elsewhere (liposuction), and on the enhancement of feminine and masculine sexuality. The latter form of body re-shaping includes, for men, pectoral implants, testicular implants, phalloplasty (penis lengthening), and, for women, breast implants and mastopexy ("firming up" of sagging breasts).

4. Anorexia nervosa is commonly defined as a form of self-starvation resulting from a distorted perception of one's appearance. The related disorder, bulimia nervosa, has similar psycho-emotional roots, but its hidden symptoms make it potentially more dangerous. As Noden (1994, p. 56) writes:

   Bulimia is a binge-purge syndrome in which huge quantities of food – sometimes totalling as much as 20,000 calories in a day – are consumed in a short period of time and then expelled through self-induced vomiting, excessive exercise, the use of diuretics or laxatives, or some combination of those methods. Stomach acids rot the teeth of bulimics and, if they are sticking their fingers down their throats to induce vomiting, their fingernails. Their throats get swollen and lacerated. Electrolyte imbalances disrupt their heart rates. But since bulimics are usually of normal weight, years may pass before a parent, roommate, or spouse learns the terrible secret.

5. While we acknowledge certain shifts in "ideal types" of female beauty, post-war ideals have consistently emphasized extreme slenderness (Nemeth, 1994).

6. For these examples from Canadian sport, we are indebted to "Play, Performance and Power: The Women," CBC Radio *Ideas on Sport,* Sept. 10, 1986.

7. Varda Burstyn, narrator, "Play, Performance and Power: The Women," CBC Radio *Ideas on Sport*, Sept. 10, 1986.

8. Caroline Davis, associate professor of psychology at York University, is one of the principle spokespersons for the position that anorexia may be linked to heavy exercise (cf. Toronto Star, Aug. 25, 1994, p. A4).

9. There is by now a sizeable criminological literature showing that hazardous work conditions are common (occupational death ranks in the top five killers of Canadians each year – Goff and Reasons, 1986; Hagan, 1994), and that they disproportionately impact blue-collar workers.

References

ALZADO, L. (1991, July 8). I'm sick and I'm scared. *Sports Illustrated*, 21-24.

BAILEY, P. (1978). *Leisure and class in Victorian England*. London : Hutchinson.

BERGER, J. (1972). *Ways of seeing*. New York, NY : Penguin.

BIBBY, R. & POSTERSKI, D. (1992). *Teen trends : A nation in motion*. Toronto, ON : Stoddart.

BORDO, S. (1990). Reading the slender body. *In* M. Jacobus, E. Fox Keller & S. Shuttleworth (Eds.), *Body/Politics : Women and the discourses of science* (pp. 83-112). New-York, NY : Routledge

CANADIAN CENTRE FOR DRUG-FREE SPORT (1992). *National school survey. Survey on drugs and sport* (Final Report).

CARLYON, W. (1984). Disease prevention/health promotion : Bridging the gap to wellness. *Health Values : Achieving High Level Wellness, 8*, 27-30.

COLQUHOUN, D. (1992). Technocratic rationality and the medicalization of physical education curriculum. *Physical Education Curriculum, 15*, 5-12.

COWARD, R. (1985). *Female desires : How they are sought, bought, and packaged*. New York : Grove Press.

CRAWFORD, R. (1980). Healthism and the medicalization of everyday life. *International Journal of Health Services, 10*, 365-388.

CRAWFORD, R. (1984). A cultural account of "health" : Control, release, and the social body. *In* J. McKinlay (Ed.), *Contemporary issues in health, medicine and social policy* (pp. 60-103). New York, NY : Tavistock.

CRAWFORD, R. (1994). The boundries of the self and the unhealthy other : Reflections on health, culture, and AIDS. *Social Science and Medicine, 38*, 10, 1347-1365.

CRIMP, D. (1988). *AIDS : Cultural analysis, cultural activism*. Boston, MA : MIT Press.

DAVIS, L. (1990). The articulation of difference : White preoccupation with the question of racially-linked genetic differences among athletes. *Sociology of Sport Journal, 7*, 179-187.

DAVIS, C., KENNEDY, S., RAVELSKI, E., & DIONNE, M. (1994). The role of physical activity in the development and maintenance of eating disorders. *Psychological Medicine, 24*, forthcoming.

DWYER, J. (1986). Reducing the great American waistline. *American Journal of Public Health, 76*, 1287-1288.

EDGLEY, C. & BRISSETT, D. (1990). Health Nazis and the cult of the perfect body : Some polemical observations. *Symbolic Interaction, 13* (2), 259-279.

EPP, J. (1986). *Achieving health for all : A framework for health promotion*. Ottawa : Ministry of Supply and Services Canada.

FALUDI, S. (1991). *Backlash : The undeclared war against American women*. New York, NY : Crown.

FELDMAN, W. FELDMAN, E., & GOODMAN, J. (1988). Culture versus biology : Children's attitudes toward thinness and fatness. *Pediatrics, 81*, 190-194.

FOUCAULT, M. (1980). *Power/Knowledge : Selected interviews and other writings, 1972-1977*. New York : Pantheon.

FRANK, A. (1991a). *At the will of the body: Reflections on illness.* Boston, MA: Houghton Mifflin.

FRANK, A. (1991b). For a sociology of the body: An analytical review. *In* M. Featherstone, M. Hepworth, & B. Turner (Eds.), *The Body*, (pp. 36-102), London: Sage Publications.

GIDDENS, A. (1991). *Modernity and self-identity: Self and identity in the late modern age.* Stanford, CA: Stanford University Press.

GILLETT, J. (1993, July). *The careful reassertion of social space: A study of amatuer bodybuilders.* Paper presented at the annual meeting of the International Committee for the Sociology of Sport, Vienna, Austria.

GILLETT, J. & WHITE, P. (1992). Male bodybuilding and the reassertion of hegemonic masculinity: A critical feminist perspective. *Play and Culture, 5*, 358-369.

GILLICK, M. (1984). Health promotion, jogging, and the pursuit of moral life. *Journal of Health, Politics, Policy and Law, 9*, 369-387.

GLASSNER, B. (1989). Fitness and the postmodern self. *Journal of Social Behaviour, 30*, 180-191.

GOFF, C.H. & REASONS, C. (1986). Organizational crimes against employees, consumers, and the public. *In* B. Maclean (Ed.), *The political economy of crime: Readings for a critical criminology.* Scarborough, ON: Prentice Hall, (pp. 204-231).

GOLDSTEIN, M. (1992). *The health movement: Promoting fitness in America.* New York: Twayne.

GRIGEL, F. (1989). *Players" reactions to the elimination of bodychecking in minor hockey.* Unpublished M.A. thesis, University of Calgary, Calgary, AB.

GRUNEAU, R. (1983). *Class, sports, and social development.* Amherst, MA: University of Massachusetts Press.

HAGAN, J. (1994). *Crime and disrepute.* London: Pine Forge Press.

HALEY, B. (1978). *The healthy body and Victorian culture.* Cambridge, MA: Harvard University Press.

HALL, S. (1984, January). The culture gap. *Marxism Today*, 18-22.

HARGREAVES, J. (1987). The body, sport and power relations. *In* D. Horne, D. Jary, & A. Tomlinson (Eds.), *Sport, leisure and social relations* (pp. 139-159). London: Routledge and Kegan Paul.

HARVEY, J. (1986). The rationalization of bodily practices. *Arena Review, 10*, 55-65.

HEARN, J. (1992). *Men in the public eye: The construction and deconstruction of public men and public patriarchies.* New York: Routledge.

INGHAM, A. (1985). From public issue to personal trouble: Well-being and the fiscal crisis of the state. *Sociology of Sport Journal, 2*, 43-55.

KROKER, A., KROKER, M., & COOK, D. (1989). *Panic encyclopedia: The definitive guide to the postmodern scene.* Montreal: New World Perspectives.

LABONTE, R. (1982). Half-truths about health. *Policy Options, 3*, 54-55.

LALONDE, M. (1974). *A new perspective on the health of Canadians: A working document.* Ottawa: Ministry of Health and Welfare.

MACNEILL, M. (1990). Fit to be looked at: Aerobicized women in the media. *Media Watch Bulletin, 3*, 4-7.

MALONEY, M., MCGUIRE, J., DANIELS, S., & SPECKER, B. (1989). Dieting behaviour and eating attributes in children. *Pediatrics*, 84, 482-489.

MANGAN, J. (1981). *Athleticism in the Victorian and Edwardian public school.* Cambridge: Cambridge University Press.

MORGAN, D. (1992). *Discovering men.* New York: Routledge.

MORIARITY, D. & MORIARITY, M. (1986, July/August). Sport/Fitness programs and sociocultural influences in eating disorders : Intervention techniques and coping strategies. *CAHPER National Journal*, 4-9.

NEMETH, M. (1994, May 2). Body obsession: Fitness, dieting, and the tyranny of the image. *Maclean's*, 44-52.

NICHTER, M. & NICHTER, M. (1991). Hype and weight. *Medical Anthropology, 13,* 249-284.

NODEN, M. (1994, August 8). Dying to win. *Sports Illustrated*, 52-60.

O'NEILL, M. & PEDERSON, A. (1994). Two analytic paths for understanding Canadian development in health promotion. *In* A. Pederson, M. O'Neill, & I. Rootman (Eds.), *Health promotion in Canada : Provincial, national, and international perspectives* (pp. 40-55). Toronto: W.B. Saunders Canada.

ORBACH, S. (1978). *Fat is a feminist issue.* New York, NY: Berkeley Books.

PRONGER, B. (1990). *The arena of masculinity : Sports, homosexuality and the meaning of sex.* Toronto: Summerhill.

RADER, B. (1991). The quest for self sufficiency and the new strenuosity: Reflections on the strenuous life of the 1970s and 1980s. *Journal of Sport History, 18,* 255-266.

ROJEK, C. (1992). "The eye of power": Moral regulation and the professionalization of leisure management from the 1930s to the 1950s. *Loisir et société, 15,* 355-373.

RITENBAUGH, C. (1982). Obesity as a culture-bound syndrome. *Culture, Medicine and Psychiatry, 6,* 347-261.

SCHILLING, C. (1993). *The body and social theory.* London: Sage.

SCHOENBORN, C. (1987). Findings from the National Health Interview Survey. *Evaluation and the Health Professions, 10,* 438-459.

SOBAL, J. & STUNKARD, A. (1989). Socioeconomic status and obesity: A review of the literature. *Psychological Bulletin, 105,* 260-275.

SONTAG, S. (1978). *Illness as metaphor.* Toronto, ON: Doubleday.

SPARKS, R. (1990). Social practice, the bodily professions and the state. *Sociology of Sport Journal, 7,* 72-82.

STEIN, H. (1982). Neo-Darwinism and survival through fitness in "Regan's" America. *Journal of Psychohistory, 10,* 163-187.

TINNING, R. (1991). Health oriented physical education (HOPE): The case of physical education and the promotion of healthy lifestyles. *ACHPER National Journal,* Summer, 4-10.

VERTINSKY, P. (1985). Risk benefit analysis of health promotion : Opportunities and threats in physical education. *Quest, 37,* 71-83.

WAGNER, G. (1987). Sport as a means for reducing the cost of illness—some theoretical, statistical, and empirical remarks. *International Review for the Sociology of Sport,* 22, 217-227.

WALDEN, K. (1985). The road to fat city: An interpretation of the development of weight consciousness in Western society. *Historical Reflections*, *12*, 331-373.

WHITSON, D. (1991, November). *Gendered identities: Discipline, power, and pleasure.* Paper presented at the North American Society for the Sociology of Sport, Milwaulkee, WI.

WOLF, N. (1990). *The beauty myth.* Toronto, ON: Vintage Books.

YATES, A. (1991). *Compulsive exercise and eating disorders: Toward an integrated theory of activity.* New York, NY: Brunner/Mazel.

YOUNG, K. (1992, December 2). *Panic or political double jeopardy? Youth crime in communities and schools.* Paper presented at the annual meeting of the Alberta School Boards Association, Calgary, AB.

YOUNG, K. (1993). Violence, risk, and liability in male sports culture. *Sociology of Sport Journal*, *10*(4), 373-396.

YOUNG, K. and WHITE, P. (1995). Sport, physical danger, and injury: The experiences of elite women athletes. *Journal of Sport and Social Issues*, *19*(1), 45-62.

YOUNG, K., WHITE, P., & McTEER, W. (1994). Body talk: Male athletes reflect on sport, injury, and pain. *Sociology of Sport Journal*, *11*(2), 175-194.

Philip WHITE, Kevin YOUNG et James GILLETT
L'impérialisme moral du culte du corps: notes critiques sur la santé et la forme physique

RÉSUMÉ

Cet article présente une critique des processus par lesquels la santé et la forme physique ont acquis une place de premier plan dans notre culture. Les auteurs montrent que si le développement et la promotion de croyances culturelles relatives à la santé relèvent souvent de bonnes intentions, ils découlent néanmoins de structures d'inégalité et de relations de domination, et aident à les reproduire. Selon eux, le mouvement en faveur de la santé et de la forme physique se teinte d'impérialisme moral et influe sur les relations entre les classes et les sexes. Leur analyse bat en brèche certaines hypothèses généralement reconnues, à l'origine des croyances populaires au sujet de la relation entre l'exercice, la forme et la santé. Leur conclusion remet en question certains principes et pratiques répandus concernant la pression sociale actuelle en faveur de l'adoption de styles de vie à caractère ascétique.

Philip WHITE, Kevin YOUNG and James GILLETT
*Bodywork as a Moral Imperative : Some Critical Notes on Health
and Fitness*

ABSTRACT

This paper provides a critique of the processes by which health and fitness have
moved forward on the cultural agenda. It is argued that the development and
promotion of cultural beliefs about health, while often well intended, flow from
and help reproduce structures of inequality and relations of dominance. It is also
suggested that the health and fitness movement incorporates a moral imperative
which has consequences for class and gender relations. Our analysis demystifies
some of the taken-for-granted assumptions underlying popular beliefs about the
relationship between exercise, fitness, and health. We conclude by challenging
some of the orthodoxies surrounding current social pressures to pursue ascetic
lifestyles.

Philip WHITE, Kevin YOUNG y James GILLETT
*El imperialismo moral del culto del cuerpo: notas críticas sobre la salud
y la forma física.*

RESUMEN

Este artículo presenta una crítica de los procesos por los cuales la salud y la
forma física han adquirido una importancia en nuestra cultura. Aunque el
desarrollo y la promoción de creencias culturales relativas a la salud realzan muy
a menudo buenas intenciones, sostienen los autores, de éstas se desprenden
estructuras de desigualdad y relaciones de dominación, y ayudan a reproducirlas.
El movimiento en favor de la salud y de la forma física se tiñe de imperialismo
moral e influye sobre las relaciones entre las clases y los sexos, según los
autores. Su análisis refuta algunas hipótesis generalmente reconocidas, al origen
de las creencias populares con respecto a la relación entre el ejercicio, la forma
y la salud. Su conclusión pone en duda algunos principios y prácticas difundidas
concernientes a la presión social actual en favor de la adopción de estilos de vida
de carácter ascético

La politique du sport
et de l'éducation physique en France

Michel JAMET
UFR STAPS
Université P. Sabatier
Toulouse, France

L'article est consacré à l'analyse des interactions entre l'État et la société en France, en matière de sport et d'éducation physique, au cours des dernières décennies. Il cherche à mettre en évidence « les incertitudes de l'État en action » (Jobert & Muller, 1987), aux prises, différemment selon les périodes et les conjonctures, avec des contraintes, des remises en question inattendues, des modifications de comportement à l'égard des pratiques physiques, l'émergence et l'affirmation d'enjeux parfois mal compris par des responsables politiques et leurs interlocuteurs traditionnels, les fédérations sportives. La conclusion vise à dégager des types d'action de l'État, en France, dans le champ du sport et de l'éducation physique.

Le sens et la portée des politiques sportives

Depuis J. Meynaud (1966), l'analyse des politiques sportives s'est développée en France. Sans entrer dans une mise en perspective – qui serait nécessairement partielle –, des approches théoriques des rapports sport, État, société, on peut considérer qu'elles ont oscillé entre deux pôles en fonction des conceptions de l'État, affichées ou sous-entendues. Le premier se distingue par une représentation de l'État comme un ensemble cohérent et unifié, exerçant son action coercitive et légitimatrice sur la société selon un plan d'ensemble, avec des moyens d'intervention afférents (Brohm, 1976). Le second met l'accent sur les insuffisances, les incohérences de l'État, faisant face à la diversité des intérêts et des attentes, et à ses difficultés à concilier actions rationnelles et maintien de la cohésion sociale (Amar, 1987). Selon les approches, l'accent est mis sur l'un ou l'autre pôle avec, cependant, des modes d'intelligibilité spécifiques pouvant articuler certains éléments contradictoires des deux pôles (Defrance, 1994 ; Harvey & Cantelon, 1988).

La thèse mise en œuvre ici est que les politiques successives élaborées par l'État en matière de sport et d'éducation physique procèdent d'une intention plus large que les actions sectorielles auxquelles elles donnent lieu. Cette intention s'inscrit dans un processus constant de régulation et de légitimation des rapports sociaux. Régulation au sens de processus « d'intégration systémique », défini comme exercice des « capacités de contrôle et d'apprentissage d'un système » ; légitimation au sens « d'intégration sociale », c'est-à-dire « la stabilité assurée par des systèmes d'interprétation garantissant une identité, par des consensus d'ordre axiologique et par la reconnaissance de normes réglant l'action » (Habermas, 1985, p. 202).

Cependant, cette action du politique – défini comme niveau spécifique d'exercices du pouvoir dans la société – ne va pas de soi. Elle met en jeu des acteurs concrets, individus et groupes qui se rencontrent, éventuellement s'affrontent sur la définition des formes sociales acceptables, reconnues, valorisées. Dans ces interactions, les agents de l'État – au sens « d'organisation politique-juridique » (Gramsci, 1975, p. 577) disposant de la légitimité démocratique et de moyens d'intervention –, s'affirment au-dessus des contingences particulières, au nom de « l'intérêt général ». Ils interagissent avec les acteurs organisés de la société civile, notion qui désigne ici l'ensemble des activités économiques, sociales, culturelles, idéologiques à l'œuvre dans la société. Ces acteurs font valoir leurs attentes spécifiques, leur intérêts, leurs croyances, en fonction des contextes et surtout de leur compréhension des règles de leur action. Dans cet ensemble d'interactions, les agents de l'État, comme les acteurs de la société civile, se heurtent aux limites des systèmes d'action – au sens d'actions concertées et coordonnées – qu'ils mettent en place. Ces limites sont dues aux contraintes rencontrées et aux ressources limitées dont ils disposent, mais aussi à leur « compétence limitée » en tant qu'acteurs sociaux capables d'appréhender les conditions de leur action (Giddens, 1987).

Ainsi, l'action de l'État en matière de sport et d'éducation physique peut-elle être appréhendée, partiellement, sous l'angle des processus de régulation et de légitimation mis en œuvre pour assurer la gestion de ce secteur du social. Comment le politique définit-il les règles formelles d'exercice et d'organisation du sport et de l'éducation physique dans la société française ? Comment intervient-il pour favoriser « l'acceptation par des sujets capables de jugement » (Jobert & Muller, 1987, p. 23) de règles sociales explicites et implicites, dans la mise en œuvre des pratiques sportives et d'éducation physique ?

Une telle démarche analytique resterait cependant partielle si elle ignorait les incertitudes de l'État en action, qui tiennent à la capacité limitée des acteurs du politique d'interpréter les situations, de définir des orientations, de trouver les formes de médiation nécessaires à la mise en œuvre d'une politique, de faire face à des effets imprévus de procédures en cours, d'inscrire des politiques sectorielles dans le cadre d'une perspective d'action globale de l'État. Comment, dans la société française de la seconde partie du XXᵉ siècle, les acteurs du politique ont-ils fait face à ces problèmes ? Avec quels effets sur la dynamique de construction sociale du sport et de l'éducation physique ? C'est donc bien dans l'articulation entre un niveau d'action globalisant de régulation et de légitimation, et la mise en œuvre de procédures partielles, marquées par des incertitudes, des hésitations, des engagements partiels, fortement marqués par des enjeux conjoncturels, qu'on cherchera à caractériser les dynamiques de construction sociale et historique des politiques sportives dans la société française.

Les dynamiques de l'État en action

On peut utilement aborder l'analyse de l'intervention étatique dans le domaine des activités physiques et sportives sur la base de l'affirmation du sport comme activité souhaitable pour tous. L'émergence de cette conviction est étroitement associée à la concrétisation du droit à l'instruction, à l'éducation, puis aux loisirs.

L'État et la démocratisation du sport

C'est par l'éducation physique, avec la genèse d'une compétence spécifique de l'État dans ce domaine au cours de la première partie du XXᵉ siècle, que des pratiques physiques deviennent progressivement – avec de très grandes disparités selon les régions, les milieux, les écoles – un élément de la formation de la jeunesse dans les écoles primaires. Des actions expérimentales sous l'impulsion de responsables pédagogiques et médicaux (Arnaud, 1983) ainsi que la mise en œuvre partielle de choix politiques contribuent à doter progressivement l'État d'outils administratifs d'intervention, en éducation physique, mais aussi – sous le gouvernement du Front Populaire – en faveur du développement des pratiques sportives pendant le temps de loisir de la jeunesse.

Pendant la période d'occupation – alors même que sous le régime de Vichy, « l'État français » poursuit son action d'encadrement de la jeunesse en faisant largement appel aux pratiques physiques (Guy Lescot, 1991) –, les revendications pour un accès élargi à l'éducation et à la culture trouvent, dans le programme d'action « du Comité National de la Résistance » (C.N.R.), une expression fondée sur le principe de l'égalité des chances. Les rédacteurs du programme d'action du C.N.R. y proclament leur intention de « rester unis après la libération » afin de mettre en œuvre un ensemble de mesures politiques, économiques et sociales dont *la possibilité effective pour tous les enfants français de bénéficier de l'instruction et d'accéder à la culture la plus développée quelle que soit la situation de fortune de leurs parents, afin que les fonctions les plus hautes soient réellement accessibles à tous ceux qui auront les capacités*

*requises pour les exercer et que soit ainsi promue une élite véritable, non de
naissance mais de mérite et constamment renouvelée par les apports populaires*
(Dupeux, 1969, p. 126).

Le Comité Français de Libération Nationale, en mettant en place un
service de la jeunesse et des sports et en émettant une ordonnance sur les
conditions d'agrément des groupements sportifs (ordonnance du 2-10-1943),
veut contrer symboliquement « l'organisme dit gouvernement de l'État français
ou ses agents » qui, depuis 1940, a mis en place une administration étatique qui
contrôle étroitement l'action des fédérations sportives et les contenus officiels
de l'éducation physique dans le cadre de « l'éducation générale ».

Le gouvernement provisoire du Général de Gaulle amorce la mise en
œuvre de cette politique sociale en matière de pratiques physiques dans le cadre
d'une Direction générale de l'éducation physique et des sports au sein du ministère de l'Éducation nationale. Les principes d'action de cette direction et leur
application font cependant l'objet de tensions au sein de l'appareil d'État entre
les tenants de conceptions différentes de l'éducation physique et du sport, mais
aussi et surtout, rencontrent le scepticisme de responsables locaux se heurtant
aux priorités d'action des collectivités locales.

Bien que la volonté politique de favoriser le développement des pratiques
sportives au sein de la jeunesse ne résiste pas aux contraintes économiques et
aux choix prioritaires de la « reconstruction », à l'époque où se met en place la
IVe République, le droit au sport, affirmé comme droit social, continue d'être
entretenu et diffusé par les organisations se réclamant de la gauche communiste
et socialiste. Cependant, les clivages entre socialistes et communistes, dans le
contexte de la guerre froide qui s'installe, l'instabilité gouvernementale chronique de la IVe République ainsi que l'importance des problèmes de la décolonisation, sont autant de conditions défavorables à une relance d'une action
politique d'envergure en faveur du développement de pratiques sportives en
France. Sous l'égide des hauts fonctionnaires, c'est donc la gestion quotidienne
des contraintes qui prévaut en matière d'éducation physique et de sport dans
la seconde partie des années 50, période où une jeunesse plus nombreuse
commence à affirmer un intérêt accru pour le sport. Les populations adultes,
pour leur part, se familiarisent avec des pratiques physiques de loisir, partiellement à caractère compétitif, mais plus largement inscrites dans des perspectives
ludiques et de bien-être. Ce processus se situe dans le cadre des entreprises,
des associations locales, des organismes de vacances (la troisième semaine de
congé payé est acquise en 1956) ou dans des groupes familiaux ou électifs
(Dumazedier, 1966).

En dépit de la relative inertie du politique en matière d'éducation physique
et de sport – il se cantonne dans des mesures de soutien et d'accompagnement –, les pratiques sportives organisées dans le cadre des fédérations con-

naissent une très nette progression au cours de la seconde partie des années 50 (2,2 millions de licences en 1954; 2,5 millions en 1958; 2,8 millions en 1960), cette progression bénéficiant d'abord aux groupements scolaires et universitaires (+ 300 000 licenciés). En effet, les pratiques sportives, au sens de pratiques compétitives, attirent une partie – environ le quart d'une classe d'âge (les enquêtes sur ce point indiquent une grande stabilité depuis les années 60) des enfants du «baby boom» désormais en âge de s'intégrer au système des compétitions sportives. Cette pression démographique, articulée avec l'émergence d'une «culture juvénile» (Morin, 1962) dont le sport est partie prenante, est un élément essentiel de compréhension de l'action étatique des années 60. Cette dernière s'exerce sur le système éducatif, y compris l'éducation physique, sur l'organisation des pratiques sportives au sein des clubs et des fédérations, de même que sur la construction des équipements et la formation des cadres sportifs.

Cette politique globale de l'État en matière d'éducation physique et de sport va s'inscrire dans le cadre de l'action d'un État «moderne» dans lequel «efficacité» et «continuité» deviennent des maîtres-mots. L'action du politique se place explicitement dans une perspective de «progrès», tant sur les plans scientifique et technique qu'économique et social. À cet égard, le discours du Général de Gaulle, le 4 septembre 1958 à Paris, est significatif :

> Ce qui, pour les pouvoirs publics, est désormais primordial, c'est leur efficacité et leur continuité. Nous vivons en un temps où des forces gigantesques sont en train de transformer le monde. Sous peine de devenir un peuple périmé et dédaigné, il nous faut dans les domaines scientifique, économique, social évoluer rapidement. D'ailleurs, à cet impératif répondent le goût du progrès et la passion des réussites techniques qui se font jour parmi les Français et, d'abord, dans notre jeunesse. Il y a des faits qui dominent notre existence nationale et doivent, par conséquent, commander nos institutions (Dupeux, 1969, p. 251).

En matière de sport et d'éducation physique, les choix décisifs sont effectués dans le contexte et à la faveur de l'émoi que suscitent les piètres résultats des sportifs français aux Jeux Olympiques de Rome en 1960. Dans ce cas, «la force de l'événement» intervient pour accélérer un processus, donner une tonalité particulière à l'action et renforcer l'adhésion des tenants d'une action majeure de l'État en matière de sport et d'éducation physique tout en atténuant la portée des protestations de ceux qui dénoncent cette politique.

Sans entrer dans une analyse détaillée des actions menées par l'État au cours des années 60 (Jamet, 1989), on peut faire quelques remarques. Les choix politiques de la Ve République ne sont affirmés que progressivement, après une période transitoire où les continuités l'emportaient sur les changements. C'est ainsi que les instructions officielles de 1959 en éducation physique, bien plus que celles de 1945, sont marquées par l'influence des tenants d'une éducation physique «fondamentale», inspirée des préceptes de la Ligue Française d'Éducation Physique, bien représentée au sein du corps des inspecteurs chargés de la préparation de ce texte. Les partisans d'une éducation physique à dominante sportive ne réussissent pas à se faire entendre, alors que l'approche psychophysiologique du mouvement humain, développée par J. Boulch reçoit des échos favorables de la part des professionnels de l'éducation physique qui ne se satisfont plus des connaissances anatomiques et physiologiques ainsi que des principes moraux constituant l'ossature des instructions de 1959.

Pourtant, à la faveur de l'impact des Jeux de Rome, télévisés en direct pour la première fois en France, l'État va mettre en place une politique globale en matière d'éducation physique et de sport, par le biais d'une série de mesures (législatives, réglementaires, organisationnelles). Au fil des mois et des années, ces mesures vont constituer un ensemble relativement cohérent et donner à la politique sportive française ce caractère unifié (hégémonique, diront certains) qui fera craindre à des acteurs et des observateurs de ce domaine, un processus « d'étatisation du sport ». M. Herzog (figure emblématique, vainqueur de l'Annapurna), Haut-Commissaire puis Secrétaire d'État à la Jeunesse et aux Sports de 1958 à 1966, est amené à répondre à ces critiques et à ces craintes en mettant de l'avant ce que doit être le rôle de l'État dans un système d'État-Providence (*Welfare State*). Reprenant ses propos, J. Meynaud résume ainsi les termes du débat :

> *Il est curieux, note Maurice Herzog, que le rôle exercé par l'État en matière d'éducation sportive soit réputé mauvais alors qu'il est généralement tenu pour bon au titre de l'éducation intellectuelle. On accepterait certes que l'État versât des subsides mais on lui refuse le droit d'apprécier les services rendus par les bénéficiaires à la collectivité nationale. En réalité, le système actuel ne donne pas à chaque citoyen une droit d'accès égal à la pratique sportive. Seul, l'État est en mesure de mettre fin à cette situation d'inégalité et d'organiser la pratique sportive sur une base qui écarte les divergences dues à l'inégalité des ressources ou à la variété des charges familiales et sociales* (Meynaud, 1966, p. 137-138).

Et J. Meynaud prend à son compte la position ministérielle en ajoutant : « Pour reprendre une expression à la mode, la démocratisation du sport ne saurait être entreprise si l'on ne fait pas de cette activité un service public. Et il suffit de considérer les modalités et les résultats du sport commercialisé pour accorder un large crédit à cette proposition » (p. 138). L'enjeu d'accessibilité aux pratiques sportives, au-delà des conditions sociales d'existence, est donc bien posé ici, à la fois par un responsable politique et par un observateur qui associe « sport » et « service public ». Cependant, la mise en œuvre du principe d'égalité des chances face aux pratiques sportives prend une forme spécifique au cours des années 60.

Dans son « plan de rénovation du sport français » présenté au printemps 1961 aux membres du « Conseil National des Sports » nouvellement créé, M. Herzog avait défini les axes prioritaires de son action. Il s'agit – en raison des critiques suscitées par les résultats des Français aux J.O. de Rome – de redonner à la France un rang conforme à la place qu'elle occupe dans les relations entre les États, sur la scène sportive internationale. Pour ce faire, les fédérations bénéficiant de l'aide financière de l'État seront contrôlées dans leur action par un « observateur » nommé par le Haut-Commissaire. De plus, la préparation olympique est placée sous la responsabilité d'un délégué général également nommé (ce sera Marceau Crespin), et centralisée à l'Institut National des Sports. Au chapitre des infrastructures, un plan d'équipement sportif est mis en œuvre dans le cadre du IVe plan (61-65) afin de rattraper le retard accumulé dans ce domaine. Enfin la liaison est faite entre le sport à l'école et « le sport civil », en particulier dans le cadre de l'Office du Sport Scolaire et Universitaire (OSSU), avec le projet énoncé par le Haut-Commissaire et rappelé par J. Le Boulch d'une « reconversion des méthodes pédagogiques » en raison de la place accrue accordée au « sport à l'école » (Le Boulch, 1978, p. 226).

Les années suivantes sont celles de la concrétisation de cette politique qui associe explicitement trois objectifs : la généralisation de la pratique sportive dans le cadre scolaire, le développement du « sport civil » et l'émergence d'une élite sportive susceptible de s'imposer sur la scène internationale. L'efficacité de cette politique est incontestable au cours des années 60. Elle s'inscrit dans le paysage urbain avec la construction d'installations sportives ; elle permet au système éducatif de faire face en éducation physique, difficilement parfois, à l'afflux des jeunes scolarisés dans l'enseignement du second degré ; elle permet d'améliorer l'encadrement sportif dans les clubs ; et elle se traduit par un bilan en nette progression des résultats sportifs sur la scène internationale.

En dépit d'oppositions internes – dans les fédérations, en éducation physique –, l'adhésion de nombre d'acteurs sociaux impliqués dans ce domaine est acquise à cette politique, renforcée encore par l'organisation d'une réflexion des responsables sportifs sur les significations du sport. Cet accord se traduit par la publication, en 1965, de l'*Essai de doctrine du sport*, largement diffusé sans les milieux sportifs et même au-delà du cercle des spécialistes. La rédaction du texte est placée sous l'égide de J. Borotra. Il s'agit d'un discours global de légitimation de la pratique sportive comme modèle de pratique physique dans une société industrielle et urbaine, que ce soit dans une perspective éducative, d'entretien et de loisir, de compétition, de haute performance ou encore de spectacle. Ce discours contribue ainsi à conforter l'action gouvernementale et à renforcer sa position de premier plan dans la structuration de ce domaine de la vie sociale.

Des processus de rationalisation de l'action publique

Cette action organisatrice et de légitimation menée par l'État dans le champ de l'éducation physique et du sport ne résistera pas cependant aux effets conjugués des mouvements de contestation de la fin des années 60 et de la première partie des années 70, ainsi qu'à l'émergence puis à l'aggravation de difficultés économiques. Après avoir officialisé l'objectif des cinq heures d'éducation physique dans le second degré par les instructions de 1967, après avoir instauré le tiers-temps pédagogique à l'école primaire en 1969, qui prévoit six heures d'éducation physique, les responsables gouvernementaux font rapidement face aux limitations budgétaires. Ainsi s'établit un décalage entre des énoncés de politique, ambitieux en matière d'éducation physique, et des moyens financiers insuffisants pour faire face à la multiplication des attentes. De 1970 à 1973, la progression moyenne du budget global de la Jeunesse et des Sports a été de 9,3 % alors que la croissance de l'indice des prix à la consommation était de 6,2 % en moyenne. De 1973 à 1979, le budget croît de 14 % en moyenne pour un indice de prix à la consommation en augmentation de 10,5 % (Énault et al., 1979 ; INSEE, 1988). Cette progression est jugée insuffisante par les principales organisations « de gauche », en éducation physique en sport et en plein air. Elles lancent le mot d'ordre « du doublement du budget » de la Jeunesse et des Sports à l'occasion des « Assises nationales de l'éducation physique, du sport et des activités de pleine nature » au printemps 1970.

Ce qui était décalage devient fracture lorsque l'État annonce en 1972 – après avoir réduit « provisoirement », l'année précédente, l'horaire d'éducation physique à trois heures dans les collèges et à deux heures dans les lycées – sa décision de compléter l'horaire d'éducation physique par « un enseignement sportif » permettant « d'offrir à des scolaires ou des non-scolaires une initiation sportive déjà plus spécialisée, débouchant normalement sur la pratique sportive organisée par les associations et fédérations sportives ». Cet enseignement sportif sera confié à des « Centres d'animation sportive » (CAS) et aux écoles de sport, dans le cadre de l'enseignement optionnel à l'école. Il fera ainsi la jonction « avec les deux dernières catégories de pratiques – les deux premières étant « l'éducation physique » d'une part, « l'enseignement sportif » d'autre part – : celle orientée vers « la haute compétition », « la performance », pouvant déboucher sur un engagement total quoique temporaire dans la vie sportive » ; et celle orientée vers « la détente », adaptée aux « différents âges », pratiquée sous forme « compétitive ou non » correspondant aux « goûts » et aux « talents » de chacun (circulaire du 1-07-1972). Ainsi est dessinée une vision totalisante de l'activité physique pratiquée à toutes les étapes de la vie. Mais c'est surtout l'intention gouvernementale de faire réaliser un enseignement sportif hors de l'école, avec l'aide de cadres techniques des fédérations sportives – ceux-ci peuvent se prévaloir d'un diplôme d'État avec l'instauration d'une formation placée sous l'égide de la Jeunesse et des Sports (décret du 15-06-1972) – qui mobilise l'attention et les réactions des professionnels de l'éducation physique. Le courant « Unité et Action », proche de la gauche communiste, qui dirige désormais le Syndicat National de l'Éducation Physique (SNEP), fort de ses 6 000 membres sur 17 000 enseignants en EPS, mobilise ses adhérents contre la mise en place des CAS et pour l'obtention de « 2 000 nouveaux postes à la rentrée » (en 1972). Ainsi, le système d'action en faveur d'une éducation physique fondée sur le sport, qui avait associé de fait les responsables gouvernementaux et les organisations sportives « de gauche » au cours des années 60, ne résiste pas aux actions de rationalisation menées par l'État au cours de la décennie suivante.

Cet effort de rationalisation de l'action étatique porte sur l'éducation physique dans le primaire. Il s'agit de la mise en œuvre progressive, bien qu'incomplète, de pratiques en progression quantitative et qualitative grâce à l'action des conseillers pédagogiques et au développement de publications en éducation physique destinées à l'école primaire. Dans le second degré, c'est la réorganisation des ressources disponibles qui l'emporte, dans un climat d'oppositions et d'incertitudes, sous l'égide du ministre J.P. Soisson. On assiste alors à la normalisation des trois heures et des deux heures d'EPS, respectivement dans les collèges et les lycées en 1978, et à la réduction de trois à deux heures du forfait hebdomadaire reconnu aux enseignants pour l'animation de l'association sportive scolaire.

Par ailleurs, cette période est celle de la reconnaissance par l'État d'une nécessaire action de formation et d'aide financière en faveur des sportifs de haut niveau. Cette action semble d'autant plus nécessaire aux responsables gouvernementaux et des fédérations sportives que les résultats obtenus par les sportifs français sur la scène internationale, en particulier olympique, ne font que régresser depuis la fin des années 60. Ce qui amène M. Crespin à écrire, dans un rapport soumis au Conseil Économique et Social, que dans le domaine du sport d'élite, la représentation nationale est en jeu dans un système de concurrence exacerbée entre les États ; la France ne peut se désister en raison de l'impact de ces compétitions, elle doit donc prendre les moyens de la réussite sans tomber dans la logique des pays à « sport d'État ». Pour réussir, il faut procéder rationnellement, scientifiquement, tant dans le dépistage des athlètes que dans leur formation, leur préparation et leur réinsertion sociale (Crespin, 1978).

L'enjeu de la représentation nationale sur la scène sportive internationale reste donc au cœur des préoccupations gouvernementales. La mise en place d'une commission de concertation puis d'une « commission de sport de haut niveau, chargée de préparer les mesures à prendre en faveur du sport de haut niveau, spécialement en ce qui concerne l'élite susceptible de participer aux Jeux Olympiques » (arrêté du 10-10-78), dans laquelle les représentants de l'État ont voix prépondérante, illustre l'importance qu'accordent les responsables politiques à cet enjeu. Paradoxalement le « laisser-faire » du gouvernement français à l'occasion des Jeux Olympiques de Moscou manifeste l'intégration de la politique du sport de haut niveau dans la stratégie internationale du gouvernement français. En effet, à la suite de l'invasion de l'Afghanistan par les troupes soviétiques, le président américain J. Carter avait choisi de riposter en interdisant aux athlètes de son pays de participer aux Jeux de Moscou, et en pressant les pays alliés de faire de même. Le président V. Giscard d'Estaing, favorable au maintien de contacts diplomatiques étroits avec l'U.R.S.S. et connaissant l'attachement de la grande majorité des fédérations à la participation aux J.O., adopte une position officielle de « laisser-faire » – qui lui permet de ménager la susceptibilité américaine tout en favorisant la représentation française aux Jeux de Moscou.

Ce cas, loin de constituer une manifestation de l'autonomie des fédérations sportives, révèle plutôt la capacité des acteurs politiques à inclure le sport de haut niveau dans leur stratégie dès lors que la représentation française sur la scène internationale est en jeu. Les grands événements sportifs internationaux sont, plus que jamais, affaire d'État.

Ainsi, au cours des années 70, pour les responsables politiques nationaux, l'affirmation de la France sur la scène internationale d'une part, l'apprentissage des pratiques et des règles sportives à l'école d'autre part, restent les deux piliers de l'action gouvernementale. La loi de 1975 « relative au développement de l'éducation physique et du sport » (loi du 29-10-1975) s'inscrit bien dans cette perspective. Plus qu'une loi de « développement » par laquelle l'État aurait tenté d'imprimer une impulsion et des orientations nouvelles dans ce domaine de la vie sociale, la loi « Mazeaud » s'avère être un texte « d'organisation » où la rationalisation des fonctions institutionnelles existantes l'emporte nettement sur la définition de nouveaux espaces d'action. D'ailleurs, le développement des contraintes économiques et politiques (émergence d'une crise économique structurelle et renforcement de l'impact politique de l'Union de la Gauche), de même que l'échéance proche des Jeux Olympiques de 1976, ne favorisent pas un débat plus large sur l'évolution sociale et culturelle des pratiques physiques dans la société française.

Pourtant, le processus de restructuration de l'espace social des pratiques physiques, par la diffusion d'activités physiques de loisir au sein des populations adultes et par la diversification des formes de pratiques, n'échappe pas aux responsables gouvernementaux (Defrance & Pociello, 1993). Le « sport pour tous » (slogan du Conseil de l'Europe, lancé en 1966 et repris par le Comité National Olympique et Sportif Français mis en place en 1972) devient une préoccupation gouvernementale. Il incite les responsables à infléchir la loi de programmation des installations sportives et de plein air en faveur d'équipements fonctionnels à usages polyvalents après ceux, classiques et parfois monumentaux, des deux premiers plans, avec un accent mis sur le développement de bases plein air et de loisir ainsi que de centres aérés. Sur le plan des utilisateurs, priorité est donnée aux associations et, pour la première fois, aux handicapés, avec ce que cela implique dans l'aménagement des accès aux installations. Ainsi se dessine une triple orientation : 1) réaliser des équipements moins coûteux ; 2) les adapter aux usages qui en sont faits et à leur évolution ; 3) tenir compte des besoins et des aspirations exprimées par différentes catégories de la population.

Des contestations sociales et politiques

La politique gouvernementale en faveur d'un accès élargi aux activités physiques de loisir reste cependant embryonnaire. Ce n'est pas l'intégration du Secrétariat d'État à la Jeunesse et aux Sports au sein d'un ministère de la Qualité de la Vie, dans le premier gouvernement du septennat de V. Giscard d'Estaing, qui modifie les priorités, même si elle indique l'émergence de préoccupations nouvelles au niveau politique, en réaction aux « nouveaux mouvements sociaux » (Touraine, 1973). Ces mouvements « qualitatifs » – auxquels sont particulièrement sensibles les classes moyennes – centrés sur des préoccupations de vie quotidienne, en particulier sur la maîtrise du cadre de vie (la qualité de l'environnement étant un élément central) posent, aussi, le problème de l'aménagement d'espaces naturels et urbains propices à l'exercice d'activités physiques ludiques et de santé. L'affirmation des femmes sur la scène publique a des effets sur l'émergence de remises en question des normes sportives, particulièrement des normes compétitives, celles-ci étant plus adaptées aux ethos masculins qu'aux aspirations culturelles et sociales des femmes (Davisse & Louveau, 1991).

Mais ce sont surtout les organisations du mouvement social « traditionnel », le mouvement ouvrier, qui donnent le ton à la contestation de la politique gouvernementale en matière sportive. Dans l'ouvrage collectif *Sport et développement humain* , S. Goffard dénonce la manœuvre gouvernementale qui « fait diversion et se pare de plumes démocratiques en arguant d'un prétendu « sport pour tous » s'appuyant sur la prise de conscience individuelle et un état d'esprit dit « sportif ». Plus loin, il condamne la double orientation que prend, selon lui, le sport en France : d'une part le « culte des grandes rencontres, des vedettes… », d'autre part le développement d'une « propagande (toute verbale et sans financement) sur l'activité de loisirs, orientée vers l'entretien de la condition physique individuelle, par un certain standing personnel de l'individu « en forme » s'adonnant à des plaisirs « naturels » et « beaux » (Goffard, 1975, p. 13-14).

Ainsi face à un « sport populaire », parce que contrôlé par les organisations du mouvement ouvrier, se développent, selon les responsables de la Fédération Sportive et Gymnique du Travail (FSGT) proche du Parti Communiste Français (PCF), des « pratiques individuelles » qui ne sont pas toujours délibérément choisies, mais qui correspondent souvent à l'absence de solutions collectives et au manque de moyens des associations sportives et des collectivités locales ou d'entreprises ; en ce sens, ces pratiques dites nouvelles sont profondément le produit de la crise de la société. Organiser ces pratiques est actuellement un enjeu de luttes entre le mouvement associatif (pas seulement sportif) et le secteur commercial largement favorisé par l'État (Le Joliff, 1981, p. 50).

De leur côté, les socialistes ne se veulent pas en reste sur ce front politique, et mettent également l'accent sur le caractère éducatif de l'association. Dans une proposition de loi qui synthétise sa position en matière «d'activités physiques», le parti socialiste réaffirme nettement que pour lui, «les associations favorisent l'expression volontaire d'un projet éducatif spécifique et suscitent la prise en charge collective d'une action éducative de transformation» (1980).

L'arrivée «surprise» de la gauche au pouvoir à l'occasion des élections présidentielles de 1981 va amener les nouveaux gouvernants à confronter leurs positions aux contraintes du moment et à l'évolution des conditions économiques et sociales.

Une nouvelle répartition des pouvoirs

La volonté réformatrice des socialistes se concrétise dans le domaine de l'éducation physique lorsque l'État – répondant favorablement à une ancienne revendication syndicale – rattache ce secteur au ministère de l'Éducation nationale (il dépendait préalablement du ministère de la Jeunesse et des Sports). Ce rattachement n'est pas seulement symbolique, il s'accompagne d'une relance de l'intégration universitaire de la formation en sciences et techniques des activités physiques et sportives (STAPS). Après l'instauration de diplômes universitaires de 1er et 2e cycle en STAPS respectivement en 1975 et 1977, l'État avait refusé d'aller plus loin. Le nouveau gouvernement habilite les formations de maîtrise et de doctorat à partir de 1982. De plus, le concours «d'agrégation» est instauré au même titre que dans les autres disciplines scolaires en éducation physique, qui trouve également une place à l'Institut National de Recherche Pédagogique.

Tous les signes extérieurs de la reconnaissance de l'éducation physique comme discipline d'enseignement et secteur de recherche universitaire sont donc réunis, donnant aux professionnels de ce secteur une position institutionnelle renforcée éventuellement de nouvelles perspectives de carrière.

Dans le même temps, l'État relance provisoirement le recrutement des professeurs d'éducation physique (1 200 postes créés en 1982) tout en interrompant la formation des professeurs adjoints dans les Centres Régionaux d'Éducation Physique et Sportive (CREPS). Enfin le ministère de l'Éducation nationale instaure à nouveau le forfait de trois heures hebdomadaires reconnues aux enseignants d'éducation physique pour l'animation du sport scolaire.

Par ailleurs, les énergies des responsables politiques – sous l'autorité d'E. Avice, Secrétaire d'État dans l'éphémère ministère du Temps libre, puis Ministre – sont très tôt mobilisées par la préparation d'un nouveau projet de loi, destiné à se substituer à la « loi Mazeaud ». Élaboré dans un climat de réforme, tout comme l'avait été celui qu'il doit remplacer, le texte législatif n'aboutit que deux années plus tard, alors que les contraintes politiques et économiques ont mis à mal les volontés réformatrices de la gauche au pouvoir. Ainsi, à l'image du texte abrogé, la loi « relative à l'organisation et à la promotion des activités physiques et sportives » (loi du 16-07-1984) est bien plus un texte « d'organisation » que de « promotion ». Dans l'enseignement du second degré, l'exclusivité de compétence est reconnue aux « personnels enseignants d'éducation physique et sportive ». Dans le premier degré, les instituteurs peuvent se faire aider par un « personnel qualifié et agréé ». En dehors du cadre scolaire, les dispositions réglementant l'exercice rémunéré de l'enseignement des activités physiques et sportives sont reprises de la loi précédente et mises à jour (articles 43 à 49). Quant aux organismes traditionnellement chargés du développement et de la régulation des activités physiques et sportives – les fédérations –, ils voient se substituer un système « d'agrément » à ceux de « délégation » ou « d'habilitation », les fédérations unisport conservant seules la compétence d'assurer la représentation sportive française dans les grandes compétitions internationales.

Pour l'essentiel, les réformes apportées par la nouvelle loi portent sur le statut des sportifs de haut niveau et le cadre juridique du sport-spectacle. Elles confirment ainsi la situation spécifique de reconnaissance sociale acquise par ces athlètes et l'intégration croissante des pratiques de spectacle dans la logique économique. Sept articles (26 à 32) sont consacrés à définir les conditions d'octroi du statut de sportif de haut niveau, de formation et d'insertion professionnelle. Les groupements participant « habituellement à l'organisation de manifestations sportives payantes » se voient, quant à eux, offrir le choix de se constituer en « société d'économie mixte » ou en « société à objet sportif », nouvelle formule juridique créée pour la circonstance (articles 11 à 15).

Afin d'institutionnaliser des liens organiques entre l'État central et les organisations impliquées dans le développement du sport au sein de la société civile, la loi prévoit en outre la mise en place d'un Conseil National des Activités Physiques et Sportives, et – pour promouvoir une politique de recherche – d'un Comité National de la Recherche et de la Technologie. Si ces articles restent lettre morte au cours des années suivantes, il n'en est pas de même du Comité National Olympique et Sportif Français (CNOSF) dont les attributions sont désormais inscrites dans la loi (article 19), et qui voit sa position renforcée, d'autant qu'il aura à cogérer avec les représentants de l'État les fonds provenant du « loto sportif » instauré par la loi des finances de 1985.

Ainsi le CNOSF et son président, N. Paillou – élu en 1982 grâce à une modification judicieuse des règles de représentation (Bouquin, 1985, p. 281) favorable à la nouvelle majorité gouvernementale – acquièrent des pouvoirs significatifs dans la définition des objectifs d'utilisation de ces moyens financiers. Ce déplacement partiel des capacités d'orientation des politiques sportives vers les organisations sportives va s'accentuer par la suite sous l'influence de facteurs de natures diverses.

Un de ces facteurs, et non des moindres, est lié au processus de professionnalisation mis en œuvre par les fédérations sportives qui font désormais appel non seulement à des cadres techniques, mais aussi à des gestionnaires professionnels. Soumis à des règles d'efficacité, les dirigeants sportifs entrent en concurrence avec les responsables administratifs de l'État pour la définition des légitimités d'action dans ce domaine de la vie sociale. Ce glissement de légitimité est facilité – c'est un second élément d'explication – par les modifications de significations sociales associées aux résultats sportifs sur la scène internationale. Ces évolutions sont partiellement conjoncturelles : le boycottage des Jeux de Moscou par les États-Unis et les pays alliés auquel répond celui des Jeux de Los Angeles par l'U.R.S.S. et ses propres alliés ont fortement contribué à atténuer l'impact du nombre de médailles obtenues par les représentants nationaux. Les points de comparaison n'existent plus. Mais plus profondément, « la santé du sport français » – appréciée depuis les années 60, sous l'impulsion de l'État, à l'aune du nombre de médailles – est désormais perçue beaucoup plus, par nombre d'acteurs sociaux, en fonction de leur propre implication dans des pratiques physiques, souvent éloignées, dans leurs significations et leur contenu, du modèle sportif.

Ce déplacement des significations du sport accompagne le développement de la participation sportive chez les adultes, dont le poids démographique ne fait que s'affirmer. Il est encore renforcé par une autre dynamique qui touche au pouvoir de l'État : l'instauration et la mise en œuvre des lois de décentralisation au cours des dix dernières années.

Bien que « le sport » ne soit pas explicitement prévu dans la loi de décentralisation de 1983 (loi du 22-07-1983), il devient compétence partagée avec les collectivités territoriales, tout d'abord par le biais de l'école, et plus précisément par transfert de régime de propriété des biens mobiliers et immobiliers des établissements scolaires. Par étapes, l'État a été amené à préciser les compétences des collectivités territoriales dans ce domaine (Bourliaud, 1993).

Mais le déplacement de compétence ne se limite pas aux installations sportives, il se réalise aussi de fait – la loi de 1984 le prévoit – dans les interventions en éducation physique à l'école primaire. La mise en œuvre en 1994 de « la filière sportive des collectivités territoriales », en application de la loi de 1984 (modifiée en 1987) sur la Fonction Publique Territoriale, va contribuer à systématiser plus encore l'intervention « d'éducateurs » et de « conseillers » territoriaux dans l'éducation physique des enfants de l'école primaire. De plus, la politique d'aménagement des rythmes scolaires, instaurée par la circulaire « Chevènement-Calmat » en 1984, et reprise sous des dénominations différentes par les responsables ministériels suivants, accentue encore le rôle à la fois des collectivités et des associations locales dans la définition des pratiques physiques imposées ou proposées à l'enfant.

L'action des collectivités territoriales – particulièrement des communes – ne se limite pas aux enfants des écoles primaires. Elle porte bien sur toutes les formes de pratiques physiques qu'il s'agit : de coordonner, directement ou par le biais d'associations ; de promouvoir par la mise à disposition des locaux, d'installations, d'espaces appropriés ; d'encadrer par la mise à disposition et la formation de cadres techniques et pédagogiques ; de planifier et de gérer sur le plan des infrastructures. Différents types de publics s'adressent désormais aux communes pour avoir un accès régulier ou occasionnel à des pratiques qui sont orientées vers l'initiation sportive, l'entraînement, la performance de haut niveau, le spectacle, mais aussi de plus en plus vers l'entretien physique, la quête de sociabilité et d'activités ludiques . Il n'est donc pas étonnant que le financement du sport par les municipalités ait crû de 73 % en francs constants au cours des années 80, avec un déplacement progressif des dépenses d'investissement vers celles de fonctionnement (Bayeux, 1993).

Les incertitudes de l'État en action

Ce processus de « municipalisation » du sport (Bonnes, 1984) tend donc à déplacer les significations et les enjeux du « national » vers le « local ». Mais dans le même temps, une autre dynamique – l'ouverture sur l'Europe et la perspective de la liberté de circulation des biens et des personnes au sein des pays de la Communauté, initialement prévue pour 1993 – oblige les États-membres à se concerter sur la reconnaissance des formations et des diplômes, y compris dans le domaine sportif. Dans ce contexte, le système français de formation aux « métiers du sport » pose problème aux autres pays qui, pour la plupart, n'ont pas de diplôme équivalent à celui des brevets d'États. Aussi, le gouvernement est-il amené à légiférer dans le sens d'un assouplissement des conditions d'enseignement, d'encadrement ou d'animation contre rémunération, dans le domaine sportif (loi du 13-07-92). Le problème de la formation des intervenants professionnels dans ce secteur de la vie sociale est d'ailleurs l'un de ceux qui restent sans solution politique au cours des années 80 et encore actuellement (deux ministères, celui de la Jeunesse et des Sports et celui de l'Enseignement supérieur étant en concurrence plus qu'en complémentarité dans ce domaine).

Si l'intégration administrative des enseignants d'éducation physique au ministère de l'Éducation nationale ainsi que les mesures d'intégration universitaire des STAPS ont eu des effets bénéfiques sur l'affirmation de l'identité professionnelle des enseignants concernés, l'absence de coordination interministérielle a favorisé le développement de deux formations concurrentes, en particulier dans le champ du loisir et du « management » sportif : l'une en développement dans les universités (essentiellement les UFR STAPS), l'autre en réorganisation sous l'égide de la Jeunesse et des Sports, par la transformation des contenus de formation de certains brevets d'État ou la création de nouveaux diplômes destinés à répondre à l'évolution du marché. La concurrence sans arbitrage ministériel entre ces deux entités gouvernementales n'a fait qu'accentuer la confusion dans ce domaine. Et la tentative de rapprochement qui avait donné lieu aux Assises nationales des métiers du sport, organisée conjointement par les deux ministères en 1991, a été sans suite.

Si la politique nationale de formation aux métiers du sport est confuse, il en est de même pour celle de la recherche, partagée, là aussi sans coordination, entre les laboratoires universitaires, ceux dépendant de la Jeunesse et des Sports, ceux liés au Centre National de la Recherche Scientifique (CNRS), sans parler des laboratoires d'entreprises.

Il s'agit bien là de deux enjeux actuels pour les responsables politiques nationaux. Pourtant, ce ne sont pas les seuls, et d'autres peuvent sembler plus urgents en raison de leur impact social immédiat. Le plus évident est le problème de la canalisation de la violence sociale qui s'exprime à l'occasion de spectacles sportifs, essentiellement en football. Le caractère ostentatoire de cette violence en direct, sous l'œil des caméras, constitue une difficulté particulière pour les pouvoirs publics détenteurs du « monopole de la contrainte physique » (M. Weber, 1971). Les « représentants de l'ordre » sont aux prises avec des débordements épisodiques et isolés de supporters qui participent par ailleurs au processus de ritualisation d'une violence canalisée, réglée et symbolisée dans les spectacles sportifs. Mais désormais, ils font également face à une violence organisée, systématique, répondant à d'autres règles – anomique pour les responsables politiques et sportifs – qui constituent autant de simulacres de la violence ordonnée par les règles de la confrontation sportive.

Si la violence des *hooligans* tend à devenir, à l'échelon national, un symbole de contestation, sans projet ni perspective, d'un État incapable de sortir de la gestion des contraintes économiques et sociales et de susciter au sein d'une partie de la jeunesse des élans et des perspectives mobilisatrices (Vigarello, 1985 ; Dunning, 1994), à l'échelon local, le sport est – après une période de mise en question – de nouveau paré de toutes les vertus, pour maintenir ou reconstituer le lien social dans des zones urbaines où les situations sont cependant très différentes, selon les villes et les quartiers. J.P. Augustin, reprenant des éléments de l'enquête réalisée par l'Institut National de la Statistique et des Études

Économiques (l'INSEE), indique que 546 quartiers sont identifiés comme étant dans une condition détériorée. Au sein de ces quartiers, les situations sont encore loin d'être uniformes : « la majorité d'entre eux ne fait que refléter le déclin économique de l'agglomération où ils sont situés, mais 150 présentent le profil de « vrais lieux d'exclusion » et parmi eux, une trentaine cumulent les handicaps et apparaissent comme les plus problématiques (Augustin, 1993).

Les opérations « anti-été-chaud » lancées par le ministère de la Jeunesse et des Sports et organisées par les collectivités locales constituent autant de tentatives de régulation d'une violence sociale quotidienne qui prend parfois des formes exacerbées et destructrices, en des occasions diverses – l'intervention parfois maladroite ou répressive des « forces de l'ordre » n'étant pas la moins importante. Dans ce processus de délégitimation d'un ordre social au sein d'une partie de la jeunesse, la question de l'adhésion à un système démocratique se pose de manière aiguë pour ceux que l'absence de travail et de perspectives touche de plein fouet. Si les pratiques sportives peuvent aider certains à reconquérir « une bonne image d'eux-mêmes, de savoir qu'ils peuvent progresser et s'associer à d'autres dans un projet commun » (Augustin, 1993), il ne s'agit là cependant que d'opérations « d'urgence ».

L'enjeu de la définition d'une politique sportive globale de la ville s'impose donc avec d'autant plus de force (Chantelat, Fodimbin & Camy, 1994). Elle ne peut relever uniquement des collectivités territoriales. Elle ne peut se limiter – sans sous-estimer leur importance – aux activités scolaires, parascolaires, associatives et d'animation de quartier. Elle doit intégrer la nécessité d'aménagement d'espaces adaptés à des pratiques de loisir et de santé ; elle doit par ailleurs intégrer les enjeux d'affirmation du sentiment d'appartenance à une collectivité ; les rencontres sociales organisées, et pas seulement sous l'angle des spectacles sportifs, ayant leur rôle à jouer dans cette perspective.

Les types d'action du politique

Pour conclure, comment peut-on caractériser les dynamiques de construction sociale et historique des politiques sportives dans la société française de la seconde partie du XXᵉ siècle ?

Une première forme d'intervention de l'État porte sur le soutien (direct et indirect) au développement des pratiques physiques dans la société. Ce type d'action prédomine dans l'après-guerre, sous la IVᵉ République, lorsque les efforts de la planification étatique sont concentrés sur des objectifs de « reconstruction » puis de « modernisation ». Dans ce schéma, les politiques spécifiques en matière d'éducation physique et de sport restent secondes : elles accompagnent le développement – ou la stagnation – du secteur considéré en laissant l'initiative aux acteurs de la société civile.

Le second type d'action de l'État est caractérisé par la définition politique des orientations majeures dans le secteur de l'éducation physique et du sport. Il implique la mise en œuvre d'une politique globale où l'action d'orientation de l'État devient centrale. C'est le cas de figure esquissé à la Libération et développé au cours des années 60 où la politique sportive française s'articule autour de l'intégration des pratiques du sport de compétition comme activité de référence pour toute pratique physique dans les institutions et le paysage français. Ce type d'action est partiellement coercitif, mais il ne peut se réaliser sans le consentement actif des principaux acteurs chargés de le mettre en œuvre.

Le troisième type d'action du politique répond à la complexification de l'espace social sportif. Il porte plus sur la régulation générale des compétences d'action à travers une nouvelle répartition des pouvoirs. Les acteurs de la société civile se voient renforcés et confortés dans leurs responsabilités et leurs capacités d'orientation : les professionnels de l'éducation physique dans leur secteur, les cadres politiques, administratifs et techniques dans les fédérations sportives, les entreprises de biens et de services sportifs dans le leur. Ce retrait relatif de l'État national n'implique pas d'ailleurs un désengagement du politique. Il s'agit plutôt d'une redistribution des responsabilités, principalement vers les collectivités territoriales (en particulier les communes) et secondairement vers des structures supranationales : l'Union Européenne, mais aussi le Conseil de l'Europe. Ce troisième type d'action s'est mis en place progressivement, par tâtonnements successifs, dans la société française des années 70 et 80. Il place constamment l'État en situation de régulation d'un espace social marqué par des évolutions rapides dans les comportements et les modes d'organisation. Il implique par ailleurs de nouvelles formes de médiation entre les responsables politiques et ceux de la société civile.

Ainsi, depuis la fin de la Seconde Guerre mondiale, les systèmes d'action de l'État en matière de sport et d'éducation physique ont considérablement évolué. L'action de régulation administrative l'emporte sous la IVe République, lorsque s'imposent les contraintes économiques liées à l'effort de reconstruction et de modernisation d'après-guerre, associées aux contraintes politiques du système parlementaire et aux problèmes de la décolonisation. L'action planifiée sous l'égide de l'État s'impose sous la Ve République, dans des conditions économiques favorables. Dans ce cas, l'action «rationnelle-légale» (Weber, 1971) est en harmonie avec des objectifs politiques clairs (mais qui tendent à ramener la pratique sportive à la pratique compétitive) et soutenue par les principaux acteurs du sport organisé et de l'éducation physique. Ce soutien favorise la légitimation du modèle compétitif comme référence pour toute pratique physique au sein de la société française. L'action médiatrice de l'État se met progressivement en place au cours des années 70, sous le double effet des contraintes économiques (et budgétaires qui en sont la conséquence) et du développement de formes de pratiques sportives renouvelées, en particulier des loisirs sportifs. Face à ces changements, les acteurs du politique tendent à se cantonner dans leur rôle de régulation du sport et de l'éducation physique, en se concentrant sur certains enjeux (le contrôle de la violence, la formation scolaire, la représentation nationale sur la scène internationale), et en laissant aux acteurs de la société civile les initiatives de la structuration des nouvelles formes de loisirs sportifs. Ainsi, l'action de l'État qui se veut globale (définir les règles et les faire accepter) dans l'ensemble du champ des pratiques physiques, reste-t-elle le plus souvent cantonnée dans des interventions sectorielles, en réaction à des problèmes du moment. Il s'agit d'une difficulté actuelle rencontrée par les représentants de l'État en France. Elle se situe sur deux plans différents, mais qui peuvent se rencontrer.

Le premier plan a trait à la légitimité de l'action étatique. Le problème est posé par les tenants de philosophies politiques différentes. Les partisans d'une «démocratie républicaine» mettent l'accent sur le primat du politique, les tenants d'une «démocratie libérale» privilégient l'économique. Ces conceptions se traduisent par des visions différenciées de la place de l'État dans l'orientation et la gestion du sport et de l'éducation physique. Les premiers privilégient l'intervention des «pouvoirs publics» garants de l'intérêt général, y compris dans le développement des loisirs sportifs ; les seconds insistent sur le dynamisme de la société civile, l'État devant intervenir pour corriger les injustices sociales (dans l'accès au sport et à l'éducation physique par exemple). Ce débat recouvre en partie la traditionnelle opposition «gauche-droite» dans la société française.

Le second plan est sans doute plus difficile à cerner. Il porte sur le rôle «pédagogique» de l'État (Gramsci, 1975). En se mettant progressivement en retrait dans la définition des orientations du sport, particulièrement des pratiques ludiques et de santé, en se cantonnant le plus souvent dans des actions partielles (prévention, formation des cadres et d'enseignants, sportifs de haut niveau, rythmes scolaires) ou perçues comme telles, les responsables politiques et les agents administratifs de l'État ont perdu une part de leur crédibilité d'action. En ce sens, la nécessaire acceptation, par les destinataires, des politiques ministérielles – en premier lieu, le ministère de la Jeunesse et des Sports, mais aussi ceux de l'Enseignement supérieur, de la Ville, de l'Intérieur et de l'Aménagement du territoire... – pose désormais problème en matière d'activités physiques et sportives. Qui a la légitimité d'action ? Avec quelles formes de pratiques reconnues, acceptées, à l'école, pendant les loisirs, les vacances, mais aussi au sein des organisations sportives responsables des pratiques sportives institutionnelles ? Les représentants de l'État en France éprouvent quelques difficultés à demeurer des interlocuteurs de premier plan dans ce type de débat.

Bibliographie

« Activité physique, éducation et sciences humaines » (s. d.). *Les cahiers du centre d'études et de recherches marxistes, 43.*

AMAR, M. (1987). *Nés pour courir, sports, pouvoirs et rebellions, 1944-1958.* Presse Universitaire de Grenoble.

ANDREFF, W. (1989). *Économie politique du sport.* Dalloz.

Anthropologie du sport, perspectives critiques (1991). Actes de colloque, ANDIHA, Matrice, Quel corps ?

ARNAUD, P. (1983). *Les savoirs du corps.* Presses Universitaires de Lyon.

AUGUSTIN J.P. (1993). Relégation urbaine et pratiques sportives. *Sciences et sociétés, 30,* LERASS, Toulouse, 213-217.

BAYEUX P. (1993). *La filière sportive dans les collectivités locales.* CNFPT.

BONNES, R. (1984). La municipalisation du sport... *Sports et sociétés contemporaines,* SEFSS, 43-49.

BROHM, J.M. (1975). *Corps et politique.* J.P. Delarge.

BROHM, J.M. (1976). *Sociologie politique du sport.* J.P. Delarge.

BOUQUIN, C. *et al.* (1985). *Le service public des APS,* R. ESP.

BOURDIEU, P. (1980). Comment peut-on être sportif ? *In Questions de sociologie,* Minuit.

BOURLIAUD, G. (1993). Installations sportives, collectivités locales... *Revue juridique et économique du sport, 24,* 93-1.

CALLEDE, J.P. (1987). *L'esprit sportif.* Presses Universitaires de Bordeaux, MSHA.

CALLEDE, J.P. et DANE, M. (1991). *Sociologie des politiques sportives et locales,* MSHA.

CHANTELAT, M., FUDIMBI, M., et CAMY, J. (1994). *Sociabilités sportives et formes de citoyenneté des jeunes...* Rapport de recherche, Université Lyon I, UFRAPS.

COT, J.P. et MOUNIER, J.P. (1974). *Pour une sociologie politique,* 2 t.

CRESPIN, M. (1978). (Conseil Économique et Social). *Les différents aspects d'une politique de développement des activités sportives...* Journal Officiel, Avis et Rapports, n° 2, janvier.

DAHL, R. (1973). *L'analyse politique contemporaine.* R. Laffont.

DAVISSE, A. et LOUVEAU, C. (1991). *Sports, école, société : la part des hommes.* Actip.

DEFRANCE, J. (1987). *L'excellence corporelle, la formation des activités physiques et sportives modernes, 1770-1914.* Presses Universitaires de Rennes, Revue STAPS.

DEFRANCEJ. et POCIELLO, C. (1993). Structure and evolution of the field of sports in France (1960-1990). *In International Review for the Society of Sport* 28(1), 1-21.

DEFRANCE, J. *et al.* (1994). *Sport et pouvoirs au XXe siècle.* Presses universitaires de Grenoble.

DELETANG, B. (1979). *Sport – histoire – idéologie. L'exemple français du sport travailliste.* INSEP.

DION, L. (1972). *Société et politique, la vie des groupes.* 2 t., Presses de l'Université Laval, Québec.

DUMAZEDIER, J. et RIPERT, A. (1966). *Loisirs et culture.* Seuil.

DUNNING, E. et ELIAS, M. (1994). *Sport et civilisation, la violence maîtrisée.* Fayard.

DUPEUX G. (1969). *La France de 1945 à 1969.* A. Colin, Coll. U2.

EHRENBERG, A. (1980). Aimez-vous les stades ? Les origines historiques des politiques sportives en France (1870-1930). *Recherches, 43,* avril, 280 p.

EHRENBERG, A. (1983). *Le corps militaire : politique et pédagogique en démocratie.* Aubier-Montagne.

EHRENBERG, A. (1986). Des stades sans dieux. *Le Débat, (40),* mai-sept, 47-61.

ELIAS, N. (1976). Sport et violence. *Actes de la recherche en sciences sociales,* déc. 1976.

ENAULT, G. *et al.* (1979). *Le sport en France. Bilan et perspectives.* Berger Levrault.

GAY-LESCOT, J.L. (1991). *Sport et éducation physique sous Vichy,* Presses Universitaires de Lyon.

Géopolitique du sport (1990). Actes de colloque, Université de Franche-Comté.

GIDDENS, A. (1987). *La constitution de la société.* PUF.

GRAMSCI, A. (1975). *Gramsci dans le texte.* Éditions sociales.

HABERMAS, J. (1985). *Après Marx,* Fayard.

HARVEY, J. et CANTELON, H. (1988). *Sport et pouvoir.* Presses Universitaire d'Ottawa.

HOUEL, J. (1979). *Le rôle de l'État dans la pratique sociale des APS (en France sous la Ve République).* INSEP.

JAMET, M. (1980). *Les sports et l'État au Québec.* Montréal, Éditions St-Martin.

JAMET, M. (1989). *Pour une analyse sociétale des pratiques physiques en France.* Thèse d'État, Université Toulouse-le-Mirail.

JAMET, M. (1991). *Le sport dans la société, entre raison(s) et passion(s).* L'harmattan.

JOBERT, P. et MULLER, P. (1987). *L'État en action.* PUF.

LE BOULCH , J. (1978). *Face au sport.* Éditions ESF.

LE POGAM, Y. (1979). *Démocratisation du sport : mythe ou réalité ?* J.P. Delarge.

MORIN, E. (1962). *L'esprit du temps.* Grasset.

MEYNAUD, J. (1986). *Sport et politique,* Payot, 321 p.

PAILLOU, N. (1986). Conseil Économique et Social. *Les trois enjeux du sport français.* Dalloz.

Philosophie politique (1993). n° 2-3, PUF

POCIELLO, C. (1981). *Sports et société.* Vigot.

POULANTZAS, N. (1968 et 1971). *Pouvoir politique et classes sociales.* Maspéro, 2 t.

ROSENVALON, P. (1983). *La crise de l'État-Providence.* Seuil.

Sport, culture et répression (1968). *Partisans , 43,* 199 p.

Sport et changement social (1987). *Actes de colloque,* MSHA, 343 p.

Sport et développement humain (1975). Éditions Sociales, 320 p.

Sport et société (1983). *Problèmes politiques et sociaux, 407,* La Documentation française.

Sports et sociétés contemporaines (1983). *Actes de colloque,* SFSS, Paris, INSEP.

Sport: l'autre politique des activités physiques (1980). Club socialiste du livre.

TOURAINE, A. (1973). *Production de la société*. Seuil.

TOURAINE, A. (1984). *Le retour de l'acteur, essai de sociologie*. Fayard.

VIGARELLO, G. (1985). Les deux violences sportives. *Esprit*, 8-9, 17-19.

VIGARELLO, G et MONGIN, O. (1987). Le nouvel âge du sport. *Esprit*, avril, 317 p.

Ville, sports, citoyenneté (1992). Actes du colloque, Brest.

WEBER, M. (1971). *Économie et société*. Plon.

Michel JAMET
La politique du sport et de l'éducation physique en France

RÉSUMÉ

L'étude porte sur les politiques nationales en matière de sport et d'éducation physique en France. L'action de l'État est analysée pour la période couvrant la seconde partie du XXe siècle dans une double perspective : comme processus de régulation et de légitimation des pratiques, et comme ensemble d'interventions marquées par des incertitudes, des engagements partiels, des enjeux conjoncturels. De l'analyse des dynamiques de l'État en action émergent trois types d'interventions : une action de soutien partiel aux initiatives sportives de la société civile ; une action de définition des orientations et des règles d'organisation du sport et de l'éducation physique ; une action de régulation et de médiation entre les acteurs du champ.

Michel JAMET
Sports and Physical Education Politics in France

ABSTRACT

This study focused on national policies regarding sport and physical education in France. State intervention was analyzed during the period covering the second half of the twentieth century, from two perspectives: as a process that regulated and legitimized leisure practices, and as a set of interventions marked by indecision, partial commitments and economic restraints. An analysis of the government's actions showed three types of intervention: partial support for sports organisations' initiatives; definition of the orientations and rules for organizing sports and physical education; and regulation and mediation between the various groups involved.

Michel JAMET
La política del deporte y de la educación física en Francia.

RESUMEN

El estudio se refiere a las políticas nacionales en materia de deporte y educación física en Francia. La acción del Estado es analizada por el período que cubre la segunda parte del siglo XX con una doble perspectiva: como proceso de regulación y de legitimación de las prácticas, y como un conjunto de intervenciones marcadas por incertidumbres, compromisos parciales y apuestas coyunturales. Del análisis de las dinámicas del Estado en acción, emergen tres tipos de intervenciones: una acción de sostén parcial a las iniciativas deportivas de la sociedad civil, una acción de definición de las orientaciones y de las reglas de organización del deporte y de la educación física, y una acción de regulación y mediación entre los actores del campo.

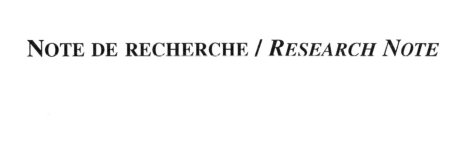

NOTE DE RECHERCHE / *RESEARCH NOTE*

Niveau de pratique de loisirs et influence des caractéristiques personnelles et environnementales chez des personnes ayant une déficience motrice

Luc NOREAU

Centre François-Charon
et Département de physiothérapie
Université Laval.
Québec, Canada.

Gilles MURPHY
Georges TREMBLAY
Roger CANTIN

Centre François-Charon
Québec, Canada

Introduction

Une maladie, un traumatisme ou une anomalie congénitale peuvent perturber la réalisation des activités quotidiennes et ainsi diminuer la qualité de vie et l'intégration sociale des personnes atteintes. Ces conséquences sont fréquentes puisque l'*Enquête sur la santé et les limitations d'activités (ESLA*, Lavigne et Morin, 1991 ; MSSS, 1992) a estimé le nombre de personnes aux prises avec une incapacité au Canada à plus de 3 millions (dont 830 000 Québécois). Ce nombre correspond approximativement à 12-14 % de la population, pourcentage important et qui risque d'augmenter avec le vieillissement prévisible de la population.

Modèle de réadaptation

Afin de minimiser l'impact des incapacités, ces personnes peuvent bénéficier d'une intervention d'adaptation/réadaptation pendant une période de temps plus ou moins longue. Cette intervention est définie comme « le regroupement sous forme d'un processus personnalisé, coordonné et limité dans le temps, des différents moyens mis en oeuvre pour permettre à une personne handicapée[1] de développer ses capacités physiques et mentales et son potentiel d'adaptation sociale » (OPHQ, 1984).

Comme une approche globale et interdisciplinaire est de plus en plus valorisée, ce mode de fonctionnement nécessite un cadre de référence afin de favoriser une meilleure coordination des interventions auprès de la personne atteinte d'incapacités. L'Organisation mondiale de la santé (OMS, 1981) a proposé un cadre conceptuel : la classification internationale des déficiences, incapacités et handicaps (CIDIH), dont l'utilisation permet une vision d'ensemble du processus de réadaptation. Ce cadre conceptuel est en constante évolution, et des modifications au modèle original (*Tableau 1 et Figure 1*) ont été proposées afin de

FIGURE 1

**Modèle conceptuel du processus d'apparition
des situations de handicap (CQCIDIH)**

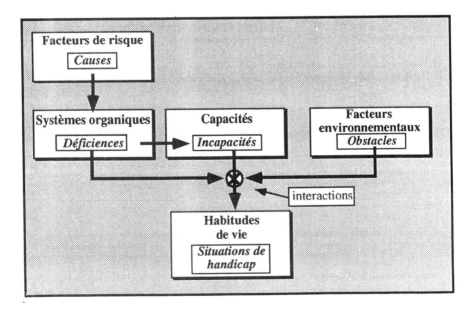

---

1. Il faudrait lire « personne ayant des incapacités » (Comité québécois de la CIDIH, Fougeyrollas, 1991).

permettre de considérer davantage l'interaction entre les caractéristiques de l'individu (déficiences et incapacités) et son milieu de vie (facteurs environnementaux) dans la détermination des situations de handicap (Fougeyrollas, 1991).

TABLEAU 1

**Définitions des concepts reliés à l'apparition
des situations de handicap (Fougeyrollas, 1991)**

Déficience	Toute anomalie ou modification physiologique, anatomique ou histologique d'un système du corps humain.
Incapacité	Toute réduction résultant de la déficience, des activités physiques et mentales considérées comme normales pour un être humain (selon ses caractéristiques biologiques).
Facteurs environnementaux	L'ensemble des dimensions sociales, culturelles et écologiques qui déterminent l'organisation et le contexte d'une société.
Habitudes de vie	Activités qui assurent la survie et l'épanouissement d'une personne dans sa société tout au long de son existence. Ce sont les activités quotidiennes et domestiques ainsi que les rôles sociaux valorisés par le contexte socioculturel de la personne selon son âge, son sexe et son identité sociale et personnelle.
Situation de handicap	Perturbation, pour une personne, dans la réalisation de ses habitudes de vie compte tenu de son âge, de son sexe, de son identité socioculturelle, résultant d'une part, de ses déficiences ou de ses incapacités, et d'autre part, d'obstacles découlant de facteurs environnementaux.

Intégration sociale

Au cours des deux dernières décennies, le concept d'intégration sociale est apparu un critère important de réussite des interventions d'adaptation et de ré-adaptation. Il devenait impératif de favoriser le retour de la personne dans son milieu de vie ainsi que sa participation à la vie sociale de ce milieu – donc de minimiser la probabilité d'apparition de situations de handicap. L'intégration sociale est définie comme la participation des personnes ayant une ou des incapacités aux interactions et interrelations sociales qui surviennent lors d'activités normatives dans des lieux et contextes valorisés, en présence des personnes sans incapacité (Flynn, 1993 ; Commission des centres de réadaptation, 1992). Malgré des interventions soutenues de plusieurs professionnels de la réadaptation, tout indique que l'intégration sociale de la personne atteinte d'inca-pacités est souvent limitée (Flynn, 1993). L'atteinte de résultats plus probants est extrêmement justifiée et nécessite un examen plus objectif de la contribution potentielle de certaines interventions au processus menant à l'intégration sociale.

Loisir et santé

L'intervention en loisir fait partie de ces nouvelles disciplines de la réadaptation dont l'impact est trop peu documenté. Avant d'aborder l'aspect spécifique de cette intervention auprès des personnes ayant une ou des incapacités, il importe de situer le loisir dans un contexte de santé et de bien-être, et d'en vérifier la contribution potentielle. De façon opérationnelle, le loisir désigne une activité pratiquée dans un contexte de liberté et de spontanéité (Tremblay, 1991). Bien qu'il puisse être pratiqué pour lui-même, par plaisir et liberté, le loisir peut également représenter un moyen d'atteindre des objectifs particuliers (sécurisation, adaptation du rythme de fonctionnement, valorisation et intégration sociale). Sur le plan de la santé, certaines évidences permettent de croire que l'impact du loisir se situe aux niveaux psychologique, physique, social et spirituel (Caldwell et Smith, 1988). Par exemple, Iso-Ahola (1982,1983) mentionne qu'il réduit les sensations d'impuissance et de manque de contrôle, et ainsi contribue à la perception de compétence personnelle (*self-efficacy*) et au maintien d'une bonne santé psychologique. Bien que la pratique d'activités physiques favorise le maintien d'une bonne santé physique, certaines de ces activités comportent également un impact social, car elles facilitent les contacts interindividuels. Il en est de même pour des activités à caractère communautaire (bénévolat) qui, à certains moments, sont plus pratiquées pour l'occasion qu'elles offrent à la personne d'établir des contacts sociaux que pour de simples raisons altruistes (Caldwell et Smith, 1988). Enfin, certains résultats ont montré que le loisir peut servir de compensation partielle à un faible niveau de satisfaction au travail (Spreitzer et Snyder, 1987).

Loisir et incapacités

En considérant ces divers bénéfices sur la qualité de vie de l'individu, on peut faire l'hypothèse que le loisir possède des caractéristiques intrinsèques qui favorisent le processus d'intégration sociale, surtout lorsque les incapacités de la personne limitent sa participation sociale (travail rémunéré, études, etc.). Toutefois, peu d'études ont documenté la question de la participation au loisir des personnes ayant une ou des incapacités, et de son impact réel sur la qualité de vie et l'intégration sociale. Niemi *et al.* (1988) ont étudié la qualité de vie chez 46 personnes ayant subi un accident cérébrovasculaire en fonction de la récupération et de la reprise d'un certain nombre d'activités (travail, loisirs, activités domestiques et familiales). Malgré une récupération fonctionnelle adéquate, 83 % des personnes ont indiqué une détérioration de leur qualité de vie après une période de quatre ans. Un pourcentage élevé de personnes ont noté une telle détérioration sur les plans du travail (39 %) et du loisir (80 %) en comparaison avec leur situation prémorbide. Dans une étude effectuée auprès de 344 personnes ayant une ou des incapacités, Kinney et Coyle (1992) ont observé que la satisfaction tirée des activités de loisirs constituait un fort prédicteur de la satisfaction de vie (*life satisfaction*) (42 % de la variance expliquée) ; ils ont suggéré l'inclusion d'une intervention en loisir lors du processus de réadaptation afin d'assurer le maintien de certaines habiletés susceptibles d'être affectées par la présence d'incapacités.

Objectifs de l'étude

Bien que certains bénéfices reliés à l'intervention en loisir auprès des personnes ayant une ou des incapacités apparaissent probables, une démonstration sans équivoque de ces bénéfices n'est toujours pas disponible, surtout quant à son potentiel d'influence sur l'intégration sociale. De plus, on note l'absence d'information relative au niveau de pratique de loisirs jugé normal pour ce type de personnes.

Le présent projet vise donc à : 1) déterminer le niveau réel de pratique de loisirs d'un échantillon de personnes ayant une déficience motrice ; 2) déterminer le niveau de pratique de loisirs pouvant être considéré comme une « norme de pratique » pour différents types d'activités ; 3) comparer le niveau de pratique de loisirs de l'échantillon à celui de la population québécoise ; et 4) déterminer, de façon exploratoire, les caractéristiques personnelles et environnementales susceptibles de favoriser ou de limiter la pratique de loisirs des personnes ayant une déficience motrice.

Compte tenu de l'utilisation grandissante des propositions du CQCIDIH en tant que cadre de référence clinique ou de planification de la réadaptation au Québec (MSSS, 1992), ce modèle conceptuel a été utilisé pour la planification du présent projet.

Méthodologie

Recrutement des sujets

L'échantillonnage et le recrutement ont été effectués à partir des personnes possédant un dossier actif au centre François-Charon entre avril 1991 et décembre 1992 (n = 1824). Elles étaient réparties à l'intérieur de huit programmes d'intervention selon le type de déficience : lésion médullaire, amputation, maladies dégénératives, traumatisme crânien, accident vasculaire-cérébral, maladie rhumatismale, polytraumatisme et neuropathie, déficience motrice cérébrale. Comme le contexte de cette étude (faisabilité, critères d'inclusion) ne permettait pas un échantillonnage aléatoire, la participation volontaire des sujets n'a donc pas permis de constituer un échantillon rigoureusement représentatif des proportions d'individus inscrits dans les différents programmes. Les critères d'inclusion – âge = 18-65 ans et résidence sur le territoire de la Communauté urbaine de Québec – ont permis de retenir 350 personnes qui ont été jointes par lettre. Un total de 112 personnes ont signifié leur intention de participer à l'étude.

Procédures de collecte des données

Un questionnaire portant sur les caractéristiques de la personne (socio-démographiques, occupationnelles, fonctionnelles, mobilité, soutien pour la réalisation des activités quotidiennes) et de son environnement (barrières architecturales, moyens de déplacement et transport) a été élaboré. Certaines sections ont été tirées d'instruments validés (p. ex., l'*Index de Barthel* pour la mesure des habiletés fonctionnelles) ou ont été inspirées par les travaux récents de la CIDIH et de l'*ESLA*.

La technique du budget-temps a également été utilisée pour déterminer la pratique de loisirs de la personne sur une base hebdomadaire (7 jours consécutifs). Sous forme d'un journal quotidien, l'outil permet l'enregistrement des principales activités réalisées au cours d'une journée (de 6h00 à 24h00, par intervalles de 30 minutes) ainsi que le lieu de l'activité (domicile, chez des ami(e)s ou dans la communauté) et le nombre de personnes présentes.

Ces instruments de mesure ont fait l'objet de deux phases préexpérimentales auprès d'un nombre restreint de sujets (n = 18) afin de vérifier la compréhension des consignes et les procédures de collecte de données, et, le cas échéant, d'apporter les correctifs appropriés. L'utilisation du mode de collecte par entrevue et d'un interviewer unique durant toute la phase expérimentale a été retenue à la suite de ces préexpérimentations.

Les sujets étaient rencontrés individuellement par l'interviewer à deux reprises à intervalle d'une semaine (2 x 1 heure). La première rencontre permettait de remplir le questionnaire portant sur les caractéristiques personnelles et environnementales, et de fournir les renseignements et consignes relatifs à l'utilisation du budget-temps. Pendant la période de 7 jours qui suivait, chaque participant devait enregistrer avec le plus de précision possible ses activités journalières (travail, loisirs, etc.). La deuxième rencontre permettait de vérifier l'exactitude des données contenues dans le budget-temps et d'identifier avec la personne (ou ses proches) les activités considérées comme du loisir.

Traitement des données et analyses statistiques

Les budgets-temps ont été analysés individuellement, et les activités de loisirs ont été codifiées en fonction du jour de la semaine, du type d'activités, de la durée, du lieu et du nombre de personnes présentes. Ces activités étaient regroupées en quatre types d'activités principales : 1) *Associatif* : bénévolat, activités religieuses, activités liées à une organisation ; 2) *Distraction* : assister à des manifestations sportives ou culturelles ; 3) *Sports et passe-temps* : participer à des activités sportives, pratiquer un instrument de musique, artisanat ; et 4) *Médias et communication : écoute de la télévision, journaux, etc.* Ces quatre catégories ont été intégralement tirées d'une enquête de Statistiques Canada sur l'emploi du temps (Mercier, 1990). Cette procédure a permis de comparer la pratique de loisirs de l'échantillon à celle de la population québécoise.

L'analyse des résultats a débuté par une description de la pratique de loisirs à l'aide de statistiques descriptives (moyenne, écart-type). De plus, une représentation graphique par diagrammes en boîte (*box plot*) a servi à illustrer le niveau de pratique de loisirs (totale et par type d'activités).

L'association entre la pratique de loisirs et certaines caractéristiques personnelles et environnementales (âge, scolarité, etc.) a été vérifiée à l'aide de l'analyse de régression et de la corrélation (Pearson ou Spearman). Le niveau de signification des différences de pratique de loisirs entre les degrés d'un même facteur (p. ex., occupation, sexe) a été vérifié par le test-t ou l'analyse de la variance. Ces différences ont été illustrées graphiquement par des diagrammes en boîte. À partir des données brutes, les valeurs de chaque décile (10e, 20e, 30e, etc.) ont été fournies par le programme SYSTAT 5.2 pour la pratique totale et pour chaque catégorie d'activités.

Résultats

TABLEAU 2

**Répartition des sujets de l'échantillon
et proportions attendues par programme-cadre**

Programme-cadre	Nombre	%	Proportions attendues *
Lésions médullaires	n = 13	13.4 %	14.6 %
Amputations	n = 7	7.2 %	15.1 %
Maladies dégénératives (S.E.P.)	n = 24	24.8 %	6.3 %
Traumatismes craniens	n = 12	12.4 %	8.3 %
Accidents vasculaires-cérébraux	n = 14	14.4 %	33.4 %
Maladies rhumatismales	n = 15	15.5 %	7.4 %
Polytraumatismes et neuropathies	n = 4	4.1 %	2.1 %
Déficiences motrices cérébrales	n = 8	8.2 %	12.8 %
Total	n = 97	100 %	100 %

* proportions attendues de sujets selon les personnes inscrites dans les différents programmes entre avril 91 et août 92.

TABLEAU 3

Caractéristiques de l'échantillon (n = 97)

Sexe	Hommes	Femmes		
	54	43		
Occupation principale	Emploi	Études	Autres	
	15	17	65	
Revenu personnel ($)	< 10 000	10 000 - 30 000	> 30 000	
	47	25	28	
Autonomie fonctionnelle (Index de Barthel)	< 44	44-80	81-99	100
	11	25	29	32
Scolarité terminée	Primaire	Secondaire	Collégiale	Universitaire
	19	44	15	19

Description de l'échantillon

Quatre-vingt-dix-sept sujets (âge moyen = 42 ± 12 ans) parmi les 112 personnes initialement recrutées ont effectué le processus expérimental complet : rencontres 1 et 2, budget-temps). La participation volontaire a entraîné une disproportion dans le nombre de sujets de certains programmes (Tableau 2). Ainsi, l'échantillon comptait une surreprésentation de personnes souffrant de maladies dégénératives (p. ex., sclérose en plaques, dystrophie) et une sous-représentation de celles qui avaient subi un accident vasculaire-cérébral. La répartition des sujets par sexe indique une plus grande proportion de sujets masculins (Tableau 3). Seulement le tiers des sujets (32) ont mentionné avoir un emploi ou être aux études, ce qui dénote un faible taux de maintien des activités professionnelles. Près de 50 % des sujets ont rapporté un revenu personnel annuel inférieur à 10 000 dollars malgré une scolarité moyenne de 12,1 ± 4,7 années. Enfin, la mesure de l'autonomie fonctionnelle a révélé que les déficiences motrices ont un impact très variable selon les individus. Un score à l'indice de Barthel inférieur à 44 indiquait un faible niveau d'autonomie dans les activités quotidiennes ; à l'opposé, un score de 100 suggérait un faible impact de la déficience physique sur l'autonomie fonctionnelle.

FIGURE 2

FIGURE 2

**Comparaison du temps de pratique de loisirs
selon les types d'activités**

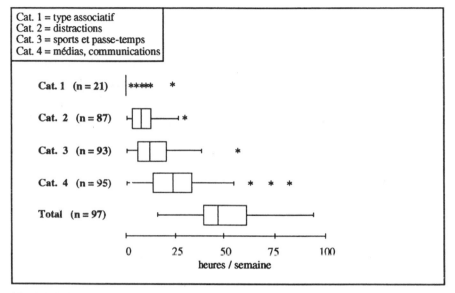

Légende de la distribution de fréquence
d'un diagramme en boîte

PC25 = percentile 25, PC75 = percentile 75
* Valeurs extrêmes à l'extérieur
de la distribution.

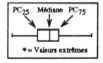

Pratiques de loisir

Comptabilisé à partir des budgets-temps, le temps moyen de pratique de loisirs chez les sujets se situait à 48 h/sem., et 50 % de l'échantillon présentaient une pratique de loisirs se situant entre 40 et 60 h/sem. (Figure 2). Toutefois, on observe une grande variabilité dans le temps de pratique : il était inférieur à 20 h/sem. pour certains et supérieur à 90 h/sem. pour d'autres. Les loisirs de type associatif (bénévolat, activités liées à une organisation) étaient pratiquées par 21 personnes, et seulement 9 s'y adonnaient plus de 5 h/sem. Les activités de type distractions (cinéma, musée, visite, etc.) et celles de type sports et passe-temps (marche, artisanat, musique, etc.) étaient pratiquées par plus de 90 % des sujets, avec une valeur médiane respective de 7 h/sem. et 12 h/sem. Les activités de type médias et communications (radio, télévision, lecture, conversation) étaient les plus pratiquées par les sujets de l'échantillon, avec une valeur médiane de 24 h/sem. ; elles comptaient globalement pour la moitié de la pratique totale de loisirs. La distribution de la pratique de loisirs (totale ou par type d'activités) peut également être visualisée à partir d'une courbe de percentiles (Figure 3).

FIGURE 3

**Distribution en percentiles du temps de pratique de loisirs
pour les activités de distraction, sports et passe-temps,
médias et communications, et la pratique totale**

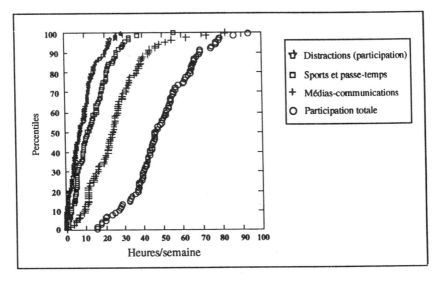

FIGURE 4

**Comparaison du temps de pratique de loisirs pour les activités reliées
à la catégorie « Médias et communications »**

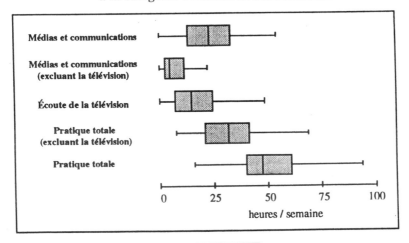

Légende de la distribution de fréquence
d'un diagramme en boîte

PC$_{25}$ = percentile 25, PC$_{75}$ = percentile 75
* Valeurs extrêmes à l'extérieur
   de la distribution.

Compte tenu de l'importance de l'écoute de la télévision (médiane = 15 h/sem.) parmi les habitudes de loisirs, il était justifié de quantifier son influence sur le temps de loisirs (Figure 4). En l'excluant de la catégorie médias et communications, le temps de pratique de cette catégorie diminue significativement (médiane = 5 h/sem.), et la pratique totale enregistre une baisse moyenne de 35 %. La comparaison des moyennes d'heures de pratique de loisirs avec celles de la population (québécoise et canadienne) indique un temps de pratique supérieur des sujets du présent échantillon (Figure 5). Cet écart de 12 h/sem. est attribuable surtout à une pratique plus importante d'activités de type sports et passe-temps (+ 9 h/sem.). Les autres types d'activités (catégorie 1, 2 et 4) étaient pratiqués par les sujets de façon similaire à celle de la population générale.

FIGURE 5

**Comparaison du temps de pratique de loisirs (heures/sem.)
entre l'échantillon et les moyennes québécoise et canadienne**

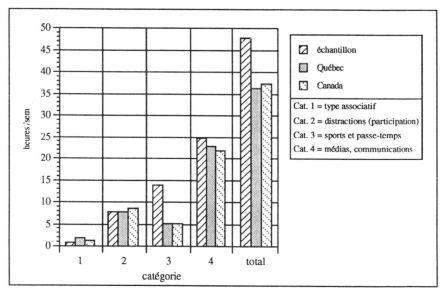

Lieu de pratique et présence de personnes

Globalement, plus de 55 % des activités de loisirs pratiquées par les participants se déroulaient à leur résidence (Figure 6). On observe que les activités de type associatif (catégorie 1) avaient majoritairement lieu dans la communauté. Inversement, les activités de type médias et communications (catégorie 4) se pratiquaient presque exclusivement à la résidence. Plus de 60 % des activités de loisirs des sujets étaient réalisées en présence d'autres personnes (Figure 7). Les activités de type distraction (catégorie 2) étaient particulièrement intéressantes à cet égard puisqu'elles se pratiquaient dans 97 % des cas en compagnie d'autres personnes. L'analyse combinée du lieu de pratique et de la présence de personnes à l'intérieur de chaque type d'activités de loisirs fait ressortir deux éléments qui semblent contradictoires quant à leur capacité d'engendrer des interactions et interrelations sociales. Les activités de type associatif qui se déroulaient surtout dans la communauté n'entraînaient pas toujours d'interrelations personnelles puisqu'elles étaient pratiquées de façon solitaire dans 50 % des cas. À l'opposé, les activités de type médias et communications, malgré un fort taux de pratique à la résidence, se déroulaient majoritairement en présence d'autres personnes.

FIGURE 6

Comparaison du lieu de pratique de loisirs selon les types d'activités

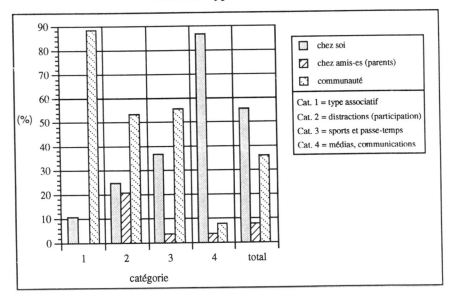

Facteurs influant sur la pratique de loisir

Une association significative a été observée entre la pratique de loisirs et certaines caractéristiques personnelles des individus ou de leur environnement. L'analyse des corrélations montre que l'association est faible, mais néanmoins significative ($p < .05$) entre l'âge et la pratique de certains types d'activités (type associatif, $r = .25$; médias et communications, $r = .20$; pratique totale, $r = .25$). Le niveau d'indépendance fonctionnelle tel que le mesure l'index de Barthel fait ressortir un association significative avec la pratique de loisirs (type distraction, $r = .27$; type sports et passe-temps, $r = .34$; médias et communication, $r = -.29$).

FIGURE 7

**Comparaison de la pratique de loisirs (seul ou en groupe)
selon les types d'activités**

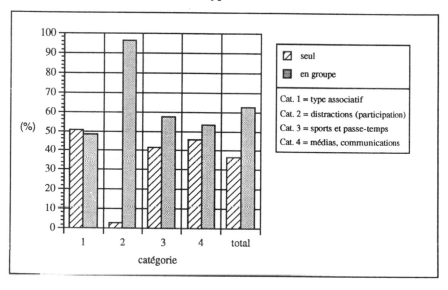

L'influence de la scolarité sur la pratique s'observait uniquement dans la catégorie médias et communication. Initialement, ce type d'activités ne semblait pas être associé à la scolarité ($r = -.04$, $p > .05$). L'association devenait positive ($r = .35$, $p > .01$) lorsqu'on excluait l'écoute de la télévision. Aucune association significative n'a été observée entre le revenu (personnel et familial) des sujets et leur pratique de loisirs.

Des analyses de régression ont été utilisées pour tenter de quantifier l'influence des variables personnelles et environnementales sur la pratique de loisirs et de prédire la pratique à partir de différents arrangements de variables indépendantes. La plupart des arrangements de variables n'expliquaient qu'un faible pourcentage de variance dans la pratique de loisirs analysée globalement et par type d'activités (< 15 % de variance commune). L'écoute de la télévision était la seule variable dépendante pour laquelle la variance expliquée atteignait 30 % à partir de variables telles que le transport, l'autonomie fonctionnelle, l'âge et l'occupation.

FIGURE 8

**Comparaison du temps de pratique de loisirs (heures/sem.)
pour l'écoute de la télévision et la pratique totale
selon l'occupation principale**

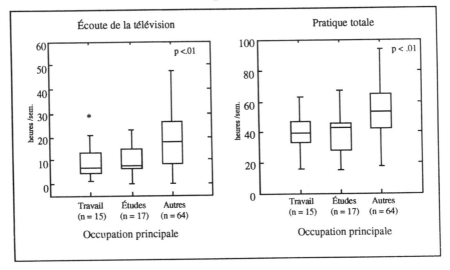

Légende de la distribution de fréquence
d'un diagramme en boîte

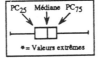

PC$_{25}$ = percentile 25, PC$_{75}$ = percentile 75
* Valeurs extrêmes à l'extérieur
    de la distribution.

L'influence potentielle de quatre variables nominales ressort à partir de représentations graphiques de la pratique de loisirs (Figures 8-11). Parmi celles-ci, l'occupation principale est la seule variable qui semblait influer sur la pratique totale (Figure 8). Les individus sans emploi ont un niveau de pratique de loisirs significativement plus élevé que les autres sujets de l'échantillon. Cette différence est directement reliée à une écoute plus élevée de la télévision. Le regroupement des scores de l'*Index de Barthel* en quatre catégories indique bien l'influence de l'autonomie fonctionnelle sur la pratique de loisirs (Figure 9). Les activités de type sports et passe-temps sont peu pratiquées par les sujets dont l'autonomie fonctionnelle est diminuée ; elles semblent être remplacées par l'écoute de la télévision. De même les individus à mobilité réduite qui doivent recourir à des dispositifs d'accès à leur résidence pour diminuer l'impact des barrières architecturales tendent à pratiquer moins d'activités de type distraction, sport et passe-temps (Figure 10). Enfin, la possibilité d'employer un véhicule automobile pour les déplacements augmente la pratique des activités de type distraction à l'extérieur du domicile (Figure 11), alors que la pratique d'activités de type médias et communications au domicile augmente significativement chez ceux qui ne disposent pas d'un véhicule pour leurs déplacements.

FIGURE 9

**Comparaison du temps de pratique de loisirs (heures/sem.)
pour les activités de sports et passe-temps et d'écoute de la télévision
selon le niveau d'habiletés fonctionnelles**

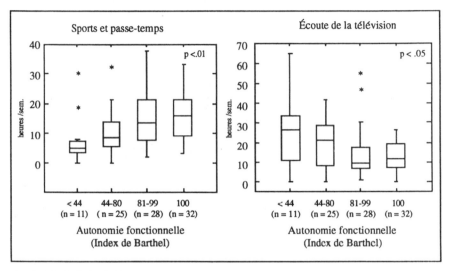

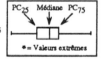

Légende de la distribution de fréquence
d'un diagramme en boîte

PC₂₅ = percentile 25, PC₇₅ = percentile 75
* Valeurs extrêmes à l'extérieur
   de la distribution.

Discussion

Les objectifs de la présente étude étaient : 1) de déterminer le niveau de pratique de loisirs et les types d'activités pratiquées par les personnes ayant une déficience motrice ; 2) de comparer cette pratique à celle de la population québécoise ; et 3) d'identifier des caractéristiques de la personne ou de son environnement susceptibles d'exercer une influence sur la pratique de loisirs et sur les types d'activités pratiquées. Le modèle conceptuel de la *Classification internationale des déficiences, incapacités et handicaps,* tel qu'il est modifié par le CQCIDIH, a servi de cadre de référence pour cette recherche. Dans ce contexte, la pratique d'activités de loisirs constitue une habitude de vie (*voir la définition au tableau 1*) puisqu'elle contribue à l'épanouissement de la personne tout au long de son existence. En présence d'une déficience physique, cette habitude peut être perturbée soit par des incapacités physiques ou mentales, soit par des obstacles de nature sociale, culturelle et écologique rencontrés dans le milieu de vie de la personne. Ce modèle a donc orienté le choix des variables indépendantes pouvant agir sur la pratique de loisirs et ainsi permettre d'améliorer les interventions des travailleurs en loisir auprès des personnes ayant une ou des incapacités.

FIGURE 10

**Comparaison du temps de pratique de loisirs (heures/sem.)
pour les activités de distraction, sports et passe-temps
selon l'utilisation de dispositifs d'accès à la résidence**

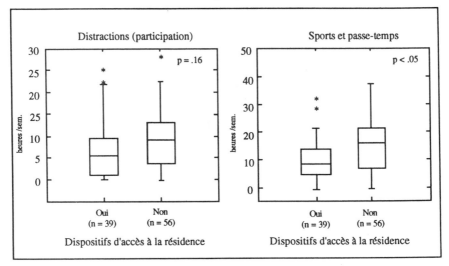

Légende de la distribution de fréquence
d'un diagramme en boîte

PC₂₅ = percentile 25, PC₇₅ = percentile 75
* Valeurs extrêmes à l'extérieur
    de la distribution.

Représentativité de l'échantillon

Bien que le nombre d'individus recrutés par type de déficiences n'ait pas atteint les proportions attendues, le présent échantillon (n = 97) est apparu représentatif, sur les plans socio-économique et démographique, des personnes ayant une ou des incapacités dans la population canadienne. La faible proportion de personnes dont l'occupation principale était le travail ($n = 5$, 15.5 %) reflète bien la situation précaire sur le plan professionnel de ce type de personnes. L'*Enquête sur la santé et les limitations d'activités* rapporte que près des trois quarts de toutes les personnes d'âge actif ayant une ou des incapacités sont, dans une certaine mesure, limitées dans leur capacité de travailler (Ross et Shillington, 1990) et que dans la catégorie d'âge de 45-64 ans, seulement 30 % occupent un emploi. Une proportion encore plus faible de personnes travaillant à temps plein (19 %) est rapportée par Kinney et Coyle (1992) sur une cohorte de 344 personnes ayant une ou des incapacités. Cette situation permet d'expliquer en grande partie les faibles revenus observés chez ces personnes. Dans les études mentionnées, y compris la présente, on note que près de 50 % des personnes ayant une ou des incapacités disposent d'un revenu personnel inférieur à 10 000 dollars

FIGURE 11

**Comparaison du temps de pratique de loisirs (heures/sem.)
pour les activités de distractions et de médias et communications
selon l'utilisation de l'automobile**

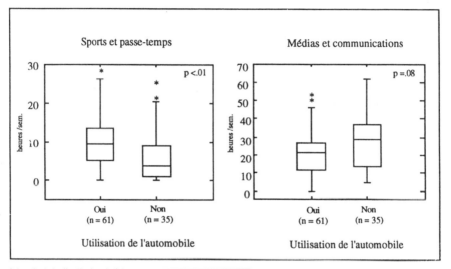

annuellement (Kinney et Coyle, 1992 ; Ross et Shillington, 1990). Une scolarité de niveau universitaire a été notée chez 20 % des personnes du présent échantillon alors qu'habituellement, elle ne dépasse pas 10 % dans la population des personnes ayant une ou des incapacités. Malgré ce taux élevé de scolarisation, le nombre de personnes sur le marché de l'emploi est très faible, ce qui semble confirmer que l'instruction à elle seule ne suffit pas à surmonter tous les obstacles à l'entrée dans la population active (Ross et Shillington, 1990).

Habitudes de loisirs

À notre connaissance, la présente étude serait la première à décrire les habitudes de loisirs de personnes ayant une déficience motrice et à tenter de cerner les facteurs qui influent sur les types d'activités pratiquées. Donc, la comparaison de nos résultats avec ceux d'études similaires s'est avérée impossible. Seulement deux sources d'information québécoise ou canadienne sur le temps de loisirs ont été recensées dans la population générale (Pronovost, 1988 ; Mercier ; 1990).

Le faible niveau de participation des individus de l'échantillon à des activités productives (travail, études, bénévolat) permet d'anticiper que la pratique de loisirs constitue un élément clé de l'augmentation du rythme de fonctionnement, de la valorisation et de l'intégration sociale des personnes ayant une ou des incapacités. Le temps total de pratique de loisirs tend à confirmer que ces personnes s'adonnent de façon substantielle à diverses activités de loisirs, puisque 75 % des participants rapportaient un temps de pratique supérieur à celui de la moyenne de la population générale. L'écart observé s'explique majoritairement par la pratique d'activités de type sports et passe-temps, alors qu'aucune différence significative n'était observée pour les autres types d'activités. Outre les activités de type associatif, qui étaient peu pratiquées, les activités de type sports et passe-temps sont celles qui semblent les plus susceptibles d'augmenter l'estime de soi, car elles requièrent une participation active de l'individu. Comme la présence d'une déficience physique affecte significativement l'estime de soi, nous pouvons faire l'hypothèse que la pratique d'une activité exigeant une implication personnelle est de nature à augmenter la valorisation ; il n'est donc pas étonnant de constater que ce type d'activités est davantage pratiqué par les personnes ayant une ou des incapacités.

Contexte de réalisation et intégration sociale

Le lieu où se déroule l'activité et la présence de personnes significatives lors du déroulement de l'activité constituent des éléments essentiels d'une analyse adéquate de la pratique de loisirs. À cet égard, il est intéressant de remarquer que 45 % des activités de loisirs se pratiquaient à l'extérieur du domicile. Ce résultat révèle, chez un nombre substantiel de sujets, la présence d'un niveau d'indépendance suffisant pour permettre la pratique des activités dans la communauté, ce qui constitue un facteur d'intégration sociale. L'approche habituelle en faveur de la participation au sein de la communauté doit donc être maintenue. Toutefois, le fait que plus de la moitié des activités de loisir des participants à l'étude se déroulaient au domicile devrait être considéré dans l'approche d'intervention. Cette nécessité ressort davantage pour les personnes dont les incapacités reliées à la locomotion sont graves et qui sont souvent très limitées dans leur capacité de déplacement. Chez une majorité de ces personnes, la pratique de loisirs à domicile serait un moyen privilégié d'atteindre des objectifs reliés à : 1) l'augmentation du rythme de fonctionnement ; 2) la valorisation ; et 3) l'intégration domiciliaire.

Un des éléments majeurs de l'intégration sociale des personnes ayant une ou des incapacités se situe au niveau de leur participation aux interactions et interrelations qui surviennent lors d'activités normatives en présence des personnes sans incapacité. Une des premières prémisses aux interactions est la possibilité de rencontrer des personnes et d'interagir avec celles-ci. Puisque 65 % des activités énoncées par les participants se déroulaient en présence d'autres personnes, la pratique du loisir semble favoriser les contacts interpersonnels, et conséquemment, augmenter la probabilité d'une meilleure intégration sociale. Par contre, la pratique de loisir individuel ne doit pas nécessairement être rejetée, car certains types d'activités, telles que la lecture et l'écoute de la musique, favorisent le calme et la relaxation souvent nécessaires à un rythme de fonctionnement optimal de l'individu. Cependant, il serait souhaitable que les personnes souffrant d'incapacités ne se limitent à ce type d'activités de loisir qui ne favorisent pas les interactions personnelles.

Caractéristiques personnelles et facteurs de l'environnement

La présente étude visait, entre autres, à déterminer les caractéristiques personnelles ou environnementales susceptibles de prédisposer les sujets à la pratique de certains types d'activités de loisir. Au chapitre des caractéristiques personnelles, il est apparu évident que la gravité des incapacités physiques tendait à influer sur le type de pratique de loisir sans pour autant diminuer le temps total de pratique. Ainsi, un niveau d'incapacité plus élevé (faible indice de Barthel et nécessité de recourir à des dispositifs d'accès à la résidence) semblait diminuer le temps de pratique d'activités de type distraction ou sports et passe-temps, lesquelles nécessitent une plus grande autonomie et se déroulent davantage à l'extérieur du domicile. Dans le cas d'un faible niveau d'autonomie fonctionnelle, l'écoute de la télévision devenait une des activités les plus prépondérantes.

L'occupation principale de la personne agit également sur sa participation au loisir. Plus spécifiquement, nos résultats révèlent que les individus sans emploi ou qui ne sont pas aux études disposent de plus de temps pour pratiquer une activité de loisir. Cependant, ils ne semblent pas pratiquer davantage de loisirs exigeant un implication personnelle, puisque la majorité du temps additionnel dont ils disposent est occupé par l'écoute de la télévision. Ce résultat tend à confirmer que la télévision constitue une activité « tampon » qui remplit le temps libre supplémentaire.

Sur le plan environnemental, parmi les variables mesurées, la disponibilité d'une automobile pour les déplacements semblait favoriser la pratique d'activités de sports et passe-temps ; dans le cas contraire, les personnes tendaient à occuper davantage leur temps libre avec des activités de type média et communications, dont l'écoute de la télévision. Ces observations soulèvent une interrogation quant à la capacité des services de transport adapté de remplacer l'usage d'un véhicule personnel et quant à leur valeur comme éléments favorisant l'intégration sociale (communautaire).

Limites de l'étude

Malgré son intérêt, cette étude présente certaines limites relatives à l'échantillon et à la mesure. Tout d'abord, le mode d'échantillonnage non aléatoire fondé sur la participation volontaire des sujets n'a pas permis d'obtenir un échantillon représentatif quant aux différents types de déficiences motrices. De plus, nous ne pouvons écarter la possibilité que les participants aient entretenu un biais favorable vis-à-vis de la participation au loisir. Aucune mesure des fonctions supérieures ou de la personnalité n'a été effectuée. La présence de séquelles psychiques peut, par exemple, exercer une influence sur le type d'activités pratiquées à la suite d'un traumatisme cranio-cérébral. Certains facteurs reliés à l'environnement n'ont pu être mesurés. Entre autres, l'organisation et la connaissance des services ou ressources disponibles seraient de nature à influer sur la participation au loisir. La structure familiale et sociale de l'individu ainsi que les attitudes à l'égard du loisir constituent également des sources potentielles d'influence sur la pratique de loisir qui n'ont pu être mesurées.

Portée clinique de l'étude

La présente étude revêt une signification clinique importante pour les intervenants en loisir du domaine de la réadaptation. D'une part, elle permet de vérifier la faisabilité de l'utilisation de la technique du budget-temps dans un processus de mesure des habitudes de loisir chez des personnes avec des incapacités. D'autre part, elle constitue un important outil d'intervention grâce aux données quantifiables sur la pratique de loisir d'une cohorte importante de personnes ayant une déficience motrice qu'elle contient. L'élaboration de normes de pratique à partir de ces données pourra permettre à l'intervenant de situer le niveau de participation au loisir d'un individu par rapport à la population de personnes ayant une déficience motrice. Le client pourra être informé sur l'état de sa pratique actuelle et établir des objectifs réalistes en fonction de ses intérêts et aptitudes. Enfin, l'identification de facteurs qui exercent une influence sur le choix des activités de loisirs devrait favoriser l'élaboration d'objectifs compatibles avec les caractéristiques de la personne et de son environnement, ou la mise au point de stratégies permettant de contrer l'effet négatif de ces facteurs.

Conclusion

Somme toute, cette étude représente la première étape d'un examen plus objectif de la contribution potentielle du loisir au processus menant à l'intégration sociale des personnes ayant une ou des incapacités. Les résultats indiquent que la participation au loisir des personnes ayant une déficience motrice se compare à celle de la population générale, et que cette pratique favorise les interactions et interrelations personnelles. Malgré l'identification de certains facteurs qui influent sur le choix des activités de loisir, plusieurs questions demeurent sans réponse et devront faire l'objet de recherches ultérieures. Entre autres, il apparaît important de documenter la question des attitudes des personnes à l'égard du loisir et celle de l'impact de la satisfaction en ce domaine sur la qualité de vie. Comme l'intégration sociale demeure un objectif majeur de l'intervention de réadaptation, les recherches devront se poursuivre afin de préciser l'impact du loisir à cet égard.

Références

CALDWELL, L.L. et SMITH E.A. (1988). Leisure : an overlooked component of health promotion. Canadian Journal of Public Health, 79, S44-S48.

COMMISSION DES CENTRES DE RÉADAPTATION (1992). Rôles et orientations des établissements de réadaptation en déficience physique. Associations des centres d'accueil du Québec.

FLYNN, R.J. (1993). L'intégration sociale entre 1982 et 1992 : Définitions conceptuelles et opérationnelles. Réseau International CIDIH, 6(2), 36-45.

FOUGEYROLLAS, P. (1991). Proposition du modèle de production des handicaps révisés. Réseau International CIDIH , 4 (1), 17.

ISO-AHOLA, S.E. (1982). People today : withdrawing, coping, adapting. Parks ans Recreation, 62-66.

ISO-AHOLA, S.E. (1983). Social, psychological foundations for leisure and resultant implications for leisure counseling. in Dowd TE (Ed.), Leisure counseling : Concepts and applications, Springfield, IL : CC Thomas.

KINNEY, W.B. et COYLE, C.P. (1992). Predicting life satisfaction among adults with physical disabilities. Archives of Physical and Medical Rehabillitation, 73, 863-869.

LAVIGNE, M. et MORIN, J.P. (1991). Loisirs et habitudes de vie des personnes ayant une incapacité au Canada. Statistiques Canada, Série thématique spéciale : Enquête sur la santé et les limitations d'activités, Ottawa : Approvisionnements et Services Canada.

MERCIER, M. (1990). Emplois du temps des Québécois : comparaisons avec l'ensemble des Canadiens. Québec : Ministère du loisir, de la chasse et de la pêche.

MINISTÈRE DE LA SANTÉ ET DES SERVICES SOCIAUX (MSSS). (1992). Programme-cadre pour les personnes ayant une déficience physique : document de consultation. Québec : Gouvernement du Québec.

NIEMI, M.L., LAAKSONEN, R., KOTILA, M. et WALTIMO, O. (1988). Quality of life four years after stroke. Stroke, 19, 1101-1107.

OFFICES DES PERSONNES HANDICAPÉES DU QUÉBEC (1984). À part égale. Politique de prévention et d'intégration sociale des personnes handicapées : Gouvernement du Québec.

ORGANISATION MONDIALE DE LA SANTÉ (1981). *Prévention des incapacités et réadaptation des handicapés.* Genève : OMS (séries de rapports techniques 668).

ROSS, D.P. et SHILLINGTON, E.R. (1990). *Profil économique des personnes ayant une ou des incapacités au Canada.* Ottawa : Secrétariat d'État du Canada.

SPREITZER, E. et SNYDER, E. (1987). Educational-occupational fit and leisure orientation as related to life satisfaction. *Journal of Leisure Research, 19* (2), 149-158.

TREMBLAY, G. (1991). *La méthode IMPACT : programme-cadre en loisirs cliniques.* Fédération québécoise du loisir en institution.

Luc NOREAU, Gilles MURPHY, Georges TREMBLAY et Roger CANTIN
Niveau de pratique de loisirs et influence des caractéristiques personnelles et environnementales chez des personnes ayant une déficience motrice

RÉSUMÉ

La présente étude vise à déterminer, d'une part, le niveau réel de pratique de loisirs des personnes ayant une déficience motrice, et, d'autre part, les caractéristiques personnelles et environnementales susceptibles de favoriser ou de limiter la pratique de loisirs. Comptabilisé à partir d'un budget-temps, le temps moyen de pratique de loisirs se situe à 48 h / sem. La comparaison du temps de pratique de loisirs des sujets avec celui de la population générale indique un temps supérieur des premiers, attribuable à une plus grande quantité d'activités de type sports et passe-temps (+ 9 h / sem.). La gravité des incapacités physiques tend à influer sur le type de pratique de loisir, sans pour autant en diminuer le temps total. L'occupation principale de la personne semble également exercer une influence sur sa participation au loisir. Plus particulièrement, les individus sans emploi ou qui n'étudient pas écoutent davantage la télévision. Ce résultat tend à confirmer que ce média constitue une activité « tampon » qui remplit le temps libre supplémentaire.

Luc NOREAU, Gilles MURPHY, Georges TREMBLAY and Roger CANTIN
Level of Leisure Practice and Impact of Individual and Environmental Characteristics on People with a Motor Disability

ABSTRACT

The present study is aimed at determining, firstly, the actual level of leisure practice of subjects with a motor disability and, secondly, the personal and environmental characteristics likely to promote or limit the practice of leisure activities. A time-budget analysis shows that the average time spent for leisure practice is 48 hours/week, which is higher than in the general population, and is attributed to a greater quantity of sports and hobbies (+ 9 hours/week). The severity of the physical handicap tends to influence the type of leisure activity practiced but does not reduce the total time. The main occupation of the individual also seems to affect his or her participation in leisure activities. Unemployed individuals and those who are not students, in particular, spend more time watching television. This finding suggests that this medium is a "buffer" activity used to occupy extra free time.

Luc NOREAU, Gilles MURPHY, Georges TREMBLAY y Roger CANTIN
Nivel de práctica de las actividades recreativas e influencia de las características personales y de su entorno en las personas que sufren de una deficiencia motriz.

RESUMEN

El presente estudio trata de determinar, por una parte, el nivel real de la práctica de actividades recreativas entre las personas atacadas de una deficiencia motriz, y por otra parte, las características personales y del entorno susceptibles de favorecer o de limitar la práctica de actividades de recreo. Contabilizado a partir de un presupuesto-tiempo, el tiempo medio de practica de dichas actividades se sitúa en 48 horas / semana. La comparación del tiempo de práctica de actividades recreativas con respecto a la población en general indica un tiempo superior en la presente muestra, atribuible a una práctica más importante de actividades de tipo deporte y pasatiempo (+ 9 h / scm.). La gravedad de las incapacidades físicas tiende a influenciar el tipo de practica de diversión, sin por lo tanto afectar el tiempo total. La ocupación principal de la persona parece ejercer una influencia sobre su participación en las actividades recreativas. Particularmente, los individuos sin empleo o que no estudian, miran mucho más la televisión. Este resultado tiende a confirmar que esta media constituye una actividad «tapón» que rellena el tiempo libre suplementario.

COMPTE RENDU / *BOOK REVIEW*

HALL, A., SLACK, T., SMITH, G. ET WHITSON, D. (1991)
Sport in Canadian Society
Toronto, McClelland & Stewart Inc., 281 p.

De plus en plus, les sociologues du sport au Canada adoptent une approche critique face à l'étude de leur domaine. Les professeurs qui enseignent la sociologie du sport aux étudiants en éducation physique font face à un défi de taille : leur enseigner les rudiments de la sociologie tout en les incitant à appréhender le sport d'un oeil critique. Il s'agit d'une tâche souvent ingrate puisque, de façon générale, ces étudiants résistent et parfois se révoltent face à une approche critique du sport et de l'activité physique. En effet, la majorité d'entre eux se lancent dans ce domaine en raison de leur expérience sportive positive, de leurs croyances aux bienfaits de l'activité physique et de leur engagement dans le modèle sportif dominant. Ils sont donc réticents et refusent parfois de remettre en question le modèle dominant du sport compétitif et l'importance de la performance (McKay et Pearson, 1984)[1]. En effet, McKay, Gore et Kirk (1990)[2] remarquent que la plupart des étudiants sont inconscients des inégalités sociales fondées sur le genre, l'ethnicité, la race et le niveau socio-économique. De plus, ils sont incrédules face à l'influence du sport dans la production et la reproduction de ces inégalités. Il est donc difficile de les exhorter à adopter une position critique face au sport (McKay, Gore & Kirk, 1990).

Hall, Slack, Smith et Whitson (1991) relèvent justement ce défi d'encourager les futurs éducateurs physiques et sociologues à examiner le sport d'une façon critique dans leur ouvrage Sport in Canadian Society. Chacun des chapitres souligne à la fois les possibilités qu'offre le sport ainsi que les conséquences parfois négatives et/ou restrictives des pratiques, structures et institutions sportives. Ils présentent les deux côtés de la médaille d'une façon élémentaire et intéressante, qui s'éloigne des croyances dominantes sans aliéner les étudiants.

Sur le plan théorique, le texte est généralement assez accessible aux étudiants de premier cycle. Les éléments de théorie présentés sont rudimentaires et les nombreux exemples rendent le texte intéressant. L'utilisation d'exemples

---

1. McKay, J. et Pearson, K. (1984). Objectives, strategies and ethics in teaching introductory courses in sociology of sport. *Quest*, 36, 134-146.
2. McKay, J., Gore, J.M. et Kirk, D. (1990). Beyond the Limits of Technocratic Physical Education. *Quest*, 42(1), 52-76.

canadiens situe les explications dans un contexte familier aux étudiants, ce qui leur permet de mieux comprendre les concepts présentés. Malgré l'accessibilité du texte, certains termes et concepts auraient cependant bénéficié d'une meilleure description, et notamment le concept d'hégémonie qui demeure ambigu. De plus, bien que la simplicité du texte constitue un avantage important de ce livre, les auteurs auraient pu étoffer davantage la partie théorique afin de mieux camper la perspective sociologique et critique du sport. Trois grands thèmes sont abordés afin d'envisager le sport selon une approche sociologique : Premièrement, la situation du sport et de ses institutions en contexte historique pour mieux en saisir l'évolution et la place dans l'histoire. Deuxièmement, le sens et l'implication des changements sociaux dans la vie de tous les hommes. Troisièmement, les rapports entre les individus et les structures sociales permettant de comprendre les processus de changement social.

Ce livre, destiné aux étudiants qui suivent un cours en sociologie du sport, est l'un des premiers ouvrages à porter sur le phénomène sportif au Canada et à s'inspirer principalement des études sportives canadiennes. Les auteurs présentent les études et des exemples propres à l'expérience sportive au Canada. Cependant, le texte n'exprime pas nécessairement toute la richesse et variété des expériences et pratiques sportives du Canada. Cette lacune semble reliée au manque de recherche sur les pratiques sportives qui se démarquent du modèle dominant (entre autres, l'expérience sportive des personnes handicapées ou des personnes âgées et la popularité des activités de plein air et non compétitives). Par ailleurs, ce livre aborde surtout les études publiées en anglais, et ainsi, une perspective surtout anglophone. Une des caractéristiques importantes de la société canadienne est la présence de deux principaux groupes linguistiques : les anglophones et les francophones. Cependant, les auteurs négligent les études francophones. Cette faiblesse est d'autant plus importante que certains thèmes de la sociologie du sport au Québec s'éloignent des questions étudiées en sociologie du sport dans les universités des autres provinces canadiennes. Par exemple, la professionnalisation de l'éducation physique est une préoccupation importante chez les sociologues du sport au Québec alors qu'elle est pratiquement inexistante dans les études qui proviennent des autres provinces. En se limitant aux études publiées en anglais, les auteurs décrivent le sport dans la société canadienne selon une perspective anglophone, qui laisse de côté l'importance de la dualité linguistique du Canada et qui présente un portrait homogène de cette société.

Bien que les auteurs signalent certaines différences entre les francophones et les anglophones, surtout dans le chapitre sur les inégalités sociales, les exemples et les recherches qu'ils mentionnent sont principalement des études publiées en anglais et des exemples qui se rapportent à l'expérience sportive dominante des anglophones. De plus, les auteurs ne font pas de distinction entre les termes francophones, canadien français et Canada français, et les utilisent comme synonymes. Pourtant, ces termes représentent des groupes d'individus fort différents. Par exemple, le groupe culturel canadien-français a laissé place à diverses identités : québécoise, acadienne et celle des autres communautés francophones minoritaires (franco-ontarienne, franco-manitobaine, fransaskoise, et autres). Et puis, le groupe linguistique des francophones rassemble non seulement des individus de descendance canadienne-française, mais aussi des individus de diverses origines ethniques tels que des Français, des Marocains, des Haïtiens, des Vietnamiens, et autres. Les auteurs présentent cependant le groupe linguistique francophone comme une entité homogène ; ils oublient l'existence de communautés francophones à l'extérieur du Québec. De même, le groupe linguistique anglophone apparaît comme un groupe uniforme, alors qu'il est, lui aussi, composé de diverses ethnicités : britanniques, écossaises, ukrainiennes, italiennes, et autres.

Les auteurs démontrent un souci d'intégrer les divers groupes autochtones, inuit et francophones, et ce, sans adopter une attitude colonialiste. Malgré cette préoccupation, le texte présente un portrait uniforme du Canada et décrit des pratiques sportives qui ne s'éloignent pas vraiment de l'expérience dominante du sport en ce pays. Le chapitre consacré à l'émergence du sport moderne au Canada, par exemple, porte principalement sur les pratiques dominantes dans les milieux anglo-saxons montréalais et torontois. Malheureusement, peu d'études ont examiné l'expérience sportive des francophones et des autochtones durant cette période de développement du sport tel que l'on connaît ses formes dominantes aujourd'hui. Cependant, cela n'implique pas nécessairement l'absence d'une expérience sportive chez ces groupes. Il y aurait lieu de préciser que le texte porte sur les données et informations existantes, tout en soulignant le manque d'études pour répondre à des questions comme les suivantes : Est-ce que les activités physiques et sportives des groupes en marge ressemblaient à l'expérience sportive de l'élite anglophone ? Étaient-elles organisées selon une structure différente ?

Malgré quelques faiblesses, *Sport in Canadian Society* représente une contribution importante à la sociologie du sport au Canada. Sur le plan des initiatives, dans le chapitre examinant les liens entre les entreprises, le capital et le sport, les auteurs discutent de l'impératif économique et de son impact sur les pratiques et structures sportives, non seulement dans le milieu professionnel, mais aussi dans le milieu du sport amateur et de l'industrie des équipements sportifs. De plus, le chapitre sur les inégalités sociales soulève les problèmes reliés à la question du genre face au milieu sportif ; il présente ainsi une perspective plus complète plutôt que de se restreindre à la situation de la femme. Il importe aussi de souligner que les auteurs ne limitent pas l'examen des inégalités sociales au seul chapitre qui porte sur ce phénomène. En effet, des situations de conflits et d'inégalités décrites tout au long de l'ouvrage établissent le domaine du sport au Canada comme un lieu de luttes entre divers groupes sociaux.

Enfin, le dernier chapitre résume les éléments introduits et invite les étudiants à réfléchir sur l'avenir du sport et de ses institutions au Canada.

En conclusion, cet ouvrage nous semble constituer un bon texte d'introduction à la sociologie du sport ; il devrait réussir à conserver l'intérêt des étudiants en raison de son caractère canadien et de son accessibilité. Nul doute qu'il favorisera l'adoption d'une perspective critique face au phénomène sportif dans la société canadienne ainsi que certaines remises en question face aux pratiques et structures sportives dominantes.

Christine Dallaire

Faculty of Physical Education and Recreation
University of Alberta, Edmonton

À PARAÎTRE
FORTHCOMING ISSUES

Automne 1995 / Fall 1995

Vol. 18, n° 2
Loisir : un défi de société
Leisure : A Challenge for Society
Michel de la Durantaye et Pierre Gagnon

Printemps 1996 / Spring 1996

Vol. 19, n° 1
Les communications de Bielefeld / *The Bielefeld Papers*
Francis Lobo

Automne 1996 / Fall 1996

Vol. 19, n° 2
Temps de travail et temps hors-travail
Working time and off-work time
Jean-Yves Boulin et Diane-Gabrielle Tremblay

Printemps 1997 / Spring 1997

Vol. 20, n° 1
Numéro spécial du 20ᵉ anniversaire de la revue
20ᵗʰ anniversary Special Issue

LOISIR : UN DÉFI DE SOCIÉTÉ
Vol. 18, n° 2, automne 1995
Éditeurs invités : Michel DE LA DURANTAYE *et Pierre* GAGNON

Ce numéro inclura, entre autres, une sélection des meilleures communications présentées au Colloque international sur le loisir tenu à Trois-Rivières en novembre 1994.

Les normes de la revue diffèrent cependant de celles prévalant pour la présentation des communications à Trois-Rivières. En particulier :

- tout manuscrit doit avoir une longueur acceptable, emprunter la forme d'un article scientifique, et ne peut consister en un simple résumé de la communication ;

- il doit être rédigé en anglais ou en français ;

- il doit principalement faire état de recherches empiriques.

En conformité avec les normes en vigueur dans les revues scientifiques nord-américaines, tous les manuscrits soumis à la revue sont évalués par des lecteurs externes. La décision de publication est de la responsabilité finale du Comité de rédaction. En même temps que la décision qui leur est transmise, tous les auteurs reçoivent une copie des évaluations de leur manuscrit.

Soumission des manuscrits

Les manuscrits doivent être soumis à la rédaction avant le 8 septembre 1995 et doivent inclure :

1) Quatre copies du manuscrit, dactylographiées à double interligne ;
   la première page du manuscrit ne doit pas comporter le nom
   ou les coordonnées de l'auteur ;

2) Une page titre contenant le titre de l'article, le nom de l'auteur
   ou des auteurs, numéros de téléphone et de télécopieur ainsi que l'affiliation
   institutionnelle de chacun ;

3) Un résumé d'au plus 150 mots ;

Si le manuscrit est accepté, est également exigée une copie du texte sur disquette et la mention du logiciel utilisé ainsi que sa version.

Les tableaux, figures et notes doivent être présentés sur des feuillets séparés ; on indiquera leur emplacement dans le texte (par ex. : insérer ici Fig. 1).

Adopter le style APA (*American Psychological Association*) pour les références et la bibliographie.

Faire parvenir à : Le Directeur
Loisir et Société / Society and Leisure
Département des sciences du loisir
Université du Québec à Trois-Rivières
C.P. 500, Trois-Rivières (Québec)
Canada
G9A 5H7

LEISURE : A CHALLENGE FOR SOCIETY
Vol. 18, No. 2, Fall 1995
Guest Editors : Michel DE LA DURANTAYE and Pierre GAGNON

This issue will include among other things a selection of the best papers presented at the International Leisure Studies Conference held at Trois-Rivières in November 1994.

The norms for the journal, however, differ from those of the presentation requirements for papers at Trois-Rivières. In particular :

- the manuscript must be of an acceptable length, and be in the form of a scientific article ; it must not be simply an abstract of the paper ;
- it must be written in either English or French ;
- it should present mainly empirical research.

In compliance with the usual standards of North-American scientific journals, all the manuscripts submitted will be evaluated by outside readers. The final decision to publish is the responsibility of the Editorial Board. When authors are informed of the decision, they will at the same time receive a copy of the evaluation of their manuscript.

Submission of Manuscripts

Manuscripts should be submitted to the editors before September 8, 1995, and should include :

1) Four copies of the manuscript, typed double-spaced ; the first page must not bear the name, address or telephone number of the author or authors ;

2) A title page containing the title of the article, the name or names of the authors, their telephone and fax numbers as well as the name of their institution ;

3) An abstract of 150 words, at most ;

If accepted, a copy of the text on a diskette, identifying software and version will be required.

Tables, figures and notes should be presented on separate sheets with their location noted in the text (e.g. insert Fig. 1 about here).

References should be styled according to the American Psychological Association format.

Mail to :   The Editor
              Loisir et Société / Society and Leisure
              Département des sciences du loisir
              Université du Québec à Trois-Rivières
              P.O. Box 500, Trois-Rivières (Québec)
              Canada
              G9A 5H7

LES COMMUNICATIONS DE BIELEFELD
Vol. 19, n° 1, printemps 1996
Éditeur invité : Francis LOBO

De manière à poursuivre les liens étroits que la revue entretient avec le Comité de recherche sur le loisir de l'AIS, le Volume 18, numéro 2, automne 1995 de la revue est réservé à une sélection de communications présentées lors du 13ᵉ congrès mondial de sociologie, Bielefeld, Allemagne, juillet 1994 (on se rappellera que le volume 10-2, 1987 a été consacré aux communications présentées à New Delhi l'année précédente, et le volume 14-2, 1991, aux communications du congrès de Madrid tenu en 1990).

Les normes de la revue diffèrent cependant de celles prévalant pour la présentation des communications à Bielefeld. En particulier :

– tout manuscrit doit avoir une longueur acceptable, emprunter la forme d'un article scientifique, et ne peut consister en un simple résumé de la communication ;

– il doit être rédigé en anglais ou en français ;

– il doit principalement faire état de recherches empiriques.

Soumission des manuscrits

En conformité avec les normes en vigueur dans les revues scientifiques nord-américaines, tous les manuscrits soumis à la revue sont évalués par des lecteurs externes. La décision de publication est de la responsabilité finale du Comité de rédaction. En même temps que la décision qui leur est transmise, tous les auteurs reçoivent une copie des évaluations de leur manuscrit.

Les manuscrits doivent être soumis à la rédaction avant le 30 septembre 1995 et doivent inclure :

1) Quatre copies du manuscrit, dactylographiées à double interligne ; la première page du manuscrit ne doit pas comporter le nom ou les coordonnées de l'auteur ;

2) Une page titre contenant le titre de l'article, le nom de l'auteur ou des auteurs, numéros de téléphone et de télécopieur ainsi que l'affiliation institutionnelle de chacun ;

3) Un résumé d'au plus 150 mots ;

Si le manuscrit est accepté, est également exigée une copie du texte sur disquette et la mention du logiciel utilisé ainsi que sa version.

Les tableaux, figures et notes doivent être présentés sur des feuillets séparés ; on indiquera leur emplacement dans le texte (par ex. : insérer ici Fig. 1).

Adopter le style APA (American Psychological Association) pour les références et la bibliographie.

Faire parvenir à : Le Directeur
Loisir et Société / Society and Leisure
Département des sciences du loisir
Université du Québec à Trois-Rivières
C.P. 500, Trois-Rivières (Québec)
Canada   G9A 5H7

THE BIELEFELD PAPERS
Vol. 19, No. 1, Spring 1996
Guest Editor: Francis LOBO

So as to maintain the journal's close links with the Research Group on Leisure, ISA, Volume 18, number 2, Fall 1995 will be devoted to a selection of papers presented during the 13th World Congress on Sociology to be held at Bielefeld, Germany, in July of 1994. (We remind you that Volume 10-2, 1987, was dedicated to papers presented in New Delhi the previous year, and that Volume 14-2, 1991, presented papers from the Madrid Congress held in 1990.)

The norms for the journal, however, differ from those of the presentation requirements for papers at Bielefeld. In particular:

- the manuscript must be of an acceptable length, and be in the form of a scientific article; it must not be simply an abstract of the paper;

- it must be written in either English or French;

- it should present mainly empirical research.

Submission of Manuscripts

In compliance with the usual standards of North-American scientific journals, all the manuscripts submitted will be evaluated by outside readers. The final decision to publish is the responsibility of the Editorial Board. When authors are informed of the decision, they will at the same time receive a copy of the evaluation of their manuscript.

Manuscripts should be submitted to the editors before September 30, 1995, and should include:

1) Four copies of the manuscript, typed double-spaced; the first page must not bear the name, address or telephone number of the author or authors;

2) A title page containing the title of the article, the name or names of the authors, their telephone and fax numbers as well as the name of their institution;

3) An abstract of 150 words, at most;

If accepted, a copy of the text on a diskette, identifying software and version will be required.

Tables, figures and notes should be presented on separate sheets with their location noted in the text (e.g. insert Fig. 1 about here).

References should be styled according to the American Psychological Association format.

Mail to :   The Editor
Loisir et Société / Society and Leisure
Département des sciences du loisir
Université du Québec à Trois-Rivières
P.O. Box 500, Trois-Rivières (Québec)
Canada G9A 5H7

TEMPS DE TRAVAIL ET TEMPS HORS-TRAVAIL
Vol. 19, n° 2, automne 1996
Éditeurs invités : Jean-Yves BOULIN et Diane-Gabrielle TREMBLAY

Vers les années 60, on annonçait l'arrivée de la société des loisirs. Les récessions des années 80 et 90 ont cependant diminué la pertinence de ce concept, la situation de chômage amenant la majorité des gens à se préoccuper davantage de s'assurer un emploi. On observe en fait une polarité de situations. Bon nombre de personnes se trouvent exclues de l'emploi ou sont dans des situations transitoires (temps partiel, stages, contrats à durée déterminée) qui se prolongent. Elles connaissent de ce fait une situation de « loisir forcé ». À l'inverse, un certain nombre de personnes travaillent apparemment plus que ne l'indiquent leurs horaires officiels et d'autres font un grand nombre d'heures supplémentaires ou cumulent deux emplois à temps partiel ou réduit pour obtenir un salaire convenable.

Par ailleurs, la progression des ménages à deux revenus, et donc à deux travailleurs, de même que celle des foyers monoparentaux, entraîne des contraintes sur le plan du temps hors travail ; les tâches domestiques se substituent souvent au loisir proprement dit, entraînant parfois une redéfinition du concept du temps hors-travail, sinon du « loisir » proprement dit. Le caractère plus proprement ludique du loisir cède le pas à celui de l'utilité.

Le chômage chronique élevé que connaissent bon nombre de pays industrialisés fait émerger de nouveau le débat sur le partage du temps de travail dont les effets sur l'utilisation du temps hors travail sont parfois soulignés de façon positive. En effet, si certains mettent l'accent sur la réduction du chômage que permettrait une telle mesure, d'autres soulignent qu'elle favoriserait un nouvel équilibre des temps sociaux, considérant cette évolution préférable au présent partage entre le travail et le non-emploi. Aux yeux des premiers, le travail constitue un élément positif et enrichissant de la vie, alors que pour les seconds, il est plutôt pénible, contraignant et peu susceptible de conduire à l'épanouissement humain.

Ce numéro de *Loisir et Société* abordera différents aspects associés à l'articulation du temps de travail et du temps hors-travail. Les articles présentant les faits, les enjeux, les facteurs explicatifs des évolutions observées en ces matières sont donc les bienvenus ; ils peuvent être à caractère sociologique, économique ou politique. On pourra ainsi traiter de sujets tels que :

- l'évolution historique du temps de travail et du temps hors-travail ;
- le temps de travail par rapport au cycle de vie, notamment l'articulation entre la formation, le travail et la retraite ;
- le temps choisi, la diversification des temps de travail et des statuts d'emploi ;
- les aspirations au regard du temps libre ;
- la structuration des comportements en matière de temps de travail et de temps hors-travail par rapport à l'évolution des valeurs dont l'un et l'autre sont porteurs ;
- les rapports sociaux de sexe, ou différences hommes-femmes, relativement à ces comportements ;

– une comparaison du contenu du temps hors-travail dans différents pays ;
– etc.

Soumission des manuscrits

Les thèmes suggérés ci-dessus ne sont aucunement limitatifs ; d'autres perspectives de recherche peuvent également être abordées sur les plans méthodologique ou théorique. Les éditeurs invitent plus particulièrement les auteurs à présenter des textes portant sur des comparaisons internationales.

Les manuscrits devront être soumis aux deux éditeurs invités avant le 1er mars 1996 et inclure :

1) Quatre exemplaires du manuscrit, dactylographiés à double interligne ; la première page du manuscrit ne doit pas comporter le nom ou les coordonnées de l'auteur ;

2) Une page titre contenant le titre de l'article, le nom de l'auteur ou des auteurs, numéros de téléphone et de télécopieur ainsi que l'affiliation institutionnelle de chacun ;

3) Un résumé d'au plus 150 mots.

Si le manuscrit est accepté est également exigée une copie du texte sur disquette portant la mention du logiciel utilisé ainsi que sa version.

Les tableaux, figures et notes doivent être présentés sur des feuillets séparés ; on indiquera leur emplacement dans le texte (par ex. : insérer ici Fig. 1).

Adopter le style APA (*American Psychological Association*) pour les références.

Faire parvenir à : Diane-Gabrielle Tremblay
Télé-Université
C.P. 5250, succursale C
Montréal (Québec)
Canada
H2X 3M4
Fax : (514) 522-3608

ou   Jean-Yves Boulin
Institut de recherche et d'information socio-économique
Université Paris Dauphine
Place Maréchal de Lattre Tassigny
75775 Paris
Cedex 16
France

WORKING TIME AND NON-WORK TIME
Vol. 19, No. 2, Fall 1996
Guest Editors: Jean-Yves BOULIN and Diane-Gabrielle TREMBLAY

In the 60's we were said to be at the threshold of the *society of leisure*. However, owing to the slumps of the 80's and 90's, people now tend to focus more on having or keeping their jobs, reducing by the same token the emphasis on leisure The situation has now dichotomized. On the one hand, numerous people either do not have a job at all, or else have a temporary one (part time, field training, limited contracts) for a more or less extended period of time, thus experiencing a *forced state* of leisure. On the other hand, other people are working more and more, extending their regular working schedule, doing considerable amount of overtime or cumulating two part-time jobs in order to get a decent salary.

There are also new constraints on the non-work time of people, since they tend to either have a double income when they live as a couple or else be in a single-parent situation. In both cases, the hours formerly spent in recreational activities are now often dedicated to family chores. Thus the need of a new definition of the concept of off-work time and *leisure* itself. It seems that leisure is losing its *play* content at the expense of its *purpose* content.

With chronic unemployment being so high in numerous industrialized societies, the debate on work or employment sharing has resurfaced, and consequences of reduced working time on the use of non-work time are sometimes given a positive emphasis. For those who think that work is a positive and enriching element of life, such a measure is welcome since it would favour a decrease in unemployment. For those who consider work as hard, constraining and rarely fulfilling, such a measure would have the advantage of creating a new balance between social times and would, at any rate, be preferable to the present dichotomy between work and unemployment.

This issue of *Society and Leisure* will focus on the interrelation between working time and non-work time. Papers dealing with facts, issues and factors affecting changes in this area are welcomed. They may be of a sociological, economical or political character. Subjects such as the following will be accepted:

- The historical evolution of working time and non-work time;
- Working time in relation to life cycle, and the relationship between education, work and retirement;
- Selected time, diversification of working times and of job;
- Aspirations concerning free time;
- Structuration of behaviour with respect to working time and non-work time behaviour in relation to the implied evolution of values;
- Gendered social relationships regarding this type of behaviour;
- Comparison of the content of non-work time within different countries;
- Etc.

These subjects only provide examples of the types of papers that are expected. Other topics may be addressed either from a methodological or a theoretical perspective. The editors are particularly interested in papers reporting on international comparisons in this area.

Submission of Manuscripts

Manuscripts should be submitted to guest editors before March 1st, 1996, and should include :

1) Four copies of the manuscript, typed double-spaced ; the first page must not bear the name, address or telephone number of the author or authors ;

2) A title page containing the title of the article, the name or names of the authors, their telephone and Fax numbers as well as the name of their institution ;

3) An abstract of 150 words maximum.

Should the manuscript be accepted, a copy of the text on a diskette identifying software and version will be mandatory.

Tables, figures and notes should be presented on separate sheets with their location noted in the text (e.g. insert Fig. 1 about here).

References should be cited according to the American Psychological Association format.

Mail to :   Diane-Gabrielle Tremblay
            Télé-Université
            C.P. 5250, succursale C
            Montréal (Québec)
            Canada
            H2X 3M4
            Fax : (514) 522-3608

or   Jean-Yves Boulin
            Institut de recherche et d'information socio-économique
            Université Paris Dauphine
            Place Maréchal de Lattre Tassigny
            75775 Paris
            Cedex 16
            France

NUMÉROS DÉJÀ PUBLIÉS
NUMBERS ALREADY PUBLISHED

LOISIR ET SOCIÉTÉ / *SOCIETY AND LEISURE*

Abonnez-vous pour trois ans et recevez **GRATUITEMENT** un exemplaire du livre
Répertoire des établissements de formation et de recherche en loisir, culture et tourisme,
sous la direction de Max D'Amours, ouvrage multilingue, 1991, 602 pages. Une valeur de 35 $.

Ask for a three year subscription and receive a **FREE** book:
International Directory of Academic Institutions in Leisure, Recreation and Related Fields,
edited by Max D'Amours, multilingual, 1991, 602 pages. A 35 $ value.

FEUILLE DE COMMANDE / *ORDER FORM*

	CANADA (Taxes incluses / *Taxes included*)		ÉTRANGER *OTHER COUNTRIES*
	RÉGULIER (Preuve requise) *REGULAR* (*Requested proof*)	ÉTUDIANT *STUDENT*	
3 ans (6 nᵒˢ)	85 $ ☐	62 $ ☐	95 $ ☐
2 ans (4 nᵒˢ)	68 $ ☐	50 $ ☐	75 $ ☐
1 an (2 nᵒˢ)	38 $ ☐	28 $ ☐	43 $ ☐

VENTES À L'UNITÉ / *SINGLE COPY*   **26,75 $** (TPS incluse / *GST included*)

Faites-moi parvenir les titres suivants déjà parus :
Please send me the following back numbers :

Nombre de copies / *Copies*	Volume	Numéro	Total ($)
_____	_____	_____	_____
_____	_____	_____	_____
_____	_____	_____	_____
		TOTAL	_____

D-81

Nom / *Name* _____

Adresse / *Address* _____

Ville / *City* _____

Code postal / *Code* _____   Téléphone / *Phone number* _____

RETOURNEZ CETTE FEUILLE DE COMMANDE AVEC VOTRE PAIEMENT
PAYMENT IS REQUESTED WITH THIS ORDER FORM

☐ Visa   ☐ MasterCard   Nᵒ de compte / *Account Number* _____

Date d'expiration / *Expiration Date* _____   Signature _____

À l'extérieur du Canada, les abonnés sont invités à utiliser leur carte de crédit pour faciliter l'échange des monnaies étrangères.
Foreign subscribers are advised to use credit card in order to facilitate currency exchange.

Postez à / *Mail to* **Presses de l'Université du Québec**
2875, boul. Laurier, Sainte-Foy (Québec) Canada, G1V 2M3

ACCELERATING LEISURE ?

Leisure, Time and Space in a Transitory Society

LEISURE STUDIES ASSOCIATION (LSA)
VERENIGING VAN DE VRIJETIJDSSECTOR (VVS)
1996 CONFERENCE
12 - 14 SEPTEMBER 1996

Society as a whole and leisure in particular is changing at ever greater velocity. Leisure products and services not only circulate along routes of greater and greater distance, but also with ever quickening turnover time. For example: technological changes, the ever emerging of new forms of production and consumption in leisure, processes of globalization and localisation, the growing of various kinds of mobility and migration of people and the building up of numbers of (socio-cultural and land use) conflicts in the countryside and in the cities are causing important transformations in the use of time and space in leisure.

During the LSA-VVS-conference attention will be given to transitions in a.o.:
* the relation between leisure and the culture industry, e.g. the (new) media (from 'word' to 'image'?);
* the public and private provision of leisure (from state to market?);
* the land use in the countryside (from agriculture tot nature and/or recreation and tourism?);
* leisure and tourism attractions (from authenticity to hyper-real?);
* ethics of leisure and tourism

Sub-themes

The aim of the conference is to analyze, understand and explain these and other transformations and their consequences from several points of view. Therefore, the transitions will be dealt with from the point of view of:

* Policy, planning and designing of leisure products and services in time and space;

* Management of leisure products and services

* Research in leisure, time and space: new paradigms?

Ideas for additional themes are invited

Landbouwuniversiteit Wageningen   LEISURE STUDIES ASSOCIATION

Vereniging voor de
Vrijetijdssector

Werkgroep Recreatie en Toerisme

Journal of

APPLIED
RECREATION
RESEARCH

The *Journal of Applied Recreation Research* is prepared quarterly by the Ontario Research Council on Leisure and is devoted to applied research articles on a wide array of topics concerning recreation and leisure. Of interest to both academic researchers and practitioners, the *Journal of Applied Recreation Research* emphasizes the practical implications of empirical and conceptual recreation and leisure research.

Ontario Research Council on Leisure

Conseil ontarien de recherche en loisir

The Ontario Research Council on Leisure (ORCOL) was founded in 1975 and is devoted to the promotion and dissemination of research on all aspects of leisure and recreation including sports, fitness, culture, and tourism. The Council is composed of researchers in the leisure field drawn from government, academe, consultancies, and other agencies, and membership is open to any individual with interests in leisure and recreation research.

Editor: **Mark E. Havitz**, Department of Recreation and Leisure Studies, University of Waterloo, Waterloo, ON   N2L 3G1

Editorial Policy: Open to contributors from Canada and abroad, the *Journal of Applied Recreation Research* publishes articles and reviews in all areas of leisure, recreation, and tourism. All manuscripts are refereed anonymously by three reviewers.

Subscription Information: The *Journal of Applied Recreation Research* is published four times per year by Wilfrid Laurier University Press. A subscription for each volume of four issues is $50.00 (or US$50.00 outside Canada) per year.

Subscriptions and address changes should be sent to:
Wilfrid Laurier University Press
Wilfrid Laurier University
Waterloo, ON, Canada   N2L 3C5
Telephone: (519) 884-0710, ext. 6124
Fax: (519) 725-1399
Make cheques payable to **Wilfrid Laurier University Press**.

Cahiers de recherche sociologique

numéro 24:

L'État dans la tourmente

Bon de commande

JE DÉSIRE RECEVOIR

_____ copies du numéro **L'État dans la tourmente**
($17.33 taxes incluses)

❑chèque.. **Retourner à cette adresse**:
❑Visa No .... Service des publications/CRS
Date d'expiration....................................... Université du Québec à Montréal
❑Master Card No .... C.P. 8888, Succ. Centre-ville
Date d'expiration....................................... Montréal (Qc) H3C 3P8
Nom:..
Organisme ou compagnie: ....
Adresse: ....
Ville:..
postal: ....

À paraître

| #25 | À l'ombre de la souveraineté, nouveaux questionnements (septembre 1995) |
| #26 | La littérature. État des lieux (mai 1996) |

Abonnement

Prix de l'abonnement en dollars canadiens (T.P.S. et T.V.Q. incluses)

	1 an (2 numéros)	2 ans (4 numéros)	3 ans (6 numéros)
au Canada	27$	48$	69$
à l'étranger	30$	54$	77$
institution au Canada	40$	72$	102$
institution étrangère	45$	81$	115$
étudiant	17$	30$	44$

Sixth International Symposium on Society and Resource Management :

Call for papers

All individuals interested in presenting a paper, poster, or organizing a roundtable discussion at the Sixth International Symposium on Society and Natural Resource Management are encouraged to submit an abstract by November 1, 1995 to the address listed below.

The Sixth Symposium is being hosted by the Department of Agricultural Economics and Rural Sociology and The School of Forestry of the College of Agricultural Sciences and the Department of Hotel, Restaurant, and Recreation Management of the School of Health and Human Development at The Pennsylvania State University. It is scheduled for May 18-23, 1996 and will be held on the Penn State campus.

This year's symposium will focus on a better integration of social and natural resource sciences in addressing resource and environmental issues. A commitment to the role of social perspectives in policy development and managing natural resources is underscored.

Symposium activities include concurrent paper and poster sessions, plenary theme addresses, roundtables and dialogue sessions, exhibits, field trips and receptions. Special efforts are being made to encourage and accommodate participation by students this year.

Those wishing to present at the conference should submit abstracts no longer than two, double-spaced, typewritten pages to:

> A.E. Luloff, Program Co-Chair
> Department of Agricultural Economics and Rural Sociology
> 111 Armsby Building
> The Pennsylvania State University
> University Park, PA 16802

The organizers of the Symposium have arranged a variety of publication outlets for some of the papers being presented at the conference. For more information about publication opportunities or topics being addressed at the Symposium, write to the above address.

• Cap-Saint-Ignace
• Sainte-Marie (Beauce)
  Québec, Canada
  1995

«L'IMPRIMEUR»

SOMMAIRE / *CONTENTS*

9 782760 508392

ISBN 2-7605-0839-0

LOISIR & SOCIÉTÉ

SOCIETY AND LEISURE

Vol. 18, n° 2

Temps libre : enjeux contemporains
Free Time : Contemporary Issues

Presses de l'Université du Québec

LOISIR ET SOCIÉTÉ / *SOCIETY AND LEISURE*

Vol. 18, n° 2, automne / *Fall 1995*
Temps libre : enjeux contemporains
Free Time : Contemporary Issues

Éditeurs invités / *Guest Editors*

Michel DE LA DURANTAYE et Pierre GAGNON

Monique Choquette

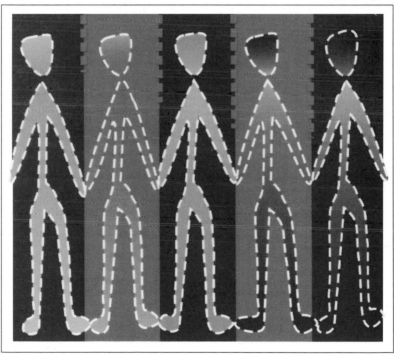

1995
Presses de l'Université du Québec
2875, boul. Laurier, Sainte-Foy (Québec)   G1V 2M3

Directeur / *Editor* : Max D'AMOURS
Éditeurs associés / *Associate Editors*
    Walter TOKARSKY, Allemagne / *Germany*
    Shinji MORINO, Japon / *Japan*
    Karla HENDERSON, États-Unis / *United States*
    Grant CUSHMAN, Nouvelle-Zélande / *New Zealand*
    Nelson MELENDEZ, Porto Rico / *Porto Rico*
Responsables des comptes rendus / *Book Review Editors* : Michel BELLEFLEUR,
    Université du Québec à Trois-Rivières, Jean HARVEY, Université d'Ottawa,
    Louis JOLIN, Université du Québec à Montréal.

Pour toute correspondance
concernant le contenu de la revue
prière de s'adresser à :

For any correspondance
about the content of the review,
please contact :

Loisir et Société / *Society and Leisure*
Département des sciences du loisir
Université du Québec à Trois-Rivières
C.P. 500, Trois-Rivières (Québec)
Canada   G9A 5H7
Tél. : (819) 376-5132 / Télécopieur : (819) 373-1988
Courrier électronique : Loisir_et_Societe@uqtr.uquebec.ca

Pour toute correspondance
concernant les abonnements,
les droits d'auteur et la publicité :

For any correspondance
concerning subscriptions, copyright
and advertizing :

Presses de l'Université du Québec
2875, boulevard Laurier, Sainte-Foy (Québec)
Canada   G1V 2M3

Cette revue est publiée grâce à une subvention accordée par le Fonds FCAR pour l'aide aux revues scientifiques du ministère de l'Enseignement supérieur et de la Science du Québec.

Les articles sont indexés dans *Repère, Loreto, Leisure Research and Tourism Abstract, Sociological Abstract, Bulletin signalétique, SPORT Database, SPORT Discus, Social Welfare Social Planning* et *Women Stud. Abstracts* / *Articles are indexed in* Repère, Loreto, Leisure Research and Tourism Abstract, Sociological Abstract, Bulletin signalétique, SPORT Database, SPORT Discus, Social Welfare Social Planning *and* Women Stud. Abstracts.

Traductions anglaise et française : Diane Leclerc
Traduction espagnole : Oscar Calderon
Secrétariat : Hélène S. Dubois

Créée par le Comité de recherche sur le loisir de l'Association internationale de sociologie, la revue *Loisir et Société* tient à reconnaître ce lien historique en réunissant tous les anciens et nouveaux présidents de ce Comité au sein du Comité international conseil / Society and Leisure *was founded by the Committee on Leisure Research of the International Association of Sociology. The Editorial Board of* Society and Leisure *would like to maintain this historical relationship by appointing all past and new presidents of the Committee on Leisure Research to the journal's International Advisory Board.*

SOMMAIRE / *CONTENTS*

COMPTES RENDUS / *BOOK REVIEWS*

ONT COLLABORÉ À CE NUMÉRO
CONTRIBUTORS TO THIS ISSUE

ALLAIRE, André, Service de la recherche et de l'évaluation, Musée de la civilisation, 85, rue Dalhousie, C.P. 155, succursale B, Québec, Québec, G1K 7A6, téléphone (418) 643-2159, télécopieur (418) 646-8779.

ARCHAMBAULT, Michel, Chaire du Tourisme de l'UQAM, Université du Québec à Montréal, C.P. 8888, succursale Centre-ville, Montréal, Québec, H3C 3P8, téléphone (514) 987-7882, télécopieur (514) 987-3797.

ARSENEAULT, Paul, Chaire du Tourisme de l'UQAM, Université du Québec à Montréal, C.P. 8888, succursale Centre-ville, Montréal, Québec, H3C 3P8, téléphone (514) 987-7882, télécopieur (514) 987-3797.

BARABÉ, André, Département des sciences du loisir, Université du Québec à Trois-Rivières, C.P. 500, Trois-Rivières, Québec, G9A 5H7, téléphone (819) 376-5132, télécopieur (819) 373-1988.

BEAUREGARD, Myriam, Département des sciences du loisir, Université du Québec à Trois-Rivières, C.P. 500, Trois-Rivières, Québec, G9A 5H7, téléphone (819) 376-5132, télécopieur (819) 373-1988.

BELLEFLEUR, Michel, Département des sciences du loisir, Université du Québec à Trois-Rivières, C.P. 500, Trois-Rivières, Québec, G9A 5H7, téléphone (819) 376-5132, télécopieur (819) 373-1988.

DAGENAIS, Michèle, Département d'histoire, Faculté des arts et des sciences, Université de Montréal, C.P. 6128, succursale Centre-ville, Montréal, Québec, H3C 3J7, téléphone (514) 343-6234, télécopieur (514) 343-2483.

DE LA DURANTAYE, Michel, Département des sciences du loisir, Université du Québec à Trois-Rivières, C.P. 500, Trois-Rivières, Québec, G9A 5H7, téléphone (819) 376-5132, télécopieur (819) 373-1988.

DE LA GARDE, Roger, Département d'information et de communication, Université Laval, Cité universitaire, Sainte-Foy, Québec, G1K 7P4, téléphone (418) 656-5191, télécopieur (418) 656-7807.

GAGNON, Pierre, Département des sciences du loisir, Université du Québec à Trois-Rivières, C.P. 500, Trois-Rivières, G9A 5H7, Québec, téléphone (819) 376-5132, télécopieur (819) 373-1988.

LEMIEUX, Jacques, Département d'information et de communication, Université Laval, Cité universitaire, Sainte-Foy, Québec, G1K 7P4, téléphone (418) 656-5191, télécopieur (418) 656-7807.

MARTIN, Claude, Département de communication, Université de Montréal, C.P. 6128, succursale Centre-ville, Montréal, Québec, H3C 3J7.

OUELLET, Gaétan, Département des sciences du loisir, Université du Québec à Trois-Rivières, C.P. 500, Trois-Rivières, Québec, G9A 5H7, téléphone (819) 376-5132, télécopieur (819) 373-1988.

PAQUIN, Maryse, Faculté d'éducation, Université d'Ottawa, C.P. 450, succursale A, Ottawa, Ontario, K1N 6N5, téléphone (613) 562-5800 poste 4136, télécopieur (613) 562-5146.

PRONOVOST, Gilles, Département des sciences du loisir, Université du Québec à Trois-Rivières, C.P. 500, Trois-Rivières, Québec, G9A 5H7, téléphone (819) 376-5132, télécopieur (819) 373-1988.

SKY, Pauline, School of Sport and Leisure Studies, The University of New South Wales, St. George Campus, P.O. Box 88, Oatley, NSW 2223, Australia, phone 61 2 385 9999, fax 61 2 385 9864.

INTRODUCTION
TEMPS LIBRE : ENJEUX
CONTEMPORAINS

Michel DE LA DURANTAYE
Pierre GAGNON

À la suite du Colloque international sur le loisir tenu à l'Université du Québec à Trois-Rivières, en novembre 1994, auquel 1300 personnes ont participé, la revue Loisir et Société a décidé de produire un numéro spécial regroupant un échantillon des nombreuses communications scientifiques qui y furent présentées. Il n'est pas représentatif de la grande variété des sujets qui y furent traités, mais il illustre bien les enjeux et défis contemporains qui interpellent la triade loisir-culture-tourisme.

Dans le premier texte, Michèle Dagenais nous réfère aux circonstances, au tournant du XXe siècle, entourant le début de la prise en charge, par les pouvoirs politiques locaux, d'un aspect de la vie culturelle montréalaise, la bibliothèque publique, son implantation. Elle nous explique comment les pouvoirs politiques montréalais se sont impliqués dans ce domaine bien avant la naissance des ministères provincial et fédéral de la Culture. Si les circonstances à l'origine de l'intervention municipale dans le champ culturel ont changé, par contre les défis et les enjeux urbains et nationaux se posent encore avec acuité dans ce domaine culturel.

Le texte de Pierre Gagnon vient nous rappeler, comme en parallèle, que les municipalités du Québec à l'aube du XXIe siècle, sont encore interpellées par l'accroissement de nouvelles responsabilités qui leur incombent suite notamment à la nouvelle politique culturelle du Québec de 1992, à titre de partenaires privilégiés dans le développement culturel des collectivités locales.

Au début de ce siècle comme à sa fin, la question de la fonction publique, de la fonction urbaine de la culture, pour paraphraser Michèle Dagenais, se trouve posée et renouvelée sans cesse. Des associations littéraires responsables de la création de lieux comme les bibliothèques au début du siècle à la mise sur pied de services de loisirs renouvelés dont le mandat est d'intervenir dans le secteur du développement communautaire, en cette fin de siècle, la continuité historique semble évidente. C'est celle de la formation de la conscience publique, pour utiliser un terme de Michèle Dagenais, et de sa responsabilité sociale.

Aujourd'hui, la situation actuelle des finances publiques ne fait que complexifier la situation. Cependant le problème de la prise en charge par les pouvoirs publics du développement culturel se pose toujours, mais en des termes plus dramatiques. De nos jours, les gouvernements remettent encore en question le rôle de pourvoyeur qu'ils ont tenu auprès des citoyens. De plus, un consensus semble s'imposer sur la nécessité de réduire le déficit gouvernemental. Dans ce contexte, comment justifier l'utilisation des fonds publics pour la culture, le loisir, le développement communautaire... ? Pour répondre à ce type de question, il faut, d'une part, suivre le cheminement historique de la conscience publique dans le domaine et, d'autre part, observer les tendances de fond en suivant leurs racines dans le temps.

De son enquête auprès des responsables des services de loisirs municipaux du Québec, Pierre Gagnon conclut que, de façon générale, les services municipaux de loisir ont déjà intégré assez fortement les secteurs du développement communautaire et de la culture à leur secteur d'activité traditionnel du loisir. Selon lui, la tendance générale pour l'avenir va dans le sens d'une plus forte intégration de ces secteurs d'activité. Pour Gagnon, la mission et les fonctions du service municipal des loisirs évoluent rapidement dans le sens d'un service multifonctionnel où les secteurs du développement communautaire et de la culture occuperont une place encore plus importante que présentement. Son enquête l'amène à observer un fort degré d'intégration de ces secteurs, intégration actuelle ou en cours de processus. À titre d'exemple, 112 répondants sur 130 affirment que les organismes culturels, agissant sur leur territoire, sont protégés actuellement par les politiques existantes de reconnaissance et de soutien de leur municipalité. Par ailleurs, 93 répondants sur 130 affirment que c'est le cas également pour les organismes de développement communautaire. Ces chiffres démontrent, selon Gagnon, une assez grande intégration de ces secteurs à celui du loisir.

Ce procès fondamental d'intégration entre les niveaux du temps libre semble constituer un enjeu majeur dans nos sociétés. Le texte de Maryse Paquin en est une autre illustration. Celle-ci nous montre que l'éducation ne peut pas être le monopole exclusif de l'école, si on veut développer des valeurs culturelles et une conscience sociale chez les élèves. Maryse Paquin attire notre attention sur le potentiel éducatif de divers lieux extra-scolaires qui peuvent contribuer à la formation. Dès 1986, selon Paquin, le Conseil supérieur de l'éducation reconnaissait certaines institutions culturelles dont les objectifs d'éducation sont reliés à ceux de l'école et dans lesquelles celle-ci peut puiser de nouvelles ressources : les sites naturels, les lieux historiques, les bibliothèques, les musées d'art ou de science.

Maryse Paquin nous rappelle que dès 1982 la Commission d'étude sur la formation professionnelle et socioculturelle des adultes prétendait que les activités éducatives et culturelles peuvent être considérées comme un lieu de coexistence, d'alternance et d'échange entre les objectifs spécifiques tantôt à la culture, tantôt à l'éducation : objectifs de détente et d'effort, de divertissement et d'animation, de création et de formation. Selon Paquin, le Conseil supérieur de l'éducation croit que l'école et les institutions culturelles doivent inscrire leurs actions propres dans une perspective de complémentarité. Par exemple, le musée et la bibliothèque peuvent collaborer avec le milieu scolaire pour la mise en œuvre d'activités éducatives destinées aux élèves. C'est dans ce contexte général qu'il faut comprendre l'expérimentation de Maryse Paquin et son évaluation de trois programmes éducatifs muséaux, conçus en relation avec les programmes scolaires de sciences humaines, sciences de la nature et français, dont elle nous fait part ici. Ces programmes éducatifs muséaux ont été conçus et validés selon le Modèle didactique d'utilisation du musée à des fins éducatives. Selon Paquin, ce modèle vise à harmoniser les ressources muséales et scolaires : il permet aux musées et aux écoles un programme visant des objectifs d'ordre pédagogique, ludique et scientifique sans les opposer entre eux. Encore ici, l'intégration de différents niveaux d'intervention est le concept central. Les recherches de Maryse Paquin et de ses collègues confirment l'urgence que toutes les institutions scolaires et culturelles mettent en commun leurs ressources humaines et matérielles au service de la formation des élèves.

Les retombées sociales découlant des interventions en matière de loisir-culture-tourisme prennent une importance stratégique de plus en plus grande, on le voit bien. De plus, la complémentarité des secteurs d'intervention est une réalité systémique qu'on ne peut plus ignorer même dans le domaine du temps libre. Désormais, le temps libre ne contredit pas le temps de travail, il en complète l'action.

Par ailleurs, dans le contexte actuel où les institutions culturelles voient diminuer considérablement leurs sources publiques de financement ainsi que leur fréquentation, le milieu muséal, selon André Allaire, tend de plus en plus à adopter une approche client visant, entre autres, à maintenir l'achalandage, voire à fidéliser la clientèle. Se référant à une enquête menée auprès des visiteurs du Musée de la civilisation, André Allaire étudie les déterminants de la satisfaction des clients à l'égard de la visite du Musée. Ce sont les variables définissant l'expérience muséale du visiteur beaucoup plus que les caractéristiques sociodémographiques et socioculturelles de clients qui déterminent le plus, selon lui, le degré de satisfaction. Et la variable perception de l'accueil reçu constitue de loin le meilleur déterminant du degré de satisfaction générale. En comparaison, les caractéristiques individuelles du visiteur n'influenceraient que faiblement la satisfaction. Le Musée de la civilisation à ce niveau ne se comporte pas différemment des autres organismes culturels, même publics, qui doivent de plus en plus composer avec les lois du marché, et pour ce, évaluer les déterminants de la pratique culturelle.

Jacques Lemieux, Roger de la Garde et Claude Martin abordent le sujet des produits culturels de grande consommation, s'intéressant à l'évolution de la demande pour les activités culturelles de loisir les plus populaires c'est-à-dire le visionnement de la télévision et la lecture. Ils établissent un lien fondamental entre les produits culturels de grande consommation et l'état de la conscience collective d'une société. Regarder une émission de télévision, disent-ils, écouter une pièce musicale, lire un livre, visionner un film, c'est se reconnaître une identité commune à travers des signes et des symboles qui participent et télé-participent à la construction d'une référence culturelle. Leur approche aux phénomènes culturels traite, selon eux, du processus social continu et contradictoire de la production, de la circulation et de la consommation et réception des produits culturels à grands succès comme le livre et la télévision. Il nous font remarquer que la lecture vient au deuxième rang des loisirs préférés des Québécois, après les activités physiques et de plein air. Parlant de la concurrence internationale sur le marché du livre, ils précisent que la bataille entre les éditeurs se livre ici essentiellement entre la France et le Québec. Car, selon eux, si les éditeurs québécois sont responsables de la quasi-totalité des titres provenant d'auteurs québécois ou canadiens, ce sont les maisons d'édition françaises qui exportent au Québec non seulement leurs œuvres nationales, mais également la plupart des best-sellers étrangers traduits en français. Concernant la forte présence des best-sellers étrangers au Québec, les auteurs soulignent pertinemment que cela fait très fortement contraste avec le très grand ethnocentrisme de la liste américaine du *Publisher's Weekley* (1968-1992) où les auteurs nationaux sont responsables de 87 % des titres. Ils constatent un phénomène analogue en France, où un seul titre étranger figure sur la liste des grands succès de l'Express de 1969 à 1992. Se référant aux listes de best-sellers de *La Presse* qui identifient 451 livres d'origines et de genres divers, ils indiquent que, pour ce qui concerne l'origine, les auteurs et les éditeurs québécois sont responsables de près de 40 % des titres. Cependant, ils nous fournissent des précisions intéressantes sur le genre de livres les plus vendus. Notons au passage, que la part des auteurs québécois, qui est de 40 % pour l'ensemble des best-sellers, n'est que de 25 % pour le roman, genre le plus populaire chez les récits de fiction dominant les best-sellers. Au plan télévisuel, l'équivalent du best-seller c'est le téléroman. Or, dans les deux cas, selon nos auteurs, leur succès peut en bonne partie s'expliquer par leur rapport direct avec l'actualité et les débats de la place publique sur les questions du jour.

On le voit ici au niveau de l'industrie du livre et de la télévision, le loisir de divertissement est en forte concurrence avec le loisir éducatif et formatif.

Situation prévisible dans une société de grande consommation ou de consommation de masse.

D'autres enjeux que la consommation de masse et l'identité sociale et culturelle d'une collectivité confrontent les activités de loisir. Le texte de Myriam Beauregard et Gaétan Ouellet nous en fournit un exemple. L'aspect dominant ici n'est plus la consommation sociétale par temps libre, mais la prévention de certains phénomènes sociaux à éviter grâce au temps libre et aux activités stratégiquement planifiées de loisir. Le texte de Beauregard et Ouellet s'inscrit dans une approche dite de qualité de vie par rapport aux activités de loisirs comme instruments de prévention de certains malaises sociaux et de réduction de coûts y étant associés. Les phénomènes sociaux que l'on cherche ainsi à réduire ou prévenir au moyen des activités de loisir sont ici dans le cas de Beauregard et Ouellet, le décrochage scolaire, mais aussi, par ailleurs, ce peut être des problèmes de santé provoqués par un mode de vie physiquement sédentaire (combattu par Kino-Québec) ou par le vieillissement de la population. Ce pourrait être le taux de suicide, notamment chez les jeunes. Ce pourrait être aussi le désœuvrement ou le chômage et la pauvreté chez les jeunes, ou encore, la délinquance, la consommation de drogue, le vandalisme et la criminalité, la guerre des gangs et les comportements antisociaux. On peut ajouter l'éclatement de la famille, l'isolement, notamment des personnes âgées et des minorités, l'alcoolisme.

Sans être une panacée, les activités de loisirs stratégiquement planifiées peuvent contribuer au mouvement fondamental de prévention dans nos sociétés.

Pour Beauregard et Ouellet, l'absentéisme et le décrochage scolaire constituent des symptômes manifestes que l'école secondaire ne répond plus aux besoins et aspirations d'un bon nombre de ses étudiants. Nos auteurs émettent l'hypothèse que les activités parascolaires, utilisées dans des conditions précises, pourraient contribuer à réduire la prédisposition au décrochage scolaire chez certains étudiants.

Comme les activités muséales, dans le texte de Paquin, les activités parascolaires de loisir, dans le texte de Beauregard et Ouellet, permettent une valorisation de l'éducation et de l'école. Citant une importante étude du Conseil supérieur de l'Éducation de 1987 portant sur les activités parascolaires, les auteurs rapportent que pour le Conseil, l'organisation des activités parascolaires est associée à une amélioration de la motivation scolaire, à une réduction des problèmes de discipline et des comportements délinquants, ainsi qu'à une réduction de l'absentéisme scolaire. C'est dans ce contexte que Beauregard et Ouellet ont conduit une recherche de type exploratoire sur le sujet. Leur programme expérimental a favorisé la réduction de la prédisposition au décrochage scolaire des décrocheurs appartenant à un certain profil de clientèle. L'implication dans une telle activité parascolaire semble avoir une incidence favorable sur les causes du décrochage, notamment par l'amélioration de l'estime de soi et de la perception du milieu scolaire, la motivation scolaire et l'absentéisme.

Un autre courant mondialement reconnu au plan des activités de temps libre et appartenant au mouvement fondamental de prévention dans nos sociétés est celui présenté par André Barabé dans son texte sur le tourisme et le développement durable. Voilà un enjeu majeur pour l'industrie touristique et le monde moderne. Un tourisme alternatif comme l'écotourisme va contribuer à la préservation de l'écosystème tout en respectant l'intégrité des collectivités d'accueil, selon Barabé qui cite le Conseil consultatif canadien de l'environnement. Selon l'auteur, le concept d'écotourisme favorise une préoccupation de l'intégrité des manifestations naturelles et culturelles caractéristiques des zones visitées. Au surplus, l'écotourisme se veut un stimulant économique pour les communautés d'accueil de ce type de touriste. Cette conception du tourisme se veut une conception préventive afin de protéger les zones les plus fragiles de notre milieu à visiter et à découvrir. Pour Barabé, ce tourisme durable constitue une réponse à la croissance du tourisme et de la demande pour visiter des milieux naturels et culturels de qualité mais fragiles. Bref, un compromis acceptable entre offre et demande touristiques, entre croissance et développement du secteur. Un compromis tolérable entre la société de conservation et la société de consommation. De façon à ne pas empêcher le progrès tout en préservant le principal, André Barabé nous présente un certain nombre de cas réussis, tout en montrant la portée et les limites de ces cas. Sa présentation du processus actuel d'élaboration des indicateurs du tourisme durable ainsi que la conception de codes de déontologie et d'éthique en la matière nous montrent le degré d'avancement de ce secteur qui préfigure en quelque sorte des lignes directrices qui pourraient inspirer dans le futur d'autres secteurs de la société de consommation et du temps libre.

Le texte de Michel Archambault et Paul Arsenault témoigne des grandes tendances concernant l'industrie du voyage et la croissance du tourisme. S'appuyant sur un sondage effectué auprès de la main-d'œuvre et des dirigeants des agences de voyages détaillantes et grossistes au Québec, les auteurs cernent la nature de l'industrie et identifient les enjeux qui risquent de marquer son évolution.

De nos jours, le secteur du voyage se présente, selon les auteurs, dans le cas de certaines destinations, comme un bien de consommation courante en compétition avec d'autres biens et services vendus au détail. Selon eux, les trois enjeux auxquels est confronté l'industrie concernent trois dimensions. D'abord, la structure de l'industrie, ensuite la technologie disponible et enfin la formation de la main-d'œuvre.

Les enjeux au niveau de la structure de l'industrie concernent, selon Archambault et Arsenault, les changements dans la nature de la demande de la clientèle, les besoins étant plus diversifiés et précis. De plus, l'industrie est trop peu structurée et manque de professionnalisme. Enfin, l'achat massif des technologies récentes et les économies de volume suite aux regroupements, fusions et alliances au niveau mondial, sont déterminants. Concernant les enjeux technologiques en matière informatique, de télécommunications et de services bancaires automatisés et informatisés, les auteurs indiquent que l'environnement de l'industrie sera bouleversé. Ceci aura un impact sur la réservation, l'information et la gestion, selon eux, sans mentionner l'impact de l'autoroute de l'information sur les habitudes de la clientèle. Finalement, l'enjeu concernant la formation de la main-d'œuvre concerne le manque de main-d'œuvre qualifiée dans l'industrie. En terminant, ces auteurs suggèrent des scénarios et des pistes d'action pour relever les défis mentionnés.

Quant au texte de Pauline Sky, en note de recherche, sur le rôle de l'art des femmes aborigènes australiennes dans l'identité culturelle de ces peuples, il concerne le problème de l'autonomie des femmes aborigènes et leur droit de parole dans les débats sur les droits territoriaux. Texte à teneur anthropologique et utilisant l'approche épistémologique féministe, il met l'emphase sur l'autonomie des femmes aborigènes dans le domaine des rites, des lois traditionnelles et des cérémonies tribales en Australie. L'auteure nous montre que la science ou la connaissance des femmes aborigènes est véhiculée par l'art, les chants et les danses. Dans une perspective d'étude comparée à partir de notre notion moderne de temps libre, on peut comprendre que ces manifestations dites culturelles sont loin d'être superfétatoires chez les aborigènes et qu'elles constituent le cœur même ou le fondement du statut social des femmes dans la communauté tribale australienne. L'apport de l'anthropologie dans l'étude comparative de la notion contemporaine de temps libre est indispensable aux sciences du loisir actuelles. Ce texte en témoigne dans la mesure où la notion de temps n'est pas la même dans les sociétés primitives que dans nos sociétés.

Par ce rappel des enjeux principaux soulevés par les auteurs, ce numéro de la revue contribue à illustrer de façon convaincante la multiplicité des réseaux qui se sont tissés patiemment entre le temps libre et ses manifestations, ainsi que les multiples défis relevés par le domaine du loisir, de la culture et du tourisme. Le temps libre, on le voit, prend une signification renouvelée dans le contexte de ces enjeux. Il prend une signification plus stratégique, de moins en moins abandonnée au laisser-faire et à la dimension impressive du temps. Qui affirmait que le défi du XXIe siècle était de transformer le temps libéré en quelque chose de sensé ? Sans tomber dans une approche utilitariste du temps libre, on peut tout de même reconnaître que le temps libre, comme le reste de la vie quotidienne, est de plus en plus interpellé par l'histoire et la société, et il remplit de plus en plus une fonction sociale et historique.

CULTURE URBAINE ET POUVOIRS PUBLICS LOCAUX À MONTRÉAL AU DÉBUT DU 20ᵉ SIÈCLE[1]

Michèle DAGENAIS

Département d'histoire
Université de Montréal

Introduction

Carte maîtresse de la stratégie des villes dans la concurrence qu'elles se livrent, la culture constitue aujourd'hui une sorte de vitrine qui confère aux grands ensembles urbains leur personnalité propre. Les administrations municipales l'ont bien compris et se sont impliquées activement dans ce domaine ou ont soutenu par divers moyens les activités culturelles sur leur territoire. À tel point que la culture est désormais considérée comme une fonction urbaine au même titre que le commerce ou l'industrie. De ce fait, on a bien souvent l'impression que la municipalisation du champ culturel est un phénomène nouveau ou du moins récent (Latouche, 1991). Or, il n'en est rien. Aussi bien en Grande-Bretagne (Bowker, 1990 ; Kite, 1992), qu'en France (Rioux et Sirinelli, dir., 1990) et au Canada (Bloomfield, 1981 ; Penman, 1983), les pouvoirs politiques locaux se sont impliqués dans ce domaine bien avant la naissance des ministères provinciaux ou nationaux de la culture. Si au fil du temps les liens entre culture et monde urbain ont revêtu des formes différentes et soulevé des questions particulières, il demeure qu'ils existent depuis fort longtemps.

Dans ce court article, nous présentons les premiers résultats de notre recherche sur les circonstances à l'origine de l'intervention municipale dans le champ culturel, à la lumière de l'expérience montréalaise. Ce retour aux sources nous semble particulièrement approprié dans la mesure où la culture ne faisait pas partie des secteurs d'intervention des municipalités canadiennes dès leur origine, au même titre que les travaux publics par exemple. Son étude peut donc permettre d'analyser de quelle façon s'élaborent les politiques municipales : d'identifier les différents facteurs qui vont amener les villes à considérer la culture comme faisant partie de leurs responsabilités, puis comme un service à la population, un service public qu'elles doivent assumer.

Cependant, pour parvenir pleinement à retracer cette genèse des politiques municipales dans le cas de Montréal, il faudrait établir un relevé exhaustif des actions qu'elle a menées dans ce secteur : lors de l'inauguration d'évènements spéciaux, comme bailleur de fonds, comme entrepreneur dans l'aménagement de parcs, de jardins, de terrains de jeux ou de bains, comme propriétaire de sites loués à des associations sportives ou culturelles. Cela représenterait un travail colossal même pour la période qui nous intéresse, soit le tournant du 20e siècle. C'est pourquoi, dans un premier temps, nous avons choisi de mener une enquête en profondeur sur un aspect spécifique de l'intervention municipale dans la vie culturelle : la mise sur pied d'une bibliothèque « publique » au début du 20e siècle. Un dossier particulièrement riche pour prendre la mesure du rôle joué par l'administration montréalaise comme agent de ce que nous appelons, à la suite d'Yvan Lamonde (1983), la culture publique urbaine.

Un espace à définir : la vie culturelle montréalaise au 19e siècle

Cette culture publique urbaine est en pleine définition au tournant du siècle à Montréal, comme dans plusieurs autres villes d'Amérique du Nord (Barth, 1980 ; Bender, 1988). C'est une période de croissance rapide des villes, marquée également par un processus d'industrialisation intense. À Montréal, la composition sociale et ethnique de la population se transforme radicalement dans la seconde moitié du 19e siècle avec l'émergence d'une bourgeoisie d'affaires prospère, la formation d'une main-d'œuvre salariée abondante, les nombreuses vagues d'immigration en provenance de la Grande-Bretagne et l'arrivée des populations rurales (Linteau, 1992).

Ce brassage de population se répercute tout particulièrement sur les composantes et la définition de la vie culturelle. Jusqu'au milieu du 19e siècle, en effet, cette vie culturelle était l'apanage d'un petit groupe sélect d'individus, apparenté à la bourgeoisie. Elle se déployait essentiellement dans les salons privés et les rares petites salles de spectacles que Montréal possédait (Lamonde, 1990). Mais les transformations majeures que subit la société montréalaise font naître le besoin d'un élargissement des cadres de cette vie culturelle à caractère plutôt privé. Plusieurs recherches sur les loisirs publics et commerciaux (Dufresne, 1990, 1983 ; Lamonde et Montpetit, 1986 ; Montpetit, 1979), sur la vie intellectuelle et culturelle (Gagnon, 1995 ;

Lajeunesse, 1982 ; Lamonde, 1990 ; Wyczynski, 1972), sur les sports (Janson, 1995 ; Metcalfe, 1983, 1978) rendent compte du processus d'élaboration d'espaces multiples concourant à l'émergence d'une vie culturelle davantage publique mais aussi urbaine.

Ce processus est le résultat des actions menées par de multiples acteurs dans leur tentative d'aménager des lieux de rencontre et d'échange propices à la constitution de nouvelles formes de sociabilité plus ou moins organisées : à travers la formation d'associations littéraires responsables de la création de lieux de discussion ou de bibliothèques, l'ouverture de musées, l'organisation de concerts dans les parcs, la mise sur pied de loisirs dans les terrains de jeux, la production d'évènements ou de manifestations culturels tels les carnavals, les expositions, etc.

Dans la majorité des études produites à ce jour sur la vie culturelle montréalaise, référence est faite à la présence de l'administration municipale, à divers titres. Bien que ces recherches n'analysent pas en elle même cette présence, certaines de leurs remarques donnent à penser que la Ville a été un agent important dans le processus de redéfinition de la vie culturelle qui s'amorce à partir de la seconde moitié du 19ᵉ siècle. Cependant, plus que de sa propre initiative, c'est sous l'effet des multiples demandes sociales que la Ville consent à agir. Ses interventions se font donc surtout par à coup, sans planification préalable, au gré des requêtes et des pressions exercées à son endroit.

La création d'une bibliothèque publique à Montréal : un débat houleux

Même si certaines bibliothèques sont fondées dès le 17ᵉ siècle au Canada (Drolet, 1965), c'est au cours du 19ᵉ siècle que prend véritablement son envol le mouvement de création des temples du livre. Ils sont alors mis sur pied par des organismes aussi divers que les hommes d'affaires, les syndicats de métiers, les associations culturelles anglophones et francophones, les institutions d'enseignement ou le clergé (Lamonde, 1979). Mais il s'agit là de bibliothèques de collectivités, c'est-à-dire d'institutions ayant un caractère plutôt privé, financées par des groupes restreints et qui offrent des services à leurs seuls membres. Ancêtres des bibliothèques publiques, elles jouent néanmoins un rôle majeur dans le développement de la vie culturelle en milieu urbain, et en particulier à Montréal.

S'inspirant notamment des expériences américaine puis torontoise, un important mouvement d'opinion composite lutte, à partir du dernier tiers du 19ᵉ siècle, pour la démocratisation du savoir et dénonce la pauvreté des moyens dont dispose la population montréalaise pour y accéder. Il réclame la fondation d'une biliothèque publique à Montréal : une bibliothèque laïque, ouverte à tous, gratuite et donc financée par les pouvoirs publics. Cette demande d'ouverture d'une bibliothèque municipale se démarque donc radicalement des institutions culturelles existantes puisqu'elle implique la création « ... (d')une *Bibliothèque populaire* indépendante de toute dénomination ou subordination religieuse »[2] et nécessite l'intervention de l'administration municipale. Mais, comme le révèlent les premiers résultats de notre recherche sur la Bibliothèque municipale[3], cette intervention des autorités politiques locales va engendrer de très vives tensions au sein de la société montréalaise de cette époque. Deux questions fondamentales se retrouvent au cœur du litige. La première concerne la définition même de la notion de culture publique et la deuxième, celle du mandat des pouvoirs publics locaux dans ce domaine. Examinons les principales composantes de ce débat.

Tout d'abord, comment définir et que doit comprendre une culture dite publique, dans une société telle que la société montréalaise, divisée par une foule de clivages à la fois sociaux, ethniques et religieux ? Comme le rapporte si justement un grand quotidien montréalais à cette époque : « Notre société est composée de catholiques et de protestants, d'Anglais, de Canadiens... Quel est le criterium qui devra former la conscience publique ? »[4] Cette question prend tout sons sens dans le Montréal du tournant du 20e siècle où les tensions, résultant de la cohabitation entre Canadiens d'origines française et britannique, demeurent vives en dépit de l'existence d'une stratégie dite de cloisonnement institutionnel. Élaborée depuis le début du 19e siècle par les élites, cette stratégie a conduit à la mise en place de tout un réseau d'institutions sur une base confessionnelle. Comme l'explique alors l'archevêque de Montréal, Paul Bruchési : « Nous avons à Montréal deux sociétés distinctes, la société catholique et la société non catholique. (...) Nous avons nos écoles, nos asiles de charité, nos orphelinats ; les protestants ont les leurs... et c'est là que se trouve le secret de la paix qui règne parmi nous, en même temps que du respect de la liberté de conscience qui règne à Montréal. Il y a certains terrains sur lesquels la fusion n'est pas possible. »[5]

La crainte de voir les élus municipaux remettre en question ce fragile équilibre, en érigeant une bibliothèque publique, est surtout vivement ressentie par les élites francophones, clergé en tête. Mais au-delà de son souci de préserver la paix sociale, l'épiscopat montréalais craint le vent de laïcisation qui souffle sur la société montréalaise, tout comme dans le monde occidental de l'époque, dans cette période de valorisation du progrès matériel et de déploiement des valeurs marchandes. La laïcité est menaçante non seulement en ce qu'elle propose de nouveaux modèles d'organisation sociale où sont mises au second plan les références aux croyances religieuses, mais aussi parce qu'elle s'exprime souvent contre l'Église catholique elle-même. La laïcité est également menaçante car elle présuppose une implication plus grande des pouvoirs publics dans la gestion des questions sociales, au détriment de l'Église bien entendu. Pour faire face à la tempête, cette dernière va d'ailleurs chercher à occuper le plus possible de terrains tout spécialement dans le monde du travail, dans les domaines de l'éducation, de la culture et des loisirs.

La campagne en faveur de l'ouverture d'une bibliothèque municipale à Montréal révèle donc l'existence d'un second enjeu : celui de l'affranchissement des laïcs de la tutelle du clergé. S'étendant sur plusieurs années, cette lutte réunit plusieurs intellectuels et des membres de l'élite libérale francophone[6]. Elle vise l'instauration d'institutions véritablement publiques qui favorisent la circulation d'œuvres et d'idées critiques y compris à l'égard des institutions catholiques et de leur pouvoir sur la société. En ce sens, le processus de définition d'une culture publique auquel contribue le débat sur la bibliothèque municipale implique la constitution d'espaces nouveaux, de lieux de rencontre, d'échanges et de sociabilité pluralistes et modernes, à l'image du siècle naissant.

Il importe de noter que cet aspect des débats entourant la Bibliothèque municipale concerne essentiellement les francophones de la ville, car le besoin d'une bibliothèque publique se fait sentir ici plus cruellement qu'au sein de la communauté anglophone. Tout d'abord, le réseau de cette dernière est beaucoup plus ancien et important qu'en milieu francophone. Outre les bibliothèques d'association telles celle du *Montreal Mechanics' Institute* (Robins, 1978) ou du *Young Men Christian Association* (Lamonde, 1979 : 67), on relève la présence de celle du *Fraser Institute* qui, à partir de 1885, renferme près de 30 000 livres. De plus, Westmount fonde une bibliothèque publique en 1899. Même si elle est destinée à la population habitant sur son territoire, elle s'adresse elle aussi à la clientèle anglophone.

Mais au-delà de l'importance des ressources du milieu anglophone, il est une autre dimension qui semble centrale dans cette bataille si fondamentale pour bien des intellectuels et des membres de l'élite libérale francophone de l'époque : celle de leur affranchissement vis-à-vis du clergé. Ce que les anglophones n'ont pas à vivre, du moins de la même manière, puisque les membres du clergé protestant ne cherchent pas à contrôler le développement des bibliothèques en autant qu'une certaine morale, définie de manière assez large, soit sauvegardée[7].

Finalement, le projet d'ouverture d'une bibliothèque publique est aussi contesté dans la mesure où il implique une démocratisation du savoir, de l'accès à la connaissance. Portée par les syndicats, les partis ouvriers (J. Rouillard, 1989 : 43, 56) et certains groupes d'intellectuels tels les membres des loges maçonniques montréalaises (LeMoine, 1991 ; Heap, 1982), cette revendication heurte l'élite bien pensante qui s'oppose à la libre circulation d'ouvrages jugés frivoles et craint, par dessous tout, de mettre à la disposition du peuple des œuvres critiques, des lectures subversives et contestataires : « Il s'agit, écrit-on à l'époque, de protéger l'âme de nos enfants et de veiller à la conservation de notre foi nationale et de nos bonnes mœurs »[8].

Si, à la rigueur, des bibliothèques voyaient le jour, il ne pourrait s'agir que de lieux d'étude et de référence, comportant des essais, des ouvrages scientifiques et techniques et, peut-être, certains classiques de la littérature. Tout comme les écoles du soir, établies en 1889 sous le gouvernement d'Honoré Mercier pour améliorer le niveau d'instruction des ouvriers (J. Rouillard, 1989 : 56), les bibliothèques sont alors perçues strictement comme des instruments destinés à : « ... former, développer et éclairer l'esprit et le cœur de l'ouvrier et ... fortifier en lui le sentiment du devoir. » (E. Rouillard, 1890 : 8) C'est pourquoi dans l'esprit de plusieurs, il ne saurait être question d'ériger : « ... (des) établissements qui feraient la plus large part à cette catégorie d'ouvrages frivoles dont le marché est inondé et qui n'apprennent rien. On ne pourrait... prononcer l'exclusion totale du roman... mais le genre sérieux, le livre utile doit prédominer, si l'on tient à former des hommes capables d'engager avec courage et succès les batailles de vie... En résumé, il faut à l'ouvrier comme à tout autre homme une nourriture intellectuelle qui laisse son âme calme et pure et qui n'y fasse naître que de généreux sentiments. » (E. Rouillard, 1890 : 25)

Ainsi, quelles que soient les raisons invoquées, plusieurs éléments de la société montréalaise s'opposent à l'érection d'une bibliothèque publique et de là, à la constitution d'espaces propices au développement d'une culture publique urbaine. La brèche ainsi créée risque de compromettre les anciennes divisions et hiérarchies en favorisant l'émergence d'institutions et de pratiques d'un nouveau genre, c'est-à-dire ouvertes à tous indépendamment de leurs croyances, de leurs origines sociale et professionnelle et de leur ethnie.

La culture : une responsabilité municipale ?

Toutefois, l'élément déterminant qui va conférer un caractère résolument public à cette culture urbaine en pleine élaboration, c'est l'implication directe des pouvoirs locaux. De fait, en assumant le financement d'institutions telle que la bibliothèque, l'administration municipale les rend accessibles à tous. Les groupes favorables à l'érection d'une bibliothèque publique l'ont bien compris et réclament très tôt l'intervention des institutions politiques locales. Mais c'est précisément aussi pour cette raison que le projet d'ouverture d'une bibliothèque publique soulève de vives objections. La culture est alors considérée comme une affaire privée et doit de ce fait relever d'associations, de clubs ou d'entrepreneurs.

À une époque où une bonne partie de l'élite perçoit le vote des toutes premières lois sociales québécoises et canadiennes comme autant de fautes graves qui trahissent sa conception libérale du rôle de l'État (Fecteau, 1986 : 135-136), il ne saurait donc être admissible que la culture soit prise en charge par les pouvoirs publics, fussent-ils municipaux. Il serait trompeur d'interpréter cette opposition à l'extension du rôle des institutions politiques comme n'étant qu'une manifestation de plus de la résistance des classes dirigeantes québécoises face à l'État. Cette opposition s'élève bien davantage contre la redéfinition en cours du domaine étatique, du domaine public face au domaine privé ; redéfinition qu'implique, à sa manière, tout le débat autour du projet de fondation de la Bibliothèque municipale.

Cette opposition prend une coloration particulière aussi en bonne partie parce que le débat fait intervenir les institutions politiques municipales. Comment même imaginer que les villes, dont le mandat est d'assurer la sécurité des citoyens, de voir à l'entretien des voies de communication et au maintien de la salubrité des lieux publics, soient capables d'assumer une telle responsabilité ? En vertu de quel principe seraient-elles autorisées à intervenir dans un domaine qui, estiment certains, relève de l'éducation ? Comme l'expose de manière très éloquente un journal conservateur de l'époque : « ... en bonne vérité, choisit-on les conseillers en vue de l'administration intelligente d'une bibliothèque publique ? Personne, assurément n'oserait le soutenir. On nomme des conseillers municipaux, parce qu'on les croit compétents pour discuter et résoudre les questions qui sont du ressort naturel d'un conseil municipal : finances municipales, impôts et perceptions d'impôts, voirie, police... »[9]

Pourtant, dès le départ, la question de la bibliothèque est posée et débattue sur la scène municipale, parce qu'elle constitue pour ses promoteurs un aspect central de la culture urbaine en voie d'élaboration. Mais c'est aussi la répartition des rôles dévolus aux institutions politiques aux différents échelons – municipal, provincial, fédéral – qui explique que cette responsabilité soit d'emblée associée aux gouvernements municipaux. Jusqu'aux années 1930, faut-il le rappeler, les administrations municipales jouent un rôle de premier plan dans la régulation des problèmes reliés au monde urbain et à son aménagement, de même que des conditions de vie en général (Collin, Dagenais, 1996). Bien que le gouvernement provincial élargit progressivement ses domaines d'intervention, en direction des services sociaux notamment, il demeure pratiquement absent de celui de la culture et des loisirs (Bellefleur, 1986 ; Harvey *et al.*, 1990).

Par ailleurs, le vote d'une série de lois dans la seconde moitié du 19e siècle va aussi contribuer à faire du domaine de la culture – en premier lieu par l'intermédiaire des bibliothèques – un secteur d'intervention municipal[10].

Plus spécifiquement la loi de 1890, votée par le gouvernement d'Honoré
Mercier, accorde clairement aux municipalités le pouvoir d'établir et
d'entretenir des bibliothèques en leur attribuant cette responsabilité, jusque-là
dévolue au surintendant de l'instruction provinciale (Gallichan, 1994 :148-149).

Même si elles contribuent à accentuer le caractère urbain et public des
bibliothèques, dans l'immédiat ces lois ne sont cependant pas suffisantes en
elles-mêmes pour susciter un mouvement de création de telles institutions.
En effet, tout ce débat sur la culture publique et sur les attributions des pouvoirs politiques locaux va refaire surface à intervalles réguliers, durant les
quelque trente ans précèdant l'ouverture de la Bibliothèque municipale de
Montréal en 1917. Son étude aussi fait ressortir d'autres obstacles avec
lesquels l'administration municipale devra composer. Car même parmi ceux
qui envisagent favorablement une telle réalisation, les conceptions divergent
sur un certain nombre d'aspects, reliés notamment à son emplacement sur le
territoire montréalais. Ces obstacles, eux aussi, sont révélateurs des clivages
profonds qui divisent la population montréalaise et les autorités politiques
locales, et de la difficulté à parvenir à établir un concensus en matière de
culture publique, à plus forte raison lorsque celle-ci est en pleine définition.

Conclusion

En 1917, Montréal parvient enfin à se doter d'une bibliothèque publique :
une institution déjà présente dans plusieurs villes du continent. Cette réalisation s'inscrit dans un contexte où, par l'aménagement de parcs, de terrains
de jeux, de bains publics ou le soutien à diverses associations, les administrations municipales s'impliquent de plus en plus dans la vie culturelle
urbaine. Mais à la différence des promoteurs privés qui en font des activités
lucratives, les initiatives des pouvoirs publics locaux dans ce secteur ont une
résonnance bien particulière. Du point de vue municipal, cela représente une
rupture avec les pratiques habituelles. Comme le dit si bien un protagoniste
au tournant du siècle, le mandat des municipalités est plutôt de s'occuper des
égouts, des rues et des incendies. Mais c'est aussi parce que cette intervention municipale amène une remise en question du domaine étatique, du
domaine public, que le projet d'ouverture d'une bibliothèque municipale
soulève autant de débats au sein de la société montréalaise.

Il reste à rendre compte de manière plus approfondie de la teneur de
tous ces débats, à peine évoqués ici, pour illustrer notre propos. En effectuant
ce retour dans le passé, notre objectif était d'abord de souligner la nature
changeante du rapport à la culture et les nombreuses luttes que ce rapport a
pu engendrer. Ce bref rappel des cironstances entourant le début de la prise
en charge par les pouvoirs politiques locaux d'un aspect de la vie culturelle
montréalaise et de certains enjeux qui en découlent apparaît aussi éclairant

dans le contexte actuel. Aujourd'hui, en effet, la culture redevient un enjeu important, spécialement dans le monde municipal québécois mais aussi nord-américain dans son ensemble. Au tournant du 20e siècle, le débat sur la question culturelle a favorisé le développement de l'intervention des pouvoirs politiques locaux. À l'aube du prochain siècle, cependant, se pose désormais la question de la pertinence de cette intervention municipale dans le champ culturel. Sur fond de crise de la fiscalité, on évoque de plus en plus l'éventualité de la re-privatisation de ce domaine qui s'y prête encore mieux que d'autres, dans la mesure où il est bien souvent considéré comme non essentiel.

NOTES

1. Cette recherche a bénéficié de l'octroi d'une bourse postdoctorale de l'Institut national de la recherche scientifique (Université du Québec) en 1993-1994. Je remercie sincèrement le professeur Jean-Pierre Collin, de l'INRS-Urbanisation, pour la qualité de son encadrement et de nos échanges, lors de mon stage.

2. « Une année de lutte », *Canada-Revue*, III, 28 (31 décembre 1892) 434. (C'est la rédaction de la revue qui souligne.)

3. L'essentiel des sources utilisées dans cette recherche se retrouve à la Division de la gestion de documents et des archives de la Ville de Montréal. Nous avons aussi consulté les quelques documents sur le sujet que possèdent les Archives de l'Archevêché de Montréal et les Archives nationales du Québec à Montréal. Pour une liste détaillée, se référer à notre rapport de recherche postdoctorale : *L'administration municipale de Montréal, un agent central dans la constitution d'une culture publique urbaine au tournant du siècle. L'exemple de la fondation de la Bibliothèque municipale de Montréal*, INRS-Urbanisation, mai 1994, 70 p.

4. Propos de *La Presse* rapportés par M. Lajeunesse, 1982 : 213.

5. Archives de l'Archevêché de Montréal (AAM), *Registre des lettres de Mgr Bruchési*, Tome 2 (18 janvier 1901 - 2 mai 1904), lettre au maire de Montréal et aux échevins, 6 mars 1901.

6. Pour un aperçu rapide, voir J.-C. Robert, *Atlas historique de Montréal*, 1994, p. 84-85. Lire également les mémoires de certains membres de l'élite de l'époque (Montpetit, 1949 ; Morin, 1967).

7. C'est nettement l'impression qui se dégage à la lecture d'un ouvrage tel que celui de E. C. Moodey, *The Fraser-Hickson Library. An Informal History*, 1977.

8. (AAM), dossier 759.112, extrait du quotidien *La Presse*, 8 mars 1907.

9. *La Vérité*, 18 octobre 1902 : 2.

10. Tout d'abord, l'« Acte pour pourvoir à l'incorporation et à une meilleure administration des associations de bibliothèques et des instituts d'artisans », adopté en 1851, va servir de guide pour l'octroi de subventions gouvernementales à ces organismes. Votée en 1856 et s'adressant plus directement aux milieux ruraux, la deuxième loi vise à soutenir l'établissement de bibliothèques de paroisses et

de townships. Comme l'explique Yvan Lamonde : « ... la loi de 1856 met l'accent sur la dimension civile de la paroisse et inaugure ce long processus vers la responsabilité publique de la bibliothèque... on assiste... à l'apparition des caractères propres, contemporains, de la bibliothèque « publique » : financée par fonds publics, régie par législation publique, ouverte à un public. » (Y. Lamonde, 1990 : 21, 23).

11. Dès avant cette date, en 1903, la Ville de Montréal met sur pied une petite « bibliothèque technique », installée dans l'édifice du Monument national, rue Saint-Laurent. Mais il s'agit d'une « bibliothèque scientifique et industrielle... (qui met) à la disposition des classes industrielles, les publications... traitant des sciences, des arts et métiers, de commerce et d'industrie en tout genre. » Sont ainsi exclus tous les ouvrages littéraires ou les essais « qui seraient dangereux pour la foi et la morale... ». Pour plus de détails (Dagenais, 1994 : 34 et suivantes).

RÉFÉRENCES

BARTH, G. (1980). *City People : The Rise of Modern City Culture in Nineteenth Century America*, New York, Oxford University Press, 1980.

BELLEFLEUR, M. (1986). *L'Église et le loisir au Québec avant la Révolution tranquille*, Québec, Presses de l'Université du Québec.

BENDER, T. (1988). Metropolitan Life and the Making of Public Culture. In J.H. MOLLENKOPF, (dir.). *Power, Culture and Place : Essays on New York City*, Russell, Sage Foundation, 261-271.

BLOOMFIELD, E. et G. *et al.* (1983). *Urban Growth and Local Services. The Development of Ontario Municipalities to 1981*, Guelph, University of Guelph, Department of Geography.

BOWKER, D.(1990). Parks and Baths : Sport, Recreation and Municipal Government in Asthon-under-Lyne Between the Wars. In R. HOLT, (dir.). *Sport and the Working Class in Modern Britain*, Manchester, Manchester University Press, 84-100.

COLLIN, J.-P. et M. DAGENAIS (1996). Évolution des enjeux politiques locaux et des pratiques municipales dans l'île de Montréal, 1840-1950. In J.-L. PINOL et D. MENJOT, (dir.).*Enjeux et expressions de la politique municipale (Moyen Âge - XXᵉ siècle)*, Paris, l'Harmattan, (à paraître).

DAGENAIS, M. (1994). *L'administration municipale de Montréal, un agent central dans la constitution d'une culture publique urbaine au tournant du siècle. L'exemple de la fondation de la Bibliothèque municipale de Montréal*, INRS-Urbanisation, 70 p.

DROLET, A. (1965). *Les bibliothèques canadiennes, 1604-1960*. Ottawa, Le cercle du livre de France.

DUFRESNE, S. (1983). Le carnaval d'hiver à Montréal, 1883-1889. *Urban History Review/ Revue d'histoire urbaine*, XI (3), 25-45.

DUFRESNE, S.(1990). Attractions, curiosités, carnaval d'hiver, expositions agricoles et industrielles : le loisir public à Montréal au XIXe siècle. In J.-R. BRAULT, (dir.). *Montréal au XIXe siècle. Des gens, des idées , des arts, une ville*, Montréal, Léméac, 233-267.

FECTEAU, J.-M.(1986). Prolégomènes à une étude historique des rapports entre l'État et le droit dans la société québécoise de la fin du XVIIIe siècle à 1929. *Sociologie et sociétés*, XVIII (1), 129-138.

GAGNON, H. (1995). Divertissement et patriotisme : la genèse des musées d'histoire à Montréal au XIXe siècle. *Revue d'histoire de l'Amérique française*, 48 (3), 317-349.

GALLICHAN, G. (1994). *Honoré Mercier. La politique et la culture*. Québec, Septentrion.

HARVEY, J. *et al.* (1990). Le loisir municipal et l'État-Providence. *Recherches sociographiques*, XXX (1), 25-44.

HEAP, R. (1982). La Ligue de l'enseignement (1902-1904) : héritage du passé et nouveaux défis. *Revue d'histoire de l'Amérique française*, 36 (3), 339-373.

JANSON, G. (1995). *Emparons-nous du sport. Les Canadiens français et le sport au XIXe siècle*, Montréal, Guérin.

KITE, J. (1992). « A Good Bargain » : The Struggle for a Public Library, 1850-1924. *Bath History*, 4, 136-154.

LAJEUNESSE, M.(1982). *Les Sulpiciens et la vie culturelle à Montréal au XIXe siècle*, Montréal, Fides.

LAMONDE, Y.(1979). *Les bibliothèques de collectivités à Montréal (17e-19e siècle)*, Montréal, Bibliothèque nationale du Québec.

LAMONDE, Y. (1983). Une problématique de culture urbaine : Montréal 1820-1920. *Questions de culture*, 5, 131-148.

LAMONDE, Y.(1990). *Gens de parole. Conférences publiques, essais et débats à l'Institut canadien de Montréal (1845-1871)*, Montréal, Boréal.

LAMONDE, Y. et R. MONTPETIT. (1986). *Le parc Sohmer de Montréal, 1889-1919. Un lieu populaire de culture urbaine*, Québec, IQRC.

LATOUCHE, D. (1991). La ville dans ses rapports à la culture et aux arts : le cas des équipements culturels à Montréal. In A. GERMAIN, (dir.). *L'aménagement urbain. Promesses et défis*, Québec, IQRC, 201-231.

LEMOINE, R. (1991). *Deux loges montréalaises du Grand Orient de France*, Ottawa, Presses de l'Université d'Ottawa.

LEVASSEUR, R. (1982). *Loisir et culture au Québec*, Montréal, Boréal Express.

LINTEAU, P.-A. (1992). *Histoire de Montréal depuis la Confédération*, Montréal, Boréal.

MELLER, H.E. (1976). *Leisure and the Changing City, 1870-1914*, Londres, Routledge and Kegan Paul.

METCALFE, A. (1978). The Evolution of Organized Physical Recreation in Montreal, 1840-1895. *Histoire sociales / Social History*, XI(21), 144-166.

METCALFE, A.(1983). Le sport au Canada français au XIXe siècle : le cas de Montréal. *Loisir et société*, 6 (1), 105-120.

MONTPETIT, É. (1949). *Souvenirs II : Vous avez la parole*, Montréal, Éditions Chanteclerc.

MONTPETIT, R.(1979). Loisir public et société à Montréal au XIXe siècle. *Loisir et société*, 2 (1), 101-125.

MONTPETIT, R. (1982). La culture populaire au Québec et son histoire en milieu urbain. In G. PRONOVOST, (dir.). *Cultures populaires et sociétés contemporaines*, Sillery, Presses de l'Université du Québec, 91-102.

MOODEY, E. (1977). *The Fraser-Hickson Library : An Informal History*, Londres, Clive Bingley.

MORIN, R. (1967). *Un bourgeois d'une époque révolue : Victor Morin notaire 1865-1960*, Montréal, Éditions du Jour.

PENMAN, M. (1983). *A Century of Service : Toronto Public Library 1883-1983*, Toronto, Toronto Public Library.

RIOUX, J.-P. et J.-F. SIRINELLI, (dir.). (1990). *Les politiques culturelles municipales. Éléments pour une approche historique*, Paris, Cahiers de l'Institut d'histoire du temps présent, Cahier n° 16.

ROBERT, J.-C. (1994). *Atlas historique de Montréal*, Montréal, Art Global et Libre Expression.

ROUILLARD, J. (1989). *Histoire du syndicalisme au Québec des origines à nos jours*, Montréal, Boréal.

WYCZYNSKI, P.(1972). L'École littéraire de Montréal, origines - évolution - rayonnement. In *id., et al.. Archives des lettres canadiennes. Tome II. l'École littéraire de Montréal*, Montréal, Fides, 12-35.

Michèle DAGENAIS
*Culture urbaine et pouvoirs publics locaux à Montréal
au début du 20e siècle*

RÉSUMÉ

Il est de coutume, au Québec notamment, de faire remonter le début de l'intervention des villes dans le secteur des loisirs et de la culture aux années 1940 ou 1950. Pourtant, dès la fin du 19e siècle, plusieurs municipalités sont amenées à s'impliquer à ce niveau en aménageant tout un réseau d'espaces publics. Ce faisant, elles contribuent à l'émergence de ce que d'aucuns appellent une culture publique urbaine. En présentant succinctement les débats entourant la création de la Bibliothèque municipale de Montréal au début du 20e siècle, cet article examine la difficulté d'établir un consensus en matière de culture publique, à plus forte raison lorsque celle-ci est en pleine définition.

Michèle DAGENAIS
*Urban Culture and Municipal Public Authorities in Montreal at the Turn
of the XXth Century*

ABSTRACT

In Québec as well as elsewhere, it is generally thought that municipal authorities began to be involved in recreation and culture during the 40's or 50's. However, the participation of several municipalities in this area can be traced back to the end of the XIXth century when a whole network of public spaces was being planned. In so doing, they contributed to the emergence of what is often called an urban public culture. Focussing on the debates surrounding the creation of the *Bibliothèque municipale de Montréal* at the turn of the XXth century, the article shows how difficult it is to achieve a consensus in matters of public culture, especially when culture is in the process of being defined.

Michel DAGENAIS
*Cultura urbana y poderes públicos locales en Montreal al comienzo del
siglo XX*

RESUMEN

Es costumbre, en el Quebec particularmente, de remontar el principio de la intervención de las ciudades en el sector de las diversiones y de la cultura a los años 1940 ó 1950. No obstante, desde el final del siglo XIX muchas municipalidades fueron llevadas a implicarse a este nivel, fomentando una red de espacios públicos. Haciendo esto, éstas contribuyen a la emergencia de lo que algunos llaman una cultura pública urbana. Presentando sucintamente los debates que rodearon la creación de la Biblioteca municipal de Montreal, al principio del siglo XX. Este artículo examina la dificultad para establecer un consenso en materia de cultura pública, con más razón cuando está en plena definición.

Intégration des secteurs d'activité de la culture et du développement communautaire au sein du service municipal des loisirs

Pierre GAGNON
Département des sciences du loisir
Université du Québec à Trois-Rivières

Introduction

Les municipalités du Québec sont préoccupées par l'accroissement de nouvelles responsabilités qui leur incombent, soit par des transferts provenant des autorités gouvernementales supérieures, soit par des demandes émanant de groupes de citoyens de leur milieu. La culture et le développement communautaire sont deux secteurs majeurs d'activité où les municipalités sont de plus en plus sollicitées.

Le Québec vient de se doter, en 1992, d'une politique culturelle où les municipalités sont interpellées à titre de partenaire privilégié dans le développement culturel des collectivités. Le financement des soins de santé et des services sociaux subit une profonde remise en question, et bien souvent le monde municipal est appelé à gérer des services locaux ou supporter des groupes locaux d'action communautaire, faute de programmes adéquats au niveau provincial.

Les services municipaux de loisir au Québec sont concernés directement par l'accroissement de ces nouvelles responsabilités. C'est à eux que revient généralement le rôle de gérer et d'encadrer les interventions de la Ville en matière culturelle et de développement communautaire. Leur savoir-faire en matière d'encadrement et de support aux organismes locaux ou encore, les liens étroits existant entre les champs du loisir et de la culture font en sorte que ces nouvelles responsabilités leur échoient naturellement.

Dans cette problématique, l'enquête entreprise auprès des directrices et directeurs de loisirs municipaux du Québec veut faire le bilan de l'intégration ou non, en 1993, des secteurs d'activité de la culture et du développement communautaire au sein du service municipal des loisirs.

1.   Le cadre de la recherche

1.1. Le problème

D'entrée de jeu, il importe de préciser que l'intervention des municipalités dans les champs du loisir, de la culture et du développement communautaire n'est pas un phénomène nouveau ou du moins récent. Les municipalités, en partenariat avec le clergé et le milieu scolaire, sont intervenues dans l'organisation et le développement des loisirs locaux bien avant que l'État ne mette en place des outils institutionnels et budgétaires dans ce domaine. En matière de santé et de services sociaux, les municipalités ont assumé plusieurs responsabilités dans ces secteurs d'intervention jusqu'aux années 1960. Depuis, elles ont toujours contribué à la résolution de plusieurs problèmes de type communautaire dans leur milieu, même si le domaine social et du bien-être relève d'abord des gouvernements supérieurs. Enfin, malgré le fait que traditionnellement la promotion de la dimension culturelle de la société a toujours appartenu aux deux niveaux de gouvernement supérieur, la présence des administrations municipales dans le champ culturel s'est faite sentir dès les années 1960 avec la création de services municipaux d'activités culturelles et de loisirs et a pris une part toujours croissante depuis.

Jusqu'à ce jour, le rôle de la municipalité dans les champs du loisir, de la culture et du développement communautaire n'était consacré que dans celui du loisir. En effet, la politique québécoise du loisir énoncée dans le Livre blanc sur le loisir en 1979, confiait à la municipalité la responsabilité du développement et de l'organisation du loisir au niveau local. Or, au cours des dernières années, les municipalités ont été fortement sollicitées à réajuster et à accroître leur intervention dans plusieurs secteurs liés à la santé et aux services sociaux comme entre autres, le soutien aux organismes d'aide et d'entraide, les garderies et les problématiques spécifiques à certains groupes de la population tel la famille et les personnes âgées. De plus, la réforme de la Loi sur les services de santé et des services sociaux adoptée en 1991 invite les élus municipaux à participer à la gestion du réseau public par le biais des Régies régionales.

Il en est de même dans le champ culturel. La politique culturelle adoptée en 1992 interpelle les municipalités à titre de partenaire privilégié dans le développement culturel des collectivités. Dorénavant, le rôle de l'État consiste essentiellement à soutenir et à accompagner le milieu dans le développement culturel. Cette décentralisation des activités culturelles place les administrations publiques locales dans une situation nouvelle où elles sont confrontées à une demande accrue et de plus en plus diversifiée de la part de certaines catégories de leur population.

L'accumulation des gestes posés par l'État dans les champs culturel et de développement communautaire sur fond de crise des finances publiques laisse présager que les municipalités auront à jouer un rôle accru dans ces domaines. Or, tel que mentionné en introduction, c'est au service municipal des loisirs qu'échoit naturellement, dans la majorité des villes au Québec, la responsabilité d'encadrer les interventions municipales en matière culturelle et de développement communautaire. Leur savoir-faire en matière d'encadrement et de support aux organismes locaux, ou encore les liens étroits qui unissent les champs d'intervention du loisir et de la culture les prédisposent davantage, que d'autres services municipaux, à assumer ces responsabilités. En outre, la taille des municipalités joue également un rôle important dans cette problématique. Les municipalités de plus petite taille n'ont généralement par les moyens de confier à des services spécialisés l'encadrement de nouveaux secteurs d'intervention.

Cependant, les secteurs d'intervention de la culture et du développement communautaire ont chacun leur problématique. Leurs objets et leur mode d'intervention diffèrent de ceux du loisir proprement dit. L'intégration de ces nouveaux secteurs d'intervention au sein du service municipal des loisirs ne peut que soulever de nombreuses questions.

La remise en question de la vocation du service municipal des loisirs et de son identification vient au premier plan. Quels devraient être la mission, les rôles et les fonctions d'un service municipal œuvrant dans des secteurs d'intervention aussi variés ? Comment harmoniser les orientations et les interventions de ces différents secteurs d'activité ? Comment un tel service devrait-il s'appeler pour projeter dans le milieu une image juste de la nature de ses interventions auprès des citoyens ?

L'intégration des secteurs d'activité du développement communautaire et de la culture au sein du service municipal des loisirs ne peut que modifier, à la baisse, les ressources affectées aux loisirs communautaires. Dans le contexte actuel des finances publiques municipales, tout accroissement des responsabilités ne signifie pas automatiquement l'accroissement des ressources financières. C'est à partir des ressources humaines, matérielles et financières existantes que les services municipaux de loisir devront chercher à satisfaire les nouveaux besoins des citoyens. Comment s'effectuera cette nécessaire rationalisation administrative et quels seront ses effets sur les services actuellement offerts aux groupes du milieu et aux citoyens ?

L'intervention professionnelle au sein des services municipaux de loisir ne peut qu'être remise en question dans un tel contexte. Dans quelle mesure les intervenants actuels sont-ils prêts à intervenir dans ces nouveaux secteurs d'activité ? Comment évoluera la nature de leurs tâches dans l'avenir afin de pouvoir répondre adéquatement à tous ces besoins des groupes et des citoyens ?

1.2. Les objectifs

Afin de mieux comprendre les perspectives de cette recherche, en voici les objectifs :

« Tenter de mesurer jusqu'à quel point les services municipaux de loisir au Québec ont intégré ou s'apprêtent à intégrer, s'il y a lieu, à leur secteur d'activité traditionnel qu'est le loisir, les secteurs d'activité du développement communautaire et de la culture ».

Plus précisément,

► Identifier les effets de cette intégration sur l'appellation du service municipal des loisirs ;

► Mesurer à quel rythme s'est effectuée ou s'effectuera cette intégration ;

► Mesurer les effets de cette intégration sur les tâches du directeur du service municipal des loisirs et celles de son personnel ;

► Mesurer les effets de cette intégration sur la dotation de personnel ;

► Identifier les effets de cette intégration sur les politiques du service.

1.3. Le cadre d'analyse

Pour atteindre les objectifs de cette étude, il a fallu au départ définir chacun des secteurs d'activité en cause. Dans le contexte de cette recherche, on entend par :

LE SECTEUR DU LOISIR : l'intervention de la municipalité dans le champ du loisir ou de la récréation. Cette intervention peut prendre les formes suivantes : mise en place d'espaces et d'équipements récréatifs, offre de programmes récréatifs (sports, socioculturels amateurs, socio-éducatifs, plein air), support technique et (ou) financier à des organismes du milieu offrant des programmes récréatifs à la population.

LE SECTEUR DU DÉVELOPPEMENT COMMUNAUTAIRE : l'intervention de la municipalité dans le champ des services de santé et des services sociaux : développement et aide à la personne, amélioration de sa qualité de vie et de ses besoins de dépassement dans sa collectivité. Cette intervention peut prendre la forme principalement d'un support technique et (ou) financier à des organismes du milieu s'occupant d'aide ou de développement de la personne.

LE SECTEUR DE LA CULTURE : l'intervention de la municipalité dans le champ des affaires culturelles : le soutien aux artistes créateurs, l'accessibilité des citoyens à la vie culturelle, la diffusion culturelle, la protection et l'interprétation du patrimoine. Cette intervention peut prendre les formes suivantes : mise en place d'équipements culturels (bibliothèque, salle de spectacle, salle d'exposition, musée), offre de programmes culturels, soutien technique et (ou) financier à des artistes ou organismes culturels professionnels.

1.4. La méthodologie de l'étude

Nous avons privilégié le questionnaire comme instrument d'enquête. Après avoir réalisé une revue de littérature sur le sujet, des entrevues exploratoires ont été menées auprès de quelques directeurs de loisirs municipaux afin d'en valider l'orientation et le contenu. Par la suite, un questionnaire a été élaboré et prétesté auprès des municipalités de taille différente de la région de Trois-Rivières. La version finale du questionnaire a ensuite vu le jour. Elle comportait 55 questions fermées.

L'enquête a été conduite auprès de l'ensemble des municipalités de 4 000 habitants et plus ayant à leur emploi un directeur de loisir permanent au moment de l'enquête (N = 206). Nous avons choisi le directeur du service des loisirs comme répondant privilégié car le questionnaire touchait un certain nombre d'informations historiques et techniques, et nous avons assumé que le cadre supérieur était plus en mesure de les fournir et ainsi réduire au maximum le nombre de valeurs manquantes.

Tous les directeurs de loisir des villes retenues dans l'échantillon ont été invités à compléter le questionnaire. Une lettre précisant l'objet de l'enquête et le questionnaire ont été envoyés au début du mois de mars 1993. Aucun rappel ne fut effectué.

1.5. Les limites de l'étude

Près de 80 % des répondants ont retourné le questionnaire (163 questionnaires pour un taux de réponses global de 79,1 %) à temps ou légèrement en retard, soit à la fin du mois de mars 1993. Aucun d'eux n'a été rejeté. En outre, les municipalités regroupées par catégories (selon la taille et les régions administratives) sont représentées de façon équivalente dans chacune des strates. Comme les tableaux 1 et 2 nous l'indiquent, les taux de répondants les moins élevés s'observent dans les municipalités de la classe de 4 000 à

4 999 (64,1 %) et dans les régions administratives de Chaudière-Appalaches (53,3 %) et de Mauricie-Bois-Francs (68,4 %). Toutes les autres catégories ont eu un taux de répondants avoisinant le taux de réponses global (79,1 %) ou supérieur à celui-ci.

TABLEAU 1

Distribution des répondants par classe de population

Classe de population	Municipalités (N = 206)	Répondants (N = 163)	Pourcentage (79,1)
50 000 et plus	20	16	80,0
25 000 à 49 999	24	20	83,3
10 000 à 24 999	68	62	91,2
5 000 à 9 999	55	40	72,7
4 000 à 4 999	39	25	64,1

TABLEAU 2

Distribution des répondants par régions administratives

Régions administratives	Municipalités (N = 206)	Répondants (N = 163)	Pourcentage (79,1)
01 Bas Saint-Laurent	8	8	100,0
02 Saguenay – Lac St-Jean	11	9	81,8
03 Québec	22	21	95,5
04 Mauricie – Bois-Francs	19	13	68,4
05 Estrie	10	8	80,0
06 Montréal	22	17	77,3
07 Outaouais	9	7	77,7
08 Abitibi - Témiscamingue	6	5	83,3
09 Côte-Nord	4	3	75,0
10 Nord-du-Québec	2	2	100,0
11 Gaspésie - Îles-de-la-Madeleine	3	3	100,0
12 Chaudière-Appalaches	15	8	53,3
13 Laval	1	1	100,0
14 Lanaudière	12	11	91,6
15 Laurentides	21	16	76,2
16 Montérégie	41	31	75,6

2. Les résultats

Nous avons regroupé les résultats de l'enquête sous quatre (4) rubriques principales, soit :

1)   des données concernant le profil des acteurs en cause (les directeurs de service, les services municipaux de loisir) ;

2)   des données sur les secteurs d'intervention du service municipal des loisirs ;

3)   des données sur les tâches du directeur et du personnel du service des loisirs et enfin ;

4)   des données sur les politiques du service municipal des loisirs.

2.1. Le profil des acteurs concernés

Profil du répondant

Le profil type du répondant se caractérise comme suit :

→   il porte le titre de directeur du service municipal des loisirs (89,6 % des répondants). Les autres répondants, tout en ayant la responsabilité du service, portent un titre différent de celui de directeur (ex. coordonnateur des loisirs) ;

→   en moyenne, il occupe ce poste depuis un peu plus de neuf ans (67,9 % des répondants occupent le poste de directeur du service depuis cinq ans et plus et 31,1 % occupent ce poste depuis moins de cinq ans) ;

→   il est à l'emploi de sa municipalité depuis près de 12 ans (près de 80 % des répondants sont à l'emploi de leur municipalité depuis cinq ans et plus et près de 60 % des répondants le sont depuis dix ans et plus ;

→   il détient un diplôme universitaire dans une proportion de 64,8 % des répondants (baccalauréat ou plus) ;

→   près de 50 % des répondants ont reçu une formation spécifique en loisir, que ce soit au niveau collégial ou universitaire.

Profil du service municipal des loisirs
quant à son appellation

Nous avons voulu mesurer jusqu'à quel point l'appellation « service des loisirs » était encore représentative. Compte tenu des nouvelles responsabilités qui incombent ou incomberont dans le futur à ce service municipal, l'appellation « service des loisirs » se justifie-t-elle encore ? Nous avons constaté que des changements importants sont en cours.

Dans un premier temps, il ressort que les principales appellations actuelles du service municipal des loisirs sont :

→   « service des loisirs » dans près de 60 % des services (96 sur 163) ;

→   « service des loisirs et de la culture » dans près de 15 % des services (24 sur 163) ;

→   « Services récréatifs et communautaires » dans près de 6 % des services (10 sur 163) ;

→   « service des loisirs et des parcs » dans près de 5 % des services (8 sur 163).

L'appellation du service municipal fait donc ressortir encore majoritairement et de façon prépondérante la mission « loisir » du service (95 % de services incluent le terme « loisir » et/ou une appellation apparentée, par exemple, récréatifs, parcs, etc.). En outre, l'addition de nouveaux termes dans leur appellation suggère que les services municipaux ont tendance à procéder de cette façon afin d'indiquer leur mission et leurs secteurs d'intervention plutôt que de rechercher un terme plus englobant.

Par ailleurs, 14,7 % des services municipaux de loisir porte leur appellation actuelle depuis moins de quatre ans, 36,2 % depuis moins de six ans. Ces données nous suggèrent que plusieurs services municipaux de loisir ont changé d'appellation au cours des dernières années. De fait, 14,4 % des services municipaux de loisir (23 répondants sur 163) affirment avoir modifié l'appellation de leur service au cours des trois dernières années.

Cette tendance de procéder à un changement d'appellation des services semble vouloir s'étendre au cours des prochaines années. En effet, 21 services (13,0 %) envisagent de changer d'appellation au cours des prochaines années et 13 autres services (8,0 %) s'interrogent sur cette question.

L'analyse des appellations envisagées nous suggère que trois grands types d'appellation seront utilisés dans les prochaines années pour identifier le service municipal des loisirs :

►   le service des loisirs

►   les Services récréatifs et communautaires

►   le service des loisirs et de la culture

L'appellation « service des loisirs » tendra à changer pour l'une ou l'autre des autres appellations, incluant les termes « culture » ou « communautaire ». Enfin, il n'y a aucune unanimité pour qualifier le terme « communautaire » dans l'appellation du service des loisirs. Certains parlent de « vie communautaire », de « services communautaires », de « développement communautaire » ou encore « d'activités communautaires ».

L'ensemble de ces résultats sur les appellations actuelle et envisagée pour les services municipaux de loisir nous indique que le service municipal des loisirs est en mutation et que cette mutation prend différentes directions. Ces diverses mutations posent de sérieuses questions d'image, de mission et de rôle du service municipal des loisirs dans la collectivité pour laquelle devront répondre les professionnels en place.

2.2. Les secteurs d'intervention du service municipal des loisirs

Nous nous sommes interrogés sur les secteurs d'intervention actuels et envisagés pour le service municipal des loisirs. Encore ici, nous avons voulu mesurer les principaux changements en cours à cet effet. Le tableau 3 nous indique que les deux tiers des services municipaux de loisir (109 répondants sur 163, soit 66,9 %) interviennent présentement dans les trois secteurs d'activité à l'étude, soit le loisir, le développement communautaire et la culture ; 22,1 % des services municipaux (36 répondants sur 163) interviennent uniquement dans les secteurs du loisir et de la culture tandis que 4,9 % des services municipaux de loisir interviennent uniquement dans les secteurs du loisir et du développement communautaire. Enfin, 6,1 % des services n'interviennent que dans le secteur du loisir (10 répondants sur 163). Ces résultats nous indiquent clairement que la grande majorité des services municipaux de loisir ont déjà intégré, à leur secteur d'activité traditionnel qu'est le loisir, les secteurs d'activité du développement communautaire et de la culture.

Par ailleurs, le tableau 4 nous indique que c'est dans les municipalités de plus petite taille qu'on retrouve principalement les services municipaux œuvrant uniquement dans le secteur du loisir. C'est principalement dans les municipalités de 5 000 à 9 999 habitants qu'on retrouve les services municipaux œuvrant uniquement dans les secteurs du loisir et du développement communautaire, tandis que c'est dans celles de 24 999 habitants et moins qu'on retrouve principalement les services municipaux œuvrant uniquement dans les secteurs du loisir et de la culture. Enfin, on remarque une croissance du nombre de services œuvrant dans les trois secteurs d'activité pour les municipalités allant de moins de 5 000 habitants jusqu'à celles de 10 000 à 24 999 habitants pour observer une décroissance, par la suite, jusqu'aux municipalités de plus forte taille.

TABLEAU 3

**Secteurs d'intervention actuels du service
municipal des loisirs selon la taille de la municipalité**

Secteur d'intervention	Moins de 5 000		5 000 à 9 999		10 000 à 24 999		25 000 à 49 999		50 000 et plus		Total	
	N	%	N	%	N	%	N	%	N	%	N	%
En loisir uniquement	2	20,0	2	20,0	4	40,0	1	10,0	1	10,0	10	6,1
En loisir et développement communautaire	0	0,0	6	75,0	1	12,5	0	0,0	1	12,5	8	4,9
En loisir et culture	8	22,2	7	19,4	13	36,1	5	13,9	3	8,3	36	22,1
En loisir, développement communautaire et culture	15	13,8	25	22,9	44	40,4	14	12,8	11	10,1	109	66,9
Total %	**25**	**15,3**	**40**	**24,5**	**62**	**38,0**	**20**	**12,3**	**16**	**9,8**	**163**	**100,0**

Pour leur part, les résultats présentés au tableau 4 indiquent que lorsque la municipalité intervient ou a l'intention d'intervenir dans le secteur du développement communautaire, que c'est principalement au service des loisirs qu'elle confie ou confiera la responsabilité de gérer ce secteur d'activité. Dans l'ensemble, il ressort que :

▶ seulement 3,7 % des municipalités (six répondants sur 162) affirment disposer au sein de leur structure organisationnelle d'un service autre que le service des loisirs dont le mandat est d'intervenir dans le secteur du développement communautaire ;

▶ plusieurs services municipaux de loisir n'intervenant pas actuellement dans le secteur du développement communautaire (N=46) ont l'intention d'y intervenir dans un avenir rapproché : c'est le cas de 34,8 % de ceux-ci ;

▶ seulement trois municipalités n'intervenant pas actuellement dans le secteur du développement communautaire (N = 46) ont l'intention de créer un service pour y intervenir directement plutôt qu'en confier la responsabilité au service des loisirs.

TABLEAU 4

Interventions actuelles et projetées dans le secteur du développement communautaire

	Réponses	Nombre de répondants (N = 162)	Pourcentage
Existence, au sein de la structure organisationnelle de la municipalité d'un service autre que le service des loisirs dont le mandat est d'intervenir dans le secteur	Oui	6	3,7
du développement communautaire	Non	156	96,3
Services municipaux de loisir n'intervenant pas actuellement dans le secteur du		**(N = 46)**	**(100,0)**
développement communautaire et ayant	Oui	16	34,8
l'intention d'y intervenir dans un avenir	Non	13	28,3
rapproché	Ne savent pas	17	36,9
Municipalités n'intervenant pas actuellement dans le secteur du développement		**(N = 46)**	**(100,0)**
communautaire et ayant l'intention de	Oui	3	6,5
créer un service pour y intervenir	Non	29	63,0
spécifiquement	Ne savent pas	14	30,5

Tout comme pour le secteur du développement communautaire, il apparaît aussi clairement, comme nous l'indiquent les résultats présentés au tableau 5, que lorsque la municipalité intervient ou a l'intention d'intervenir dans le secteur de la culture, que c'est principalement au service des loisirs qu'elle confie ou confiera la responsabilité de gérer ce secteur d'activité. Ainsi, il ressort que :

▶ seulement 14,2 % des municipalités (23 répondants sur 162) affirment disposer au sein de leur structure organisationnelle d'un service autre que le service des loisirs dont le mandat est d'intervenir dans le secteur de la culture. Dans la grande majorité des cas, il s'agit du service de la bibliothèque qui concerne surtout les municipalités de 24 999 habitants et moins. L'existence d'un service « culturel » proprement dit est principalement le cas des municipalités de plus forte taille ;

▶ plusieurs services municipaux de loisir n'intervenant pas actuellement dans le secteur de la culture (N = 18) ont l'intention d'y intervenir dans un avenir rapproché : c'est le cas de 33,3 % de ceux-ci ;

▶ seulement une municipalité n'intervenant pas actuellement dans le secteur de la culture (N = 18) a l'intention de créer un service pour y intervenir directement plutôt qu'en confier la responsabilité au service des loisirs. Notons cependant un degré d'incertitude assez grand à cet égard : 50 % des répondants (9 sur 18) disent ne pas savoir si leur municipalité a l'intention de créer un service de la culture.

TABLEAU 5

Interventions actuelles et projetées dans le secteur de la culture

	Réponses	Nombre de répondants	Pourcentage
Existence, au sein de la structure organisationnelle de la municipalité d'un service autre que le service des loisirs dont le mandat est d'intervenir spécifiquement dans le secteur de la culture		(N = 162)	(100,0)
	OUI	23	14,2
	NON	139	85,8
Appellation du service municipal dont le mandat est d'intervenir spécifiquement dans le secteur de la culture		(N = 23)	(100,0)
	• Bibliothèque municipale	15	65,2
	• Autres appellations (ex. : services culturels, des arts)	8	44,8
Existence d'un service municipal dont le mandat est d'intervenir spécifiquement dans le secteur de la culture selon la taille de la municipalité		(N = 34)	(100,0)
	Moins de 5 000	1	4,3
	5 000 à 9 999	4	17,4
	10 000 à 24 999	10	43,5
	25 000 à 49 999	2	8,7
	50 000 et plus	6	26,1
Services municipaux n'intervenant pas actuellement dans le secteur de la culture et ayant l'intention d'y intervenir dans un avenir rapproché		(N = 18)	(100,0)
	OUI	6	33,3
	NON	7	38,9
	Ne savent pas	5	27,8
Municipalités n'intervenant pas actuellement dans le secteur de la culture et ayant l'intention de créer un service pour y intervenir spécifiquement		(N = 18)	(100,0)
	OUI	1	5,6
	NON	8	44,4
	Ne savent pas	9	50,0

2.3 Les tâches du directeur et du personnel du service des loisirs

Nous avons voulu mesurer jusqu'à quel point le directeur du service des loisirs ainsi que son personnel intervenaient actuellement dans les secteurs d'activité du loisir, du développement communautaire et de la culture. Nous avons voulu mesurer également leur degré d'intervention envisagé dans le futur ainsi que leur degré de préparation afin d'intervenir dans ces différents secteurs d'activité. Pour ce faire, nous avons demandé aux répondants de nous indiquer leurs réponses sur une échelle de 0 (pas du tout) à 5 (beaucoup). Les résultats présentés au tableau 6 indiquent le rang moyen obtenu pour chacune des questions.

Les résultats exprimés dans le tableau 6 nous suggèrent que les tâches du directeur du service municipal des loisirs sont appelés à changer dans le sens d'une plus grande intervention dans les secteurs d'activité du développement communautaire et de la culture. Ils nous suggèrent également que les besoins de formation sont ressentis par le directeur du service municipal des loisirs afin de pouvoir mieux se préparer à intervenir dans ces secteurs d'activité. Plus précisément, il ressort que :

►   actuellement, les tâches du directeur du service des loisirs sont orientées principalement vers le secteur du loisir (rang moyen = 4,64), ensuite vers le secteur de la culture (rang moyen = 3,35) et celui du développement communautaire (rang moyen = 2,46) ;

►   les directeurs de services municipaux de loisir envisagent différemment l'orientation de leurs tâches dans le futur. Ils devraient se consacrer un peu moins au secteur du loisir (rang moyen = 4,45) pour se consacrer un peu plus au secteur de la culture (rang moyen = 3,83) et davantage au secteur du développement communautaire (rang moyen = 3,45). Ils envisagent donc un meilleur équilibre de leurs tâches et de leurs préoccupations entre les trois secteurs d'activité ;

►   C'est dans le secteur d'activité du loisir qu'ils se sentent le mieux préparés à intervenir actuellement (rang moyen = 4,64). Ils se sentent relativement à l'aise pour intervenir dans le secteur de la culture (rang moyen = 3,69), mais moins dans le secteur du développement communautaire (rang moyen = 2,98).

Tout comme pour celles du directeur du service des loisirs, les résultats exprimés dans le tableau 6 nous suggèrent que les tâches du personnel du service municipal des loisirs sont appelées à changer dans le sens d'une plus grande intervention dans les secteurs d'activité du développement communautaire et de la culture. Ils nous suggèrent encore ici que des besoins de formation sont ressentis par le directeur du service municipal des loisirs afin de pouvoir mieux préparer son personnel à intervenir dans ces secteurs d'activité. Dans l'ensemble, les données indiquent :

►   qu'actuellement les tâches du personnel du service des loisirs, lorsque ce dernier en dispose, sont orientées presque également vers les secteurs du loisir (rang moyen = 4,41) et de la culture (rang moyen = 4,33) et par la suite, vers celui du développement communautaire (rang moyen = 2,15) ;

► par contre, les directeurs de services municipaux de loisir envisagent différemment la répartition des tâches de leur personnel dans le futur. Celui-ci devrait se consacrer un peu moins aux secteurs d'activité du loisir (rang moyen = 4,33) et de la culture (rang moyen = 3,69) pour se consacrer davantage au secteur du développement communautaire (rang moyen = 3,27) ;

► c'est dans le secteur du loisir que les directeurs de services municipaux de loisir sentent leur personnel le mieux préparé à intervenir actuellement (rang moyen = 4,24). Ils le jugent relativement prêt à intervenir dans le secteur de la culture (rang moyen = 3,27) mais beaucoup moins dans le secteur du développement communautaire (rang moyen = 2,38).

TABLEAU 6

Importance des tâches actuelles et projetées du directeur du service des loisirs et son personnel et leur degré de préparation en fonction des secteurs d'intervention

| Secteurs d'intervention | Le directeur du service des loisirs | | | Personnel du service des loisirs | | |
| | Degré d'intervention | | Degré de préparation | Degré d'intervention | | Degré de préparation |
	actuel	futur		actuel	futur	
Loisir	4,64	4,45	4,64	4,41	4,33	4,24
Développement communautaire	2,46	3,45	2,98	2,15	3,27	2,38
Culture	3,35	3,83	3,69	4,33	3,69	3,27

2.4 Les politiques du service municipal des loisirs et de la municipalité

Nous nous sommes interrogés sur les politiques dont dispose le service municipal des loisirs et de façon plus large, la municipalité à l'égard des trois secteurs d'activité à l'étude.

Les politiques du service municipal des loisirs

La politique de reconnaissance et de soutien des organismes du milieu et la politique de tarification des usagers (individus et/ou groupes) sont les deux (2) politiques dont se dotent habituellement les services municipaux de loisir. Nous avons cherché à savoir jusqu'à quel point ces politiques intégraient ou non les secteurs d'activité du développement communautaire et de la culture.

Les résultats concernant ces aspects sont présentés au tableau 7. Dans l'ensemble, il ressort que :

▶ les organismes culturels sont couverts actuellement à 86,2 % (112 répondants sur 130) par les politiques de reconnaissance et de soutien, tandis que les organismes de développement communautaire le sont à 71,5 % (93 répondants sur 130). Ces résultats nous démontrent une assez grande intégration des secteurs d'activité du développement communautaire et de la culture à celui du loisir ;

▶ les usagers du secteur culturel sont concernés actuellement à 79,2 % (103 répondants sur 130) par les politiques de tarification des usagers, tandis que les usagers (groupes) du secteur d'activité du développement communautaire le sont beaucoup moins, soit à 44,6 % (58 répondants sur 130) ;

▶ les services municipaux de loisir ont l'intention d'étendre leur politique de reconnaissance et de soutien à d'autres catégories d'organismes dans une proportion de 20,2 % (33 répondants sur 163), tandis que 38,1 % ne le savent pas tout en y songeant sérieusement (voir le tableau 50). Les catégories d'organismes touchées par cette extension de la politique seraient principalement les organismes communautaires (26 cas) suivis des organismes culturels (15 cas).

TABLEAU 7

Intégration actuelle et projetée des secteurs du développement communautaire et de la culture dans les politiques du service municipal des loisirs

Types de politiques	Catégories d'organismes et d'usagers couverts par les politiques de reconnaissance et de soutien et les politiques de tarification			Catégories d'organismes et d'usagers touchés par l'intention du service municipal de loisir d'étendre des politiques de reconnaissance et de tarification	
	Catégories d'organismes ou d'usagers	*Nombre de répondants (N = 130)*	*Pourcentage (100,0)*	*Catégories d'organismes ou d'usagers*	*Nombre de répondants (N = 33)*
Reconnaissance et soutien des organismes	Loisir	130	100,0		
	Communautaire	93	71,5	Communautaire	26
	Culturel	112	86,2	Culturel	15
Tarification des usagers	Loisir	130	100,0		
	Communautaire	58	44,6	Communautaire	16
	Culturel	103	79,2	Culturel	10

Les politiques spécifiques de la municipalité

Nous avons cherché également à savoir si les municipalités disposaient ou s'apprêtaient à disposer de politiques spécifiques à l'égard des secteurs d'activité du développement communautaire et de la culture. Les résultats sont présentés au tableau 8. Dans l'ensemble, il ressort :

▶ que 25,2 % des municipalités (41 répondants sur 163) affirment disposer actuellement d'une politique culturelle et que 12,3 % (20 répondants sur 163) d'une politique de développement communautaire. Le pourcentage ou le nombre de municipalités disposant de politiques spécifiques à l'égard des jeunes, de la famille, des aînés et des handicapés est relativement élevé. Il faut préciser ici que plusieurs répondants nous ont mentionné que ces politiques ne sont pas toujours formelles, c'est-à-dire ayant fait l'objet d'échanges et d'une approbation par le conseil municipal. Il s'agit, dans la majorité des cas, davantage de documents d'orientation que de réelles politiques ;

▶ que l'intention des municipalités de se doter, au cours des trois (3) prochaines années, de politiques spécifiques, c'est prioritairement sur le développement de politiques culturelles (34,3 % des répondants), de politiques à l'égard de la famille (31,3 % des répondants) et du développement communautaire (29,4 % des répondants) que s'orienteront les interventions de la municipalité.

TABLEAU 8

Politiques municipales actuelles et projetées à l'égard des secteurs du développement communautaire et de la culture

	Municipalités qui disposent actuellement de politiques spécifiques		Municipalités ayant l'intention de se doter de politiques spécifiques au cours des trois prochaines années	
Politique de développement communautaire	20	12,3	48	29,4
Politique actuelle	41	25,2	56	34,3
Politique à l'égard des jeunes	42	25,8	31	19,0
Politique à l'égard de la famille	41	25,2	51	31,3
Politique à l'égard des aînés	34	20,9	34	20,9
Politique à l'égard des handicapés	26	16,0	19	11,7
Politique à l'égard des communautés culturelles	9	5,5	8	4,9

Conclusion

Notre conclusion générale est que, de façon générale, les services municipaux de loisir au Québec ont déjà intégré assez fortement les secteurs d'activité du développement communautaire et de la culture à leur secteur d'activité traditionnel qu'est le loisir, et que la tendance générale est à une plus forte intégration encore de ces secteurs d'activité dans le futur. L'image, la mission et les fonctions du service municipal des loisirs au Québec évoluent assez rapidement vers un service « multifonctionnel » où les secteurs d'activité du développement communautaire et de la culture occuperont une place plus importante que celle qu'ils occupent présentement.

L'analyse des changements de dénomination effectués au cours des trois (3) dernières années et ceux envisagés pour les trois (3) prochaines (35 % des services municipaux ont procédé ou procéderont à de tels changements) nous indique que trois (3) grands types d'appellations seront privilégiées dans les prochaines années pour le service municipal des loisirs :

1)   Le service des loisirs ;

2)   Les Services récréatifs et communautaires, et ;

3)   Le service des loisirs et de la culture.

L'analyse de ces résultats nous suggère que l'appellation pure « service des loisirs » tendra à changer pour l'une ou l'autre des deux (2) autres appellations, par addition principalement des termes « culture » ou « communautaire ». À noter ici qu'il n'y a aucune unanimité pour qualifier le terme « communautaire » dans l'appellation du service des loisirs. Certains parlent de « vie communautaire », de « services communautaires », de « développement communautaire » ou encore « d'activités communautaires ».

Par sa part, l'étude des secteurs d'intervention actuels ou envisagés pour le service municipal des loisirs nous indique un assez fort degré d'intégration des différents secteurs d'activité, loisir, développement communautaire et culture et que, c'est principalement au Service municipal des loisirs que les municipalités ont l'intention de confier la gestion des secteurs d'activité du développement communautaire et de la culture. Il ressort d'ailleurs assez fortement que les services municipaux de loisirs n'intervenant pas actuellement dans un ou l'autre de ces secteurs d'activité ont l'intention d'y intervenir dans un proche avenir.

Les tâches du directeur du service municipal des loisirs ainsi que celles de son personnel nous indiquent encore ici une tendance vers l'intégration des secteurs d'activité du développement communautaire et de la culture à celui du loisir proprement dit. Le directeur du service et son personnel interviennent tous deux présentement, à des degrés divers dans les trois (3) secteurs d'activité : plus fortement en loisir et en culture, moins en développement communautaire. On envisage cependant un accroissement des tâches vers les secteurs d'activité du développement communautaire et de la culture au détriment de celui du loisir dans un futur assez rapproché. Enfin, des besoins de formation pour mieux intervenir dans le secteur d'activité du développement communautaire sont ressentis par les directeurs de services municipaux de loisir ainsi que par leur personnel en place.

L'analyse des politiques de reconnaissance et de soutien des organismes du milieu et de tarification nous indique que le secteur de la culture y est déjà intégré assez fortement et un peu moins dans le cas du secteur de développement communautaire. La tendance pour le futur va vers une plus grande intégration de ces secteurs d'activité dans les politiques actuelles plutôt que vers le développement de politiques spécifiques pour les différents secteurs.

Enfin, les résultats de notre étude nous indiquent également que 25,2 % des municipalités disposent actuellement d'une politique culturelle et que 12,3 % d'entre elles disposent d'une politique de développement communautaire. Le nombre de municipalités affirmant disposer de politiques spécifiques à l'égard des jeunes, de la famille, des aînés et des handicapés est relativement élevé (de 20 à 25 %). Il faut préciser ici que plusieurs répondants nous ont mentionné que ces politiques ne sont pas toujours formelles et qu'il s'agit, dans la majorité des cas, davantage de documents d'orientation que de réelles politiques. Les municipalités ayant l'intention de se doter de nouvelles politiques dans un avenir rapproché le feront prioritairement pour le développement de politiques culturelles (34,3 %), de politiques à l'égard de la famille (31,3 %) et du développement communautaire (29,4 %).

Cette recherche nous a appris beaucoup de choses sur la question principale à l'étude, à savoir l'intégration des secteurs d'activité du développement communautaire et de la culture au secteur d'activité traditionnel des services municipaux de loisir. Les résultats soulèvent plusieurs questions quant au devenir de ce dernier pour ce qui a rapport à son image, sa mission, ses rôles et fonctions. Le service municipal des loisirs est en train d'évoluer vers quelque chose d'autre.

Cette étude mériterait des prolongements. Une étude plus approfondie sur la même question nous apporterait un éclairage beaucoup plus grand. Chercher à mesurer des indicateurs tels que les budgets consacrés aux différents secteurs d'activité par les services municipaux de loisir, la nature des équipements, des services et des activités mis en place dans les différents secteurs nous permettraient, entre autres, de connaître un peu mieux encore comment s'effectue cette intégration et l'importance de cette dernière.

Bibliographie

ASSOCIATION DES DIRECTEURS DE LOISIRS MUNICIPAUX DU QUÉBEC (1968). *Le loisir défi d'aujourd'hui*, déclaration de Montmorency, ADLM.

ASSOCIATION DES DIRECTEURS DE LOISIRS MUNICIPAUX DU QUÉBEC (1970). *Le loisir et la municipalité*, Guide d'intervention, ADLM.

BELLEFLEUR, Michel, LEVASSEUR, Roger, *Loisir Québec 1976*, Les dossiers Beaux-jeux 1, Montréal, Bellarmin-Desport, 1976.

CHAIRE DE GESTION DES ARTS DE L'ÉCOLE DES HAUTES ÉTUDES COMMERCIALES DE MONTRÉAL (1993). *L'intervention culturelle des municipalités québécoises*, Regroupement québécois du loisir municipal, Montréal.

DAGENAIS, Michèle (1994). *Culture urbaine et pouvoirs publics locaux : autour de la fondation de la bibliothèque municipale de Montréal*, Texte de communication scientifique, Colloque international sur le loisir, Trois-Rivières, 4 novembre.

D'AMOURS, Max C. (1981). *Municipalisation des loisirs au Québec : bilan et perspectives*, Cahiers des sciences du loisir, Trois-Rivières, Département des Sciences du loisir, Université du Québec à Trois-Rivières.

GAGNON, Pierre (1980). *Programmes municipaux de loisir. Orientation et évaluation*, Montréal, Intrinsèque.

GAGNON, Pierre (1993). *Intégration des secteurs d'activités de la culture et du développement communautaire au sein du service municipal des loisirs*, Études du loisir - Cahier 5, Trois Rivières, Département des Sciences du loisir, Université du Québec à Trois-Rivières.

GAREAU, Serge (1994). *La municipalité maître d'œuvre du développement communautaire*, Texte de conférence, Colloque international sur le loisir, Trois-Rivières, Université du Québec à Trois-Rivières, 3 et 4 novembre 1994.

GOUVERNEMENT DU QUÉBEC (1977). *Prendre notre temps - Livre vert sur le loisir au Québec*, Québec, Haut-commissariat à la jeunesse, aux loisirs et aux sports.

GOUVERNEMENT DU QUÉBEC (1979). *On a un monde à récréer - Livre blanc sur le loisir au Québec*, Québec, Haut-commissariat à la jeunesse, aux loisirs et aux sports.

GOUVERNEMENT DU QUÉBEC (1990). *Une réforme axée sur le citoyen*, Québec, ministère de la Santé et des Services sociaux, Bibliothèque nationale du Québec.

GOUVERNEMENT DU QUÉBEC (1992). *La politique culturelle du Québec*, Québec, ministère des Affaires municipales, Bibliothèque nationale du Québec.

GRANDMONT, Gérald (1994). *Le rôle de l'État*, Texte de conférence, Colloque international sur le loisir, Trois-Rivières, Université du Québec à Trois-Rivières, 3 et 4 novembre 1994.

LEVASSEUR (1982). Roger, *Loisir et culture au Québec*, Montréal, Boréal Expres.

PRONOVOST, Gilles (1983). *Temps, culture et société*, Sainte-Foy, Presses de l'Université du Québec.

PRONOVOST, Gilles (1993). *Loisir et Société : traité de sociologie empirique*, Sainte-Foy, Presses de l'Université du Québec.

SAMSON, BÉLAIR, DELOITTE ET TOUCHE (1993). *Étude sur le financement des arts et de la culture*, Novembre 1993.

UNION DES MUNICIPALITÉS DU QUÉBEC (1994). *Rapport du comité de travail sur le développement communautaire*, Mars 1994.

Pierre GAGNON
*Intégration des secteurs de la culture et du développement communautaire
au sein du service municipal des loisirs*

RÉSUMÉ

Cette étude entreprise en 1993 auprès des directrices et directeurs de loisirs des municipalités de 4000 habitants et plus du Québec visait à mesurer jusqu'à quel point les secteurs d'activités de la culture et du développement communautaire sont intégrés au sein du service municipal des loisirs. Il ressort que, de façon générale, les services municipaux de loisir au Québec ont déjà intégré assez fortement ces secteurs à leur secteur d'activité traditionnel qu'est le loisir, et que la tendance générale est à une plus forte intégration encore de ces secteurs d'activités dans le futur. En outre, les résultats de cette étude indiquent que l'image, la mission et les fonctions du service municipal des loisirs au Québec évoluent assez rapidement, vers un service « multifonctionnel » où les secteurs d'activité du développement communautaire et de la culture occuperont une place plus importante que celle qu'ils occupent présentement.

Pierre GAGNON
*Integration of Culture and Community Development in Municipal
Recreation Services*

ABSTRACT

The study was undertaken in 1993 among the recreation directors of municipalities of over 4000 people in the province of Québec. The purpose of the study was to evaluate the degree of integration of culture and community developmentæ within recreation services. The findings show that these two sectors of activity have been quite well integrated into the traditional areas of recreation services provided by those agencies, and that this trend should even get stronger in the future. The results also suggest that the image, mission and role of a municipal recreation service in Québec are changing at a fast pace in such multifunctional agencies. Therefore, it is expected that community development and culture will increase in importance among other recreational services in the years to come.

Pierre GAGNON
Integración de los sectores de actividad de la cultura y del desarrollo comunitario en el seno del servicio municipal de las diversiones.

RESUMEN

Este estudio realizado en 1993, con las directoras y directores de diversiones de las municipalidades de 4000 habitantes y más del Quebec, pretendía medir hasta que punto los sectores de actividades culturales y de desarrollo comunitario están integrados en el seno del servicio municipal de las diversiones. Sobresale que, de manera general, los servicios municipales de diversión en el Quebec ya han integrado muy fuertemente estos sectores a su sector de actividad tradicional que es la diversión, y que la tendencia general consiste en una más grande integración de estos sectores de actividades en el futuro. Además, los resultados de este estudio indican que la imagen, la misión y las funciones del servicio municipal de las diversiones en el Quebec evolucionan muy rápidamente, considerado como un servicio « multi-funcional » donde los sectores de actividad del desarrollo comunitario y de la cultura ocuparán un espacio más importante que ése que ocupan actualmente.

Modèle didactique d'utilisation d'institutions culturelles québécoises à des fins éducatives

Maryse Paquin

Faculté d'éducation
Université d'Ottawa

Depuis une vingtaine d'années au Québec, le système scolaire se conçoit comme « un système ouvert, composé de ressources, d'activités et de connaissances, lui appartenant en propre ou tirées d'autres savoirs [...], dont le but est de permettre aux être humains de développer au maximum leurs dispositions et d'atteindre progressivement l'autonomie dans la recherche du sens de leur existence et de leur environnement » (Legendre, 1988).

En tenant compte de cette définition, l'éducation ne peut plus se rattacher exclusivement à l'école et ne se limite plus uniquement à l'acquisition de connaissances. Tels qu'en font foi les objectifs des nouveaux programmes du ministère de l'Éducation du Québec, ceux-ci visent également à développer des valeurs culturelles et une conscience sociale chez les élèves (MEQ, 1981).

À ce sujet, Deronzier (1987) souligne, qu'en dépit que l'institution scolaire demeure la seule à prendre en charge l'enseignement de base, elle n'a pas pour but de répondre à tous les besoins d'éducation des membres de la société québécoise. Cette prise de conscience concorde avec une vaste réflexion portant sur le potentiel éducatif de divers lieux extra-scolaires qui peuvent contribuer à la formation des élèves, en complémentarité avec l'école.

Dans un avis adressé au ministre québécois de l'Éducation, le Conseil supérieur de l'éducation du Québec soutient que,

> La mission éducative de la société déborde largement les cadres de l'institution scolaire et trouve dans un nombre croissant de lieux, des voies valables d'approfondissement et de diffusion (Conseil supérieur de l'éducation, 1986).

À ce sujet, l'organisme souhaite que des collaborations se multiplient entre l'école et les différents partenaires de la communauté préoccupés par des questions d'éducation. De plus, il identifie certaines institutions culturelles dont les objectifs d'éducation sont reliés à ceux de l'école, tels les sites naturels, les lieux historiques, les bibliothèques, les musées d'arts ou de sciences, pour ne nommer que ceux-là (Conseil supérieur de l'éducation, 1986).

Le partenariat école-communauté

Les conclusions du Conseil supérieur de l'éducation s'inspirent d'un courant de pensée déjà existant, qui considère primordiale la relation école-communauté pour assurer la survie et le développement du système éducatif actuel.

Selon Lemerise (1993), « la relation école-communauté implique un lien étroit entre l'école et les différentes institutions culturelles présentes dans la communauté. Cette relation se situe dans un contexte où le partenariat, les alliances entre les institutions culturelles et l'école sont jugés des moyens importants, sinon essentiels, pour sauvegarder et enrichir la mission éducative d'une société ».

D'autre organismes américains, tels Task Force on Museum Education (Bloom et Mintz, 1990) et Carnegie Corporation (Atkin et Atkin, 1989), conçoivent cette relation comme un lien permanent et réciproque.

Au Québec, l'avis de la Commission d'étude sur la formation professionnelle et socio-culturelle des adultes abonde également en ce sens.

> On peut très bien imaginer que toutes les activités éducatives et culturelles, quels qu'en soient la forme, l'endroit ou le support, peuvent être considérées comme un lieu de coexistence, d'alternance et d'échange entre les objectifs spécifiques tantôt à la culture, tantôt à l'éducation : détente et effort, divertissement et animation, création et formation (CEFPSA, 1982).

Également, la vision socio-historique de Fantini (1985) nous aide à situer la relation école/institutions culturelles dans un contexte beaucoup plus large que la relation école/communauté décrite ci-haut. Ce dernier illustre de manière éloquente l'évolution du rôle et des besoins de l'école par rapport à tous les acteurs présents dans la société (gouvernement, monde du travail, famille, etc.), depuis une cinquantaine d'années.

Fantini (1985) décrit le partage des rôles dans une société rurale et agricole, la délégation dans une société industrielle et urbaine, la coordination et collaboration dans une société post-industrielle et la coopération entres les différentes ressources d'une communauté. Ce partage est illustré dans les figures de la page suivante. Fantini (1985) soutient que nous nous situons à la figure 3 tout en se dirigeant vers le partage décrit à la figure 4.

FIGURE 1

Shared Stage : Division of Educational Responsibility

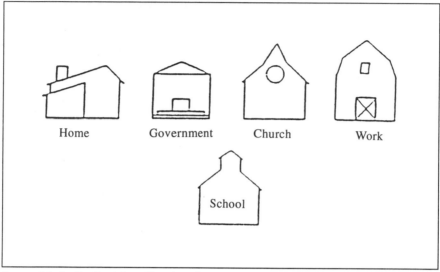

Source: Marlo D. Fantini, « Changing Concepts of Education : From School System to Educational System », in *Community, Educational, and Social Impact Perspectives,* ed. Donna Hager Schoeny and Larry E. Decker (Charlottesville, Va. : Mid-Atlantic Center for Community Education, University of Virginia, 1983), p. 32. Reprinted with permission.

FIGURE 2

Delegative Stage : Delegation of Educational Responsability

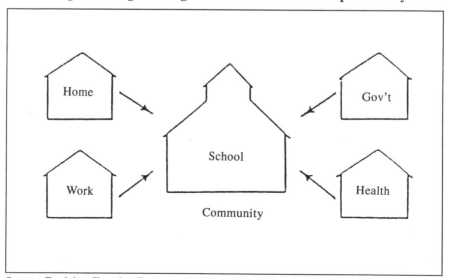

Source : Fantini, « Changing Concepts of Education », p. 33. Reprinted with permission.

FIGURE 3

Coordinative Stage : Coordination of Educational Responsibilities

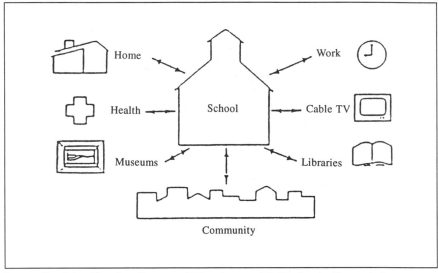

Source : Fantini, « Changing Concepts of Education », p. 35. Reprinted with permission.

FIGURE 4

The facilitative Learning Stage : Facilitation of Community Learning Educational Resources and Services

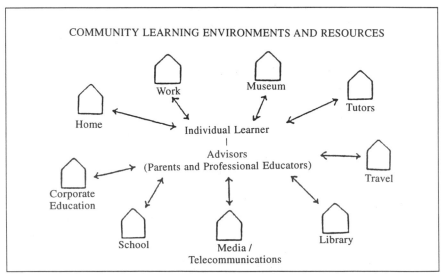

Source : Fantini, « Changing Concepts of Education », p. 40. Reprinted with permission.

Quoique les institutions culturelles québécoises ont un rôle réel et re-connu en éducation depuis les vingt dernières années, elles sont pourtant loin d'avoir atteint le statut de partenaires à part entière de l'école. À l'heure actuelle, au Québec, seuls quelques projets de partenariat impliquant les diverses instances institutionnelles scolaires et culturelles, sont encouragés et se situent au delà d'une relation récréative ou occasionnelle (Paquin, 1989). Malgré l'existence de nombreux projets de collaboration entre les écoles et les musées, industries, organisations sociales et religieuses, visant des objectifs éducatifs (Hein, 1991 ; Harrison, 1988, Orr, 1987), ceux-ci ne font généralement pas l'objet d'un projet éducatif offert aux élèves québécois du primaire et du secondaire.

La relation de complémentarité école/institutions culturelles

Au seuil de l'an 2000, bien que l'école québécoise trouve valable de puiser des ressources extra-scolaires pour atteindre ses objectifs d'éducation, de leur côté, certaines institutions culturelles proposent des programmes répondant aux besoins de sa clientèle scolaire. À ce propos, le Conseil supérieur de l'éduca-tion du Québec se fait loquace sur la question, tel que cité par Allard (1993).

> La relation entre l'école et les institutions culturelles est importante, tant et si bien qu'à deux reprises, au cours des dernières années, le Conseil supérieur de l'éducation a invoqué, dans des avis rédigés à l'intention du ministre de l'Éducation, la nécessité que ces institutions inscrivent leurs actions propres dans une perspective de complémentarité (Allard, 1993).

Toutefois, afin que des liens complémentaires s'établissent entre l'école et les institutions culturelles, celles-ci doivent y trouver leur part de bénéfices. Par exemple, le musée et/ou la bibliothèque peuvent élaborer des programmes éducatifs qui tiennent compte ou non des programmes scolaires. Quant au milieu scolaire, il peut participer à ces programmes éducatifs dans la mesure où ces derniers complètent la formation dispensée à l'école. À ce sujet, Allard (1993) fournit un excellent exemple,

> En classe, on peut décrire un canot d'écorce. On peut aussi montrer aux élèves une illustration. Mais au musée, les élèves peuvent le voir, l'ob-server et parfois le toucher. Le musée ajoute à leur compréhension de la réalité (Allard, 1993).

Si les structures permettant à l'école québécoise d'accomplir sa tâche éducative sont généralement connues des institutions culturelles, à l'inverse, le milieu scolaire connaît mal les structures dont disposent les institutions culturelles pour accueillir les écoliers (Hansen, 1984). Par ailleurs, les insti-tutions culturelles ne tiennent pas toujours compte de toutes les dimensions de la réalité scolaire lorsqu'elles planifient des activités s'adressant aux élèves. De son côté, l'école ne possède pas toujours une connaissance suffisante des impératifs auxquels les institutions culturelles sont soumises. Bref, malgré leur désir de collaborer ensemble, l'école et les institutions culturelles font face à certaines barrières, soit une méconnaissance mutuelle de leurs services, infrastructures, personnel. Cette situation explique en partie pourquoi les ressources éducatives des institutions culturelles sont encore utilisées essentiellement de manière expérimentale par le milieu scolaire québécois.

Des recherches sur les programmes éducatifs école/musée

Dans ce contexte, de 1987 à 1993, des recherches ont été conduites sur les programmes éducatifs école/musée. À cet effet, l'auteure a travaillé à l'expérimentation et à l'évaluation de trois programmes éducatifs muséaux, conçus en relation avec les programmes scolaires de sciences humaines, sciences de la nature et français de l'ordre primaire (Paquin, 1993 ; 1989 ; 1987).

Ces programmes éducatifs ont été conçus et validés selon un modèle didactique muséal, élaboré par le Groupe de recherche éducation et musée (GREM), de l'Université du Québec à Montréal (UQAM). Notamment, ce modèle didactique muséal propose l'élaboration de programmes éducatifs de manière à ce que leur application soit généralisable quelle que soit l'école ou l'institution culturelle. Avant de présenter les résultats de ces recherches, il semble opportun de définir le concept de modèle, de didactique et, enfin, de modèle didactique.

Les modèles en éducation

Selon L'Écuyer (1990), l'utilisation de modèles en éducation constitue le point de départ de toute recherche et de toute description des choses et des phénomènes.

> Parce qu'ils permettent de décortiquer les phénomènes ou les objets, de les analyser sous diverses facettes et d'en décrire les principales composantes, ils sont essentiels au développement scientifique et constituent la voie obligée de la connaissance d'une nature trop riche pour être appréhendée d'un seul coup (L'Écuyer, 1990).

Un modèle est une représentation simplifiée d'une réalité complexe, pour en permettre une meilleure compréhension. C'est une représentation abstraite d'un phénomène complexe décrivant les éléments essentiels de son adéquation avec la réalité. Également, un modèle est un idéal à atteindre tout en étant transitoire dans l'attente d'une représentation plus explicite (Legendre, 1988).

La didactique

Quant à la didactique, elle se définit comme « l'art et la science de l'éducation dont l'objet est la planification de la situation pédagogique » (Legendre, 1988).

Considérée dans sa totalité, la didactique se définit comme la science ayant pour objet l'acte d'enseigner, non pas uniquement comme la simple transmission de connaissances, mais comme une relation entre un agent et un sujet visant l'apprentissage d'un objet, soit d'un savoir intégral (Boucher, 1991).

Le modèle appliqué à la didactique

Selon Desrosiers-Sabbath (1984), un modèle appliqué à la didactique est un schéma d'action pourvu d'une base scientifique, découlant de principes psycho-pédagogiques et se concrétisant en une multitude de stratégies d'intervention. En éducation, faute d'une théorie générale orientant toute situation d'apprentissage et éclairant la complexité de l'acte d'enseigner, le praticien peut recourir à des modèles didactiques pour structurer des situations pédagogiques (Desrosiers-Sabbath, 1984).

Le modèle didactique muséal mis au point par le GREM, s'inspire largement du Modèle de la situation pédagogique (Legendre, 1988). Ce modèle, comprenant les composantes interreliées sujet-objet-milieu-agent (SOMA), n'est pas uniquement propre à l'école, c'est pourquoi il peut servir de point de départ pour tenter de cerner la complexité de l'éducation dans les institutions culturelles, dont le musée fait partie. Le Modèle de la situation pédagogique (Legendre, 1988) et celui du GREM sont illustrés aux figures 5 et 6 de la page suivante.

Selon Legendre (1988), l'apprentissage est fonction des caractéristiques personnelles du sujet apprenant, de la nature et du contenu des objectifs, des influences d'un milieu éducationnel et de la qualité d'assistance de l'agent.

Un modèle didactique appliqué à l'éducation au musée

Cette définition du Modèle de la situation pédagogique (Legendre, 1988) s'applique en tous points à la définition du modèle didactique muséal du GREM. Toutefois, ce dernier comprend deux milieux plutôt qu'un seul, où se déroule la situation pédagogique, soit à l'école et au musée. D'un point de vue général, le modèle du GREM vise à harmoniser les ressources muséales et scolaires. Spécifiquement, « il permet aux musées et aux écoles de façonner un programme éducatif muséal visant des objectifs d'ordre pédagogique, ludique et scientifique, sans opposer ces qualificatifs entre eux » (Allard et Boucher, 1991).

Les phases du modèles didactique muséal

Validé au cours d'expérimentations, ce modèle didactique muséal comprend trois phases, à savoir, la planification du programme éducatif muséal,

FIGURE 5

Le Modèle de la situation pédagogique (Legendre, 1988)

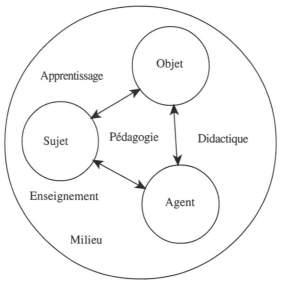

FIGURE 6

Le Modèle de la situation pédagogique du GREM

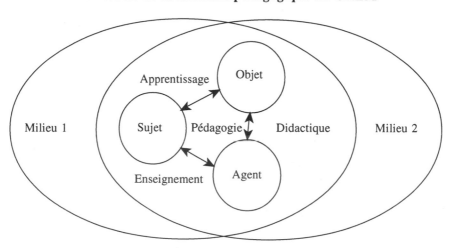

l'expérimentation et l'évaluation. Pour faciliter la compréhension du modèle didactique muséal du GREM, nous présentons le contenu de ses trois phases. La planification consiste à définir les composantes interreliées de la situation pédagogique (SOMA) : sujet, objet, milieu et agent, telles que définies par Legendre (1988). Une fois les composantes interreliées identifiées, celles-ci permettent d'élaborer un programme éducatif muséal qui tient compte des besoins et des limites tant du musée que de l'école.

Le sujet est l'élève-visiteur, caractérisé par diverses variables, telles que l'âge, le sexe, les intérêts, les connaissances acquises, l'expérience, l'état de développement, le style cognitif, les attitudes, les aspirations, les potentialités, etc. (Boucher, 1991). L'objet comprend les objectifs, le contenu, les moyens et les stratégies d'apprentissage propres au programme éducatif muséal. Les objectifs peuvent être généraux ou spécifiques, d'ordre cognitif, affectif ou psychomoteur. Le contenu d'apprentissage est basé sur les collections du musée et du programme scolaire. Les moyens permettent au sujet de s'approprier le contenu. La stratégie est l'approche employée pour présenter l'objet au sujet (Racette, 1989). Le milieu désigne l'endroit où la situation pédagogique se déroule. Le milieu interne comprend les équipements, les installations et les commodités. Le milieu externe se réfère à l'environnement géographique dans lequel la situation pédagogique se déroule (Racette, 1989). L'agent signifie l'ensemble des ressources humaines requises dans une situation pédagogique donnée. L'agent est la personne qui facilite l'apprentissage chez le sujet. L'agent sélectionne les moyens et les approches les plus appropriés, les organise et les planifie de manière à favoriser l'apprentissages chez le sujet à l'aide d'un objet (Racette, 1989).

La deuxième phase du modèle consiste en l'expérimentation du programme éducatif muséal en trois étapes, soit la préparation en classe, la visite au musée et le prolongement en classe. « Ces étapes se situent dans une approche inductive, faisant appel à la participation active de l'élève » (Allard, 1993). Les trois étapes du programme s'inscrivent dans une démarche d'apprentissage semblable à celle menée dans un processus de recherche.

Le point de départ consiste en la formulation d'hypothèses à partir d'interrogations posées sur un fait, une situation ou un problème donné. Par la suite, une recherche est menée dans le but de trouver des réponses à ces questions. Une telle démarche d'apprentissage est privilégiée par les programmes de sciences humaines et de sciences de la nature au primaire du ministère de l'éducation du Québec.

Selon le MEQ (1983), c'est en exprimant ses perceptions, en formulant des hypothèses et en recueillant des données afin de les interpréter et d'élaborer de nouvelles conclusions, que les élèves ont le plus de chances d'apprendre l'histoire et la biologie. À cet effet, le programme des sciences humaines du second cycle du primaire, suggère un processus se réalisant en quatre temps, soit l'exploration, la recherche, le traitement des données et l'échange (MEQ, 1983). Ce processus s'arrime bien avec les trois étapes du programme éducatif muséal du GREM, se déroulant tantôt à l'école, tantôt au musée.

L'exploration se prête très bien aux activités suggérées pour la préparation en classe. Ces activités consistent à faire formuler des questions auxquelles l'élève trouve les réponses au musée. Quant à la recherche, elle est tout à fait indiquée lors de la visite au musée car elle permet à l'élève d'effectuer une collecte d'informations, c'est-à-dire de lui faire chercher les réponses à ses questions. Pour ce qui est du traitement des données et de l'échange des résultats, ils se prêtent bien aux activités suggérées lors du prolongement en classe. Ces activités consistent à analyser les données recueillies au musée, à en faire une synthèse permettant à l'élève de tirer ses propres conclusions et finalement, de les partager avec ses pairs par le biais d'une communication orale.

Une démarche d'apprentissage intégrée

La démarche du programme éducatif muséal intégrant les moments, les lieux, les étapes et le processus impliqués dans le programme des sciences humaines au primaire (Allard, 1993), est illustrée au tableau 1 suivant.

TABLEAU 1

La démarche du programme éducatif muséal

	Moments	**Lieux**	**Étapes**	**Processus**
1.	Avant	École	Préparation	Exploration
2.	Pendant	Musée	Visite	Recherche
3.	Après	École	Prolongement	Traitement des données et échange

En ce qui a trait à la dernière phase du modèle didactique muséal, elle consiste en l'évaluation des objectifs, du contenu d'apprentissage, des activités et du matériel didactique du programme éducatif muséal. C'est un processus continu d'analyse et de synthèse dans le but de mesurer l'atteinte chez les élèves, des résultats d'apprentissage escomptés par le programme éducatif muséal.

Quelques recherches ont été menées par l'auteure en relation avec les phases et les étapes du modèle didactique muséal. Ces recherches traitent des effets d'un programme éducatif muséal, conçu et validé en fonction du programme des sciences humaines au second cycle du primaire et du contenu de la collection permanente du Musée d'archéologie de l'Université du Québec à Trois-Rivières.

Un de ces programmes, intitulé *Le mode de vie des Amérindiens de la préhistoire* (Paquin, 1989), vise la compréhension du mode de vie des premiers habitants du Québec et des premiers arrivants en Nouvelle-France. Par le biais de ses collections encyclopédique, le Musée d'archéologie permet d'enseigner la préhistoire amérindienne et du début de la période historique, du « contact » jusqu'au XIXᵉ siècle (Paquin, 1990). De plus, ce programme tient compte tant des objectifs terminaux et intermédiaires prescrits dans les programmes d'études que des objets de la collection du musée. À ce titre, il permet d'atteindre les objectifs 5.3 du programme de sciences humaines au second cycle du primaire (MEQ, 1981 : 44) : À l'aide de cartes géographiques et de représentations diverses, décrire en ses propres mots, l'origine et le mode de vie des populations qui habitaient le Québec jusqu'à l'arrivée des premiers européens.

Quelques résultats de recherche

De 1987 à 1993, diverses formes d'activités éducatives ont été expérimentées et évaluées au Musée d'archéologie à l'aide d'instruments de collecte de données : Un questionnaire d'ordre cognitif ayant trait aux faits, aux événement et à certains concepts (transport, alimentation, sédentarisme vs nomadisme) ; un questionnaire d'ordre affectif portant sur les attitudes envers le musée et envers les sciences humaines. Ces instruments étaient soumis aux élèves en prétest / post-test, avant et après la tenue du programme éducatif muséal. À l'aide de ces instruments, plusieurs variables ont été étudiées : Type d'activités mises en œuvre (simulation ; manipulation, démonstration) ; stratégies pédagogiques (visite active et visite-guidée ; agents impliqués (enseignant et éducateur de musée).

Quant au programme éducatif muséal, celui-ci consistait à faire effectuer aux élèves des activités de préparation en classe (mini-recherche, manipulation d'objets, exercice sur la carte), suivies d'une visite au musée visant essentiellement à recueillir des informations à l'aide de cahiers thématiques, pour se terminer par des activités de prolongement en classe (dessin, jeu de rôle, composition).

Signalons au passage, que d'autres recherches ont été conduites simultanément dans d'autres musées et en relation avec d'autres objectifs des programmes de sciences humaines, d'art et de français de l'ordre primaire du MEQ. En outre, le Musée David M.-Stewart situé à l'île Sainte-Hélène a évalué un programme éducatif ayant pour thème la traversée et l'implantation des colons français dans la vallée du Saint-Laurent, au XVIIᵉ et XVIIIᵉ siècles. Des études similaires ont été également poursuivies au site archéologique de la Pointe-du-Buisson, au Centre d'histoire de Montréal, pour ne nommer que ceux-là.

Les résultats de toutes ces expérimentations montrent que les élèves participant au programme éducatif muséal réalisent des progrès significatifs au niveau cognitif et affectif. À ce sujet, Allard (1993) écrit que plus les activités exigent des élèves une participation active, plus grand est le progrès observé. Ces progrès consistent en l'acquisition de connaissances et la compréhension de concepts ainsi que le développement d'attitudes positives envers le musée. De plus, l'état des recherches permettent de tirer certaines conclusions sur les stratégies, les approches, les étapes et les contenus d'apprentissage mis en œuvre dans les programmes. Notamment, les élèves réalisant une excursion à l'aide de cahiers thématiques dans le musée obtiennent de meilleurs résultats que ceux soumis à une visite-guidée ; l'analyse des programmes éducatifs mettant l'accent sur les attitudes et les habiletés intellectuelles et sociales présente des résultats plus positifs que ceux misant essentiellement sur les connaissances.

Dans un article qui sera publié dans la Revue canadienne de l'éducation, l'auteure présente les résultats de sa recherche doctorale. Celle-ci montre que l'agent d'éducation muséale joue un rôle déterminant dans l'apprentissage des élèves (Paquin, 1993). Par exemple, les connaissances approfondies dont il dispose sur les collections du musée sont avantageusement mises à profit lorsqu'il se déplace en classe pour faire effectuer aux élèves des activités de préparation et de prolongement autant que lors de la visite au musée. De même, lorsque l'agent d'éducation muséale travaille étroitement avec les enseignants à la conception d'un programme éducatif respectant les limites et les contraintes tant de l'école que du musée, il augmente considérablement les chances de stimuler l'intérêt et la curiosité des élèves qui y participent. À cet effet, en développant des habiletés et des attitudes plus favorables face au lieu muséal, les élèves risquent d'aimer davantage les musées et d'y retourner souvent plus tard (Boucher, 1986).

Bref, les résultats obtenus jusqu'à ce jour confirment l'importance, non seulement que les écoles et les musées mais, également, que toutes les institutions éducatives et culturelles de la société mettent en commun leurs ressources au service de la formation des élèves de l'ordre primaire et secondaire du Québec. Dans cette optique, un modèle didactique d'utilisation d'institutions culturelles québécoises à des fins éducatives s'envisagent à long terme, puisque l'école recèle une large part de la clientèle future de ces lieux.

Bibliographie

ALLARD, M. (1993). Le musée comme lieu d'apprentissage, *Vie Pédagogique*, (84). 41-43.

ALLARD, M., BOUCHER, S. (1991). *Le musée et l'école,* Montréal : Hurtubise HMH.

ATKIN, J.M., ATKIN, A. (1989). *Improving Science Education Through Local Alliances*, New-York : A report to the Carnegie Corporation.

BLOOM, J., MINTZ, A. (1990). Museum and the future of education, *Journal of Museum Education*, 15(3). 12-15.

BOUCHER, S. (1991). Le rôle de l'agent dans la mise en place des approches didactiques au musée, *À propos des approches didactiques au musée*, Montréal : Société des musées québécois, 8-14.

COMMISSION D'ÉTUDE POUR LA FORMATION DES ADULTES. (1982). *Apprendre : une action volontaire et responsable*, Québec : Gouvernement du Québec.

CONSEIL SUPÉRIEUR DE L'ÉDUCATION (Ed.). (1986). *Les nouveaux lieux éducatifs*, Québec : Gouvernement du Québec.

DERONZIER, J-R. (1987). L'éducation hors des murs, *L'Alliance*, 24(5). 40-41.

DESROSIERS-SABBATH, R. (1984). Des modèles d'apprentissage à la recherche et par la recherche dans la formation des enseignants, *L'apprentissage à la recherche ou par la recherche dans les programmes universitaires de sciences sociales et de formation des enseignants*, Montréal : Université du Québec à Montréal, 128-135.

FANTINI, M. (1985). Changing Concepts of Education, *Education in School and non-school Settings*, New-York : National Society for the Study of Education, 33-34.

HANSEN, T.H. (1984). Le rôle éducatif du musée, *Museum*, 36(4), 176-183.

HARRISON, J.A. (1988). The effects of educational programs in art museums on the artistic perceptions of elementary school children, *Journal of Research and Development in Education*, 21(3), 44-52.

HEIN, G.E. (1991). More than a field trip : Science programmes for elementary school groups at museums, *International Journal of Science Education*, 13(5), 505-520.

L'ÉCUYER, J. (1990). Les modèles dans les sciences de l'éducation, *Les modèles en éducation*, Montréal : Université du Québec à Montréal, 3-11.

LEGENDRE, R. (1988). *Dictionnaire Actuel de l'Éducation*, Montréal : Larousse.

LEMERISE, T. (1993). Le musée : un environnement favorable au dévoilement et au développement des théories naïves chez les élèves, Société canadienne pour l'étude de l'éducation, Ottawa : Université Carleton.

MINISTÈRE DE L'ÉDUCATION (Ed.). (1983). *Guide pédagogique, primaire, sciences humaines : histoire, géographie, vie économique et culturelle*, Québec : Gouvernement du Québec.

MINISTÈRE DE L'ÉDUCATION (Ed.). (1981). *Programme d'étude, primaire, sciences humaines : histoire, géographie, vie économique et culturelle*, Québec : Gouvernement du Québec.

ORR, M.T. (1987). *Keeping Students in School*, San Francisco : Jossey-Bass.

PAQUIN, M. (Article inédit accepté pour fins de publication), L'impact de *l'agent d'éducation muséale sur l'apprentissage d'ordre cognitif et affectif chez des élèves de la quatrième année du primaire, Revue canadienne de l'éducation.*

PAQUIN, M. (1993). *L'impact de l'agent d'éducation muséale sur l'acquisition de connaissances et le développement d'attitudes positives envers le musée et les sciences humaines chez des élèves de la quatrième année du primaire réalisant un programme éducatif muséal en trois étapes,* Thèse de doctorat en éducation, Trois-Rivières : Université du Québec à Trois-Rivières.

PAQUIN, M. (1991). Le rôle de l'agent en éducation muséale, *À propos des approches didactiques au musée,* Montréal : Société des musées québécois, 20-25.

PAQUIN, M. (1990). Apprendre et s'amuser au Musée d'archéologie de l'Université du Québec à Trois-Rivières, *Vie Pédagogique,* 64, 13-18.

PAQUIN, M. (1989). *Rendre la vie aux pierres : Programme éducatif et évaluation,* Trois-Rivières : Musée d'archéologie de l'Université du Québec à Trois-Rivières.

PAQUIN, M. (1987). *Le mode de vie des Amérindiens de la préhistoire : Programme éducatif et évaluation,* Trois-Rivières : Musée d'archéologie de l'Université du Québec à Trois-Rivières.

RACETTE, G. (1989). Applicabilité et universalité d'un modèle didactique muséal, *Les modèles en éducation,* Association internationale de pédagogie expérimentale de langue française, Montréal : Université du Québec à Montréal, 307-317.

Maryse PAQUIN
Modèle didactique d'utilisation d'institutions culturelles québécoises à des fins éducatives

RÉSUMÉ

Le présent article expose les composantes d'un modèle didactique utilisé en éducation muséale. L'auteure montre de quelle manière le modèle proposé ne se limite pas uniquement à une collaboration musée-école, puisque son application s'avère généralisable quelque soit l'institution culturelle ou scolaire. À ce sujet, l'état de la réflexion concernant le potentiel éducatif de divers lieux culturels contribuant à la formation des élèves est présenté. Bien que l'école et différentes institutions culturelles s'associent dans l'expérimentation de programmes éducatifs, beaucoup de barrières les empêchent de généraliser ces collaborations à l'ensemble du système scolaire. Dans ce contexte, l'auteure a travaillé de manière expérimentale à la planification et à l'évaluation de trois programmes éducatifs muséaux, conçus en relation avec les programmes scolaires du ministère de l'Éducation du Québec. Ses travaux ont été menés en collaboration avec le Groupe de recherche sur l'éducation et le musée (GREM), de l'Université du Québec à Montréal. En fournissant quelques exemples et en résumant les principaux résultats obtenus par ses recherches, l'auteure montre que les élèves retirent beaucoup de bénéfices d'un partenariat entre l'école et le musée. Les résultats atteints tendent à confirmer l'importance que toutes les institutions de la société mettent en commun leurs ressources afin de mieux former la clientèle future des lieux culturels.

Maryse PAQUIN
*Didactic Model of the Use of Cultural Institutions for Educational
Purposes in Quebec*

ABSTRACT

For almost twenty years, a major assessment of the educational potential of various cultural environments contributing to students' education has been made by education specialists. Although schools and various cultural institutions wish to get involved in experimenting with some educational programs, a lot of barriers prevent them from generalizing their findings across the whole of the school system. The author of the article has been involved, on an experimental basis, in the planning and assessment of three educational programs related to museums and designed to fit in the curriculums offered by the *ministère de l'Éducation du Québec*. These programs have been evaluated based on a didactic model of museums which applies to the cultural institutions of Québec. Studies carried out by the Research Group on Education and Museums of the Université du Québec à Montréal show that students derive a lot of benefits from such partnership. The findings suggest the necessity for all social institutions to share their resources in order to stimulate the interest of the future clientele of cultural institutions.

Maryse Paquin
Modelo didáctico de utilización de instituciones culturales quebequenses para fines educativos.

Resumen

Desde hace una veintena de años, el mundo de la educación emprende una vasta reflexión con respecto al potencial educativo de diversos lugares culturales que contribuyen a la formación de los alumnos. Aunque la escuela y diferentes instituciones culturales desean asociarse en la experimentación de programas educativos, muchas barreras les impiden de generalizar estas colaboraciones al conjunto del sistema escolar. La autora ha trabajado de manera experimental en la planificación y evaluación de tres programas educativos con respecto a los museos, concebidos en relación con los programas escolares del ministerio de educación del Quebec. Estos programas han sido validados según un modelo didáctico de los museos aplicable a las instituciones culturales quebequenses. Al final de algunas investigaciones realizadas por el grupo de investigación sobre la educación y el museo, los resultados muestran que los alumnos obtienen muchos beneficios de tal asociación. Estos resultados confirman la importancia que todas las instituciones de la sociedad meten en común sus recursos con el fin de formar mejor la clientela futura de los sitios culturales.

LES DÉTERMINANTS DE LA SATISFACTION À L'ÉGARD DE LA VISITE DES MUSÉES

André ALLAIRE
Service de la recherche et de l'évaluation
Musée de la civilisation
Québec

Dans le contexte actuel où les musées voient diminuer leurs sources publiques de financement ainsi que leur fréquentation, le milieu muséal tend de plus en plus à adopter une « approche client » visant, entre autres, à maintenir l'achalandage, voire à fidéliser la clientèle[1]. Le présent article porte sur une dimension importante de cette approche, soit la satisfaction des visiteurs. Deux variables dépendantes seront étudiées ici : 1) le degré de satisfaction générale à l'égard de la visite ; et 2) l'intention de retour au musée.

Plus précisément, nous chercherons à identifier empiriquement un certain nombre de *prédicteurs* de ces deux dernières variables, et à évaluer leur impact *net* sur la satisfaction. Notons que la présente recherche a été réalisée dans le cadre du programme d'évaluation et d'études de public du Musée de la civilisation de Québec.

Méthode

Notre étude s'appuie sur les données d'une enquête menée à l'été 1993 auprès d'un échantillon représentatif de visiteurs âgés de 18 ans et plus du Musée de la civilisation[2]. Lors de cette enquête, 1 996 personnes sélectionnées au hasard avaient dûment répondu, à la fin de leur visite du Musée, à un questionnaire auto-administré de six pages. Le taux de réponse obtenu s'établissait à 63,9 %. L'enquête visait à mesurer les caractéristiques socio-démographiques et socioculturelles des visiteurs, les modalités de la visite, le comportement au Musée, l'appréciation envers les différentes expositions, les services offerts aux publics et certains éléments muséographiques, et à connaître, enfin, le niveau de satisfaction générale.

L'analyse statistique des données se basera principalement sur l'analyse discriminante. Cette méthode d'analyse causale « multivariée » permet d'évaluer la contribution spécifique de chaque variable indépendante introduite dans un modèle explicatif en terme de sa capacité à *prédire* l'appartenance à l'un ou l'autre des groupes définissant la variable dépendante. Pour respecter l'un des postulats de l'analyse discriminante voulant que les variables indépendantes soient des mesures métriques, certaines variables qualitatives du questionnaire ont été transformées en variables dichotomiques prenant les valeurs 0 ou 1, où 0 signifie l'absence de l'attribut et 1 sa présence. Les analyses discriminantes ont été effectuées au moyen du progiciel SPSSX/PC+ et en utilisant le fichier pondéré des données de l'enquête.

TABLEAU 1
Les variables explicatives utilisées

1. Les caractéristiques sociodémographiques et socioculturelles du visiteur
- Sexe (1 = homme, 0 = femme) ;
- Groupe d'âge
  (4 variables dichotomiques : 25-34 ans, 35-44 ans, 45-54 ans, 55 ans et plus) ;
- Langue d'usage (1 = francophone, 0 = non-francophone) ;
- Niveau de scolarité
  (2 variables dichotomiques : 13-15 années d'études ; 16 années ou plus) ;
- Statut d'activité (1 = actif, 0 = inactif) ;
- Lieu d'origine (1 = province de Québec, 0 = extérieur du Québec) ;
- Nombre de visites dans les autres musées au cours des 12 derniers mois
  (0 = aucune, à 15 = 12 visites ou plus).

2. Le contexte de la visite
- Nombre de visites au Musée de la civilisation au cours des 12 derniers mois
  (0 = aucune, à 15 = 12 visites ou plus) ;
- Journée de la visite (1 = mardi gratuit, 0 = autre journée) ;
- Nombre de personnes accompagnant le visiteur (0 à 8).

3. L'expérience muséale
- Perception de l'accueil au Musée (1 = très bon, 0 = bon, moyen ou mauvais) ;
- Degré de gêne exprimé à l'égard de l'affluence et du bruit
  (indice variant de 0 = aucunement gêné, à 4 = très gêné) ;
- Degré de gêne exprimé à l'égard de certains éléments muséographiques :
  orientation dans le Musée, éclairage, lisibilité des textes dans les salles,
  bris de matériels d'exposition
  (indice variant de 0 = aucunement gêné, à 8 = très gêné) ;
- Nombre d'expositions vues au cours de la visite (0 à 10) ;
- Durée de la visite
  (3 variables dichotomiques : 2-3 heures ; 3-4 heures, 4 heures et plus) ;
- Satisfaction générale à l'égard de la visite
  (1 = très satisfait, 0 = plutôt satisfait ou insatisfait).

Le tableau 1 présente l'ensemble des variables que nous avons retenues du questionnaire de l'enquête comme « déterminants » potentiels du degré de satisfaction du visiteur et de l'intention de retour au Musée. Ces variables réfèrent à trois catégories de déterminants, soit : 1) les caractéristiques sociodémographiques et socioculturelles ; 2) le contexte de la visite ; et 3) l'expérience muséale.

Les modèles explicatifs présentés ici ne sont évidemment pas exhaustifs, en ce sens qu'ils ne tiennent pas compte de tous les facteurs pouvant influer sur la satisfaction des publics. Par exemple, cette étude ne considère aucune variable psychosociologique. En outre, elle ne mesure pas l'effet spécifique de la programmation sur la satisfaction générale, c'est-à-dire l'effet de l'ensemble des produits et services offerts par un musée pendant une période donnée.

Résultats

Le degré de satisfaction

La variable dépendante étudiée dans cette première partie de l'analyse des résultats est définie par l'appartenance à l'un ou l'autre des deux groupes suivants :

–   les visiteurs qui se sont dits très satisfaits de la visite du Musée de la civilisation (n = 1 077 ou 61,4 % de l'échantillon global) ;

–   tous les autres visiteurs, c'est-à-dire les répondants qui se sont dits plutôt satisfaits ou insatisfaits de la visite (n = 677 ou 38,6 %)[3].

Les analyses ont été réalisées à partir d'un échantillon de 1 754 répondants[4]. Avant de décrire les résultats de l'analyse discriminante, comparons d'abord les deux groupes étudiés au niveau des moyennes rattachées aux variables explicatives sélectionnées.

Comme l'indique le tableau 2, les plus grandes différences de moyennes se retrouvent parmi trois variables définissant l'expérience muséale, soit : la perception de l'accueil, le degré de gêne exprimé à l'égard de l'affluence et du bruit, et le degré de gêne exprimé à l'égard d'éléments muséographiques[5]. Ainsi, les visiteurs qui se disent très satisfaits jugent l'accueil plus souvent très bon que les autres qui se montrent plutôt satisfaits ou insatisfaits (83 % contre 48 %), et se disent moins gênés par l'affluence et le bruit (0,73 contre 1,04) ainsi que par certains éléments muséographiques comme l'éclairage dans les salles et la lisibilité des textes (0,72 contre 1,08). L'examen des moyennes fournit déjà une idée des principaux *prédicteurs* potentiels du degré de satisfaction. Afin de connaître plus précisément l'effet net des variables explicatives précédentes, référons-nous maintenant aux résultats de l'analyse discriminante[6].

TABLEAU 2

**Moyennes et écarts - types de l'ensemble des variables explicatives
utilisées, selon le degré de satisfaction générale à l'égard de la visite,
ensemble des visiteurs, juillet 1993**

Variable	(1) Plutôt satisfaits ou insatisfaits (*n* = 677)		(2) Très satisfaits (*n* = 1 077)	
	Moyenne	Écart-type	Moyenne	Écart-type
1. Les caractéristiques sociodémographiques et socioculturelles				
– Sexe (% hommes)	0,51	0,50	0,49	0,50
– Groupe d'âge				
25-34 ans	0,32	0,47	0,24	0,43
35-44 ans	0,25	0,43	0,28	0,45
45-54 ans	0,15	0,36	0,23	0,42
55 ans et plus	0,07	0,26	0,10	0,31
– Langue d'usage				
(% francophones)	0,86	0,35	0,89	0,31
– Niveau de scolarité				
13-15 années	0,33	0,47	0,33	0,47
16 années ou plus	0,42	0,49	0,43	0,49
– Statut d'activité				
(% personnes actives)	0,72	0,45	0,79	0,40
– Lieu d'origine				
(% de Québécois)	0,76	0,42	0,77	0,42
– Nombre de visites dans les autres musées				
(12 derniers mois)	2,01	2,91	2,10	2,97
2. Le contexte de la visite				
– Nombre de visites au Musée				
(12 derniers mois)	0,49	1,18	0,63	1,58
– Journée de la visite				
(% venus le mardi gratuit)	0,34	0,48	0,31	0,46
– Nombre de personnes accompagnant le visiteur	1,83	1,59	1,77	1,49
3. L'expérience muséale				
– Perception de l'accueil au Musée (% jugé très bon)	0,48	0,50	0,83	0,38
– Degré de gêne vs l'affluence et le bruit	1,04	1,29	0,73	1,07
– Degré de gêne vs éléments muséographiques	1,08	1,36	0,72	1,20
– Nombre d'expositions vues au cours de la visite	6,53	2,93	6,57	2,87

Le tableau 3 présente le poids que possèdent différents ensembles de variables (modèles) pour *prédire* le degré de satisfaction générale du visiteur. On note d'abord que le modèle saturé, c'est-à-dire celui incluant l'ensemble des 14 variables indépendantes retenues, explique 16,8 % de la variance totale de la variable dépendante[7]. Plus précisément, ce sont les variables définissant l'expérience muséale du visiteur qui déterminent le plus le degré de satisfaction, expliquant à elles seules 15,1 % de la variance totale. En comparaison, les caractéristiques sociodémographiques et socioculturelles n'expliquent que

TABLEAU 3

Poids relatif des différents types de déterminants de la satisfaction générale à l'égard de la visite, ensemble des visiteurs, juillet 1993

**Modèle 1 : Les caractéristiques sociodémographiques
        et socioculturelles du visiteur**
1. Sexe ;
2. Groupe d'âge ;
3. Langue d'usage ;
4. Niveau de scolarité ;
5. Statut d'activité ;
6. Lieu d'origine ;
7. Nombre de visites dans les autres musées au cours des 12 derniers mois.
Pourcentage de la variance totale expliquée : $R^2 = 3,3$ %

Modèle 2 : Le contexte de la visite
1. Nombre de visites au Musée de la civilisation au cours des 12 derniers mois ;
2. Journée de la visite ;
3. Nombre de personnes accompagnant le visiteur.
    Pourcentage de la variance totale expliquée : $R^2 = 0,4$ %*
    (* non statistiquement significatif au seuil de confiance de 0,05.)

Modèle 3 : L'expérience muséale
1. Perception de l'accueil au Musée ;
2. Degré de gêne exprimé à l'égard de l'affluence et du bruit ;
3. Degré de gêne exprimé à l'égard de certains éléments muséographiques ;
4. Nombre d'expositions vues au cours de la visite ;
    Pourcentage de la variance totale expliquée : $R^2 = 15,1$ %

**Modèle 4 : Les variables antérieures à la visite
        (Modèle 1 + Modèle 2)**
Pourcentage de la variance totale expliquée : $R^2 = 3,5$ %

**Modèle 5 : Modèle saturé : l'ensemble des variables précédentes
        (Modèle 1 + Modèle 2 + Modèle 3)**
Pourcentage de la variance totale expliquée : $R^2 = 16,8$ %

TABLEAU 4

Résultats de l'analyse discriminante sur la satisfaction générale à l'égard de la visite, ensemble des visiteurs, juillet 1993

Variable dépendante = Degré de satisfaction
    1 = Plutôt satisfait ou insatisfait (38,6 %)
    2 = Très satisfait (61,4 %)

Les prédicteurs les plus importants, par ordre décroissant :	*Lambda* de Wilks	Coefficient standardisé de discrimination
1. Perception de l'accueil au Musée	0,8689	0,843
2. Degré de gêne exprimé vs certains éléments muséographiques	0,8543	-0,263
3. Degré de gêne exprimé vs l'affluence et le bruit	0,8487	-0,271
4. Âge : 45-54 ans	0,8450	0,146
5. Langue d'usage : francophone	0,8428	0,213
6. Nombre de visites dans les autres musées (12 derniers mois)	0,8405	0,099
7. Statut d'activité : actif	0,8384	0,154
8. Âge : 25-34 ans	0,8372	-0,074
9. Journée de visite : mardi gratuit	0,8361	0,098
10. Lieu d'origine : province de Québec	0,8351	-0,141
11. Nombre de visites au Musée (12 derniers mois)	0,8341	0,089
12. Âge : 55 ans et plus	0,8334	0,082
13. Scolarité : 13-15 années	0,8328	0,068

Nombre de cas utilisés pour l'analyse = 1 754
% de la variance totale expliquée   = 16,7 %
% de cas classés dans le bon groupe   = 70,1 %
                                 51,0 % pour groupe 1
                                 82,0 % pour groupe 2

Variables non discriminantes = Sexe, nombre de personnes accompagnant le visiteur et nombre d'expositions visitées.

3,3 % de la variance totale alors que les variables reliées au contexte de la visite n'influencent aucunement le degré de satisfaction ($R^2 = 0,4$ %, $p = 0,08$). Ces résultats qui montrent clairement la prédominance de l'expérience du visiteur pour expliquer la satisfaction corroborent donc l'analyse des moyennes effectuées précédemment.

Pour connaître cette fois l'effet net de chaque variable du modèle dans la détermination de l'appartenance aux deux groupes étudiés (très satisfaits / plutôt satisfaits ou insatisfaits), nous avons utilisé la procédure dite « pas à pas » (*stepwise*) du programme d'analyse discriminante, qui trie une à une les variables sur la base du critère de minimisation de la valeur du coefficient *lambda* de Wilks.

Les résultats de ce type d'analyse présentés au tableau 4 montrent que la variable *perception de l'accueil* constitue de loin le meilleur déterminant du degré de satisfaction du visiteur : on se dit d'autant plus très satisfait de la visite que l'on juge très bon l'accueil au Musée. La comparaison de la valeur des coefficients standardisés de discrimination révèle que cette variable exerce un effet net trois fois plus élevé que le degré de gêne exprimé à l'égard de certains éléments muséographiques, variable qui occupe le deuxième rang (0,843 contre − 0,263). Ensuite, on retrouve, à peu près sur le même pied (−0,271), le degré de gêne exprimé envers l'affluence et le bruit.

L'impact des autres variables du modèle sur la satisfaction générale, quoique statistiquement significatif, est somme toute assez faible puisque la valeur des coefficients standardisés varie entre un minimum de 0,068 et un maximum de 0,213[8]. Notons quand même que, toutes choses étant contrôlées, le fait d'être francophone augmente quelque peu les chances de se dire très satisfait du Musée alors que, curieusement, le fait de résider au Québec tend à diminuer cette probabilité. Donc, être un francophone de l'étranger accroît plus les chances de se dire très satisfait qu'être Québécois francophone. Par ailleurs, être âgé de plus de 44 ans augmente les chances de se dire très satisfait tandis qu'appartenir à la tranche des 25 à 34 ans réduit cette probabilité.

Comme autres caractéristiques qui tendent à accroître la probabilité d'être très satisfait, signalons le fait d'être un habitué du Musée et aussi celui de visiter souvent les autres musées, le fait d'être « actif » sur le marché du travail et, enfin, le fait d'avoir complété de 13 à 15 années d'études. Notons de plus que visiter le Musée lors de la journée gratuite exerce un effet autonome positif sur le degré de satisfaction, et ce, malgré que les conditions de visite soient souvent moins bonnes durant cette journée (plus d'affluence et de bruit notamment). Par ailleurs, il est intéressant de signaler ici que la scolarité n'exerce qu'une faible influence nette (0,068) sur la satisfaction générale.

Enfin, parmi les variables qui n'affectent pas du tout le degré de satisfaction, on retrouve le sexe, le nombre de personnes accompagnant le visiteur et le nombre d'expositions vues.

L'intention de retour au musée

Le délai de l'intention de retour au Musée représente un autre indicateur de la satisfaction à l'égard de la visite. Cette variable dépendante est ici définie par l'appartenance à l'un ou l'autre des deux groupes suivants :

—   les visiteurs qui ont affirmé vouloir revenir au Musée dans les six mois (*n* = 438 ou 25,5 %) ;

—   tous les autres visiteurs qui ont affirmé qu'ils reviendront dans plus de six mois ou jamais (*n* = 1 280 ou 74,5 %).

TABLEAU 5

Moyennes et écarts – types de l'ensemble des variables explicatives utilisées, selon le délai de l'intention de retour au Musée, ensemble des visiteurs, juillet 1993

Variable	(1) Dans plus de 6 mois (*n* = 1 280)		(2) Avant 6 mois (*n* = 438)	
	Moyenne	Écart-type	Moyenne	Écart-type
1. Les caractéristiques sociodémographiques et socioculturelles				
– Sexe (% hommes)	0,50	0,50	0,48	0,50
– Groupe d'âge				
25-34 ans	0,30	0,46	0,21	0,41
35-44 ans	0,27	0,44	0,28	0,45
45-54 ans	0,20	0,40	0,20	0,40
55 ans et plus	0,08	0,27	0,11	0,31
– Langue d'usage (% francophones)	0,86	0,35	0,95	0,22
– Niveau de scolarité				
13-15 années	0,32	0,47	0,36	0,48
16 années ou plus	0,41	0,49	0,45	0,50
– Statut d'activité (% personnes actives)	0,78	0,41	0,71	0,45
– Lieu d'origine (% de Québécois)	0,72	0,45	0,94	0,24
– Nombre de visites dans les autres musées (12 derniers mois)	2,02	2,95	2,16	2,95
2. Le contexte de la visite				
– Nombre de visites au Musée (12 derniers mois)	0,22	0,57	1,67	2,40
– Journée de la visite (% venus le mardi gratuit)	0,27	0,44	0,51	0,50
– Nombre de personnes avec le visiteur	1,89	1,55	1,54	1,48
3. L'expérience muséale				
– Perception de l'accueil (% jugé très bon)	0,67	0,47	0,76	0,43
– Degré de gêne vs l'affluence et le bruit	0,76	1,11	1,12	1,29
– Degré de gêne vs éléments muséographiques	0,87	1,28	0,80	1,21
– Nombre d'expositions vues au cours de la visite	7,05	2,76	5,10	2,81
– Durée de la visite				
2-3 heures	0,40	0,49	0,43	0,50
3-4 heures	0,17	0,38	0,13	0,33
4 heures et plus	0,08	0,28	0,05	0,22
– Satisfaction générale à l'égard de la visite (% de très satisfaits)	0,57	0,49	0,73	0,40

TABLEAU 6

Poids relatif des différents types de déterminants de l'intention de retour au Musée, ensemble des visiteurs, juillet 1993

Modèle 1 : Les caractéristiques sociodémographiques et socioculturelles du visiteur

1. Sexe ;
2. Groupe d'âge ;
3. Langue d'usage ;
4. Niveau de scolarité ;
5. Statut d'activité ;
6. Lieu d'origine ;
7. Nombre de visites dans les autres musées au cours des 12 derniers mois.

Pourcentage de la variance totale expliquée : $R^2 = 8,8\%$

Modèle 2 : Le contexte de la visite

1. Nombre de visites au Musée de la civilisation au cours des 12 derniers mois ;
2. Journée de la visite ;
3. Nombre de personnes accompagnant le visiteur.

Pourcentage de la variance totale expliquée : $R^2 = 21,9\%$

Modèle 3 : L'expérience muséale

1. Perception de l'accueil au Musée ;
2. Degré de gêne exprimée à l'égard de l'affluence et du bruit ;
3. Degré de gêne exprimée à l'égard de certains éléments muséographiques ;
4. Nombre d'expositions vues au cours de la visite ;
5. Durée de la visite ;
6. Satisfaction générale à l'égard de la visite.

Pourcentage de la variance totale expliquée : $R^2 = 12,7\%$

Modèle 4 : Les variables antérieures à la visite (Modèle 1 + Modèle 2)

Pourcentage de la variance totale expliquée : $R^2 = 25,3\%$

Modèle 5 : Modèle saturé : l'ensemble des variables précédente (Modèle 1 + Modèle 2 + Modèle 3)

Pourcentage de la variance totale expliquée : $R^2 = 30,6\%$

Les analyses de cette dernière partie reposent sur un échantillon de 1 718 répondants[9]. Comme le montre le tableau 5, il existe, sur plusieurs variables, des différences de moyennes assez prononcées entre les deux groupes considérés. Ainsi, comme on pouvait s'y attendre, les personnes qui mentionnent vouloir revenir bientôt au Musée, c'est-à-dire dans les six mois, résident plus souvent au Québec que les autres (94 % contre 72 %) et sont donc plus souvent francophones (95 % contre 86 %). Elles fréquentent plus assidûment le Musée (1,67 visite en moyenne au cours de la dernière année contre 0,22 visite), voient moins d'expositions en moyenne lors de leur séjour au Musée (5,10 contre 7,05) et viennent plus souvent au cours de la journée gratuite fort achalandée du mardi (51 % contre 27 %). Ce dernier constat explique sans doute qu'elles signalent avoir été plus gênées par l'affluence et le bruit (1,12 contre 0,76) que les autres visiteurs. Notons enfin que les personnes qui souhaitent revenir bientôt au Musée sont proportionnellement plus nombreuses à se dire très satisfaites de leur visite (73 % contre 57 %).

Le tableau 6 présente les résultats de l'analyse discriminante en ce qui a trait au poids explicatif de différents ensembles de variables dans la détermination du délai de l'intention de retour au Musée. Si l'on introduit dans l'équation toutes les variables indépendantes, on peut expliquer 30,6 % de la variance totale, pourcentage nettement plus élevé que celui obtenu à la section précédente (16,8 %). Notons qu'en ne retenant que les variables statistiquement significatives, ce modèle permet de classer 82,4 % des cas dans le bon groupe d'appartenance (tableau 7), proportion bien supérieure à celle attendue du hasard (74,5 %). Par ailleurs, il réussit beaucoup mieux à prédire l'appartenance au premier groupe, composé des visiteurs affirmant qu'ils ne reviendront pas au Musée dans les six mois, qu'au second. Ainsi, 95,5 % des répondants appartenant au premier groupe ont été classés dans ce même groupe, comparativement à seulement 44,2 % des répondants du second groupe.

On remarque que ce sont d'abord les variables reliées au contexte de la visite qui contribuent le plus à différencier les deux groupes ($R^2 = 21,9$ %). On retrouve ensuite les variables définissant l'expérience muséale ($R^2 = 12,7$ %), suivies des caractéristiques sociodémographiques et socio-culturelles ($R^2 = 8,8$ %).

Examinons de façon plus précise, à l'aide du tableau 7, l'effet net de chaque *prédicteur* retenu. La variable de loin la plus discriminante de l'intention de revenir ou non au Musée dans les six mois est le nombre de visites qu'on y a effectué au cours de la dernière année (coefficient standardisé = 0,621). Tel qu'attendu, on revient d'autant plus tôt au Musée qu'on le fréquente souvent.

Le nombre d'expositions vues au cours de la dernière visite constitue le deuxième *prédicteur* le plus important (-0,395) : toutes choses étant égales par ailleurs, le fait de visiter un grand nombre d'expositions diminue la probabilité de revenir au Musée dans les six mois. Cette dernière observation révèle sans doute un comportement assez singulier d'un bon nombre de visiteurs d'été de la région, qui consiste en quelque sorte à faire le « plein » d'expositions lors de leur visite au Musée et à n'y revenir que lorsque la programmation aura complètement changé.

Ensuite, au troisième rang, on retrouve le lieu d'origine (0,409) : résider au Québec plutôt qu'à l'extérieur de la province accroît évidemment les chances de retourner bientôt au Musée. La satisfaction générale à l'égard de la dernière visite exerce aussi, comme on pouvait s'y attendre, un impact significatif positif (0,268) sur le délai de l'intention de retour. Par ailleurs, il est intéressant de constater que la variable *perception de l'accueil* influence ici directement l'intention de retour au Musée, quoique de façon moins marquée que le degré de satisfaction (0,074 contre 0,268). Ainsi, on a plus de chances de faire une nouvelle visite dans les six mois si l'on a perçu l'accueil comme étant très bon.

Comme autres caractéristiques qui, toutes choses contrôlées, accroissent les chances de retour avant six mois, mentionnons le fait d'avoir visité le Musée au cours de la journée gratuite du mardi, d'être « inactif », de fréquenter souvent les musées et, enfin, de posséder plus de 12 années d'études.

TABLEAU 7

Résultats de l'analyse discriminante sur l'intention de retour au Musée, ensemble des visiteurs, juillet 1993

Variable dépendante = Intention de retour au Musée 1 = Dans plus de 6 mois (74,5 %) 2 = Avant 6 mois (25,5 %)		
Les prédicteurs les plus importants, par ordre décroissant :	*Lambda* de Wilks	Coefficient standardisé de discrimination
1. Nombre de visites au Musée (12 derniers mois)	0,8097	0,621
2. Nombre d'expositions vues au cours de la visite	0,7676	-0,395
3. Lieu d'origine : province de Québec	0,7360	0,409
4. Satisfaction générale à l'égard de la visite	0,7201	0,268
5. Journée de visite : mardi gratuit	0,7077	0,221
6. Statut d'activité : actif	0,7032	-0,145
7. Nombre de visites dans les autres musées (12 derniers mois)	0,7015	0,082
8. Nombre de personnes accompagnant le visiteur	0,7005	-0,069
9. Perception de l'accueil au Musée	0,6995	0,074
10. Durée de la visite : 3-4 heures	0,6986	-0,062
11. Degré de gêne exprimé vs l'affluence et le bruit	0,6980	0,073
12. Âge : 25-34 ans	0,6975	-0,057
13. Scolarité : 16 années ou plus	0,6971	0,114
14. Scolarité : 13-15 années	0,6958	0,101
15. Degré de gêne exprimé vs certains éléments muséograpghiques	0,6952	-0,054

Nombre de cas utilisés pour l'analyse = 1 718
    % de la variance totale expliquée = 30,5 %
  % de cas classés dans le bon groupe = 82,4 %
                                95,5 % pour le groupe 1
                                44,2 % pour le groupe 2
Variables non discriminantes = Sexe et langue d'usage.

À l'inverse, le fait d'être accompagné de plusieurs personnes, de faire une visite d'une durée de 3 à 4 heures, d'être âgé entre 25 et 34 ans[10], et d'avoir été gêné par certains éléments muséographiques (orientation dans le musée, lisibilité des textes, éclairage dans les salles et bris de matériels d'exposition) sont des traits qui diminuent en soi la probabilité de revenir dans les six mois. Enfin, on constate que ni le sexe, ni la langue d'usage n'ont un impact significatif sur l'intention de retour.

Conclusion

Les résultats des analyses discriminantes que nous avons effectuées sur un échantillon de visiteurs du Musée de la civilisation pourraient, pensons-nous, en grande partie, être généralisés à d'autres institutions muséales. Ils montrent d'abord que le degré de satisfaction générale à l'égard de la visite des musées dépend beaucoup plus de l'expérience vécue lors de cette visite que de facteurs antérieurs à celle-ci, tels que les caractéristiques socio-démographiques et socioculturelles. Parmi les variables reliées à l'expérience muséale, c'est surtout la perception de l'accueil reçu qui détermine le degré de satisfaction générale du visiteur. Viennent ensuite les aspects plus proprement muséographiques (éclairage et lisibilité des textes dans les salles, bris de matériel d'exposition, signalisation, etc.) et le confort du visiteur (affluence et bruit).

En comparaison, les caractéristiques individuelles n'influencent, somme toute, que faiblement la satisfaction. À cet égard, on remarque, comme on pouvait s'y attendre, que les visiteurs ont plus de chances de se dire très satisfaits de la visite d'un musée s'ils sont déjà des habitués de ce musée, ou encore, des amateurs de musées.

Un des résultats intrigants de la présente étude est sans doute le peu d'effet qu'exerce la scolarité sur le degré de satisfaction. Ainsi, cet important élément de *capital culturel* agirait, comme l'ont montré plusieurs recherches[11], beaucoup plus sur la fréquentation, c'est-à-dire sur la décision d'aller visiter ou non un musée, que sur l'appréciation de la visite. Toutefois, il serait bon de vérifier par d'autres études si cette dernière conclusion, qui est tirée d'un échantillon de visiteurs d'un musée thématique, s'applique également aux musées d'art dont le public apparaît traditionnellement plus élitiste.

Par ailleurs, l'analyse des déterminants de l'intention de revenir ou non au musée dans les six mois a confirmé, tel qu'attendu, l'importance des variables contrôles que sont le lieu de résidence, la fréquence annuelle des visites au musée et le nombre d'expositions vues lors du dernier séjour au musée. Un autre prédicteur non négligeable est évidemment la satisfaction à l'égard de la dernière visite : plus l'on se dit très satisfait de cette visite, plus l'on a de chances de retourner bientôt au musée.

Des résultats de la présente étude, on peut conclure que les musées devraient miser avant tout sur l'amélioration des conditions d'accueil du public s'ils veulent accroître la satisfaction, et conséquemment la fidélisation. Parmi les autres moyens susceptibles d'augmenter le nombre de visites, mentionnons l'amélioration du confort des visiteurs et de certains aspects liés à la muséographie, tels que l'éclairage, la lisibilité des textes d'expositions et la signalisation. Notons enfin que le fait d'offrir une journée de visite gratuite a un effet positif à la fois sur la satisfaction et la fidélisation.

Notes

1. Pour une présentation de ce type d'approche, voir André Coupet, « Service à la clientèle : une stratégie et une démarche pour fidéliser nos clients », *MBA bulletin de l'Association des m.b.a. du Québec*, 1994.

2. Pour une description plus détaillée de la méthode et une présentation des principaux résultats de cette enquête, voir André Allaire, *Les publics du Musée de la civilisation : portrait de l'été 1993 et évolution depuis l'ouverture*, Musée de la civilisation, collection « Cahiers de recherche », n° 7, 1994, 98 p.

3. Afin de simplifier la présentation des résultats de l'analyse discriminante, nous avons choisi d'utiliser une variable dépendante comprenant deux catégories plutôt que trois, en incluant dans la même catégorie les réponses « plutôt satisfaits » et « insatisfaits ». Notons que les visiteurs insatisfaits ne représentent en fait que 3 % de l'échantillon total.

4. Des 1 996 répondants formant l'échantillon initial, 242 cas ont dû être exclus de l'analyse, n'ayant pas donné une information complète sur l'ensemble des variables considérées dans l'étude.

5. Ces deux dernières variables sont en fait des indices additifs qui ont été construits à partir des résultats d'une analyse factorielle portant sur 8 éléments du questionnaire cherchant à mesurer divers aspects possibles de gêne que peut éprouver un visiteur lors de la visite d'un musée. Pour chacun des éléments, le degré de gêne était mesuré à l'aide de trois catégories de réponse : « pas du tout gêné(e) » (0 point) ; « un peu gêné(e) » (1 point), et « beaucoup gêné(e) » (2 points). De ces 8 éléments, l'analyse factorielle a fait ressortir deux principaux facteurs que l'on peut représenter par les deux indices suivants : 1) le degré de gêne exprimée à l'égard le l'affluence et du bruit (échelle variant entre 0 et 4) et 2) le degré de gêne exprimée à l'égard d'éléments muséographiques, indice qui se compose des 4 éléments suivants : l'orientation dans le musée, l'éclairage dans les salles, la lisibilité des textes dans les salles, et enfin, le bris de certains matériels d'exposition. Dans ce cas-ci, l'échelle des valeurs peut varier entre 0 et 8. Notons que deux éléments, soit la température dans le musée et les heures d'ouverture, n'ont pas été considérés dans la présente étude puisque leur corrélation avec les facteurs était trop faible.

6. Cette méthode d'analyse multivariée, en contrôlant les corrélations entre les variables indépendantes de l'équation, permet d'éviter d'imputer à une variable ce qui est en fait attribuable à une autre qui lui est associée.

7. Le modèle retenu est statistiquement significatif ($p < 0,001$), c'est-à-dire qu'il contribue plus que le simple hasard à prédire l'appartenance à l'un ou l'autre des deux groupes considérés. En outre, en ne conservant que les variables statistiquement significatives (voir tableau 4), le modèle réussit globalement à classer correctement dans le bon groupe 70,1 % des répondants, pourcentage bien supérieur à celui que l'on attendrait du hasard (61,4 %).

8. À l'instar du coefficient standardisé de régression ß, le coefficient standardisé de discrimination peut fluctuer entre -1 et +1.

9. 278 cas ont été exclus de l'analyse parce qu'ils n'avaient pas fourni une information complète sur l'ensemble des variables considérées dans l'étude.

10. On peut penser que cette tranche d'âge particulière correspond à une étape du cycle de vie (nouveaux mariés, familles   avec jeunes enfants) où tend à diminuer la consommation des produits culturels, comme les sorties au cinéma, au théâtre ou dans les musées. Voir à ce sujet, l'étude de Claire McAughey, *A Survey of Arts Audience Studies : A Canadian Perspective 1967-1984*, Canada Council, septembre 1984, 113 p., et celle de Les consultants Cultur'Inc et Decima Research, *Profil des Canadiens consommateurs d'art, 1990-1991*, mai 1992, 516 p.

11. Voir particulièrement à ce sujet l'étude classique de Pierre Bourdieu et Alain Darbel, *L'amour de l'art : les musées d'art européens et leur public*, Les éditions de minuit, Paris, 1969, 247 p.

André ALLAIRE
Les déterminants de la satisfaction à l'égard de la visite des musées

RÉSUMÉ

Cet article considère deux variables dépendantes : 1) le degré de satisfaction générale à l'égard de la visite ; et 2) le délai de l'intention de retour au musée. Les données analysées proviennent d'une enquête menée au Musée de la civilisation de Québec auprès d'un échantillon de 1 996 visiteurs. L'analyse statistique se base principalement sur l'analyse discriminante. Le modèle explicatif proposé comprend une quinzaine de variables mesurant trois types de déterminants, soit : 1) les caractéristiques sociodémographiques et socioculturelles du visiteur ; 2) le contexte de la visite ; et 3) l'expérience muséale. Cette recherche montre, entre autres, que la satisfaction du visiteur dépend plus de l'expérience vécue lors de la visite, et particulièrement de la perception de l'accueil, que des caractéristiques individuelles et de facteurs antérieurs à la visite. Pour une bonne part, les conclusions de la présente étude pourraient s'appliquer à tous les types de musées.

André ALLAIRE
Factors of Satisfaction in Visiting Museums

ABSTRACT

Two dependent variables are taken into account in the research : 1) the overall satisfaction of visitors, and 2) the period of time visitors intend to wait before returning to the museum. The data under analysis are drawn from a survey carried out at the Quebec's *Musée de la civilisation* among a sample of 1996 visitors. The statistical analysis is mainly based on discriminant analysis. The proposed explanatory model is comprised of about fifteen variables which measure three types of determining factors, i.e. : 1) the visitor's sociodemographic and sociocultural characteristics ; 2) the context of the visit ; and 3) the experience in the museum. The findings suggest, among other things, that the visitor's satisfaction mainly depends on the feelings he experiences during the visit, and particularly his perception of general hospitality. Individual characteristics and previous experiences seem to account less for the feeling of satisfaction. For the most part, the conclusions of the study could apply to all kinds of museums.

André ALLAIRE
Los determinantes de la satisfacción con respecto a la visita de los museos

RESUMEN

Este artículo considera dos variables dependientes : 1) el grado de satisfacción general con respecto a la visita ; y 2) el tiempo que tarda la intención de regresar al museo. Los datos analizados provienen de una encuesta realizada en el Museo de la civilización de Quebec, sobre una muestra de 1996 visitantes. El análisis estadístico se basa principalmente en el análisis discriminante. El modelo explicativo propuesto comprende una quincena de variables que miden tres tipos de determinantes, sea : 1) las características sociodemográficas y socioculturales del visitante ; 2) el contexto de la visita ; y 3) la experiencia con respecto a la visita al museo. Esta investigación muestra, entre otras cosas, que la satisfacción del visitante depende más de la experiencia vivida durante la visita, y particularmente de la percepción del recibimiento, que de las características individuales y de los factores anteriores a la visita. En gran parte, las conclusiones del presente estudio podrían ser aplicadas a todos los tipos de museos.

LES BEST-SELLERS, INDICES D'UNE IDENTITÉ CULTURELLE COLLECTIVE : LES GRANDS SUCCÈS DU LIVRE ET DE LA TÉLÉVISION AU QUÉBEC

Jacques LEMIEUX
Roger DE LA GARDE
avec la collaboration de CLAUDE MARTIN*
Département d'information et de communication
Université Laval

Le visionnement de la télévision et la lecture constituent non seulement les principales habitudes de loisirs culturels des Québécois, mais se situent également aux premiers rangs de l'ensemble de leurs activités de loisir.

Les genres de livres et d'émissions de télévision les plus populaires – les best-sellers romanesques et biographiques, ainsi que les téléromans – se caractérisent dans leurs contenus par leur double fonction de divertissement (évasion) et d'information (réflexion) ; dans la mesure où leur thématique se révèle habituellement en prise directe avec l'agenda social de l'heure.

La présence massive, au niveau de l'offre, de produits étrangers (majoritairement « usaniens ») pourrait être considérée comme une menace pour le maintien de l'identité québécoise ; toutefois, lecteurs et téléspectateurs québécois font preuve de spécificité, tant dans la sélection de produits étrangers

*   Jacques Lemieux et Roger de la Garde sont professeurs au Département d'information et communication et chercheurs au Centre de recherche sur la littérature québécoise (CRELIQ), à l'Université Laval. Claude Martin est professeur au Département de communication de l'université de Montréal et chercheur au CRELIQ. Les auteurs veulent remercier leurs auxiliaires de recherche qui ont participé de façon active aux travaux de l'équipe : Charles-Édouard Boivin, Pierre Huard et Nicolas Tremblay.

qu'ils adoptent, que dans la part de marché substantielle qu'ils persistent à accorder à leurs productions nationales.

C'est ce que nous voulons démontrer à partir de l'examen des grilles de programmation et des cotes d'écoute de la télévision, ainsi que des listes de best-sellers parues dans la presse, en rapport avec diverses enquêtes sur la lecture.

Imaginaire et production sociale de la réalité

Cette étude constitue une production d'une équipe multidisciplinaire[1] de chercheurs rattachés au Centre de recherches sur la littérature québécoise (CRÉLIQ). Notre projet conjoint porte sur l'analyse des best-sellers et se situe dans le deuxième axe de recherche du Centre. Pour le moment, il constitue la principale activité de l'axe. Nos travaux portent sur les produits à succès dans les domaines de l'audiovisuel (la télévision), de l'imprimé (le livre) et de l'enregistrement sonore (la musique populaire).

S'il fallait identifier notre problématique, nous pourrions dire que nos préoccupations se rejoignent autour de la question de l'identité commune et des signes et symboles par lesquels des individus se reconnaissent cette identité. Plus précisément, en reprenant à notre compte les mots de Fernand Dumont, il s'agit de la question de la communauté d'allégeance, ou d'appartenance, et de ses symboles (p. 15).

> Ces symboles sont liés à des pratiques et à des institutions, que des représentations et des débats leur prêtent consistance. Un cran de plus est franchi lorsque intervient le discours ; des idéologies disent la [communauté d'appartenance], en décrivent les traits, la distinguent d'autres [communautés], dénoncent les périls qui la guettent.... Des discours racontent l'histoire de la [communauté], en font voir le développement dans le temps, la gratifient d'une mémoire collective.

Nous n'allons pas, comme le fait Dumont, jusqu'à nommer cette « communauté d'appartenance » et à lui substituer le terme de *nation*. Ainsi, tout en continuant à nous inscrire dans la théorie que Dumont propose à notre réflexion, théorie qu'il définit lui-même comme « un échafaudage afin que s'exerce l'analyse » (p. 19) de ce phénomène de l'identité commune, nous acceptons sa règle de base qui stipule que « nous sommes incapables de cerner la nature d'une [communauté d'appartenance] en écartant l'incessant travail par lequel les [membres] eux-mêmes interprètent son existence. » (p. 15). Ce travail incessant d'interprétation ce sont les représentations, les discours identitaires, la « construction d'une *référence* » (p. 16). La communauté d'appartenance peut être la nation qui « est un mode parmi d'autres de structuration [des phénomènes sociaux] ». Cependant, comme toute communauté d'allégeance sa « spécificité lui vient du fait qu'elle se situe à l'échelle de la société globale. » (p. 16). Pour Dumont la société québécoise, comme toute société, existe parce qu'on peut retracer sa genèse, et sa genèse (p. 18) est achevée lorsque la *référence* est complétée : quand, à partir du sentiment d'une identité commune, on est passé aux conditions de la vie politique, au discours national, à des projets collectifs, à une mémoire historique, à l'institution d'une littérature. En d'autres termes, quand une collectivité est parvenue à la conscience historique. Certes, la genèse ainsi entendue n'est pas une implacable fatalité qui influera ensuite sur le cours del'histoire. Elle n'est pas moins la forme première d'un destin que les sociétés doivent assumer même quand elles songent à s'en affranchir.

Nous nous intéressons donc à ces modes de structuration, à ces constructions d'une référence, qui se situent à l'échelle de la société et dont les signes et symboles permettent aux individus de se reconnaître une identité commune. Puisqu'une communauté « se reconnaît au premier chef dans des représentations collectives » (p. 17), notre projet consiste à analyser un certain nombre de ces représentations collectives, ou certains de ses éléments, afin d'inférer de quelle(s) communauté(s) elles sont constitutives. De par le choix de nos matériaux d'analyse, tout indique qu'il s'agit de la communauté d'appartenance dite « la société québécoise ». Et, peut-être, la *nation* québécoise. Pour l'instant, nous réservons notre droit de nommer cette communauté. Ce n'est pas là une tâche prioritaire.

Ce qui nous motive à poursuivre ce travail d'équipe multidisciplinaire c'est l'analyse de ces modes de structuration, de ces constructions d'une référence, et de leurs signes et symboles qui permettent la reconnaissance d'une identité commune par une collectivité-à-nommer. Vouloir cerner ces modes de structuration c'est également vouloir cerner la communauté d'appartenance. À Dumont, et à plusieurs autres, nous empruntons des pans de leur échafaudage pour monter le nôtre afin que s'exerce notre analyse.

Loisirs culturels et identité sociale

Les produits culturels de grande consommation, de par leur popularité même, constituent des indices particulièrement pertinents de l'état de la « conscience collective » d'une société. Mais ils ne sont ni les seuls indices ni, *a priori*, les sources premières des remises en cause, « par le retour sur soi de la pensée, des visions accoutumées où se fige notre complicité avec la vie collective » (*ibid.* ; 12), c'est-à-dire des bouleversements des identités acquises à notre insu.

À notre avis il y a au moins trois sources auxquelles peut se nourrir une identité commune. La première, c'est cette sphère d'activités où les individus interagissent, interviennent sous le masque de leurs multiples statuts et par le jeu de leurs multiples rôles. C'est le monde de l'organisation politique, de la vie publique, et des institutions sociales ballotté par des « forces » sur lesquelles l'individu a le sentiment, et très souvent la conviction, de ne pouvoir exercer aucun contrôle ; que ce soit dans son travail, dans l'exercice de ses droits de citoyen, ou dans ses comportements de consommateur. La seconde, c'est la vie privée ou quotidienne, cette sphère d'activités où l'individu a l'impression, et très souvent la conviction, de posséder *sa* vie et d'en exercer le contrôle ; il choisit les gens avec qui interagir et la forme d'organisation de ses comportements. La troisième, celle qui nous intéresse au premier chef, c'est le pont entre la sphère du contrôle « privé » et celle de l'organisation « publique ». L'individu, seul ou en petit groupe, partage la conviction qu'il choisit son mode de participation à un monde qu'il sait ne pouvoir manipuler. Son seul contrôle s'exerce au niveau de l'accès à ce monde public et au niveau de son travail de *gatekeeping* ou de décodage (Hall, 1980). Sa seule sécurité c'est de savoir qu'il peut, à tout moment, couper ce pont qui lui sert de lien. Ce sentiment de contrôle, et donc de pouvoir, lui est fourni par un mode de participation particulier ; celui de la télé-participation, de la participation à distance. Alors que dans les deux premières sphères, la participation se déroule dans le temps et dans un espace réels, la télé-participation se déroule dans le hors-temps et dans un espace virtuel. C'est pourquoi il est tout à fait certain que le retour sur soi de la pensée prend son origine dans l'une et / ou l'autre des deux premières sphères, là où justement se confrontent représentations et organisation de l'identité commune.

Regarder une émission de télévision, écouter une pièce musicale, lire un livre, visionner un film, c'est se reconnaître une identité commune à travers des signes et des symboles, comme c'est le cas dans nos activités de tous les jours, sauf que cette activité en est une de télé-participation dont l'objectif premier est précisément la construction d'une référence culturelle.

À l'instar de Jean-Paul Baillargeon (1994 : 46) nous pouvons nous demander quelle place occupent tous ces signes et ces symboles dans le « travail incessant d'interprétation » des membres d'une communauté identitaire. Si, de prime abord, il semble peu probable qu'ils engendrent des remises en cause on peut penser qu'ils interviennent au niveau du discours, c'est-à-dire au stade d'achèvement de la *référence*, plus précisément à l'instauration d'une mémoire historique et à l'institution d'une littérature. En d'autres mots, nous pouvons nous demander à quel travail d'interprétation se livrent les membres d'une communauté identitaire quand ils télé-participent à un monde musical à dominante anglo-américaine (90 %), à un monde symbolique télévisuel à dominante francophone québécois (66 %) et à un monde symbolique romanesque à dominante francophone français (un tiers composé de romans français et un tiers de romans américains traduits en France).

Revue sommaire de la littérature pertinente

« L'intérêt pour la culture est une des tendances significatives des études sur la communication contemporaine. » (Ang, 1990 : 75). Deux ensembles d'approches caractérisent l'études des phénomènes culturels ; le premier, plus traditionnel, traduit un intérêt socio-scientifique plus restreint où la culture est « généralement connue en termes de comportements et de fonctions, qui peuvent faire l'objet d'une connaissance « objective » par la mise à l'épreuve d'hypothèses généralisables au moyen de méthodes socio-scientifiques conventionnelles. » (*idem* ; 75-76). Le second ensemble d'approches, généralement appelées *cultural studies* (études critico-culturelles), traite « du *processus social* continu et contradictoire de la production, de la circulation et de la consommation culturelles, et non pas de la « culture » définie comme un ensemble plus ou moins statique et objectivé d'idées, de croyances et de comportements. » (*ibid.* ; 76). Plusieurs auteurs (Curran, 1993 ; Schrøder, 1987) ont suggéré, ou plutôt appelé de leurs vœux, la convergence de ces deux traditions de recherche en communication en raison d'un « objet d'étude commun » (Rosengren, 1988 : 10). Mais d'autres, dont Ang, considèrent que les « différences théoriques, méthodologiques, épistémologiques et politiques » sont telles qu'il faut davantage parler de divergence paradigmatique que de convergence.

Quoi qu'il en soit, notre approche se situe davantage du côté des cultural studies. Les principaux éléments qui caractérisent ces approches, et qui les démarquent des études plus traditionnelles, sont nombreux et représentent un poids inégal dans le choix des chercheurs d'inscrire leurs travaux sous la bannière des études critico-culturelles. Voyons d'abord la liste qu'en établit Ien Ang (*ibid.* : 76) :

> les études culturelles s'intéressent à des significations historiquement situées plutôt qu'à des types généraux de comportement ; elles sont orientées vers le processus plutôt que vers le résultat, elles sont interprétatives plutôt qu'explicatives […] ce qui divise fondamentalement les deux traditions, c'est la conception qu'elles se font respectivement de leur statut discursif […] en tant que pratique intellectuelle, les études culturelles sont consciemment éclectiques, critiques et déconstructives […] Leurs ambitions intellectuelles dépassent les limites du monde universitaire pour atteindre à la critique des problèmes culturels contemporains dans le sens plus large. […] elles relèvent à la fois de la recherche sur la culture et de la critique culturelle.

D'abord tranchées, sinon retranchées, certaines des positions des culturalistes se sont relativement ouvertes aux positions des traditionalistes. Par exemple, si le statut discursif continue de faire appel au « sens critique et [à] la sensibilité pour le concret [plutôt qu'au] professionnalisme théorique et la pureté méthodologique » (*ibid.* ; 76), on note la reconnaissance de plus en plus avouée de fonder ce discours sur la « preuve par l'épreuve ». Cela se traduit par un effort concerté d'apporter aux méthodes interprétatives et herméneutiques traditionnelles le concours de la micro-informatique dans l'analyse qualitative des phénomènes culturels (Fielding et Lee, 1991 ; Dey, 1993). Par contre, l'écart épistémologique demeure quant à la « définition » de la culture comme « processus social continu et contradictoire » et non comme un « ensemble plus ou moins statique et objectivé » (voir plus haut). Notre intérêt pour les cultural studies porte sur la valeur heuristique de ce postulat de base et sur leurs efforts de doter l'analyse qualitative de moyens suffisamment puissants pour traiter un matériau d'une richesse et d'une complexité peu communes i.e., les représentations sociales (Dubois, 1995). La qualité première des cultural studies, à notre avis, c'est de s'intéresser à des « significations historiquement situées » ce qui, dans cette « période de transformations économiques, politiques et technologiques » de notre environnement médiatique (*ibid.* : 77) rend particulièrement pertinentes leurs analyses des sous-cultures, de l'hégémonie, de la culture populaire et de l'identité nationale. Il n'est donc pas surprenant que l'aire de diffusion du premier Centre d'études culturelles contemporaine à Birmingham ait surtout touché les « jeunes » sociétés capitalistes avancées, dont le Canada, l'Australie et les États-Unis, et très marginalement les anciennes sociétés (Europe de l'Est et de l'Ouest, et le Japon). C'est donc la question de l'identité collective (ou nationale) historiquement située dans un Québec dont l'environnement médiatique subit et continue de subir depuis plus de quarante ans des transformations économiques, politique et technologiques qui nous amène à aborder la question de la production, consommation et réception des produits culturels à grands succès dans les domaines du livre et de la télévision.

Nous tentons ici pour une première fois de mettre en parallèle les résultats de deux des recherches entreprises par notre équipe ; l'une, plus avancée, sur les rapports entre succès du livre et lectorat, l'autre, en démarrage, sur les rapports entre succès télévisés et téléspectateurs.

Nous traiterons donc de « best-sellers », de ces romans et téléromans à grand succès. Si la perspective se veut critique, ce n'est ni celle de la condamnation de ce que plusieurs perçoivent comme « l'américanisation de la culture québécoise », ni celle de la défense de ce que plusieurs intellectuels populistes désignent de « culture du peuple ». Nous associons culture populaire à culture publique, c'est-à-dire à ce processus social par lequel des idées, des croyances et des comportements sont, de façon continue et contradictoire, produits, diffusés et consommés. Nous insistons tout particulièrement sur les termes « produits et consommés ». Cela suppose, d'une part, des conditions matérielles de production et de consommation, c'est-à-dire « conjoncturalistes » ou socio-historiques. Cette perspective est radicalement différente de celle, plus statique, de l'émetteur-récepteur de produits culturels.

Il s'agit d'examiner dans quelles conditions économiques, politiques et technologiques une culture donnée est signifiée, diffusée et appropriée ou rendue signifiante.

La lecture des best-sellers

Notre premier exemple porte sur la lecture des best-sellers au Québec. Après avoir examiné les grandes caractéristiques socio-culturelles du lectorat des livres à succès, nous dégagerons les particularités thématiques et nationales des œuvres les plus lues, que nous mettrons enfin en rapport avec les attentes et motivations de lectrices et lecteurs rencontrés lors d'entretiens.

Nous savons, par les enquêtes quinquennales sur les activités culturelles de loisir, réalisées par le ministère de la Culture et des Communications du Québec, que la lecture vient au deuxième rang des loisirs préférés des Québécoises et des Québécois, après les activités physiques et de plein air. En effet, lors de l'enquête de 1989 (la plus récente, celle de 1994 étant à la phase de l'analyse), 33 % des personnes interrogées mentionnent la lecture comme un de leurs trois loisirs préférés (par rapport à 73 % pour les activités physiques, ou 26 % pour la télévision, la radio et le disque, regroupés en une catégorie unique). La lecture constitue également l'activité préférée numéro un de 17 % des Québécois, ce qui la situe encore une fois au second rang derrière les sports et le plein air (57 %) (Pronovost, 1990 : 24). Par ailleurs, si on examine non pas les préférences, mais plutôt le temps consacré aux divers loisirs, une autre enquête, celle-là réalisée pour le compte du gouvernement du Canada en 1991, accorde un honorable troisième rang à la lecture : le Canadien moyen y consacrerait plus de 7 heures par semaine, par rapport à 14 heures pour la télévision, 9 heures pour la musique (disque et radio), 6 heures pour la relaxation et moins de 4 heures pour les activités physiques (Graves et Dugas, 1992 : 9).

Quoi qu'il en soit, en ce qui concerne spécifiquement les loisirs culturels, la lecture partage avec la télévision la faveur du public ; cette association, qu'on pourrait d'un certain point de vue considérer comme concurrentielle, nous apparaît plutôt complémentaire, lorsqu'on centre l'analyse sur les produits à succès dans les domaines de la lecture de loisir et de la télévision de divertissement. Mais avant d'aborder les succès télévisuels et leur complémentarité avec la lecture, examinons d'abord les livres les plus lus au Québec, ainsi que leurs lecteurs.

Le public des best-sellers

En 1989, 79 % des Québécoises et Québécois disent lire des livres au moins de temps en temps ; de ce nombre, 53 % affirment lire de façon régulière

(« Très souvent » ou « Assez souvent ») ; trois variables, la scolarité, le sexe et dans une moindre mesure l'âge, influencent l'assiduité à la lecture. Les paragraphes suivants énumèrent les faits saillants des données ministérielles de 1989 (Lemieux et Martin, 1993 : 3-4).

La lecture de livres apparaît d'abord et avant tout comme « un loisir féminin », ainsi que le suggérait Garon (1984) : en effet, 64 % des femmes lisent régulièrement, mais seulement 42 % des hommes ; les femmes représentent par conséquent 58 % du lectorat total des livres. En second lieu, on constate que la lecture attire davantage les personnes scolarisées : on ne trouve en effet que 34 % de lecteurs chez les personnes ayant moins de 7 ans d'études, alors que cette proportion atteint 69 % dans le groupe ayant 16 ans

GRAPHIQUE 1

Importance numérique du lectorat général et de celui des best-sellers, selon la fréquence de lecture, Québec, 1989 (en millions).

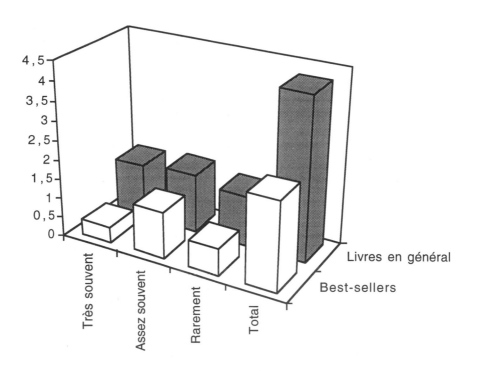

Source : Lemieux et Martin, 1993 : 14

de scolarité ou plus. Enfin, contrairement aux idées reçues, ce sont les jeunes de 15 à 17 ans qui s'avèrent lecteurs assidus dans une plus grande proportion, soit 64 % ; cette proportion diminue ensuite graduellement avec l'âge, et ne représente que 52 % des 55 ans et plus. Notons toutefois que de 1983 à 1989, la lecture progresse un peu chez les 55 ans et plus, alors qu'elle diminue sensiblement chez les 15-17 ans, surtout chez les garçons, qui constituent ainsi la « clientèle à risque » des promoteurs de la lecture.

Par rapport à ces grandes caractéristiques du lectorat général, le public lecteur des best-sellers se distingue selon ces mêmes trois variables stratégiques : il est plus fortement féminisé et scolarisé, mais davantage concentré dans les catégories d'âge moyen (Lemieux et Martin, *op. cit.* : 14-15) : ainsi, 67 % des amateurs de best-sellers sont de sexe féminin (lectorat général : 58 %) ; 43 % ont de 12 à 15 ans de scolarité (38 % du lectorat général) ; 24 % ont 16 ans d'études et plus (22 % du lectorat général) ; enfin, le groupe des 25 à 44 ans lit davantage de best-sellers (alors que les 15 à 17 dominent dans le lectorat général).

Nous estimons qu'à la fin des années 1980, sur un lectorat global de plus de 4,2 millions de Québécois (âgé de 15 ans et plus), dont 2,9 millions (69 %) de lecteurs assidus, le public des best-sellers représente 2,3 millions de lecteurs, dont 1,8 million (78 %) de personnes affirmant lire de façon régulière.

Le palmarès des plus grands best-sellers

Après avoir schématiquement décrit le public des best-sellers, il s'agit maintenant de définir les genres et les thèmes de ces livres à succès. Le problème préalable consiste toutefois à établir la liste des authentiques best-sellers. La solution semble simple : il n'y a qu'à identifier les ouvrages qui ont connu une diffusion qui sort de l'ordinaire ! La difficulté consiste dans le fait que les personnes et institutions qui détiennent les informations – éditeurs, distributeurs, libraires – n'ont aucun intérêt à divulguer ces chiffres à leurs concurrents, même pas par l'intermédiaire de chercheurs universitaires pourtant bien intentionnés. Nous avons contourné l'obstacle en recourant aux listes hebdomadaires de best-sellers produites par les quotidiens et magazines. Si la confection de telles listes comporte des risques évidents de subjectivité ou de manipulation, leur examen sur une longue période suggère que ces diverses distorsions s'annulent mutuellement ; de plus, le repérage prioritaire des titres qui se signalent par leur plus grande longévité sur les listes, permet de dégager un corpus d'œuvres que tous les spécialistes du livre de grande diffusion interrogés reconnaîtront comme d'authentiques best-sellers (sur la méthodologie de confection et de validation des listes, voir Martin, dans Saint-Jacques *et al.*, 1994, chap. 3 : 65-70).

C'est ainsi qu'ont été répertoriés, pour le Québec francophone, les 25 super-sellers annuels mentionnés de 1970 à 1992 dans le quotidien montréalais *La Presse*, ainsi que leurs équivalents français (l'*Express*), usaniens (*Publisher's Weekly*) et canadiens-anglais (*The Gazette* / chaîne Southam). Notre démonstration porte essentiellement sur le corpus québécois, cependant nous établirons des comparaisons ponctuelles avec les trois autres listes de succès.

Les listes de best-sellers de *La Presse* permettent d'identifier 451 livres d'origines et de genres divers : pour ce qui est de l'origine, les auteurs et éditeurs québécois sont responsables de près de 40 % des titres : cette proportion peut sembler modeste, mais se compare avantageusement aux 5 % de produits québécois dans le domaine des succès du cinéma, ou même aux 25 % dans le domaine de la musique populaire ; deux secteurs qui, contrairement à celui de l'édition, sont fortement subventionnés et protégés de la concurrence étrangère. On observe également que la part des éditeurs québécois dépasse globalement de 6 % celle des auteurs : c'est que l'édition québécoise publie un certain nombre d'auteurs étrangers, alors que rares sont les écrivains québécois édités en France et a fortiori ailleurs[2].

GRAPHIQUE 2

La part québécoise du marché des grands best-sellers en français.

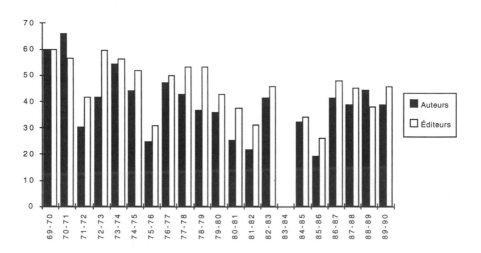

Source : Martin, dans Saint-Jacques *et al.* (1994).
À noter l'absence de liste en 1983-84.

L'analyse diachronique indique toutefois une évolution curvilinéaire dans la part québécoise de ces super-sellers : au début des années 1970, cette proportion s'établit autour de 50 % ; elle baisse sous la barre des 30 % vers le milieu des années 1980, puis se rétablit autour de la moyenne générale de 40 % (pour l'ensemble de la période 1970-1992). Comme nous le verrons ultérieurement, cette évolution s'explique dans un premier temps par une transformation de la demande qui favorise les produits étrangers, puis par une prise de conscience des créateurs et éditeurs nationaux, qui se traduit par la publication d'ouvrages québécois conformes à la « recette » des succès venus de l'étranger (on peut également identifier des facteurs liés aux politiques étatiques, aux fluctuations de l'économie mondiale, voire à une « dépression collective » de la société québécoise du début des années 1980 : Martin, 1994, *op. cit.* : 70-73).

GRAPHIQUE 3

La part du marché des best-sellers selon l'origine des auteurs.

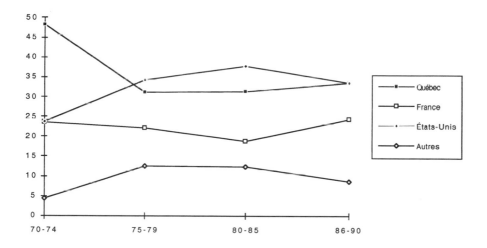

La concurrence étrangère provient essentiellement des auteurs des États-Unis et de la France, respectivement responsables de 31 % et de 24 % des super-sellers sur le marché québécois francophone ; les Canadiens anglais (2 %), les Britanniques et les autres auteurs de langue anglaise (2,6 %) comptent pour moins de 5 % des titres ; le reste de la planète se partage les derniers 4,6 % (la part québécoise, rappelons-le, est de 38 %). La concurrence entre la France et les USA pour le partage du marché québécois se traduit par une légère diminution de la part française, suivie d'une modeste remontée – mouvement analogue à celui des succès québécois – tandis que les best-sellers d'auteurs américains voient leur nombre augmenter substantiellement au début des années 1970, puis atteindre une relative stabilité, qui les situe au même niveau que les produits québécois.

Il faut noter toutefois que si la concurrence est « trinationale » lorsqu'on l'examine du point de vue du pays d'origine des auteurs, la bataille entre les éditeurs se livre essentiellement entre la France et le Québec : si les éditeurs québécois sont responsables de la quasi-totalité des titres provenant d'auteurs québécois ou canadiens, ce sont les maisons d'édition françaises qui exportent au Québec non seulement leurs œuvres nationales, mais également la plupart des best-sellers étrangers traduits en français. Si le marché se fait en proportions égales pour l'ensemble de la période 1970-92 – Québec : 47 %, France : 52 %, Autres : 1 % – on observe une légère progression de l'édition française : de 1976 à 1990, leur part dans l'importation de best-sellers américains au Québec passe de 63 % à 94 %.

Cette forte présence des best-sellers étrangers au Québec fait très fortement contraste avec le très grand ethnocentrisme de la liste états-unienne du *Publisher's Weekly* (1968-1992), où les auteurs nationaux sont responsables de 87 % des titres. On constate un phénomène analogue en France, où un seul titre étranger (*Racines*, d'Alex Haley, USA, 1977) figure sur la liste des grands succès de l'*Express* de 1969 à 1992. Néanmoins, la situation du Québec français, avec 38 % de titres d'auteurs locaux, se compare avantageusement à celle du Canada anglais, dont les écrivains ne comptent que pour 20 sur 200 (10 %) des plus grands best-sellers répertoriés de 1969 à 1987 dans les listes de la chaîne Southam (Lemieux et Saint-Jacques, 1994).

La présence persistante des succès américains sur les listes québécoises de best-sellers coïncide avec la popularité croissante du roman – genre dans lequel se distinguent auteurs et éditeurs étrangers – ainsi que la perte de popularité des essais et livres pratiques – produits où les créateurs et diffuseurs québécois connaissent leurs plus grands succès.

Dans les 451 super-sellers répertoriés dans *La Presse*, les récits de fiction (des romans pour la plupart, mais aussi quelques recueils de nouvelles et albums de bandes dessinées) dominent largement, avec 224 titres ou 49,7 % du corpus. Au second rang se situent les biographies, avec 85 ouvrages représentant 18,8 % des titres. Suivent les essais (83 livres ou 18,4 %) et les livres pratiques (52 titres, 11,5 %). Enfin, catégorie résiduelle, les ouvrages divers (poésie, théâtre, chanson,...) représentent 7 livres ou 1,6 % des titres.

Ces proportions globales changent toutefois de façon significative de 1970 à 1990 : la principale transformation concerne la présence croissante des romans et autres fictions, dont la proportion s'accroît de 32 % au début des années 1970 à 72 % à la fin des années 1980. Tandis que les autres genres voient leur popularité diminuer de façon correspondante : les biographies connaissent le déclin le plus brutal (de 22 % à 7 %) ; mais les essais (de 26 %

à 13 %) ainsi que les livres pratiques (de 19 % à 8 %) connaissent également une baisse sensible de popularité.

Or c'est précisément dans le domaine des romans que la compétition étrangère s'avère la plus menaçante : si les récits de fiction représentent environ 60 % des succès importés de France ou des USA, ils ne représentent que 32 % des titres écrits par des Québécois. En d'autres termes, la part des auteurs québécois, qui est de 40 % pour l'ensemble des best-sellers, n'est que de 25 % pour le roman ; par contre, les écrivains locaux sont responsables de 57 % des essais et de 75 % des livres pratiques. Cela n'est pas surprenant, puisque ces ouvrages « fonctionnels » sont souvent reliés au contexte socio-politique, ainsi qu'aux styles de vie (santé, éducation, consommation) d'une collectivité ; de fait, on observe également, pour ces catégories, une plus forte présence relative des auteurs nationaux dans les listes canadiennes-anglaises et américaines (Lemieux et Saint-Jacques, 1994).

Il est intéressant de constater que nos observations vont globalement dans le même sens que celles que propose Baillargeon (1991), à partir d'une méthodologie radicalement différente de la nôtre[3] : examinant la part relative des importations de livres français (originaux ou traductions) par rapport à la production québécoise, Baillargeon constate que, de 1980 à 1989, la part des importations françaises s'accroît globalement, notamment dans le domaine de la littérature générale, où le rapport France/Québec passe de 1 : 2 à 6 : 1. Ce qui pourrait s'expliquer selon lui par la croissance d'un lectorat de scolarité faible ou moyenne, attiré par les traductions françaises des best-sellers usaniens (*op. cit.* : 195-196, 200-202, 208-209). On peut en conclure que le principal défi qu'ont à relever les éditeurs et auteurs québécois, con-siste à proposer à leur lectorat des récits aussi intéressants que ceux qu'on importe de l'étranger.

Le récit-type

Il nous semble que c'est précisément ce que les écrivains et éditeurs ont compris depuis une dizaine d'années ; le rétablissement de la part québécoise des livres à succès depuis ce moment, serait le fruit de cette prise de cons-cience. Mais quelle est la recette de base ? Nous avons repéré, dans les best-sellers étrangers ayant connu un grand succès au Québec depuis les années 1970, la présence fréquente d'un *récit-type* (ou « scénario motif », d'après les catégories d'Eco : 1985), celui de la réussite sociale et affective probléma-tique du protagoniste, dans un environnement difficile (et souvent exotique). Ce récit-type connaît certes de nombreuses variantes : romans ou biogra-phies, récits d'action ou sentimentaux, contemporains ou historiques, prota-gonistes uniques ou multiples, de sexe masculin ou féminin, etc. (Lemieux et Saint-Jacques, 1990 ; Saint-Jacques, dans Saint-Jacques *et al.*, 1994, chap. 3 : 150-163).

GRAPHIQUE 4

Évolution de la répartition des genres de best-sellers, 1970-90

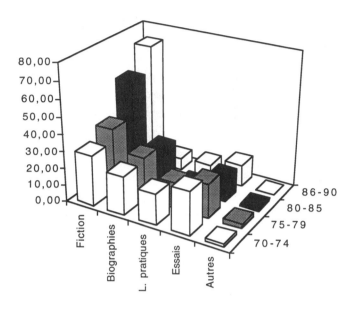

Source : Martin, dans Saint-Jacques *et al.* (1994)

GRAPHIQUE 5

Répartition des genres de best-sellers selon l'origine nationale des auteurs

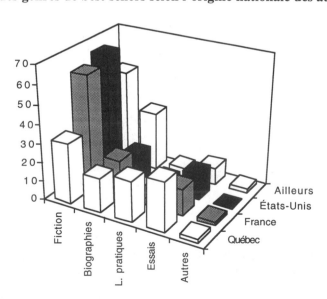

Ce n'est toutefois qu'en 1981, avec *Le Matou*, d'Yves Beauchemin, que ce récit-type apparaît dans un best-seller québécois. Il fera par la suite école, étant suivi notamment par son *Juliette Pomerleau*, mais aussi par les récits à succès des Arlette Cousture (*Les filles de Caleb, Ces enfants d'ailleurs*), Francine Ouellette (*Au nom du père et du fils, Le sorcier, Le Grand Blanc...*), Alice Parizeau (*Une vie*), Paul Ohl (*Drakkar, Katana, Soleil noir*), etc.

La liste des 30 plus grands super-sellers québécois de 1970 à 1992 (voir en Annexe) montre bien l'évolution de la concurrence entre best-sellers nationaux et étrangers : dix des treize ouvrages québécois de la liste sont postérieurs à 1985, par rapport à onze des dix-sept titres étrangers. Les trois ouvrages québécois de la première période (1970-1984) sont un roman littéraire (*Kamouraska*), un essai polémique (*Petit manuel d'histoire du Québec*) et un livre de cuisine (*Recettes de Sœur Berthe*). Tandis que sept des onze titres étrangers – cinq romans et deux biographies – constituent diverses variantes du récit-type (*Jonathan Livingston le goéland, Le Parrain, Au nom de tous les miens, Les oiseaux se cachent pour mourir, Papillon, Les Jordache, L'espace d'une vie*). Par contre, dans la période plus récente (1985-1992), au moins cinq des treize titres québécois – quatre romans et une biographie – peuvent à leur tour se rattacher au scénario de la réussite problématique (*Les filles de Caleb 1 et 2, Soleil noir, Juliette Pomerleau, Christophe Colomb*).

Liens avec l'agenda privé et social

Ce palmarès des grands succès établit par ailleurs divers liens avec l'agenda privé ou social : ainsi, les problèmes de la vie personnelle et familiale sont particulièrement visibles dans les essais, dont cinq sur neuf portent sur le développement personnel (*Le chemin le moins fréquenté, Ces femmes qui aiment trop, Défi alimentaire de la femme, Ecoute ton corps, Le stress sans détresse*) ; par contre, les quatre autres essais (*Le choc du futur, Petit manuel d'histoire du Québec, l'État du monde en 1992* et *La femme eunuque*) se situent résolument au plan sociétal.

Dans ces essais, mais également dans les récits, on sent le poids du lectorat féminin : par exemple, 12 (40 %) des 30 titres dominants, dont 7 (54 %) des 13 romans sont écrits par des femmes, alors que la proportion correspondante pour l'ensemble du corpus de 451 titres n'est que de 27 % d'œuvres produites par des écrivaines. De même, la moitié des 14 récits romanesques ou biographiques où s'observe (au moins en partie) le scénario-type de la réussite, mettent en scène des protagonistes de sexe féminin.

Autre élément digne de mention, l'ouverture sur le monde et sur l'Histoire de ces best-sellers, dont l'action se situe à diverses époques et aux quatre coins de la planète. Il est à cet effet intéressant d'observer que cette ouverture sur le monde était, dans les années 1970 et 1980, le monopole exclusif des auteurs étrangers (*Au nom de tous les miens, Papillon, Les oiseaux se cachent pour mourir*). Toutefois, deux des titres québecois les plus récents (*Soleil noir* et *Christophe Colomb*), deux visions ambigües de la colonisation européenne des Amériques, montrent que le récit populaire québecois peut non seulement sortir de l'ethnocentrisme où il s'était confiné, mais même développer une vision planétaire originale, celle d'une collectivité qui doit vivre avec son double statut de colonisateur et de colonisé.

On observe de nombreux autres exemples de thématiques sociales « progressistes » dans d'autres titres québecois de la liste globale des grands succès du livre. Ainsi, dans les romans de Francine Ouellette, on constate l'importance attribuée à l'écologie (*Sire Gaby du lac*) ou aux rapports harmonieux entre Québecois « de souche » et Amérindiens (*Le Grand Blanc*). De même, les rapports entre « pure laine » et Québecois d'autres origines, ambigus dans *Le Matou* (du fait des personnages antipathiques de Slipskin et Ratablavasky), deviennent positifs dans le second best-seller d'Yves Beauchemin (*Juliette Pomerleau*), où le musicien Martinek « fait partie de la famille » ; le thème de l'immigration au Québec – du point de vue des Néo-Québecois – constitue également l'élément dominant des deux tomes de *Ces enfants d'ailleurs*, d'Arlette Cousture.

Qui plus est, si on compare globalement la liste québecoises des best-sellers et son équivalent usanien, on constate que le roman d'action violent, très présent chez nos voisins du Sud, avec les récits des Ludlum, Clancy et autres, tient chez nous (quasi uniquement en traduction) une place beaucoup moindre. Tandis que le thème des relations personnelles et communautaires harmonieuses y figure davantage. De fait, le thème de la réussite sociale, que nous avons identifié précédamment comme scénario-type du best-seller, prend dans les récits québecois une tournure à la fois plus modeste ou plus égalitaire : le héros ne vise pas, comme dans de nombreux récits usaniens, à sauver le monde d'un conflit international ou à devenir une star du capitalisme mondial, mais plutôt à assurer le bonheur des siens, comme *Juliette Pomerleau*, ou à devenir une femme autonome dans une petite collectivité dominée par les hommes, comme *Les filles de Caleb* : Émilie Bordeleau ou sa fille Blanche Pronovost (Lemieux et Saint-Jacques, 1994).

Ces quelques observations générales sur les caractéristiques des grands best-sellers québecois sont à mettre en relation avec les attentes du lectorat : la lecture de loisir, nous apprennent diverses enquêtes[4], répond à un double besoin de divertissement et d'enrichissement intellectuel : on aime retrouver dans les best-sellers des personnages ou des situations exemplaires, dans des contextes différents de son univers quotidien, mais décrits de façon détaillée et plausible ; de sorte qu'on puisse non seulement y apprendre des choses, mais aussi s'y reconnaître et en tirer des leçons de vie. On souhaite surtout faire la connaissance, par l'intermédiaire du livre, d'un auteur qui, tel un ami intime, deviendra un conseiller, voire même un « confident de papier ».

Le récit-type de la réussite problématique, en particulier tel qu'il s'incarne dans les œuvres québecoises, mais aussi dans la sélection que fait le lectorat québecois parmi l'offre étrangère, s'avère par conséquent tout à fait conforme à ces motivations des lecteurs (en majorité des lectrices) de scolarité et de classe moyennes qui constituent le public des best-sellers (Lemieux, dans Saint-Jacques *et al.*, *op. cit.* : 205-208). C'est en ce sens que nous estimons proposer ici un premier exemple de « construction d'une référence » spécifique à la collectivité québecoise.

Le marché de la télévision

Notre second exemple portera sur les émissions de télévision les plus populaires, dont l'auditoire s'avère encore plus nombreux et plus diversifié que le public des livres à succès. Comme nous l'avons signalé précédamment dans la problématique, nos recherches sur les rapports entre produits et réception sont moins avancées dans le domaine de la télévision que dans celui du livre. L'essentiel de notre argumentation portera par conséquent sur les relations entre l'offre de programmes proposés par les diffuseurs et le choix qu'en fait le public téléspectateur. Nous suggérerons néanmoins par la suite, à la lumière de résultats d'études en cours, quelques observations préliminaires sur la thématique des téléromans et sur leur réception.

Il est vrai que les francophones du Québec consomment, en moyenne, plus d'une journée entière par semaine d'émissions télévisuelles. On note cependant, depuis 1985, un mouvement à la baisse qui suggère que la fragmentation très poussée de l'offre et de la consommation transformera à tout jamais, en les complexifiant, les habitudes des téléspectateurs. En effet l'année 1986 marque le dernier sommet dans les annales de la consommation ; de 25,2 heures par personne par semaine en 1985, la consommation hebdomadaire est passée à 26,3 heures en 1986 pour chuter à 24,6 heures en 1989 (Baillargeon : 27-28).

Ces chiffres ne sont que la partie visible d'un phénomène complexe et comme tels doivent servir de point de départ à la réflexion et non de jugement d'un état de fait. Par exemple, affirmer une légère baisse générale du temps moyen hebdomadaire c'est affirmer, du même souffle, une hausse considérable (plus de deux heures) chez la population des personnes à la retraite et des préretraités, hommes et femmes. C'est aussi affirmer une baisse marquée chez les adolescents et chez les jeunes hommes de 18 à 24 ans (plus de deux heures par semaine). Baillargeon (p. 29) cite à cet effet des chiffres qui indiquent des écarts considérables autour d'une moyenne devenue fictive :

> [...] les femmes de 60 ans et plus ont écouté une moyenne de 36 heures de télévision par semaine en 1985 et près de 39 heures en 1989. Ajoutons aussi que les 60 ans et plus représentaient moins de 14 % de

la population francophone de 2 ans et plus en 1989, mais que leur masse d'heures d'écoute de la télévision a compté pour près de 20 % de toutes les heures d'écoute des téléspectateurs francophones, cette même année.

La réaction que nous suggèrent ces chiffres est de comparer la consommation télévisuelle par groupe d'âge et, lorsque c'est possible, par communauté linguistique. À partir des données du Broadcast Bureau of Measurement (BBM), une coopérative regroupant radiotélédiffuseurs et agences de publicité et qui établit par enquête statistique les cote d'écoute des émissions télévisuelles et radiophoniques, nous avons analysé le marché de la télévision pour la zone métropolitaine du grand Montréal, pour les année 1987 et 1993.

Ce que nous disent les grilles de programmation et les BBM

Nous avons comparé l'offre télévisuelle de dix stations émettrices en 1987 (trois américaines, cinq québécoises affiliées à des réseaux de langue française et deux québécoises affiliées à des réseaux de langue anglaise) et de douze stations en 1993 (cinq américaines, quatre québécoises affiliées à des réseaux de langue française et trois stations affiliées à des réseaux de langue anglaise), à la consommation de l'audience francophone montréalaise. En 1993 nous avons comparé la consommation télévisuelle des deux grandes communautés linguistiques de Montréal. Voici quelques détails.

1987 et 1993 : la communauté francophone

1. L'offre télévisuelle est demeurée relativement stable sauf une légère baisse des émissions de divertissement et une hausse des émissions éducatives, en raison de l'accès à un deuxième poste du réseau américain PBS

TABLEAU 1

Répartition de l'offre et de la consommation télévisuelles, selon les grands genres, Montréal, 1987 et 1993

	1987 *offre*	1987 *consommation*	1993 *offre*	1993 *consommation*
information	30 %	33 %	30 %	27 %
divertissement	59 %	56 %	52 %	68 %
éducation	10,6 %	10,5 %	18 %	05 %

2. Par contre la consommation, qui en 1987 était le reflet fidèle de l'offre télévisuelle, a nettement favorisé, en 1993, les émissions divertissantes au détriment des émissions éducatives et informatives.

3. Cette poussée de la consommation des émissions de divertissement, chez tous les groupes d'âge, s'accompagne d'une plus grande consommation d'émissions de langue française, y compris des émissions américaines postsynchronisées. Par conséquent, les émissions de langue française ont augmenté leur part de l'écoute totale, passant de 88 % (dont 66 % vont aux stations québécoises de langue française) à 92 % (dont 75 % aux stations québécoises). Ces chiffres deviennent plus éloquents quand on les compare à la part de l'offre que représentent les stations québécoises. Ces chiffres renforcent, à nos yeux, cette idée que la popularité des produits culturels de grande consommation est un indice de l'achèvement de la *référence*, et que nous touchons là le stade de l'institution d'une littérature (livresque et audiovisuelle).

TABLEAU 2

Répartition de l'offre et de la consommation des émissions télévisuelles de langue française, Montréal, 1987 et 1993

	offre	*consommation*
émissions de langue française, y compris la postsynchronisation, 1987	46 %	88 %
émissions de langue française, y compris la postsynchronisation, 1993	39 %	92 %

1993 : l'offre francophone et anglophone

1. En 1993, 61 % de l'offre télévisuelle étaient de langue anglaise. Parce que les émissions américaines sont également offertes via les stations canadiennes et québécoises (par la postsynchronisation réalisée en France), nous pouvons également dire que 63 % de l'offre étaient américaine, 12 % canadienne et 25 % québécoise.

2. En 1993, 59 % de l'offre provenaient du secteur privé.

3. En 1993, l'offre globale était composée de contenu divertissant (41 %), informatif (23 %), publicitaire (22 %) et éducatif (14 %). En somme, l'offre télévisuelle dans le grand Montréal est à dominante américaine, anglaise et divertissante, ce qui rendent les chiffres de la consommation d'autant plus contrastants.

4. En raison de la présence massive de l'*entertainment* américain sur nos ondes, les stations québécoises et canadiennes produisent proportionnellement plus d'émissions d'information que leur part du marché global. Par contre, comme les américaines, la production des stations québécoises et canadiennes est orientée vers le divertissement. À cet égard, la télévision canadienne est la plus divertissante de toutes.

TABLEAU 3

Répartition de l'offre télévisuelle, selon les réseaux et les grands genres d'émissions télévisuelles, Montréal, 1993

Réseaux	Total	information	divertissement	éducation	publicité
québécois	25 %	38 %	14 %	27 %	23 %
canadiens	12 %	19 %	10 %	10 %	12 %
américains	63 %	43 %	76 %	62 %	64 %
Total	**100 %**	**100 %**	**100 %**	**100 %**	**100 %**

TABLEAU 4

La part de l'offre télévisuelle selon les grands genres d'émissions et les réseaux télévisuels, Montréal, 1987

Réseaux	Total	information	divertissement	éducation	publicité
québécois	100 %	27 %	39 %	14 %	20 %
canadiens	100 %	25 %	47 %	08 %	20 %
américains	100 %	19 %	38 %	19 %	24 %

5.   Si nous comparons, pour les années 1987 et 1993, le contenu « national » des trois groupes de télévision (publique de langue anglaise, publique de langue francaise et privée), nous remarquerons que seules les télévisions publiques de langue française (SRC et Radio-Québec) ont accru la part « nationale » de leur contenu. La télévision américaine, déjà hermétique en 1987, devient en 1993 totalement étanche à toute importation.

TABLEAU 5

Répartition du contenu « national » des réseaux de télévision, selon les chaînes publiques et privées, Montréal, 1987 et 1993

Québec	Contenu québécois 1987	Contenu québécois 1993
SRC	79 %	82 %
Radio-Québec	79 %	82 %
privé	71-79 %	61 %
Canada	**Contenu canadien 1987**	**Contenu canadien 1993**
CBC	66 %	57 %
privé	47 %	35 %
États-Unis	**Contenu américain 1987**	**Contenu américain 1993**
PBS	non disponible	94,5 %
privé	91-99 %	100 %

1993 : la consommation francophone et anglophone

1. Si, en 1993, l'abonné à un service régulier de câblodistribution voulait consommer l'offre totale d'une semaine de télévision rendue disponible par son accès à douze stations émettrices il lui faudrait y consacrer 11,3 semaines de son temps, 24 heures sur 24. L'offre hebdomadaire télévisuelle totale peut se stocker sur 316 vidéocassettes d'une durée chacune de six heures (au total, 1 896 heures). Le chercheur qui veut consacrer au visionnement de l'offre télévisuelle ses semaines de 40 heures, devra y passer une année entière, soit 47,5 semaines de travail et 4,5 semaines de vacances.

2. De toute évidence la consommation télévisuelle n'est pas répartie uniformément. Certaines émissions, en raison de leur heure de diffusion (en soirée), rejoignent une plus grande audience et deviennent par le fait même plus « populaires ». Ainsi estimons-nous que 7 % de l'offre télévisuelle de langue française attirent 60 % de l'écoute francophone et qu'il faut 9 % de l'offre télévisuelle de langue anglaise pour obtenir le même résultat chez la communauté anglophone. Ce sont là les véritables émissions « locomotives » qui financent les heures de programmation les moins rentables.

3. Ces deux programmations « locomotives » suggèrent que les émissions d'information de langue française ont plus « d'attirance » que leur contrepartie de langue anglaise

TABLEAU 6

Répartition de la programmation « locomotive » francophone et anglophone selon les grands genres d'émissions télévisuelles, Montréal, 1993

	Total	information	divertissement	éducation	publicité
« locomotive francophone »	100 %	34 %	46 %	00 %	20 %
« locomotive anglophone »	100 %	23 %	54 %	03 %	20 %

4. Les Québécois francophones consomment plus d'heures de télévision que leurs concitoyens anglophones, sauf chez les enfants.

5. Alors que l'auditoire francophone répartit également ses heures d'écoute entre les secteurs public et privé, les anglophones privilégient dans un rapport de presque 3 pour 1 le secteur privé, y compris les stations canadiennes et américaines. Les francophones, tous âges confondus, consacrent moins de 10 % de son temps d'écoute à des émissions de

TABLEAU 7

**Répartition des heures d'écoute télévisuelle
chez les communautés de langue française et anglaise,
selon des groupes d'âge, Montréal, 1993**

Audience	Total	tous 2-11 ans	tous 11-18 ans	H 18 ans +	F 18 ans +
francophone	24,6 h	18,9 h	17,9 h	23,6 h	28,8 h
anglophone	23,2 h	20,1 h	15,7 h	21,7 h	26,7 h

langue anglaise, malgré le fait qu'environ le tiers soit bilingue, alors que la communauté anglophone consacre moins de 2 % aux émissions de langue française. Si le francophone est « fidèle » aux postes québécois de langue française, l'anglophone est plutôt « bigame » puisque ses heures d'écoute sont également partagées entre les réseaux canadiens et américains.

6.   Quant au contenu des heures d'écoute, il est composé en majeure partie de produits québécois chez les francophones et de produits américains chez les anglophones. La différence pourrait se résumer ainsi : la communauté francophone consomme des émissions québécoises diffusées par les réseaux public et privé de langue française alors que la communauté anglophone consomme les émissions américaines diffusées par les télédiffuseurs canadiens.

7.   Quant aux genres, nous pouvons dire que la communauté francophone apprécie davantage la production québécoise dont, tout particulièrement, les téléromans, les émissions de variétés et les spectacles vivants. Pour sa part, la faveur de la communauté anglophone va du côté des *sitcom* et des séries dramatiques américains.

8.   Les habitudes d'écoute des jeunes téléspectateurs des deux communautés linguistiques se ressemblent beaucoup. Dans les deux communautés également les habitudes des jeunes diffèrent de celles de leurs aînés.

9.   Les jeunes francophones consomment moins de télévision que leurs aînés mais plus de contenu américain. Doit-on s'inquiéter ? Nous savons que les habitudes de consommation télévisuelle fluctuent selon l'âge et, en vieillissant, les jeunes très probablement vont augmenter leur temps d'écoute. Est-ce dire qu'il vont continuer à s'alimenter auprès de la production américaine ? Une première indication permet d'en douter car si nous comparons la consommation « jeunesse » des téléromans nous remarquons qu'elle est plus élevée en 1993 qu'en 1987. Pour nous cela signifie que la production québécoise non seulement attire un public large et fidèle mais qu'elle est capable de renouveler ce public en terme de génération. Ce qui, dans un marché aussi compétitif que Montréal, n'est pas une mince tâche.

Ce que racontent les téléromans et leurs adeptes

L'une des principales raisons qu'évoquent les téléspectateurs quand on leur demande pourquoi ils apprécient si grandement les téléromans c'est, disent-ils, leur qualité de vraisemblance. Ce jugement, prononcé par des téléspectateurs de grande expérience qui ont su développé leur sens critique au fil de plus de trente années de consommation téléromanesque, est appuyé par une analyse de contenu des plus sommaires. On dit souvent qu'on trouve « de tout » dans les téléromans, et c'est vrai. Cependant il ne faut pas prendre cette expression comme l'équivalent d'un *melting-pot* ou d'un marché aux puces. On retrouve « de tout » dans les téléromans au même titre qu'on trouve de tout dans les actualités, soit télédiffusées soit écrites.

La série *Scoop*, diffusée par Radio-Canada durant quatre saisons hivernales (de 1992 à 1995), constitue un exemple particulièremment éloquent de ce rapport entre fiction et réalité ; rapport d'autant plus évident, il faut bien le dire, que l'intrigue se situe dans l'univers du journalisme écrit au Québec[5]. Les personnages de la série évoluent donc parmi des événements fictifs symétriques à ceux de l'actualité : conflits entre les travailleurs et l'État à l'ère des compressions budgétaires, relations difficiles entre Blancs et autochtones, criminalité, délinquance et pauvreté… À un point tel que *Scoop* devient, dans les médias eux-mêmes, le point de référence pour définir la « bonne information » : on verra, à l'émission d'affaires publiques *Le Point Médias*, des journalistes venir discuter sérieusement de ce qu'il y a de semblable ou de différent entre eux et les personnages de la série ; encore mieux, dans un dossier sur l'euthanasie, le magazine *L'Actualité* prendra comme point de référence deux « cas types » : l'un sera une personne paraplégique « en chair et en os », l'autre un personnage de la série *Scoop* devenu handicapé (Émile Rousseau).

Il y aurait donc une grande similitude de contenu entre les téléromans et les actualités en termes de « questions du jour » et de matière à interprétation par les communautés identitaires. La différence majeure, c'est que le téléroman situe cette matière dans le hors-temps et dans le hors-espace, ou plutôt dans un contexte spatio-temporel vraisemblable, marqué au coin de la vérisimilitude ; alors que les actualités la situent dans un temps et dans un espace bien délimités, grâce à leur mode de construction de la réalité, qui consiste à toujours ancrer les événements et les idées dans le « quand », le « où », le « qui », le « pourquoi » et le « comment ».

Roman, téléroman et construction du sens

Certes, les téléspectateurs sont parfaitement capables de faire cette distinction entre le réel et l'imaginaire. Néanmoins, comme les lecteurs de best-sellers, les amateurs de téléromans admettent volontiers que les séries télévisées peuvent susciter chez eux et chez leurs proches la réflexion, voire même la discussion, en même temps que la détente et le divertissement. La nature du média télévision produit toutefois une relation texte-récepteur différente de celle du livre. Alors que le lecteur développe un dialogue intime avec l'écriture du roman et avec l'auteur qu'il y imagine, le téléspectateur s'attache davantage aux péripéties des personnages, tels qu'interprétés par des comédiens-vedettes. De même, tandis que l'amateur de best-sellers ne discute que peu de ses lectures (sinon avec un ami très proche), le passionné de téléromans, compte tenu du visionnement habituellement familial, confronte fréquemment ses opinions – avant, pendant et après les émissions – avec celles de son entourage. De plus, contrairement au lecteur de best-sellers, qui considère habituellement le réalisme d'un récit comme condition essentielle de sa qualité, le téléspectateur s'accomode fort bien d'un peu d'invraisemblance, si cela met du piquant à l'intrigue.

En somme, la réception du téléroman s'effectue dans un contexte plus collectif que celle du best-seller, sans doute aussi sur un mode plus superficiel et plus éphémère : si la relecture passionnée d'un roman aimé est fréquente, le revisionnement d'une émission diffusée en reprise ne suscite que peu d'enthousiasme ; de même, les mordus de téléromans et les passionnés de romans s'entendent pour préférer la version imprimée d'un récit à son adaptation télévisuelle ou cinématographique : le cas des *Filles de Caleb* – super-succès du livre et du petit écran au Québec – constitue un exemple typique. En fait, bien qu'on consacre en moyenne plus d'heures de loisir à la télévision qu'à la lecture, on affirmera généralement, même chez les grands télévores, préférer la lecture à la télévision.

Ce qui nous amène à suggérer les hypothèses suivantes : en terme de structuration d'une culture spécifique au Québec, romans et téléromans à succès contribuent tous deux à la production de références symboliques parallèles et homologues aux structures sociales et à l'évolution historique de la collectivité québecoise ; cette « production de sens » par ces deux médias s'avère toutefois plus complémentaire que concurrentielle : non pas tellement parce que les succès du livre sont fréquemment adaptés pour la télévision, ni même parce que de telles adaptations permettent aux récits d'atteindre un auditoire plus vaste que celui des livres. La complémentarité tiendrait davantage, dans la thématique des récits autant que dans les attentes des récepteurs, à un rapport différent à l'actualité : si la télévision colle de plus près à l'ordre du jour immédiat, aux débats collectifs du moment, le livre joue davantage sur « l'actualité lente », c'est-à-dire sur les changements de valeurs qui imperceptiblement modifient nos vies personnelles.

Synthèse et conclusions

Telles sont les pistes principales que suggèrent nos recherches en cours. Autant pour le livre que pour la télévision, nous constatons la capacité des créateurs québécois de proposer des œuvres populaires dont la qualité se compare à celle des produits étrangers concurrents, en particulier des produits usaniens. Le succès de ces œuvres locales auprès du public du livre et de la télévision, permet à ces deux industries culturelles québécoises de conserver une part du marché qu'envient leurs homologues de bien d'autres collectivités plus populeuses, à commencer par celles du Canada anglais.

On remarque de plus que le succès des best-sellers et des téléromans peut en bonne partie s'expliquer par leur rapport direct avec l'actualité immédiate ou à plus long terme : ce qui ressort autant des enquêtes auprès des publics que des analyses de contenus des œuvres. Notre analyse des romans à succès et de leurs lecteurs laisse même entrevoir une « vision du monde » québecoise, qui serait moins individualiste, moins violente et plus égalitaire que celle que nous propose la culture publique usanienne ; il nous reste à voir si l'étude des téléromans et de leur auditoire permet d'observer un système de valeurs similaire.

Quoi qu'il en soit, nous croyons que le temps de loisir consacré à la télévision et au livre ne constitue pas une simple détente, une évasion hors du temps professionnel et social. Nous le considérons plutôt comme le moment où l'imaginaire médiatise les débats de la place publique, permettant par la suite au téléspectateur ou au lecteur de réactualiser ces débats dans son micro-milieu social.

NOTES

1. L'équipe est composée de six membres : trois sociologues (Line Grenier, de l'Université de Montréal, et Jacques Lemieux et Roger de la Garde de l'Université Laval) ; deux professeurs de littérature de l'Université Laval (Denis Saint-Jacques et Roger Chamberland) ; et un économiste de l'Université de Montréal (Claude Martin).

2 On notera dans le Graphique 2 l'absence de liste de best-sellers dans *La Presse* en 1983-84, due à un long conflit de travail. Notre équipe s'est mise « à la recherche des best-sellers perdus » et compte en produire la liste en 1995-96.

3. Les importations de France sont estimées par Baillargeon à partir du poids total (en tonnes métriques) des livres importés, divisé selon le poids moyen (en grammes) par catégorie de volumes (livres scolaires, scientifiques, littérature générale, etc...) : p. 192-194.

4. En particulier, une quarantaine d'entretiens réalisés par notre équipe en 1990-92 auprès de lectrices et lecteurs de best-sellers, dont les résultats détaillés figurent dans Saint-Jacques *et al.* (1994).

5. Nous soumettons ici des résultats préliminaires d'une étude sur *Scoop* et son public, commencée en 1994 et parvenue au stade l'analyse en 1995-96. L'étude comporte plusieurs volets : une analyse de contenu des 52 épisodes de la série et de sa couverture de presse, ainsi qu'une enquête par questionnaires, entretiens et « focus group »auprès de 48 téléspectateurs réguliers de la série. Les résultats détaillés de cette recherche devraient faire l'objet de deux ou trois articles dans des revues savantes en 1996. Un ouvrage collectif est envisagé pour 1997.

Bibliographie

ANG, Ien (1992). « Culture et communication. Pour une critique ethnographique de la consommation des médias dans le système médiatique transnationale », *Hermès*, no 11-12 ; 75-93.

BAILLARGEON, Jean-Paul *et al.* (1994). *Le téléspectateur : glouton ou gourmet ? Québec 1985-1989.* IQRC, Québec.

BAILLARGEON, Jean-Paul (1991). « Les livres québecois en langue française au Québec face aux livres de France », *Communication*, 12(2) : 191-217.

CURRAN, James (1993). « La décennie des révisions. La recherche en communication de masse des années 80 », *Hermès*, n°11-12 : 47-74.

DE LA GARDE, ROGER (1994). « There goes the neighborhood. Montréal's television market and Free Trade », communication présentée au colloque international *Media, Free Trade and Culture*, Austin, Texas (mars) ; à paraître en 1996 dans un collectif publié par les Presses de l'université du Texas, sous la direction d'Emile-G. McAnany.

DE LA GARDE, Roger et Denise PARÉ (1991). « La télévision : l'offre d'une programmation ou la programmation d'une demande », *Communication*, 12(1) : 101-148.

DE LA GARDE, Roger, William GILSDORF et Ilja WECHSELMANN, eds. (1993). *Small Nations, Big Neighbour. Denmark and Quebec/Canada Compare Notes on American Popular Culture*, John Libbey, London.

DEY, Ian (1993). *Qualitative Data Analysis. A User-Friendly Guide for Social Scientists.* Routledge, New York.

DUBOIS, Lise (1995). « La santé au petit écran ; entre science et fiction », *Communication*, 16 (1) : 155-173.

DUMONT, Fernand (1993). *Genèse de la société québécoise.* Boréal, Montréal.

ECO, Umberto (1985). *Lector in fabula ou la coopération interprétative dans les textes narratifs*, Grasset, Paris.

FIELDING, Nigel G. & Raymond M. LEE, eds. (1991). *Using Computers in Qualitative Research.* Sage, Newbury Park.

GARON, Rosaire (1984). « La lecture serait-elle du genre féminin ? », *Chiffres à l'appui*, II.1 (avril) : 1-11.

GRAVES, Frank L. et Timothy DUGAS (avec la collaboration de Janice REMAI et Pascale BELLIER) (1992). *La lecture et les Canadiens en 1991*, Ottawa, Les Associés de recherche Ekos Inc.

HALL, Stuart (1980), « Encoding / Decoding », dans S. Hall, D. Hobson, A. Lowe, and P. Willis (eds.), *Culture, Media, Language.* Hutchinson, London.

LEMIEUX, Jacques et Claude MARTIN (avec la participation de Pierre HUARD) (1993). « La lecture de revues et de livres au Québec », *Chiffres à l'appui*, VII.4 (mars) : 1-18.

LEMIEUX, Jacques et Denis SAINT-JACQUES (1990). « Un scénario motif dans le champ des best-sellers », *Voix et images*, XV(2) : 260-268.

LEMIEUX, Jacques et Denis SAINT-JACQUES (1994). « U.S. best-sellers in French Québec and English Canada », communication présentée au colloque international *Media, Free Trade and Culture*, Austin, Texas (mars) ; à paraître en 1996, aux Presses de l'université du Texas, dans un collectif sous la direction d'Emile-G. McAnany.

PRONOVOST, Gilles (1990). *Les comportements des Québecois en matière d'activités culturelles de loisir*, Québec, Les publications du Québec.

ROSENGREN, Karl Erik (1988). *The Study of Media Culture : Ideas, Actions, and Artefact.* Lund Research Papers in the Sociology of Communication, Report n°10. University of Lund, Lund.

SAINT-JACQUES, Denis et Roger DE LA GARDE, (dir.) (1992). *Les pratiques culturelles de grande consommation. Le marché francophone.* Nuit blanche éditeur/ CEFAN, Québec.

SAINT-JACQUES, Denis, Jacques LEMIEUX, Claude MARTIN et Vincent NADEAU (1994). *Ces livres que vous avez aimés ; les best-sellers au Québec de 1970 à aujourd'hui*, Québec, Nuit blanche éditeur.

SCHRØDER, Kim (1987). « Convergence of antagonistic traditions ? The case of audience research » *European Journal of Communication*, 12(1) : 7-32.

Les 30 plus grands best-sellers en français au Québec, selon les listes de *La Presse* (1970-1992)

1. Scott Peck, *Le chemin le moins fréquenté* (Laffont, 1989), essai, USA : 999,5 points, pour 84 parutions sur les listes hebdomaires de best-sellers.

2. Alvin Toffler, *Le choc du futur* (Denoël, 1971), essai, USA : 765,2 points, 90 parutions.

3. Anne Hébert, *Kamouraska* (Seuil, 1970), roman, Québec, : 625,8 points, 62 parutions.

4. Robin Norwood, *Ces femmes qui aiment trop* (Stanké *et al.*, 1986), essai, USA : 623,2 points, 62 parutions.

5. Betty Mahmoody, *Jamais sans ma fille* (Presses Pocket, 1990), biographie, USA : 564,3 points, 51 parutions.

6. Léandre Bergeron, *Petit manuel d'histoire du Québec* (Éd. québecoise, 1970), essai, Québec : 488,4 points, 48 parutions.

7. Louise Lambert-Lagacé, *Défi alimentaire de la femme* (L'Homme, 1988), essai, Québec : 483,4 points, 44 parutions.

8. Richard Bach, *Jonathan Livingston le goéland* (Flammarion, 1973), roman, USA : 462,6 points, 50 parutions.

9. Arlette Cousture, *Les filles de Caleb, tome 2 : Le cri de l'oie blanche* (Québec-Amérique, 1986), roman, Québec : 447,3 points, 57 parutions.

10. Louise Bourbeau, *Écoute ton corps* (E.T.C., 1989), essai, Québec : 418,9 points, 38 parutions.

11. Alexandre Jardin, *Le Zèbre* (Gallimard, 1988), roman, France : 292,6 points, 36 parutions.

12. Mario Puzo *Le Parrain* (Laffond *et al.*, 1970), roman, USA : 376,9 points, 42 parutions.

13. Arlette Cousture, *Les filles de Caleb, tome 1 : Le chant du coq* (Québec-Amérique, 1985), roman, Québec : 370,8 points, 36 parutions.

14 Alina Reyes, *Le Boucher* (Seuil, 1988), roman, France : 369,6 points, 36 parutions.

15. Martin Gray, *Le livre de la vie* (Laffont, 1973), essai, France : 355,6 points, 40 parutions.

16. Hans Selye, Le stress sans détresse (La Presse, 1974), essai, Québec / Canada : 318,8 points, 36 parutions.

17. Martin Gray, *Au nom de tous les miens* (Laffont, 1973), biographie, France / USA : 313,3 points, 41 parutions.

18. Colleen McCullough, *Les oiseaux se cachent pour mourir* (Select *et al.* 1978), roman, Australie / Grande-Bretagne / USA : 295,4 points, 33 parutions.

19. Collectif d'auteurs, *Petit Larousse illustré 1991* (Larousse, 1990), livre pratique, France : 294,8 points, 23 parutions.

20. Henri Charrière, *Papillon* (Laffont, 1970), biographie, France : 292,6 points, 36 parutions.

21. Berthe Sansregret, *Les recettes de Sœur Berthe* (Le Jour, 1973), livre pratique, Québec : 282,6 points, 26 parutions.

22. Irwin Shaw, *Les Jordache, tome 1 : Le riche et le pauvre* (Presses de la Cité, 1979), roman, USA : 282,3 points, 29 parutions.

23. Paul Ohl, *Soleil noir* (Québec-Amérique, 1991), roman, Québec : 279,7 points, 22 parutions.

24. Collectif d'auteurs, *L'état du monde en 1992* (Boréal/Découverte), essai, France : 275,3 points, 23 parutions.

25. Barbara Taylor-Bradford, *L'espace d'une vie* (Belfond, 1980), roman, Grande-Bretagne/USA : 268,8 points, 23 parutions.

26. Yves Beauchemin, *Juliette Pomerleau* (Québec-Amérique, 1989), roman, Québec : 266,2 points, 22 parutions.

27. Germaine Greer, *La femme eunuque* (Laffont *et al.*, 1972), essai, USA : 262,2 points, 36 parutions.

28. René Lévesque, *Attendez que je me rappelle* (Québec-Amérique, 1986), biographie, Québec : 262,0 points, 20 mentions.

29. Daniel Pennac, *La petite marchande de prose* (Gallimard, 1990), roman, France : 259,4 points, 30 parutions.

30. Georges-Hébert Germain, *Christophe Colomb* (Québec-Amérique, 1991), biographie, Québec : 257,9 points, 23 parutions.

Points :   Attribués selon le nombre de parutions dans les listes hebdomadaires de *La Presse* de 1970 à 1992, pondéré par le rang sur la liste (de 10 à 4,1) et le mois de publication des listes (de 2 à 1).

Source :   Saint-Jacques, Lemieux, Martin et Nadeau, 1994 : pages 74-76.

Jacques LEMIEUX, Roger DE LA GARDE et Claude MARTIN
Rapports entre réel et imaginaire
dans la réception du livre et de la télévision au Québec

RÉSUMÉ

Le visionnement de la télévision et la lecture constituent non seulement les principales habitudes de loisirs culturels des Québécois, mais se situent également aux premiers rangs de l'ensemble de leurs activités de loisir.

Les genres de livres et d'émissions de télévision les plus populaires – les best-sellers romanesques et biographiques, ainsi que les téléromans – se caractérisent dans leurs contenus par leur double fonction de divertissement (évasion) et d'information (réflexion) ; dans la mesure où leur thématique se révèle habituellement en prise directe avec l'agenda social de l'heure.

La présence massive, au niveau de l'offre, de produits étrangers (majoritairement « usaniens ») pourrait être considérée comme une menace pour le maintien de l'identité québécoise ; toutefois, lecteurs et téléspectateurs québécois font preuve de spécificité, tant dans la sélection de produits étrangers qu'ils adoptent, que dans la part de marché substantielle qu'ils persistent à accorder à leurs productions nationales.

C'est ce que nous voulons démontrer à partir de l'examen des grilles de programmation et des cotes d'écoute de la télévision, ainsi que des listes de best-sellers parues dans la presse, en rapport avec diverses enquêtes sur la lecture et le visionnement télévisuel.

Jacques LEMIEUX, Roger DE LA GARDE, Claude MARTIN
Relationships between Reality and Imagination
in the Approach to Reading and Television Viewing in Quebec

ABSTRACT

Not only are watching TV and reading the two major cultural and recreational activities of Quebecers, but they also rank as the most popular of all their recreational activities.
The most popular books (fiction and biographical best-sellers) or TV programs (series) share some distinctive characteristics : both are used as sources of entertainment (escapism) and information (reflection), inasmuch as their themes are closely related to current social issues as a general rule. Since the offer of foreign products (mainly of American origin) has become overwhelming, it could be seen as a threat to the survival of the *Québécois* identity. But both as readers and TV viewers, Quebecers show some specificity as much in terms of which foreign products they choose to adopt as in the substantial portion of the market they still devote to national productions. The article purports to show that the above observations are valid, based on the analysis of TV program grids and ratings as well as best-seller lists in newspapers compared with various surveys on reading and viewing habits.

Jacques Lemieux, Roger de la Garde y Claude Martin
Relación entre lo real y lo imaginario en la recepción del libro y de la
televisión en el Quebec

Resumen

La televisión y la lectura no constituyen únicamente los principales hábitos
de diversiones culturales de los quebequenses, pero se sitúan igualmente en
los primeros rangos del conjunto de sus actividades de recreación.

Los tipos de libros y de emisiones de televisión los más populares – los b*est*
sellers romanescos y biográficos, así que las telenovelas – se caracterizan en
sus contenidos por la doble función de entretenimiento (evasión) y de
información (reflexión) ; dentro de la medida en que su temática se revela
habitualmente en relación directa con la agenda social del momento.

La presencia masiva, en el nivel de la oferta, de productos extranjeros
(mayoritariamente Estadounidenses) podría considerarse como una amenaza
para el mantenimiento de la identidad quebequense, sin embargo, lectores y
telespectadores quebequenses hacen prueba de especificidad, tanto en la
selección de productos extranjeros que adoptan, como en la parte del
mercado substancial que persisten en acordar a las producciones nacionales.

Es lo que queremos demostrar a partir del examen de las cartas de ajuste de
programación y de las cotas de escucha de la televisión, así que de las lista
de los *best sellers* aparecidos en la prensa, con relación a diversas encuestas
sobre la lectura.

ÉLABORATION ET MISE À L'ESSAI D'UN PROGRAMME DE PRÉVENTION DU DÉCROCHAGE SCOLAIRE AXÉ SUR LES ACTIVITÉS PARASCOLAIRES

Myriam BEAUREGARD

Gaétan OUELLET

Département des sciences du loisir
Université du Québec à Trois-Rivières

Introduction

Le décrochage scolaire constitue, de l'avis de plusieurs, le signe le plus manifeste que l'école secondaire ne répond plus aux besoins et aux aspirations de bon nombre de ses étudiants. Quoique présent dans notre société depuis maintes années, l'ampleur prise récemment par le phénomène questionne et préoccupe tout à la fois.

Devant l'acuité du problème, différents programmes furent instaurés dans l'espoir de réduire les taux de décrochage scolaire. Cependant, rares sont les programmes qui ont tenté d'utiliser les activités parascolaires comme moyen de prévention du décrochage scolaire. Pourtant, la littérature tend à démontrer que la participation à ce type d'activités est associée à des attitudes et des comportements favorables à la persévérance scolaire. Au nombre de ceux-ci figurent une perception positive de soi et du milieu scolaire, un niveau élevé de motivation à fréquenter l'école, un faible taux d'absentéisme, ainsi que des résultats académiques satisfaisants.

Dans cette perspective, le but poursuivi par cette étude consistait à élaborer, puis à pré-tester un programme de prévention du décrochage scolaire axé sur les activités parascolaires, de manière à vérifier sa capacité d'agir sur les principaux facteurs de prédisposition au décrochage scolaire[1].

Loisir et société / *Society and Leisure*
Volume 18, numéro 2, automne 1995, pp. 373-394 • © Presses de l'Université du Québec

La problématique du décrochage scolaire

Le phénomène du décrochage scolaire a fluctué au rythme des différents contextes économiques et politiques qui ont animé le Québec au fil des ans. Ainsi, les statistiques divulguées par le ministère de l'Éducation du Québec (1991) révèlent que la probabilité de quitter le système scolaire avant l'obtention du diplôme d'études secondaires s'est considérablement amoindrie entre 1975 et 1985, passant de 48 % à 27 % dix ans plus tard. Là où le bât blesse cependant, c'est que cette probabilité d'abandon a connu une augmentation notable de plus de 8 % entre 1985 et 1986, pour se maintenir depuis aux environs de 35 %.

Conjuguée aux transformations qui se sont opérées sur le marché de l'emploi depuis les années quatre-vingt, cette hausse subite et substantielle des taux de décrochage scolaire n'est pas sans inquiéter les différents acteurs sociaux (Langevin, 1994 ; Hrimech,Théorêt, Hardy, Gariépy 1993). Ceux-ci craignent en effet que la sous-scolarisation des générations montantes constitue un frein tant à l'avancement économique et social de la société québécoise, qu'au développement intégral des individus qui la composent (Moisset & Toussaint, 1992).

Dans l'espoir d'accroître la persévérance scolaire des jeunes québécois, différentes recherches furent conduites afin d'identifier les facteurs de prédisposition au décrochage scolaire. La recension des écrits met en évidence trois grandes catégories de facteurs de prédisposition reliés soit à l'environnement familial et social de l'étudiant, soit au milieu scolaire, soit à l'étudiant lui-même (Langevin, 1994 ; Charest, 1980) (voir Figure 1).

Les causes qui interviennent dans le processus de l'abandon scolaire, tout en étant à la fois multiples et interreliées, diffèrent toutefois passablement d'un individu à l'autre. S'inspirant des motifs invoqués par les jeunes pour expliquer leur départ prématuré de l'école, la typologie de Violette (1991) met en évidence cinq profils de décrocheurs, deux principaux et trois secondaires, déterminés en fonction du nombre d'étudiants qu'ils regroupent.

Le premier profil majeur renferme des jeunes « aux prises avec des difficultés scolaires ». Le vécu à l'école de ces décrocheurs se résume en une longue liste d'échecs et de retards scolaires accumulés depuis le primaire. Pour sa part, le second profil principal est composé de jeunes dits « au cœur de l'adolescence type ». Contrairement aux décrocheurs du premier profil, les problèmes scolaires et personnels de ces étudiants n'apparaissent qu'au second cycle du secondaire, soit au moment où les manifestations typiques de l'adolescence sont à leur apogée.

En réponse à la complexité de la problématique du décrochage scolaire, une gamme variée de programmes et de mesures fut instaurée dans les écoles

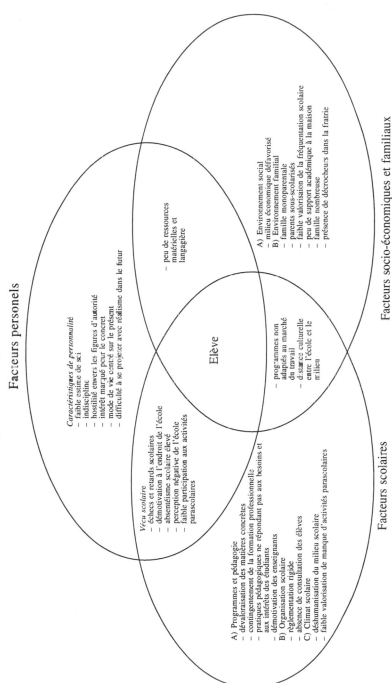

FIGURE 1

Relations entre les principaux facteurs de prédisposition au décrochage scolaire.
Adapté de Lévesque et West (1986)

Facteurs personels

Caractéristiques de personnalité
– faible estime de soi
– indiscipline
– hostilité envers les figures d'autorité
– intérêt marqué pour le concret
– mode de vie centré sur le présent
– difficulté à se projeter avec réalisme dans le futur

Vécu scolaire
– échecs et retards scolaires
– démotivation à l'endroit de l'école
– absentéisme scolaire élevé
– perception négative de l'école
– faible participation aux activités parascolaires

Élève

– peu de ressources matérielles et langagière

Facteurs socio-économiques et familiaux

A) Environnement social
– milieu économique défavorisé
B) Environnement familial
– famille monoparentale
– parents sous-scolarisés
– faible valorisation de la fréquentation scolaire
– peu de support académique à la maison
– famille nombreuse
– présence de décrocheurs dans la fratrie

– programmes non adaptés au marché du travail
– distance culturelle entre l'école et le milieu

Facteurs scolaires

A) Programmes et pédagogie
– dévaloraisation des matières concrètes
– contingentement de la formation professionnelle
– pratiques pédagogiques ne répondant pas aux besoins et aux intérêts des étudiants
– démotivation des enseignants
B) Organisation scolaire
– règlementation rigide
– absence de consultation des élèves
C) Climat scolaire
– déshumanisation du milieu scolaire
– faible valorisation de manque d'activités parascolaires

primaires et secondaires de la province Pour l'essentiel, ces programmes s'efforcent d'agir sur les principaux facteurs de prédisposition au décrochage mis en lumière par la littérature.

Sans nier le rôle prépondérant joué par l'environnement de l'étudiant ainsi que par le milieu scolaire dans le processus du décrochage scolaire, la présente étude s'est principalement attardée aux facteurs de prédisposition liés à l'étudiant lui-même.

Pour les fins de la recherche, cinq facteurs de prédisposition liés à l'étudiant furent retenus, soit la faible estime de soi, la perception négative du milieu scolaire, la démotivation à l'endroit de l 'école, le faible rendement académique et l'absentéisme scolaire. Le choix de ces variables est d'abord justifié par la prévalence de leur rôle dans le processus de l'abandon scolaire. D'autre part, la littérature tend à démontrer l'incidence directe ou indirecte des activités parascolaires sur ces variables reliées à l'étudiant.

Les bénéfices procurés par les activités parascolaires

Les activités parascolaires constituent une réalité ancrée depuis plusieurs années dans les écoles de la province. Pour les fins de la présente recherche, l'activité parascolaire fut définie comme étant celle

> organisée à l'intérieur ou à l'extérieur de l'horaire scolaire, non inscrite au curriculum proprement dit, en général facultative, qui se déroule dans l'école ou qui part de l'école, et qui poursuit des objectifs d'ordre éducatif (Conseil supérieur de l'éducation, 1988, p. 3).

Des nombreuses recherches ont démontré que les activités de loisir contribuent, entre autres choses, au bien être psychologique et au développement personnel des individus qui s'y engagent (Driver, Brown et Peterson, 1991). En ce qui a trait aux activités parascolaires proprement dites, les premières recherches furent initiées en réaction aux travaux de Coleman, (1959, 1961 ; voir Marsh, 1992) qui alléguait que la participation à ce type d'activités constituait une entrave à la réussite académique des étudiants. Les conclusions de Coleman s'inscrivaient dans une approche dite « académique », qui conçoit l'école comme un lieu de transmission du savoir formel, et dont le but premier est la poursuite de l'excellence scolaire. Dans cette perspective, les activités parascolaires ont pour but principal d'occuper les temps libres des étudiants, en plus de leur procurer plaisir et détente (Marsh, 1992).

En contrepartie, une seconde approche dite « développementale » soutient que l'école doit favoriser le développement intégral des étudiants. Les tenants de cette approche se sont donc efforcés de justifier l'importance des activités parascolaires comme lieu éducatif complémentaire aux activités traditionnelles d'enseignement (Marsh, 1992 ; Holland & Andre, 1987). Plusieurs recherches furent ainsi conduites pour établir des relations entre la participation aux activités parascolaires et certaines caractéristiques favorables à la persévérance scolaire.

Estime de soi

De nombreuses recherches ont tenté de mettre en relation le niveau d'estime de soi des étudiants impliqués dans les activités parascolaires, et différentes variables dont le sexe de l'étudiant, le type d'activité pratiqué et le degré d'engagement dans celle-ci (Holland & Andre, 1987 ; Steitz & Owen, 1992).

La recherche conduite par Yarworth et Gauthier (1978) tentait d'établir des relations entre la pratique d'activités parascolaires sportives ou non sportives et les caractéristiques psychologiques et scolaires suivantes : l'estime de soi, le type de formation académique (générale ou professionnelle), le rendement académique, le niveau scolaire et le sexe de l'étudiant. Les résultats ont révélé l'existence d'une forte relation entre la participation aux activités parascolaires (sportives ou non sportives) et un niveau élevé d'estime de soi.

Par ailleurs, Steitz et Owen (1992) ont tenté d'établir une relation entre l'estime de soi, le degré d'implication dans une activité parascolaire et le travail à temps partiel à l'extérieur des heures de cours. Les résultats révèlent que le niveau d'estime de soi des participants est plus élevé que celui des non participants. Les auteurs ont cependant constaté que le niveau d'estime de soi des premiers varie considérablement en fonction de la nature de l'activité parascolaire et du sexe du participant. Steitz et Owen (1992) avancent donc que les activités parascolaires ne procurent pas un degré d'implication identique pour les participants et, qu'en conséquence, les bénéfices retirés diffèrent d'une activité à l'autre.

En somme, ces recherches indiquent que la participation aux activités parascolaires est associée à un niveau élevé d'estime de soi. Cependant, la littérature suggère également que le sexe du participant, le type d'activité parascolaire pratiqué, le degré d'implication dans l'activité et la taille de l'école peuvent conduire à des variations importantes du niveau d'estime de soi observé chez les participants aux activités parascolaires (Holland & Andre, 1987).

Rendement scolaire

Plusieurs études américaines ont tenté d'observer la relation entre le rendement scolaire et la participation aux activités parascolaires. Au nombre des précurseurs, Schaffer et Armer (1968, voir Holland & Andre, 1987) ont révélé que les athlètes de sexe masculin obtenaient de meilleurs résultats scolaires que les étudiants non engagés dans les sports.

Lander, Feltz, Obermeir et Brouse (1978, voir Holland & Andre, 1987) ont, pour leur part, démontré que les garçons impliqués uniquement au sein des activités sportives enregistraient, aux épreuves nationales, des résultats scolaires moins élevés que ceux de la moyenne nationale. En contrepartie, les élèves qui participaient à la fois à une activité sportive et à un autre type d'activité parascolaire ont obtenu des résultats scolaires significativement plus élevés que ceux de la moyenne nationale.

Dans le même sens, les résultats de Snyder et Spreitzer (1977, voir Lebel, 1988) indiquent que les garçons et les filles qui adhèrent à la fois aux activités sportives et aux activités musicales ont des aspirations scolaires significativement plus élevées que les non participants. En revanche, les étudiants qui ne pratiquent qu'une ou l'autre de ces activités ont sensiblement les mêmes aspirations scolaires que les non participants.

S'exprimant sur les relations positives entre la participation aux activités parascolaires et le rendement scolaire, Marsh (1992) émet l'hypothèse que

> la participation aux activités parascolaires, même celles qui ne sont pas associées de façon évidente au rendement académique semblent conduire à un plus grand engagement face à l'école et aux valeurs de l'école, ce qui conduit indirectement à un meilleur rendement académique (Marsh, 1992, p. 560)

Enfin, la recension des écrits effectuée pour le compte du Conseil supérieur de l'éducation (Lebel, 1988) révèle que l'organisation d'activités parascolaires est associée à une amélioration de la motivation des étudiants, à une diminution des problèmes de discipline, ainsi qu'à une réduction des taux d'absentéisme et de décrochage scolaire (Conseil supérieur de l'éducation, 1988 ; Cheng & Ziegler, 1986).

En définitive, la littérature tend à démontrer la présence d'une relation positive entre la participation aux activités parascolaires et certains comportements et attitudes propices à la persévérance scolaire. Par ailleurs, de multiples études s'intéressant à l'abandon scolaire ont établi que les décrocheurs potentiels sont significativement moins engagés dans les activités parascolaires de leur école que leurs homologues persévérants (Langevin, 1994 ; Violette, 1993). En corollaire, ces résultats suggèrent que les étudiants susceptibles de bénéficier le plus des apports des activités parascolaires, soit les décrocheurs potentiels, sont également ceux qui y adhèrent le moins.

Contribution des activités parascolaires pour prévenir le décrochage scolaire

Des études révèlent que les écoles qui offrent une variété d'activités parascolaires à leurs étudiants et à l'intérieur desquelles la participation est encouragée et valorisée par le projet éducatif, enregistrent des taux de décrochage nettement plus bas que les écoles qui n'offrent pas cette opportunité à leurs étudiants (Cheng & Ziegler, 1986). Cette constatation donne à penser que

> les activités parascolaires peuvent atténuer, chez les jeunes qui éprouvent des difficultés dans les matières scolaires, l'image de l'école perçue comme le lieu où ils échouent. En conséquence, leur motivation peut en être améliorée. On peut donc raisonnablement penser que, en atténuant le sentiment d'inconfort vis-à-vis de soi-même et en maintenant la motivation, l'école cesse alors d'être pour les jeunes le foyer d'une multitude de frustrations contre lesquelles ils se rebellent ou qu'ils cherchent à fuir (Conseil supérieur de l'éducation, 1988, p. 23)

En dépit des apports favorables que la pratique en milieu scolaire et la littérature scientifique leur attribuent, peu de programmes ont cherché à utiliser systématiquement les activités parascolaires à des fins de prévention de l'abandon scolaire. En outre, les intervenants qui ont eu recours à ce type de programme agissent dans bien des cas de façon intuitive, sans qu'un rationnel scientifique sous-tende véritablement leur démarche. Enfin, peu de recherches ont tenté de mesurer, chez des décrocheurs potentiels, les retombées psychologiques et scolaires résultant d'une implication au sein d'une activité parascolaire.

Objectifs de la recherche

Le nombre limité de recherches empiriques traitant spécifiquement de l'utilisation des activités parascolaires à des fins de prévention du décrochage scolaire, nous a incité à conduire une recherche de type exploratoire. L'objectif premier de cette étude consiste à vérifier les possibilités d'application d'un programme de prévention du décrochage axé sur les activités parascolaires. Elle vise d'abord à s'assurer des possibilités de succès d'un tel programme s'adressant spécifiquement à des étudiants identifiés comme décrocheurs potentiels en vérifiant le bien-fondé des conditions ou des modalités d'application.

Le second but était de vérifier les impacts potentiels d'un tel programme sur les participants, en particulier, ses effets sur les principaux facteurs de prédisposition au décrochage reliés à l'étudiant. Les principaux facteurs de prédisposition dont il est possible ici de vérifier l'évolution sont l'*estime de soi*, la *perception du milieu scolaire*, la *motivation scolaire*, l'*absentéisme* et le *rendement scolaire*. Les deux premiers facteurs sont des dimensions psychologiques de base, des dispositions motivationnelles et perceptuelles, à savoir l'attitude face à soi-même et face à l'école ; des changements à ce niveau sont susceptibles d'entraîner aussi des modifications aux trois autres facteurs reliés davantage à la motivation scolaire et à l'apprentissage.

Méthodologie

Un programme de prévention du décrochage scolaire axé sur les activités parascolaires fut appliqué, entre les mois de janvier et de mai 1994, dans une école secondaire de 1000 étudiants de la région Mauricie-Bois-Francs. Cette école dessert une Municipalité Régionale de Comté parmi les plus défavorisées au Québec au niveau socio-économique.

Les *sujets* de l'expérimentation sont recrutés sur une base volontaire parmi un groupe de 43 étudiants de secondaire 3 identifiés comme décrocheurs potentiels à partir du questionnaire « L'école ça m'intéresse ? » (Ministère de l'Éducation du Québec, 1983). Ce test, qui sert à prédire l'abandon scolaire, a été administré en janvier 1994 à tous les étudiants de troisième secondaire.

Sans mentionner leur statut de décrocheur potentiel, ni à quelle clientèle s'adressait spécifiquement le programme, ces étudiants furent convoqués à une rencontre de groupe pour les informer des grandes lignes de l'activité et les inviter à s'y inscrire.

Six (6) décrocheurs potentiels (cinq filles et un garçon) exprimèrent le désir de participer, de même qu'une autre étudiante ne faisant pas partie de ce groupe d'après le test, mais présentant par ailleurs de fortes prédispositions au décrochage scolaire.

L'*activité parascolaire* proposée s'inspirait de l'émission télévisée « Fort Boyard » ; les sujets du groupe expérimental avaient pour mandat d'organiser une journée de jeux et d'épreuves à l'intention de leurs pairs et de leurs professeurs. D'une durée de dix semaines, ce programme se déroula entre le 7 février et le 15 avril 1994, à raison de deux rencontres hebdomadaires tenues pendant l'heure du midi.

L'*animation du groupe* fut assumée par une stagiaire en éducation spécialisée déjà impliquée dans ce milieu. Ses interventions visaient principalement l'atteinte des objectifs suivants : développer des aptitudes et des habiletés requises pour la prise en charge de l'activité, l'autonomie, le sens des responsabilités, l'initiative et la créativité. De plus, l'activité devait faire vivre aux étudiants des expériences de succès, favoriser la cohésion dans le groupe, en plus de créer un sentiment d'appartenance à l'école.

Le *déroulement de l'expérimentation* ne fut pas sans problème. Des sept (7) membres de l'équipe originale, seulement cinq (5) ont complété le programme. Le groupe expérimental était constitué de deux sous-groupes présentant des caractéristiques de personnalité et un vécu scolaire qui divergeaient considérablement. D'après la typologie de Violette (1991), on pouvait distinguer un premier sous-groupe de trois (3) étudiants appartenant au profil des « *jeunes aux prises avec des difficultés scolaires* », tandis que le second sous-groupe était, quant à lui, composé de quatre (4) étudiants appartenant au profil des « *jeunes au cœur de l'adolescence type* ». Cette hétérogénéité a engendré des tensions importantes au sein du groupe, ce qui amena l'abandon de deux (2) participants après la quatrième semaine. Par la suite, le respect des différences finit par s'établir, et la cohésion du groupe atteignit son apogée lors de la journée de réalisation des épreuves.

Pour évaluer les impacts du programme sur les variables à l'étude, deux (2) *questionnaires* furent administrés à deux reprises, le Self-Esteem Scale de Rosenberg (1965) pour mesurer l'estime de soi, et un questionnaire élaboré pour les besoins de cette étude pour évaluer la perception du milieu scolaire. Le pré-test eut lieu lors de la première rencontre du programme, alors que le post-test furent administrés deux semaines après la fin de celui-ci.

Le rendement scolaire, l'absentéisme et la motivation scolaire furent évalués avant, pendant et après le programme, à partir des *relevés de notes* des étapes 2 (novembre à janvier), 4 (février à avril) et 5 (mai et juin). Le rendement scolaire est évalué par la moyenne générale obtenue aux cours ; l'absentéisme est indiqué par le nombre de périodes où l'étudiant ne s'est pas présenté à ses cours. Quant à la motivation scolaire, elle fut mesurée par l'écart entre le nombre de commentaires positifs et de commentaires négatifs inscrits par les enseignants sur les relevés de notes des étapes 2,4 et 5 ; ces commentaires portent sur les comportements de l'étudiant en classe et sur ses attitudes envers les travaux scolaires.

Enfin, une *entrevue individuelle* conduite par le chercheur à la fin du programme permit d'évaluer la motivation et la satisfaction des participants, tout en fournissant des éléments utiles pour une interprétation nuancée des autres données.

Les résultats

Compte tenu du nombre restreint de sujets ayant pris part à l'expérimentation, il n'est pas possible d'effectuer de test de signification statistique, pas même avec des techniques non paramétriques. La présentation des données se fera donc de façon purement descriptive, plutôt sous forme d'études de cas, soit pour les sujets pris individuellement, soit pour les deux sous-groupes de décrocheurs potentiels.

Changements après la participation au programme

Le Tableau 1 illustre les variations observées chez les cinq (5) participants. Pour l'estime de soi et la perception du milieu scolaire, il s'agit de la différence entre la mesure initiale et celle effectuée deux semaines après la fin du programme ; pour les variables mesurées à partir du dossier scolaire, il s'agit de la différence entre l'étape 2 (précédant le programme) et l'étape 4 (pendant le programme) et entre l'étape 4 et l'étape 5 (suivant le programme). Ces résultats font état du profil de décrocheurs potentiels auquel appartient chacun des sujets, ceux « *aux prises avec difficultés scolaires* » (D1, D2 ou D3), et ceux « *au cœur de l'adolescence type* » (A1 et A2).

Les zones ombrées permettent de voir rapidement pour quels sujets et pour quelles variables les changements sont positifs, allant ainsi dans le sens d'une réduction des facteurs de prédisposition au décrochage.

On constate que quatre (4) des cinq (5) variables montrent des changements positifs chez quatre (4) des cinq (5) sujets ; c'est le cas de l'*estime de soi,* de la *perception du milieu scolaire*, de la *motivation scolaire* et de l'*absentéisme*. Pour sa part, le *rendement scolaire* s'est amélioré chez seulement trois (3) des cinq (5) participants. Ces changements sont donc très positifs et très encourageants ; ils démontrent des changements constants dans le sens attendu. Comme en témoigne le Tableau 1, tous les indicateurs sauf un montrent un changement moyen allant dans le sens d'une diminution de la prédisposition au décrochage ; seul le rendement scolaire moyen n'a pas changé du tout.

Par ailleurs, les trois variables mesurées durant les deux mois ayant suivi le programme montrent des changements négatifs très importants : la motivation scolaire a baissé chez 4 des 5 sujets ; l'absentéisme a augmenté considérablement durant cette période chez tous les participants, et le rendement scolaire montre une baisse dans trois cas.

Finalement, en examinant le tableau sous l'angle des participants plutôt que celui des variables à l'étude, on peut voir qu'un seul des cinq participants ne manifeste pas de changement positif sur au moins 4 des 5 variables mesurées immédiatement après la fin du programme. Il s'agit d'un sujet du profil aux prises avec des difficultés scolaires (D2) chez qui le processus de décrochage était déjà passablement avancé ; le programme l'a temporairement « raccroché » à l'école, allant jusqu'à améliorer sa perception de l'école et sa motivation scolaire ; il n'a pas été suffisant pour augmenter son estime de soi, et encore moins pour diminuer l'absentéisme et pour augmenter les résultats scolaires.

En reprenant une à une les variables à l'étude, il est possible de voir comment les deux sous-groupes d'étudiants se comparent entre eux.

TABLEAU 1

Variations enregistrées par les sujets pendant et après le programme

Variables	Variations	D1*	D2*	D3*	A1**	A2**	Moy.
Estime de soi	pendant	+ 2	– 2	+ 1	+ 1	+ 7	+ 1.8
Perception milieu	pendant	+ 2	+ 1	– 1	+ 3	+ 4	+ 1.8
Motivation scolaire	pendant	+ 5	+ 2	+ 3	+ 5	0	+ 3
	après	– 4	– 6	+ 1	– 7	– 2	– 3.6
Absentéisme scolaire	pendant	–13	+19	–14	– 6	– 3	– 3.4
	après	+29	+69	+24	+17	+ 7	+29.2
Rendement scolaire	pendant	– 5	– 4	+ 3	+ 4	+ 2	0
	après	+ 5	–19	0	– 5	– 7	– 5.2

Légende des couleurs

▓ Variation dans le sens de l'hypothèse
▒ Variation dans le sens opposé à l'hypothèse
☐ Aucune variation

*   Ce sujet a été identifié comme appartenant au profil de décrocheur potentiel « aux prises avec difficultés scolaires ».

** Ce sujet a été identifié comme appartenant au profil de décrocheur potentiel « au cœur de l'adolescence type ».

Estime de soi

Au niveau de cette première variable, la Figure 2 montre que les scores ont augmenté en moyenne de 4 points pour les sujets du groupe au cœur de l'adolescence type, tandis qu'ils sont restés sensiblement les mêmes pour l'autre groupe, même s'il y a une légère augmentation chez deux des trois sujets. Pour l'ensemble des sujets, l'augmentation moyenne est de 1.8 points.

À priori, cette augmentation peut paraître peu importante. Cependant, il importe de conserver à l'esprit que le niveau d'estime de soi constitue une caractéristique fondamentale de la personnalité d'un individu. Un changement profond à ce chapitre se fait généralement de façon progressive suite à des expériences répétées. Il est impossible de connaître l'importance et la permanence de ce changement. Étant donné la durée limitée du programme, il y a lieu de faire l'hypothèse qu'un programme plus soutenu et réparti sur une plus longue période serait susceptible de favoriser un accroissement important de l'estime de soi de la majorité des décrocheurs potentiels impliqués, y compris ceux qui sont aux prises avec des difficultés scolaires.

FIGURE 2

Moyennes de l'indice d'estime de soi par profil de décrocheurs et pour le goupe total, avant et après le programme

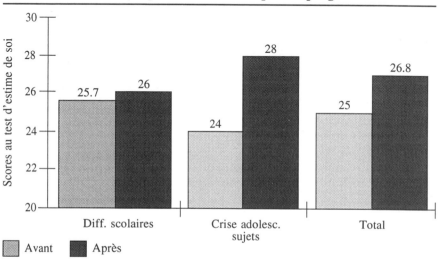

Perception du milieu scolaire

Les changements de perception du milieu scolaire illustrés à la Figure 3 montrent les mêmes tendances, à savoir une légère différence pour le groupe de décrocheurs aux prises avec des difficultés scolaires, et un changement positif assez important pour l'autre groupe (3.5 points en moyenne). Comme le démontre le Tableau 1, les sujets A4 et A5 ont enregistré des hausses de 3 et 4 points lors du post-test, tandis que les sujets D1 et D2 connaissaient des augmentations de 1 et de 2 points. Le sujet D3 a, quant à lui, enregistré une baisse peu significative de 1 point lors du second test.

Comme le confirment aussi les entrevues, la participation au programme semble avoir contribué à améliorer la perception du milieu scolaire chez les décrocheurs potentiels. On peut penser qu'une implication soutenue et généralisée des étudiants à ce genre d'activités serait de nature à faciliter leur identification à l'école en favorisant une perception positive.

FIGURE 3

Moyennes de l'indice de perception du milieu scolaire par profil de décrocheurs et pour le goupe total, avant et après le programme

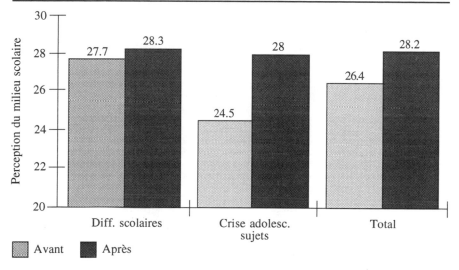

Motivation scolaire

Dans le cadre de cette recherche, la motivation scolaire des sujets fut mesurée par l'écart entre le nombre de commentaires positifs et celui des commentaires négatifs inscrits par les enseignants sur les relevés de notes des sujets. À ce propos, les résultats présentés au Tableau 1 nous apprennent que quatre des cinq sujets ont connu une hausse de leur motivation scolaire pendant le programme, tandis que le dernier demeurait au même niveau. La Figure 4 montre qu'ici, c'est le groupe D qui montre la plus grande amélioration avec une différence moyenne de 3.4, comparativement à 2.5 pour le groupe A.

Cependant, cette motivation scolaire est revenue à peu près au même point durant l'étape qui a suivi le programme, subissant une baisse dans les deux groupes.

Absentéisme scolaire

Les résultats présentés au Tableau 1 indiquent que quatre des cinq sujets ont considérablement réduit le nombre de périodes d'absence aux cours pendant le programme. Seul, le sujet D2 a augmenté de 19 périodes. Malgré ceci, les deux groupes ont réduit leur niveau moyen d'absentéisme : 2.6 périodes pour

FIGURE 4

**Moyennes de l'indice de motivation scolaire par profil de décrocheurs
et pour le goupe total, avant et après le programme**

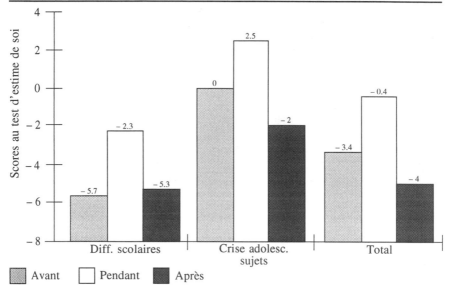

FIGURE 5

**Moyennes du nombre de périodes d'absences par profil de décrocheurs
et pour le goupe total, avant, pendant et après le programme**

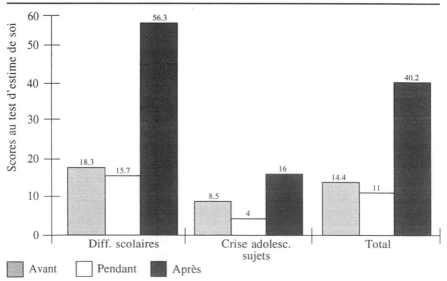

le groupe D, et 4.5 pour le groupe A. Il est à remarquer que les diminutions les plus importantes sont observées chez les sujets D1 et D3, différences allant dans le même sens que l'augmentation de la motivation scolaire de 5 et 3 points observée chez ces mêmes sujets.

Toutefois, on observe une augmentation considérable du nombre de périodes d'absences durant l'étape qui suivit le programme. On peut interpréter cette réaction comme le résultat d'un manque de suivi du programme, ou d'une démotivation généralisée suite à la disparition d'une activité significative pour ces étudiants. Il faut également se rappeler que cette étape correspond aux mois de mai et de juin, période où l'absentéisme est un phénomène généralisé dans les écoles secondaires. Ces observations donnent à penser que, n'eut été de leur participation au programme, les sujets auraient enregistré non pas une baisse, mais une hausse du nombre d'absences au cours de l'étape 4. De plus, l'augmentation du nombre d'absences au cours de l'étape 5 aurait pu être encore plus prononcée.

Rendement scolaire

Les résultats présentés au Tableau 1 indiquent que trois des cinq sujets ont vu leurs résultats scolaires s'améliorer pendant la période où s'est déroulé le programme. De fait, les deux décrocheurs « au cœur de l'adolescence type » ont amélioré leur rendement scolaire de 4 % (A4) et de 2 % (A5). Dans l'autre groupe, seul le sujet D3 a connu une hausse de 3 %. au cours du programme, les deux autres ayant des résultats scolaires plus bas de 5 % et de 4 %. La Figure 6 présente les variations moyennes des deux groupes ; le groupe avec des difficultés scolaires passe de 57,3 % à 55,3 %, tandis que le groupe aux prises avec la crise d'adolescence augmente en moyenne de 3 points, passant de 67,5 à 70,5 pour cent.

Après le programme, les changements observés chez les trois décrocheurs « aux prises avec difficultés scolaires » divergent considérablement. Le sujet D1 a connu une augmentation non négligeable de 5 % par rapport à l'étape où se déroulait le programme, revenant donc au même niveau de rendement qu'avant le programme. Le sujet D2 a pour sa part enregistré une baisse substantielle de 19 %, et enfin, le sujet D3 voyait son résultat scolaire se maintenir au même niveau que pendant le programme, soit 3 points en haut de sa moyenne pré-programme.

Ces résultats suggèrent que le programme à lui seul, et dans sa forme actuelle, n'a que peu d'incidence sur le rendement scolaire de ce type de décrocheurs.

Quant à l'autre groupe de décrocheurs, l'après-programme montre des données constantes, mais assez négatives ; en effet, ces deux sujets ont enregistré des baisses assez importantes dans leurs résultats scolaires, les ramenant à près de trois points en-dessous de leurs résultats précédant le programme (voir la Figure 6).

Cette baisse dans les résultats scolaires vont dans le même sens que les baisses de motivation scolaire et l'augmentation de l'absentéisme observées à la suite du programme. Cela pourrait aussi signifier que l'augmentation du niveau d'estime de soi et l'amélioration de la perception du milieu scolaire sont des changements précaires qui auraient besoin de programmes répétés et de plus longue durée pour se maintenir.

FIGURE 5

Moyennes du nombre de périodes d'absences par profil de décrocheurs et pour le goupe total, avant, pendant et après le programme

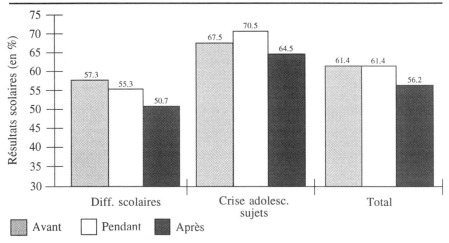

Discussion des résultats

L'analyse des résultats recueillis dans le cadre de l'expérimentation du programme met en lumière trois constats principaux. Le premier tend à révéler que l'incidence du programme sur les variables à l'étude diffère en fonction du profil de décrocheur auquel appartient l'étudiant. Ainsi, les changements observés chez les décrocheurs potentiels « aux prises avec des difficultés scolaires » sont moins importants que ceux obtenus par les sujets « au cœur de l'adolescence type ». Cependant, les améliorations observées chez les décrocheurs potentiels du premier groupe au chapitre de l'estime de soi, de la perception du milieu scolaire, de la motivation scolaire ainsi que la réduction de l'absentéisme, incitent à croire qu'il peut s'avérer judicieux d'offrir le programme à ce type de décrocheurs. Dans l'espoir d'accroître l'effet préventif du programme auprès des décrocheurs potentiels « aux prises avec des difficultés scolaires », il apparaît néanmoins nécessaire de dispenser ce dernier dès la première secondaire, en plus d'offrir, concurremment au programme, un encadrement académique approprié à ces étudiants.

Le second constat révèle, pour sa part, que les effets bénéfiques observés pendant le programme ne sont pas durables et s'atténuent rapidement à la fin de celui-ci. Ces résultats soulèvent la nécessité de prolonger la durée du programme, en plus d'offrir un encadrement particulier à chaque participant. Pour l'essentiel, cet encadrement individuel devra tenter d'identifier et de résoudre les difficultés personnelles, familiales ou scolaires susceptibles d'occasionner le départ prématuré de l'école des participants.

Le troisième constat qui se dégage de l'expérimentation concerne la difficulté de recruter des décrocheurs potentiels pour participer au programme. En effet, seulement sept (7) décrocheurs potentiels approchés ont accepté de participer au programme. De plus, on ne peut passer sous silence le fait que le programme ait attiré nettement plus de filles que de garçons. À cet égard, il est plausible de croire que le programme gagnerait à proposer différents choix d'activités parascolaires (sportives, culturelles, socio-culturelles, etc) plutôt qu'un seul, afin d'accroître son pouvoir d'attraction auprès des décrocheurs potentiels.

Les principaux constats qui émanent de l'expérimentation soulèvent donc la nécessité d'apporter certaines modifications au programme dans l'espoir d'améliorer son efficacité à prévenir le décrochage scolaire.

Enfin, à l'instar des recherches portant sur les activités parascolaires, la présente étude comporte certaines limites méthodologiques qui rendent difficile l'établissement de liens réels de causalité entre les variables étudiées. Ainsi, la sélection des sujets sur une base libre et volontaire, l'absence de groupe contrôle, de même que la durée limitée de l'expérimentation, ne permettent pas d'affirmer que les changements observés sur les cinq variables sont entièrement et uniquement attribuables à l'implication au sein du programme préliminaire.

Toutefois, la principale limite de cette recherche s'avère certes le nombre restreint de sujets ayant pris part à l'expérimentation du programme. De fait, seulement cinq sujets ont complété le programme dans son entier, ce qui a eu pour corollaire d'annihiler les possibilités d'utilisation de tests statistiques non paramétriques. Il convient néanmoins de rappeler que cette expérimentation ne visait pas à démontrer l'efficacité du programme, mais davantage à évaluer sa pertinence et sa faisabilité, tout en évaluant de façon exploratoire son impact sur les participants.

Conclusion

Au cours des dernières années, plusieurs programmes furent instaurés dans les écoles primaires et secondaires dans l'espoir de réduire l'ampleur du décrochage scolaire. Cependant, rares sont les programmes qui ont tenté d'utiliser les activités parascolaires à des fins de prévention du décrochage scolaire et ce malgré le fait que ces activités soient associées à des attitudes et à des comportements favorables à la persévérance scolaire. De fait, la littérature a démontré que la participation aux activités parascolaires est associée à une perception positive de soi et du milieu scolaire, à un niveau élevé de motivation à fréquenter l'école, à un faible taux d'absentéisme scolaire, ainsi qu'à des résultats académiques satisfaisants. Dans cette perspective, la présente étude visait à élaborer puis à pré-tester un programme de prévention du décrochage scolaire axé sur les activités parascolaires.

Les résultats obtenus dans le cadre de l'expérimentation ont permis de dégager certains constats qui laissent présager de la réussite d'un tel programme, et ce particulièrement auprès des décrocheurs potentiels dits « au cœur de l'adolescence ». Cependant, le nombre restreint de sujets composant le groupe expérimental constitue une limite certaine de cette recherche. Il s'avère par conséquent difficile de généraliser les résultats obtenus dans le cadre de l'expérimentation, et de vérifier l'efficacité réelle du programme au chapitre de la prévention du décrochage scolaire.

En définitive, nous sommes loin de prétendre que le programme élaboré constitue la panacée au décrochage scolaire. De fait, ce programme ne peut, à lui seul, répondre aux besoins spécifiques de tous les décrocheurs potentiels. Cependant, les résultats de la recherche de même que le rationnel scientifique qui la sous-tend, soulèvent l'opportunité d'utiliser les activités parascolaires, concurremment à d'autres types d'intervention, dans l'espoir d'accroître la persévérance scolaire des décrocheurs potentiels.

————————

NOTES

1.   Cet article constitue une synthèse du mémoire de maîtrise en Loisir, Culture et Tourisme présenté par l'auteur principal à l'Université du Québec à Trois-Rivières.

BIBLIOGRAPHIE

BEAUREGARD, M. (1995). *Élaboration d'un programme de prévention du décrochage scolaire axé sur les activités parascolaires.* Mémoire de maîtrise inédit, Université du Québec à Trois-Rivières.

CHAREST, D. (1980). *Prévention de l'abandon prématuré.* Québec : Direction générale des réseaux.

CHENG, M. & ZIEGLER, S. (1986). *Moving from Elementary to Secondary School Procedures : Which May Facilitate the Transition Process,* Toronto : Toronto Board of Education, Research section.

CONSEIL SUPÉRIEUR DE L'ÉDUCATION. (1988). *Les activités parascolaires à l'école secondaire : un atout pour l'éducation.* Québec : Direction des communications.

DRIVER, B.L., BROWN, P.J. & PETERSON, G.L. (1991). *Benefits of Leisure.* Pensylvania : Venture Publishing Inc.

HOLLAND, A. & ANDRE, T. (1987). Participation in Extracurricular Activities in Secondary School : What is Know, What Needs to be know ? *Review of Educational Research, 57,* 4, 437-466.

HRIMECH, M., THÉORÊT, M., HARDY, J.Y. & GARIÉPY, W. (1993). *Étude sur l'abandon scolaire des jeunes décrocheurs du secondaire sur l'Ile de Montréal.* Montréal : Conseil scolaire de l'Ile de Montréal.

LANGEVIN, L. (1994). *L'abandon scolaire : On ne naît pas décrocheur !* Montréal, Les Éditions LOGIQUES.

LEBEL, D. (1988). État de la situation au Canada et aux États-Unis : revue de littérature. In Conseil supérieur de l'éducation. *Deux études sur les activités parascolaires dans les écoles secondaires* (pp. 1- 64) Québec.

LÉVESQUE, J. & WEST W. (1986). *Le décrochage scolaire : une perspective holistique.* Mémoire de maîtrise inédit, Québec : Université Laval.

MARSH, H. W. (1992). Extracurricular Activities : Beneficial Extension of the Traditional Curriculum or Subversion of Academic Goals. *Journal of Educational Psychology, 84,* 4, 553-562.

MINISTÈRE DE L'ÉDUCATION DU QUÉBEC. (1991). *La réussite scolaire et la question de l'abandon des études.* Résumé des plus récentes données disponibles, Québec : Direction de la recherche.

MINISTÈRE DE L'ÉDUCATION DU QUÉBEC. (1983). *L'école ça m'intéresse ? Questionnaire destiné aux élèves du secondaire.* Québec : Direction générale du développement pédagogique.

MOISSET J. & TOUSSAINT, P. (1992) Pourquoi faut-il combattre l'abandon scolaire ? Une perspective économique. In CRIRES-FECS (Éds), *Pour favoriser la réussite scolaire : Réflexions et pratiques* (pp. 38-57). Montréal : Ed. Saint-Martin et Centrale de l'enseignement du Québec.

STEITZ, J.A. & OWEN, T.P. (1992) School Activities and Work : Effects on Adolescent Self-Esteem. *Adolescence, 27,* 105, 37-49.

VIOLETTE, M. (1991). *L'école... facile d'en sortir Enquête auprès des décrocheurs et des décrocheuses.* Québec : Ministère de l'Éducation, Direction de la recherche.

YARWORTH, J. S. & GAUTHIER, W. Jr. (1978). Relationship of Student Self-concept and Selected Personnal Variables and Participation in School Activities. *Journal of Educational Psychology, 70,* 3, 335-344.

Myriam BEAUREGARD et Gaétan OUELLET,
*Élaboration et mise à l'essai d'un programme de prévention
du décrochage scolaire axé sur les activités parascolaires*

RÉSUMÉ

Même s'il n'est pas nouveau, le phénomène du décrochage scolaire est devenu une problème social préoccupant. Depuis l'année 1985-86, plus de
35 % des jeunes quittent l'école sans diplôme d'études secondaires. Plusieurs
programmes ont été mis de l'avant pour prévenir ce problème. Peu d'interventions sont basées sur l'utilisation des activités parascolaires qui sont pourtant fortement associées à des facteurs de persistance scolaire, comme
l'estime de soi, la perception du milieu scolaire, la motivation aux études,
l'assiduité aux cours et la réussite scolaire. La présente étude vise à élaborer et évaluer un programme de prévention s'adressant à des décrocheurs
potentiels. Mis à l'essai auprès d'un groupe de 5 élèves de troisième année
du secondaire, le programme préliminaire s'avère réalisable et efficace. A la
suite du programme, quatre des cinq variables ont montré des changements
positifs chez 4 des 5 participants ; il s'agit de l'*estime de soi*, la *perception
du milieu scolaire*, la *motivation* et l'*absentéisme*. Les *résultats scolaires* se
sont aussi améliorés, mais chez seulement 3 des 5 participants. D'après les
observations, l'approche serait profitable aux deux principaux types de
décrocheurs potentiels, avec des activités plus variées, de plus longue durée
et offertes plus tôt dans le cheminement scolaire. Cette intervention pourrait
être complémentaire à des mesures portant sur le rattrapage des retards scolaires ou sur la solution des problèmes affectifs, sociaux ou familiaux.

Myriam Beauregard et Gaétan Ouellet,
*Development and Testing of a Dropout Prevention Program Centered
around Extracurricular Activities*

ABSTRACT

Although not new, the dropout phenomenon has become a serious social
problem. Since 1985-86, over 35 % of students have left school without
getting a high school diploma. Various programs have been developed in
order to prevent this problem. Few of them, however, are based on the use
of extracurricular activities, which strongly relate to factors of persistence in

school such as self-esteem, perception of the school environment, motivation to study, class attendance, and school success. The purpose of this study is to develop and evaluate a prevention program designed for potential dropouts. Tested among a group of 5 students of Secondary III, the preliminary program has proved to be feasible and efficient. Following its application, four of the five variables under investigation have shown positive changes, i.e. *self-esteem, perception of the school environment, motivation and class attendance.* School marks have also improved but for only 3 participants. The data suggest that this approach could work with the two major types of potential dropouts, provided that the activities are more diversified, over a longer period of time, and offered sooner in the learning path. Such a program could complement other measures like compensatory education or resolution of various psychological, social or family problems.

Myriam BEAUREGARD y Gaétan OUELLET
Elaboración y ensayo de un programa de prevención del abandono escolar orientado en las actividades paraescolares.

RESUMEN

Aún cuando no es nada nuevo, el fenómeno del abandono escolar se ha convertido en un problema social que preocupa. Desde el año escolar 1985-1986, más del 35% de los jóvenes abandonan la escuela sin obtener el diploma de estudios secundarios. Muchos programas han sido puestos en ejecución para prevenir este problema. Pocas intervenciones están basadas sobre la utilización de las actividades paraescolares que están por lo tanto fuertemente asociadas a los factores de persistencia escolar, como la autoestima, la percepción del medio escolar, la motivación en los estudios, la asiduidad a los cursos y el éxito escolar. El presente estudio tiene por objeto elaborar y evaluar un programa de prevención dirigido a los desertores potenciales. Ensayado por un grupo de cinco alumnos de tercer año de secundaria, el programa preliminar se revela realizable y eficaz. Luego del ensayo del programa, cuatro de las cinco variables permitieron percibir cambios positivos en el caso de cuatro sobre cinco participantes; se trata de la autoestima, la percepción del medio escolar, la motivación y el absentismo. Los resultados escolares fueron también mejorados, aunque solamente en el caso de tres de los cinco participantes. Según las observaciones, el enfoque sería conveniente a los dos principales tipos de desertores escolares potenciales, con las actividades más variadas, con duración más larga y ofrecidas lo más pronto durante el camino escolar. Esta intervención podría ser complementaria a las medidas que tratan sobre la recuperación de los retardos escolares o sobre la solución de los problemas afectivos, sociales o familiares.

_____

Tourisme et développement durable : état de situation et perspectives d'avenir

André Barabé

Département des sciences du loisir
Université du Québec à Trois-Rivières

Introduction

Proposé par le « Rapport Brundtland » et discuté lors du « Sommet de la Terre » à Rio, le développement durable est maintenant à l'ordre du jour des agendas nationaux, régionaux et locaux. Le secteur du tourisme n'échappe pas à cette vague de fond. Les colloques, les conférences et les sessions de formation traitant du « développement touristique durable » se multiplient à un rythme accéléré. Mais quel est donc le défi que pose le développement durable pour l'industrie touristique ?

Actuellement, pour les intervenants de l'industrie touristique, il est difficile d'avoir une vision claire de l'état de la situation. Les concepts sont confus, la littérature abondante et les pratiques se réclamant du développement durable présentent de nombreuses contradictions. Cette conjoncture donne toute sa pertinence aux travaux de synthèse qui s'amorcent. C'est précisément dans cette perspective que nous avons entrepris le présent bilan exploratoire.

L'article n'a pas pour but de présenter un bilan exhaustif de la littérature portant sur le thème du développement touristique durable. Une telle entreprise ne peut que difficilement être menée dans le format d'une revue scientifique. Plus modestement, nous avons retenu deux objectifs principaux. Le premier vise à effectuer un effort de synthèse centré sur quelques thèmes dominants dans la littérature consultée. Cet exercice a pour mérite de mettre en lumière des tendances structurantes. Le second objectif, au-delà de l'exercice de synthèse, tend à faire preuve de recul critique en distinguant les avantages et les limites des travaux actuels caractérisant les thèmes dominants analysés. Cette approche présente l'intérêt de contribuer à une meilleure compréhension du virage qui s'amorce en vue de rendre compatible le développement touristique et la conservation de l'environnement. L'enjeu de cette symbiose est de taille : il s'agit, ni plus ni moins, de la prospérité à long terme de cette industrie ! (Inskeep, 1991 ; WWF UK, 1992 ; Sources UNESCO, 1994).

Cet article se subdivise en trois sections. La première partie vise à préciser et comprendre la notion de développement durable. La seconde partie porte sur les rapports entre le développement durable, le tourisme et l'écotourisme. Enfin, de façon plus approfondie, la troisième partie traite de trois tendances récentes dans le domaine du tourisme : les études de cas réussies, les indicateurs du tourisme durable, les codes d'éthique en matière de développement touristique durable.

Développement durable : un cadre de référence global

Une stratégie mondiale

Au cours des deux dernières décennies, nous avons assisté à une mobilisation importante des organismes internationaux et nationaux préoccupés par la mondialisation des problèmes environnementaux. Citons à titre d'exemples, les travaux internationaux suivants :

1980 Stratégie Mondiale de la Conservation. La conservation des ressources vivantes au service du développement durable (UICN, PNUE, WWF).

1987 Commission Mondiale sur l'Environnement et le Développement. Notre avenir à tous (Rapport Brundtland).

1992 Conférence des Nations Unies sur l'Environnement et le Développement à Rio de Janeiro (Sommet de la Terre).

Ces réflexions et ces travaux, consacrés à la recherche d'un équilibre harmonieux des rapports de l'homme avec son environnement, débouchent sur un même constat : la nécessité d'intégrer la conservation au développement. Tous ces organismes œuvrent dans un même but : susciter des changements majeurs dans la façon actuelle de gérer les ressources vivantes en vue d'un développement durable.

Un cadre conceptuel en évolution

Les orientations théoriques et méthodologiques à adopter afin de supporter cette stratégie de développement durable sont présentement en élaboration. Nous nous contenterons, ici, de définir le concept de développement durable et d'en préciser les principes moteurs. Il existe de nombreuses définitions essayant de circonscrire la notion de développement durable. Nous en avons retenu deux (2), émanant des organismes internationaux les plus crédibles.

* « Le développement durable est un développement qui répond aux besoins du présent sans compromettre la capacité des générations futures de répondre aux leurs » (CMED, 1987).

* « Dans la présente stratégie, on entend par développement durable le fait d'améliorer les conditions d'existence des communautés humaines tout en restant dans les limites de la capacité de charge des écosystèmes » (Sauver la Planète, UICN, PNUE, WWF, 1991).

Sur la base de ces définitions, certaines caractéristiques centrales du concept de développement durable peuvent être identifiées. En premier lieu, on rappelle que la croissance et le développement ont pour but primordial la satisfaction des besoins essentiels des communautés humaines. En second lieu, on précise que la compatibilité entre développement et environnement est conditionnelle au maintien de la pérennité des ressources vivantes et au respect de la capacité de charge des écosystèmes. En troisième lieu, on insiste sur l'importance du souci d'équité dans l'utilisation des ressources naturelles entre les générations actuelles et les générations futures. En quatrième lieu, on constate que la philosophie du développement durable fait appel à une nouvelle orientation de notre pensée et implique des changements de valeurs, d'attitudes et de comportements. Voilà les principes-clés qui animent la philosophie du développement durable.

Développement durable : tourisme et écotourisme

Éléments de problématique

Le patrimoine naturel et culturel constitue la matière première de l'industrie touristique. Pourtant, les entrepreneurs touristiques sont souvent accusés d'altérer de façon irréversible ce capital patrimonial. Des projets mal planifiés, une recherche de rentabilité à court terme et une exploitation trop intensive des ressources portent atteinte à l'intégrité des milieux physiques et humains mis en valeur. Ces impacts sont bien documentés et largement diffusés dans la littérature scientifique. Pour bien des observateurs, le risque qui menace l'industrie touristique équivaut à « tuer la poule aux œufs d'or ».

Cette critique fort répandue mérite certes d'être nuancée. Cette opposition, quelque peu manichéenne, entre développement touristique et protection de l'environnement tend à s'atténuer. La mise en œuvre récente de divers projets montre que le tourisme peut également être un outil de protection du milieu. Ce changement dans les pratiques peut à la fois résulter d'une manifestation de peur ou de sagesse.

Chose certaine, un environnement détérioré fait fuir les touristes. L'analyse du comportement des touristes montre que la qualité du produit est devenu un souci majeur des voyageurs exigeant une offre plus personnalisée et une qualité supérieure de l'environnement global. L'opposition fait de plus en plus place à la convergence. Le même constat touche à la fois les touristes, les communautés d'accueil, les entrepreneurs touristiques et l'État. La réconciliation des intérêts économiques, environnementaux et éthiques s'impose pour assurer la survie et la prospérité de l'industrie touristique dans le marché mondial de demain.

Cette tendance traduit bien les efforts récents de l'industrie en vue de s'engager dans la voie du développement touristique durable. On reconnaît que pour être durable, le développement doit prendre appui sur la conservation. Cette compatibilité entre développement et environnement est conditionnelle au maintien de la pérennité des ressources. Plus encore, on y trouve l'idée que la croissance économique peut contribuer à la conservation de l'environnement en apportant une partie de ses fruits à la protection du patrimoine naturel et culturel. Cette croissance peut se faire en diminuant la consommation des ressources et la dégradation de l'environnement tout en augmentant la rentabilité de leur utilisation. À partir de l'analyse de thématiques émergentes, notre but consiste à montrer comment ces intentions se traduisent dans les pratiques de l'industrie touristique.

Écotourisme : définitions et principes

On assiste présentement à la promotion d'une forme de tourisme qui se veut plus respectueuse du patrimoine naturel et humain des zones visitées. (Blangy, 1993 ; TÉOROS, 1993). Ce tourisme alternatif est habituellement désigné sous le vocable « écotourisme ». Ce néologisme exprime l'idée d'une symbiose entre écologie et tourisme.

Il est souhaitable de disposer d'une définition qui délimite clairement le champ de l'écotourisme. En l'absence de balises précises, cette notion risque de devenir un fourre-tout servant d'étiquetage à n'importe quel produit touristique associé aux milieux naturels. Dans cette perspective, nous proposons de considérer les définitions qui suivent, élaborées par des individus ou des organismes qui font autorité en la matière.

- « ... une forme de tourisme qui consiste à visiter des zones naturelles relativement intactes ou peu perturbées, dans le but précis d'étudier et d'admirer le paysage et les plantes et animaux sauvages qu'elles abritent, de même que toute manifestation culturelle (passée et présente), observable dans ces zones » (Hector Ceballos-Lascurain, 1983).

- « L'écotourisme est une expérience de voyage pleine nature révélatrice qui contribue à la préservation de l'écosystème tout en respectant l'intégrité des collectivités d'accueil », (Conseil consultatif canadien de l'environnement, 1992).

Sur la base de ces définitions, il est possible de dégager quelques caractéristiques centrales du concept d'écotourisme. En premier lieu, on fait référence à une expérience de voyages nature de grande qualité intégrant des dimensions cognitives et affectives intenses. En second lieu, ces expériences sont principalement vécues au sein d'environnements naturels peu perturbés et favorisent des comportements susceptibles de maintenir la qualité des milieux biophysiques intacte. En troisième lieu, les écotouristes se montrent soucieux du respect et de l'intégrité des collectivités d'accueil. En quatrième lieu, les écotouristes se distinguent par leur forte préoccupation de la compréhension des manifestations naturelles et culturelles propres aux zones visitées ainsi que pour leur sensibilité à l'éthique environnementale. Finalement, l'écotourisme peut créer des retombées économiques intéressantes pour les collectivités locales et régionales. Dans cette perspective, l'écotourisme est perçu comme un moyen de protéger l'environnement tout en stimulant l'économie des communautés d'accueil qui protègent leur capital nature. L'écotourisme a le mérite de faire comprendre aux collectivités locales qu'il est souvent économiquement avantageux de préserver son environnement. (Barabé, Bourgeois, Trudel, 1995).

Potentiels et menaces de l'écotourisme

Le tourisme de masse a mauvaise presse, car on lui reproche d'entraîner une dégradation importante du patrimoine naturel et culturel des communautés d'accueil. L'écotourisme est présenté comme une forme distincte de tourisme. Par opposition, il est qualifié de nouveau tourisme respectueux de l'environnement. Pour certains, l'écotourisme est considéré comme une manifestation concrète de la philosophie du développement durable, voire même un des indicateurs pour en mesurer la réussite. Cependant, il ne nous apparaît pas souhaitable de présenter l'écotourisme comme la panacée capable de faire contrepoids au tourisme de masse . Il ne serait pas avisé, pour la prospérité à long terme de l'industrie touristique, de faire de l'écotourisme un alibi qui retarderait la responsabilisation des entrepreneurs touristiques en matière d'environnement. C'est à l'ensemble de l'industrie tourisme, dans toutes ses composantes, qu'il appartient de définir de nouvelles pratiques pour rendre possible une meilleure intégration à l'environnement.

Le développement de l'écotourisme repose sur la croissance de la demande pour la visite et la connaissance de milieux naturels de qualité, restés dans un état relativement sauvage. Cette demande constitue une force externe puissante capable de décider différents niveaux de gouvernement et différentes collectivités de préserver les joyaux de leur patrimoine naturel.

Cette demande du public est renforcée par des incitatifs économiques associés au développement des activités écotouristiques. Cette double motivation résulte présentement dans la protection de plusieurs sites parmi les plus beaux et les plus précieux au monde. Le développement de l'écotourisme en Afrique de l'Est s'inscrit dans cette perspective. Cette orientation est également en émergence en Amérique Centrale et en Amérique du Sud (Boo, 1990).

Le développement de l'écotourisme possède cependant sa contrepartie. En effet, n'est-on pas en train de répéter la légende du cheval de Troie, en introduisant volontairement, au sein des milieux naturels les plus sensibles et les plus vulnérables, les acteurs qui ouvrent la porte à la destruction du milieu même que l'on voulait protéger ? Les parcs demeurent l'un des lieux privilégiés pour la pratique de l'écotourisme. Une croissance de la fréquentation touristique, dans les zones les plus fragiles, crée une menace interne incompatible avec la mission de protection des parcs nationaux. En conséquence, on peut anticiper certaines mesures de contrôle et de limitation des activités écotouristiques dans certains lieux (Hetherington, Inskeep, McIntyre, 1992 ; OMT, 1992 ; Barabé, 1995). Par ailleurs, la menace s'avère plus inquiétante pour les territoires naturels adjacents et les zones naturelles non protégées où se pratique l'écotourisme. Dans ce dernier cas, non seulement l'écotourisme ne contribuera pas à solutionner les impacts environnementaux du tourisme de masse, mais il risque au contraire de créer de nouvelles menaces et de nouvelles destructions parmi les aires écologiques les plus précieuses au monde ! En devenant un site écotouristique, là où le randonneur individuel ne laissait derrière lui que l'empreinte de ses pas, des centaines de visiteurs sont en train d'aimer la nature jusqu'au point de la faire mourir... Pour reprendre le titre même d'un document récemment produit sur ce sujet par la Fédération des Parcs Naturels et Nationaux d'Europe, s'agirait-il d'une passion fatale ? (FPNNE, 1993).

Études de cas : apprendre par la pratique

L'étude de cas, comme moyen d'apprentissage, est une méthode largement utilisée dans différentes disciplines académiques et plusieurs milieux professionnels. Ce procédé, au cours des trois dernières décennies, a été employé dans différents secteurs des études en loisir et en tourisme. Cette approche connaît présentement un regain d'intérêt dans les milieux professionnels reliés au développement touristique durable.

Exemples de cas réussis

Examinons de plus près trois (3) de ces recueils d'études de cas récemment publiés en lien avec le tourisme, l'environnement et le développement durable.

Le tableau 1 précise les projets et les pays qui ont fait l'objet de ces analyses. Les deux premières références ont pour sujet les aires naturelles protégées en Amérique Centrale et en Europe. La référence suivante met en lumière des cas appliqués à différents secteurs de l'industrie touristique au Canada.

En premier lieu, notre attention se porte sur un ouvrage qui a connu beaucoup de succès et qui traite des potentiels et des embûches associés à l'écotourisme (Boo, 1990, volume 1 et volume 2). Le volume 1 aborde les liens entre le tourisme et les espaces naturels protégés. L'analyse des impacts du tourisme de nature sur les parcs ainsi que sur les milieux locaux, régionaux, nationaux et internationaux forme le noyau central du texte. Enfin, le document se termine sur des conclusions et des recommandations visant à appuyer les stratégies de développement pour le tourisme de nature. Le volume 2 présente et analyse dix (10) études de cas, portant sur des aires naturelles protégées, illustrant l'implication de cinq (5) pays dans le développement de l'écotourisme. Ces pays, principalement d'Amérique Latine, sont les suivants : Bélize, Costa Rica, République Dominicaine, République de l'Équateur, Mexique. Tous ces cas ayant une même structure d'information, l'auteure en dégage d'intéressantes comparaisons quant au développement du tourisme de nature.

En second lieu, citons le récent document édité par la Fédération des Parcs Naturels et Nationaux d'Europe en lien avec le tourisme durable (FNNPE, 1993). Ce document se compose des principales parties suivantes : aires protégées et tourisme en Europe, lignes directrices pour la gestion des aires protégées dans la perspective du développement touristique durable, le développement touristique durable en lien avec certains aires sensibles (Méditerranée, bloc de l'Est, aires côtières, zones humides, zones montagneuses), des recommandations pratiques valables aussi bien pour le secteur du tourisme que pour les gestionnaires des espaces protégés. Enfin, seize (16) études de cas, se rapportant principalement à des parcs, sont intégrées dans les différents chapitres du texte. Ces études de cas sont intéressantes par leur grande diversité (Angleterre, Australie, Espagne, France, Hongrie, Roumanie, Suède, etc.), mais elles demeurent cependant peu approfondies. Le sommaire et les recommandations finales présentent toutefois beaucoup d'intérêt et de pertinence.

TABLEAU 1

Recueil d'études de cas

	– Cockscomb Bassin Wildlife Sanctuary – Crooked Tree Wildlife Sanctuary	Belize
	– Monteverde Cloud Forest Reserve – Poas National Park	Costa Rica
Ecotourism : The Potentials and Pitfalls (Boo, 1990)	– Emerald Pool – Trafalgar Falls	République Dominicaine
	– Cotopaxi National Park – Galapagos National Park	République de l'Équateur
	– Izta-Pepo National Park – Canon del Sumidero National Park	Mexique
	– Parc national de la Vanoise	France
Sustainable Tourism in Europe's Nature and National Parks (FNNPE, 1993)	– Peak National Park	Angleterre
	– Hortobagy National Park	Hongrie
	– Sierra Norte Natural Park	Espagne
	– Hohe Tauern National Park	Australie
	– 11 autres études de cas	Hongrie, Roumanie, etc.
	– British Airways	Angleterre
	– Château Whistler	Canada
	– Canadian Restaurant and Food Association	Canada
The Greening of Tourism (Hawkes and Williams, 1993)	– Hôtel Ucliva	Suisse
	– Arctic Edge Tours	Canada
	– Maple Leaf Adventures	Canada
	– Trail of the Great Bear	Canada et États-Unis
	– Parc National Marin du Saguenay	Canada
	– Great Barrier Reef	Australie
	– Redberry Pelican Project	Canada

Le dernier document, produit en coopération par « The Centre for Tourism Policy and Research, Simon Fraser University » et Tourisme Canada, compte dix (10) études de cas illustrant des pratiques du développement touristique durable. Les cas sont classés sous trois principales rubriques : la gestion respectueuse des ressources naturelles et des économies d'énergie, le tourisme d'aventure durable, la protection et la mise en valeur du patrimoine (Hawkes and Williams, 1993). Les cas présentés illustrent diverses réponses et innovations développées dans différents secteurs de l'industrie touristique afin de répondre au défi du développement touristique durable : transporteur aérien, hôtellerie, restauration, opérateurs de tours, aires naturelles protégées, etc.

Portées et limites des études de cas

D'une part, la méthode des études de cas, appliquée au développement touristique durable, présente plusieurs avantages. En raison de son caractère empirique, fondé sur l'illustration d'expériences vécues et validées, cette approche est grandement appréciée par les intervenants de l'industrie touristique. Face à la rapidité des changements actuels, le partage des idées utiles et l'examen de modèles alternatifs constituent une source d'inspiration non-négligeable pour les gestionnaires. Enfin, les efforts et les réussites des entreprises touristiques, ayant développé des pratiques harmonieuses avec l'environnement, méritent d'être valorisés et largement diffusés.

D'autre part, il faut rappeler certaines limites de la méthode des études de cas. En premier lieu, précisons que la puissance explicative de cette approche repose sur la cohérence des composantes et sur la profondeur de l'analyse du cas. Un traitement trop superficiel diminue la valeur de l'enseignement retiré. En second lieu, il faut rappeler la faible capacité de généralisation des études de cas à d'autres populations et à d'autres contextes. Chaque pays et chaque région présentent des conditions géographiques, sociales, économiques et politiques différentes. Une imitation fidèle d'une réussite étrangère n'est pas une garantie de succès local. Les enseignements diffusés exigent une transposition et une adaptation à ses propres besoins. En troisième lieu, soulignons qu'il est regrettable que certains recueils d'études de cas se limitent à une phase descriptive, sans dégager les lignes de force et les leçons à retirer des expériences illustrées. Il est souhaitable de dégager les éléments communs entre les différentes études de cas permettant de faire ressortir les idées maîtresses et les pratiques innovatrices supportant le développement touristique durable.

Les indicateurs du tourisme durable

L'initiative d'élaborer des indicateurs du tourisme durable a pour origine une proposition du Canada, adressée au Comité de l'environnement de l'Organisation mondiale du tourisme (Manning, avril 1992). L'esprit de la proposition s'inspire des besoins pour les décideurs de posséder des balises capables de guider les gestionnaires touristiques vers une offre environnementale de qualité. L'OMT a accepté la proposition du Canada et a créé un groupe de travail international chargé de mener à bien ce processus.

Le processus d'élaboration des indicateurs

Pour répondre aux besoins des décideurs, il a été recommandé d'adopter une triple approche dans l'élaboration des indicateurs du tourisme durable : des indices dérivés, des indicateurs de niveau national, des indicateurs de niveau local (Manning, 1992 ; International Working Group on Indicators of Sustainable Tourism, 1993 ; Hawkes and Williams, 1993).

En premier lieu, le groupe de travail a suggéré de retenir deux indices dérivés : un indice d'intérêt de la destination et un indice des niveaux de perturbation. Ces indices dérivés ont pour fonction de jouer le rôle d'indicateurs d'alerte servant à repérer les zones vulnérables actuelles et potentielles. Ces signaux avertisseurs permettront de déclencher un processus de suivi de l'évolution de l'état et du niveau de perturbation des ressources naturelles et culturelles dans le temps. Le mérite premier de ces indices dérivés n'est pas l'exactitude quantitative. Ces indices représentent un outil de diagnostic qui doit être complété par des indicateurs plus mesurables. C'est précisément le rôle des indicateurs nationaux et locaux.

Au niveau national, le groupe de travail propose dix-sept (17) indicateurs. Pour chaque indicateur, les informations suivantes sont fournies : la description de l'indicateur, l'utilité de l'indicateur, la disponibilité à court ou à long terme des données de base, et des observations concernant la priorité et l'utilisation de l'indicateur. Le tableau 2 présente la liste des dix-sept (17) indicateurs ainsi qu'un exemple du type de mesure anticipée.

La liste sélective des indicateurs locaux compte quinze (15) éléments. Pour chaque indicateur, le Groupe international de travail précise les renseignements suivants : description de l'indicateur en lien avec l'usage local, l'utilité de l'indicateur pour la prise de décisions concrètes, la logistique de production et d'acquisition des données locales, des observations concernant la priorité et l'emploi de l'indicateur.

TABLEAU 2

Liste d'indicateurs provisoires de niveau national *

Indicateurs	Exemples de mesure **
A. Zone protégée :	- % du territoire national
B. Espaces menacés :	- indicateur de remplacement = espèces menacées
C. Protection culturelle :	- % de sites culturels protégés
D. Intensité de voyage :	- nombre de voyages intérieurs et internationaux par habitant
E. Intensité d'utilisation :	- nombre d'endroits classés comme points chauds en raison du niveau d'utilisation, des perturbations ou de la dégradation
F. Consommation des ressources essentielles :	- eau/énergie (consommation par touriste, lit ou nuitée)
G. Rapport touristes/résidents :	- annuel et en période d'affluence
H. Effet sanitaire/social :	- % de touristes inculpés/victimes de délits pouvant être signalés
I. Contrôle par des étrangers ou des non-résidents :	- % d'équipements touristiques dont des étrangers ou des non-résidents sont propriétaires
J. Densité de développement :	- mètres carrés de site par touriste (moyenne/ période de pointe)
K. Indice de stabilité politique :	- indice du PNUD
L. Normes d'environnement :	- % d'eaux usées déversées sans traitement dans les cours d'eau et/ou la mer
M. Utilisation des capacités d'infrastructure :	- eau, eaux usées, énergie, transports
N. Emploi dans le tourisme :	- % de gens du pays employés dans le secteur touristique à chaque niveau
O. Aménagement de l'environnement :	- existence d'une stratégie nationale de respect de l'environnement
P. Procédure d'examen des problèmes d'environnement :	- existence d'une procédure légale d'étude d'impact sur l'environnement pour tous les projets
Q. Fuite de devises :	- % de devises provenant du tourisme international qui quitte le pays

*   *Source :* OMT. *Rapport sur les indicateurs environnementaux,* 1993
** Il ne s'agit pas de la liste exhaustive, mais d'exemples choisis à titre d'illustration

Portées et limites du processus d'élaboration des indicateurs

Rappelons brièvement les principaux avantages reliés au processus d'élaboration des indicateurs du développement touristique durable entrepris par le Groupe de travail international. Premièrement, en étant parrainée par un organisme international tel l'OMT, la démarche acquiert plus de crédibilité et favorise davantage l'implication des pays membres. Deuxièmement, la sélection des indicateurs à partir des besoins de connaissances des décideurs confère à la démarche un caractère pratique et opérationnel attendu par les intervenants des entreprises touristiques. Troisièmement, l'adaptation des indicateurs aux échelles nationales et locales est susceptible de créer une adhésion plus étendue des intervenants touristiques à cette démarche. Quatrièmement, les indicateurs présentent l'intérêt de fournir une information synthétique facile à consulter et à interpréter. Enfin, les indicateurs proposés offrent des balises intéressantes pour planifier, mettre en œuvre et évaluer des pratiques touristiques dans une perspective de développement durable.

D'autre part, il importe de rappeler certaines limites du processus actuel d'élaboration des indicateurs du tourisme durable. Premièrement, les indices dérivés seront difficiles à mettre au point. Leur caractère arbitraire exigera l'accord des pays membres à la fois sur le contenu, la pondération et le mode de présentation des indices. Deuxièmement, pour les indicateurs nationaux et locaux, l'embûche principale demeure le temps et les ressources nécessaires pour produire et compiler les données requises à l'élaboration des indicateurs. Pour certains pays ou pour certaines régions, le défi risque de ne pouvoir être relevé. Enfin, l'élaboration de certains indicateurs forcera l'apport de modifications dans la collecte des données de certains pays, afin d'assurer cette homogénéité et cette comparabilité qui caractérisent l'utilisation d'indicateurs nationaux et internationaux.

Éthique et développement touristique durable

On constate présentement une valorisation de la responsabilisation et de l'engagement volontaire des entreprises touristiques envers la protection de l'environnement et l'éducation des consommateurs. Cet engagement dans la voie de l'autorégulation s'exprime bien par cette tendance au développement de codes d'éthique par les organismes touristiques internationaux, nationaux, régionaux et locaux. Considérant l'enjeu et l'ampleur que prennent le développement des codes d'éthique, ce sujet mérite d'être davantage approfondi.

Conception et application des codes d'éthique

On remarque présentement une implication notable de l'industrie touristique dans cette voie de l'éthique environnementale. Plusieurs codes de déontologie, élaborés à l'intention des voyageurs, existent depuis fort longtemps. Cependant, la majorité des codes d'éthique actuellement diffusés sont de conception récente. Ceux-ci peuvent être classifiés en trois catégories : ceux s'adressant aux voyageurs individuels, ceux s'adressant aux associations de tourisme, et ceux élaborés pour des secteurs spécifiques de l'industrie (Hawkes and Williams, 1993).

Les codes, s'adressant aux voyageurs individuels, fournissent des lignes de conduite à adopter dans les relations visiteurs-visités. Ils ont pour but d'inciter à faire preuve de respect envers les coutumes et les traditions locales des populations hôtes. Ils favorisent également une réduction des impacts sur les ressources naturelles et l'achat de produits respectueux de l'environnement, etc. À grande échelle, on retrouve les exemples suivants : « American Society of Travel Agents, Traveller Environmental Guidelines ; National Audubon Society Travel Ethic » (UNEP, 1992, 1995 ; Hawkes and Williams, 1993). À une échelle plus nationale, on note l'existence du code d'éthique pour les touristes de l'Association de l'industrie touristique du Canada et « The Himalayan Tourist Code » (UNEP, 1992, 1995). La figure 1 reproduit le code d'éthique et les directives générales élaborés par l'Association de l'industrie touristique du Canada dans le cadre de la Table ronde nationale sur l'environnement et l'économie.

D'émergence plus récente, les codes développés par les associations de l'industrie touristique visent à fournir des lignes directrices pour leurs membres. Ces codes couvrent un large éventail de considérations environnementales. Ce large spectre a pour but de répondre aux divers intérêts de leurs membres affiliés. Ces codes couvrent une grande variété de sujets : sécurité, gestion des déchets, évaluation environnementale, sensibilisation environnementale des employés et des visiteurs, consultation des communautés locales, respect du patrimoine local, mise en valeur des habitats naturels, implantation des équipements dans le respect de l'environnement, etc. Certains codes ont une vocation internationale : c'est le cas pour « The World Travel and Tourism Council's Environmental Guidelines ». D'autres codes ont une vocation davantage régionale, tels « the Pacific Area Tourism Association, Code for Environmentally Responsible Tourism ; et « The Travel Industry Association of Canada Codes » (UNEP, 1992 ; Hawkes and Williams, 1993 ; Association de l'industrie touristique du Canada, 1992).

Enfin, une troisième catégorie de codes d'éthique met l'accent sur des secteurs spécifiques de l'industrie touristique. De conception opérationnelle, ils visent à être utiles dans la gestion quotidienne des entreprises telles : les lignes aériennes, les chaînes d'hôtel et autres. Les thèmes abordés ont pour but de guider les intervenants vers l'adoption des meilleures pratiques environnementales : application des directives volontaires préconisées par le Protocole national sur l'emballage, achats de préférence en vrac, recyclage, compostage, réduction des déchets, conservation de l'eau et de l'énergie, achats de produits respectueux de l'environnement, éducation environnementale, etc. Les exemples suivants sont régulièrement cités : « Cruise Operators to Antartica Guidelines, Code of Conduct for Commercial Tour Operations in Gwaï Haanas/South Moresby, British Columbia » (Conseil consultatif canadien de l'environnement, 1992 ; Hawkes and Williams,

Figure 1

Code d'éthique de l'Association de l'industrie touristique du Canada [*]

L'industrie touristique canadienne reconnaît que la durabilité à long terme du tourisme au pays est fonction de la prestation de produits touristiques de haute qualité ainsi que du maintien du caractère hospitalier de ses employés et des communautés d'accueil. Elle reconnaît également être tributaire d'une utilisation rationnelle et de la conservation des ressources naturelles ; de la protection et de la mise en valeur de l'environnement ainsi que de la préservation des ressources culturelles, historiques et esthétiques. De ce fait, par ses politiques, plans, décisions et mesures, l'industrie entend :

1. Rechercher l'excellence en offrant des expériences de tourisme et d'accueil de qualité par l'entremise d'un personnel motivé et bienveillant.

2. Encourager les clients, les employés, les intervenants et les communautés d'accueil à apprécier et à respecter le patrimoine naturel, culturel et esthétique.

3. Respecter les valeurs et aspirations des communautés d'accueil et veiller à ce que les services et les installations contribuent à leur identité collective, à leur fierté, à leurs valeurs esthétiques ainsi qu'à la qualité de vie de leurs habitants.

4. S'employer à un développement touristique conciliant objectifs économiques avec protection et mise en valeur du patrimoine naturel, culturel et esthétique.

5. Utiliser à bon escient l'ensemble des ressources naturelles, gérer les déchets en respectant l'environnement et tâcher d'éliminer ou de réduire la pollution sous toutes ses formes.

6. Concourir, avec les membres du secteur touristique et les autres industries, à l'avènement du développement durable et à l'amélioration de la qualité de vie de tous les Canadiens.

7. Aider les touristes en quête d'une meilleure connaissance et d'une appréciation véritable de la nature et de leurs voisins du village planétaire. Collaborer ou participer à des organisations nationales et internationales pour mettre le tourisme au service de l'édification d'un monde meilleur.

Directives générales pour l'industrie

1. Concilier les objectifs économiques avec la conservation des ressources et les valeurs environnementales, sociales, culturelles et esthétiques au moment d'élaborer des énoncés de perspectives d'avenir, des énoncés de mission, des politiques, des plans et des processus décisionnels.

2. Permettre aux touristes de vivre une expérience de haute qualité apte à mieux leur faire apprécier notre patrimoine naturel et culturel.

[*] Association de l'industrie touristique du Canada ; Table ronde nationale sur l'environnement et l'économie

FIGURE 1 (SUITE)

Code d'éthique de l'Association de l'industrie touristique du Canada [*]

Faciliter, dans la mesure du possible, des rapports visiteurs-visités positifs ainsi que répondre aux besoins particuliers des touristes issus des divers segments de la société, dont les jeunes, les personnes d'âge mûr et les handicapés.

3. Offrir des produits et services touristiques conformes aux valeurs de la communauté d'accueil et au milieu environnant. Rehausser et mettre en valeur le caractère esthétique du paysage, le génie du lieu, l'identité collective et les avantages que procure le tourisme aux communautés d'accueil.

4. Concevoir, mettre au point et commercialiser des produits, des installations et des infrastructures touristiques de manière à concilier les objectifs économiques avec le maintien et la mise en valeur des écosystèmes ainsi que des ressources culturelles et esthétiques. En arriver à une planification intégrée englobant le développement et le marketing touristiques.

5. Protéger et mettre en valeur les ressources naturelles, historiques, culturelles et esthétiques de manière à préserver cet héritage pour les générations actuelles et futures. Encourager la création de parcs, de réserves naturelles intégrales et d'aires protégées.

6. Mettre en pratique et encourager la conservation et l'utilisation rationnelle des ressources naturelles, notamment l'eau et l'énergie.

7. Appliquer et prôner une gestion des déchets et des matériaux conciliable avec l'environnement, y compris la réduction à la source, la réutilisation et le recyclage. Réduire, voire éliminer tout rejet polluant dégradant l'air, l'eau, les sols, la flore et la faune.

8. Soutenir les efforts de sensibilisation du public à l'environnement et aux ressources culturelles par des initiatives de marketing.

9. Encourager les efforts qui, en recherche et en éducation, accordent une large place à l'éthique, à la préservation du patrimoine, aux communautés d'accueil ainsi qu'à la base de connaissances nécessaires pour pérenniser les fondements économiques, sociaux, culturels et environnementaux de l'industrie touristique.

10. Favoriser une sensibilisation accrue du public à l'importance économique, sociale, culturelle et environnementale du tourisme.

11. Concourir, avec l'industrie et les secteurs connexes, à protéger et à mettre en valeur l'environnement, à conserver les ressources, à harmoniser le développement et à rehausser la qualité de vie dans les communautés d'accueil.

12. Épouser le concept « d'une Terre, un monde » et collaborer avec divers pays et organismes internationaux au développement d'une industrie touristique qui soit socialement, écologiquement et économiquement responsable.

1993). Plus près de nous, Pêches et Océans Canada a formulé des Directives s'adressant aux plaisanciers et aux capitaines d'excursions pratiquant la navigation à proximité des baleines dans le golfe du Saint-Laurent.

Portées et limites des codes d'éthique actuels

L'élaboration des codes d'éthique présentent plusieurs avantages pour l'industrie touristique (D'Amore, 1993 ; Hawkes and Williams, 1993 ; Wight, 1993). Premièrement, les codes développés et diffusés par les grandes associations de l'industrie rejoignent un nombre considérable d'intervenants. Par exemple, le code d'éthique et les directives générales sur le développement touristique durable, récemment développés par l'Association de l'industrie touristique du Canada, seront possiblement mis en œuvre par plus de 60 000 entreprises canadiennes reliées au secteur du tourisme. Deuxièmement, l'expérience des compagnies engagées dans ce processus montre qu'il existe de réels bénéfices à agir de façon responsable en matière d'environnement. La chaîne hôtelière Inter-Continentale estime à dix millions de dollars récupérés, annuellement, depuis l'implantation d'importantes mesures d'efficacité énergétiques. De même, la chaîne d'hôtel Hyatt estime épargner plus de trois millions annuellement par suite de la mise en œuvre de son programme d'information environnementale et de recyclage (D'Amore, 1993). Troisièmement, le rayonnement des codes d'éthique et des mesures environnementales adoptées est bénéfique pour l'image corporative et le marketing des entreprises. Les enquêtes menées au Canada, aux États-Unis et en Europe continuent de montrer que l'environnement est une préoccupation importante parmi les consommateurs et confirment leur désir d'acheter des produits et services de compagnies responsables en matière d'environnement.

D'autre part, il faut aussi rappeler les limites des codes d'éthique et éviter de les considérer comme une panacée. Premièrement, rappelons que ces codes se situent dans un contexte d'autorégulation et n'ont qu'une valeur incitative. Il s'agit d'un engagement volontaire préconisant une autorégulation individuelle et collective. Deuxièmement, les mesures de contrôle, visant à vérifier l'application et la mise en œuvre des codes d'éthique, sont présentement quasi inexistantes. Par ailleurs, l'initiative de récompenser et de publiciser le mérite des organismes faisant preuve d'une application exemplaire des codes d'éthique constitue une formule intéressante de renforcement positif, allant dans le sens du contrôle endogène. Troisièmement, il faut se méfier des conséquences reliées aux entreprises qui affichent leur adhésion aux codes d'éthique exclusivement pour se donner bonne conscience et améliorer leur image publique. L'observation de contradictions, entre le contenu des codes d'éthique et les pratiques réelles des entreprises touristiques, risque d'entacher la crédibilité de cette opération auprès du public.

Conclusion

Pour conclure sur les rapports entre développement durable, tourisme et écotourisme, nous insistons sur quelques tendances susceptibles de présenter de l'intérêt pour les intervenants touristiques .

Premièrement, le tourisme doit être environnementalement durable pour être économiquement durable. Un environnement de qualité constitue l'assise de base du développement touristique durable. Deuxièmement, des bénéfices économiques immédiats sont reliés à certaines pratiques du développement touristique durable. Les entreprises engagées dans cette voie affirment qu'une réduction des coûts d'exploitation est directement associée à la diminution des déchets, à la pratique du recyclage, à l'utilisation efficace de l'énergie et des ressources. Troisièmement, un « monitoring » des pratiques innovatrices actuelles dans l'industrie touristique s'avère nécessaire afin de déterminer à long terme les bénéfices et les coûts reliés aux décisions du développement touristique durable. Cette observation dans le temps des modifications opérées peut servir à définir les pratiques touristiques à préconiser pour le 21e siècle. Quatrièmement, plusieurs cas montrent l'importance du partenariat et des alliances entre les agences gouvernementales, les entrepreneurs privés, les communautés locales et régionales. Cette collaboration permet de constituer et d'accéder à un réseau d'informations, d'expertises, d'expériences innovatrices bénéfiques à tous les participants. Cinquièmement, une implication informée et enthousiaste des employés semble constituer un élément critique dans l'introduction et la mise en œuvre des pratiques durables au sein des entreprises touristiques. Le personnel, par son contact quotidien avec les touristes et les lieux de pratique, représente une importante source d'idées novatrices et d'actions pratiques en vue de concilier tourisme et environnement. Sixièmement, l'étude de certains cas permet de rappeler l'importance de l'éducation environnementale et de l'interprétation. Comparés aux résultats tangibles des actions entreprises en matière de gestion des déchets, les effets de l'éducation environnementale peuvent apparaître nébuleux à court terme. Toutefois, l'éducation environnementale, favorisant les changements d'attitudes et de comportements, s'avère indispensable au développement d'une éthique environnementale soutenant une utilisation durable des ressources naturelles et culturelles au sein des zones touristiques.

Bibliographie

Barabé, A., Bourgeois, J.-C., Trudel, R. (1995). « Dans la vallée du fleuve Saint-Laurent. L'écotourisme au lac Saint-Pierre », *Écodécision* 15(1) : 91-94.

Barabé, A. (1995). « Parcs, tourisme et développement durable », *TÉOROS*, 14(1) : 8-12.

Blangy, S. (Ed.). (1993). « Tourisme et environnement : du tourisme de nature à l'écotourisme ». *Les Cahiers Espaces*. Paris : Éditions Touristiques Européennes.

Boo E. (1990). *Ecotourism : The Potentials and Pitfalls*. Volume 1. Washington, D.C. : World Wildlife Fund with the support of the U.S. Agency for International Development, 71 p.

Commission mondiale sur l'environnement et le développement (1987). *Notre avenir à tous*. Genève : Éditions du Fleuve.

Conférence mondiale sur l'environnement et le développement (1993). *Déclaration de Rio sur l'environnement et le développement. Action 21.* France : Publication des Nations Unies.

D'Amore, L. (1993). « A Code of Ethics and Guidelines for Socially and Environmentally Responsible Tourism ». *Journal of Travel Research*, p. 64 - 66.

Federation of Nature and National Parks of Europe (1993). *Loving them to Death ? Sustainable Tourism in Europe's Nature and National Parks.* Belgium : FNNPE

Gouvernement du Canada, Conseil consultatif canadien de l'environnement (1992). *L'écotourisme au Canada*. Ottawa : Approvisionnements et Services Canada, 42 p.

Hawkes, S., Williams, P. (Eds.). (1993). *The Greening of Tourism : from Principles to Practice*. A Casebook of Best Environmental Practice in Tourism. Simon Fraser University : Centre for Tourism Policy and Research, 104 p.

Hetherington, A., Inskeep, E., McIntyre, G. (1992). *Sustainable Tourism Development : Guide Local Planners*. Madrid : World Tourism Organization.

Inskeep, E. (1991). *Tourism Planning : An Integrated and Sustainable Development Approach*. New York : Van Nostrand Reinhold, 508 p.

International Working Group (1993). *Indicators for the Sustainable Management of Tourism*. Report of the International Working Group on Indicators of Sustainable Tourism to the Environment Committee World Tourism Organization (OMT).

OMT (1992). *Les principes directeurs de l'aménagement des parcs nationaux et des zones protégées pour le tourisme*. Madrid : Organisation mondiale du tourisme (OMT).

Sources Unesco (1994). *Tourisme et nature : le face-à-face*. Sources Unesco, no. 55. Paris : Organisation des Nations Unies pour l'éducation, la science et la culture.

Téoros (1993). « Colloque National sur l'écotourisme. Actes du colloque ». Pohénégamook Santé Plein Air, novembre 1992. *Téoros* Collection Colloques et Congrès, n° 4, 58 p.

UICN, PNUE, WWF (1991). *Sauver la planète. Stratégie pour l'avenir de la vie.* Suisse : UICN, PNUE, WWF.

UNION INTERNATIONALE POUR LA CONSERVATION DE LA NATURE ET DE SES RESSOURCES (1980). *Stratégie mondiale de la conservation. La conservation des ressources vivantes au service du développement durable.* Suisse : UICN, PNUE, WWF.

UNITED NATIONS ENVIRONMENT PROGRAMME (1995). *Environmental Codes of Conduct for Tourism,* France : UNEP IE/PAC.

UNITED NATIONS ENVIRONMENT PROGRAMME (1992). *Sustainable Tourism Development,* France : UNEP IE/PAC.

WWF UK (1992). *Beyond the Green Horizon. A Discussion Paper on Principles for Sustainable Tourism.* London : World Wide Fund For Nature.

André BARABÉ
*Tourisme et développement durable :
état de situation et perspectives d'avenir*

RÉSUMÉ

Le développement durable est à l'ordre du jour des agendas nationaux, régionaux et locaux. La première partie du texte vise à préciser l'origine et la notion de développement durable. La seconde partie s'amorce à partir de l'interrogation suivante : comment se pose la problématique du développement durable pour l'industrie touristique ? Les éléments de problématique examinés seront les suivants : la compatibilité entre le tourisme de masse et les aires naturelles protégées, ainsi que l'écotourisme comme outil de protection. La troisième partie, fondée sur une revue de la littérature scientifique et professionnelle, traite des tendances et des pratiques récentes mises en œuvre par l'industrie touristique pour appliquer concrètement la philosophie du développement durable. Les principaux thèmes retenus sont les suivants : l'apprentissage par la pratique au moyen de la diffusion des cas de réussites conciliant conservation et développement touristique, le développement d'indicateurs du tourisme durable, le développement des codes d'éthique.

André BARABÉ
Tourism and Sustainable Development : Box Score and Future Outlook

ABSTRACT

Sustainable development is a major item on national, regional and local agendas. The first part of the article focusses on the origin and the meaning of the concept of sustainable development. The second part begins with the following question : how is the issue of sustainable development related to the tourist industry ? The different aspects of this problematic are : the compatibility of mass tourism with protected natural areas, and ecotourism as a means of protection. The third part of the article is based on a survey of the scientific and professional literature. It examines new trends and recent practices that have been established by the tourist industry in order to cope with the philosophy of sustainable development. The main themes discussed are : learning-by-doing based on success stories showing the compatibility of tourist development and conservation, the development of indicators of sustainable tourism, and the development of codes of ethics.

André BARABÉ
Turismo y desarrollo durable : estado de situación y perspectivas futuras

RESUMEN

El desarrollo durable está en la orden del día de las agendas nacionales, regionales y locales. La primera parte del texto tiende a precisar el origen y la noción de desarrollo durable. La segunda parte comienza a partir de la interrogación siguiente : ¿cómo se plantea la problemática de desarrollo durable para la industria turística ?. Los elementos de la problemática examinados serán los siguientes : la contabilidad entre el turismo de masa y las áreas naturales protegidas, así que el ecoturismo como una herramienta de protección. La tercera parte, basada en una revista de literatura científica y profesional, trata de las tendencias y las prácticas recientes puestas en ejecución por la industria turística para aplicar concretamente la filosofía del desarrollo durable. Los principales temas retenidos son los siguientes : el aprendizaje por medio de la práctica utilizando la difusión de los casos de triunfo y conciliando conservación y desarrollo turístico, el desarrollo de indicadores del turismo durable, el desarrollo de códigos de ética.

L'INDUSTRIE DU VOYAGE AU QUÉBEC : LES ENJEUX DU RÉSEAU DE DISTRIBUTION

Michel ARCHAMBAULT
Paul ARSENEAULT
Chaire du Tourisme
Université du Québec à Montréal

L'industrie québécoise du voyage est confrontée à plusieurs enjeux de taille. En effet, l'introduction massive de nouvelles technologies, la déréglementation aérienne, l'évolution des besoins et des attentes du consommateur, le vieillissement de la clientèle, la concurrence élargie par l'ouverture des marchés mondiaux ainsi que la complexité grandissante des produits touristiques représentent de nouvelles réalités qui ont un impact sur l'industrie et sur sa main-d'œuvre. L'accélération brutale de ces changements et le peu de formation spécialisée des ressources humaines que connaît actuellement cette industrie entraînent, sur le plan qualitatif, des pénuries de compétences. Dans cette perspective, il nous est apparu pertinent de s'interroger sur ces problématiques générales afin de cerner les impacts prévisibles de ces changements sur la structure de l'industrie, sur sa main-d'œuvre et sur l'introduction de technologies nouvelles. L'élaboration d'un diagnostic global de l'industrie nous a permis d'identifier et d'analyser les principaux changements socio-économiques qui affectent l'évolution de l'industrie, de mettre en évidence ses forces et ses faiblesses ainsi que d'évaluer et de prioriser les causes qui engendrent ces problématiques.

Le présent article repose sur les résultats d'une recherche réalisée en 1994 qui trace un bilan situationnel de l'industrie du voyage au Québec. Il décrit l'état actuel de l'industrie et identifie ses particularités à l'aide des résultats d'une enquête menée auprès de cadres et d'employés et avec les conclusions de groupes de discussions réalisés auprès d'experts du secteur. Plusieurs constats émergent quant à l'état de cette industrie, tant au Québec que dans les pays occidentalisés. En effet, on observe quatre tendances marquantes dans l'industrie du voyage : la suroffre au chapitre du réseau de distribution, le regroupement mondial des agences détaillantes, les changements dans la nature de la demande de la clientèle et finalement le décloisonnement et la mondialisation des activités économiques – tels la déréglementation aérienne, les marchés communs et les alliances entre les fournisseurs – qui laissent présager des perturbations dans la structure de l'industrie. Notre recherche vise à illustrer certaines situations caractéristiques de l'industrie et à identifier les enjeux risquant de marquer son évolution à moyen et à long terme. Finalement, des pistes de recherche et de solution sont proposées.

L'industrie du voyage : cadre conceptuel

Intégrée à l'industrie plus large du tourisme, l'industrie du voyage joue un rôle majeur dans les activités économiques, récréatives et familiales. Elle a connu à l'échelle planétaire une croissance économique importante et toujours soutenue depuis le début des années 60. Aucune baisse au chapitre du chiffre d'affaires global n'a été enregistrée au cours des 35 dernières années et le nombre absolu de voyages effectués a lui aussi connu une croissance soutenue durant cette période (World Travel & Tourism Review, 1994). Cette situation résulte du taux d'augmentation des coûts des produits du voyage qui est toujours demeuré, en proportion, inférieur au taux d'inflation. Les économies d'échelles réalisées par le biais de regroupements entre entreprises[1], celles imputables à l'apparition de nouvelles technologies ainsi que les pressions concurrentielles sont à l'origine de cette faible hausse des coûts des produits du voyage. Cette situation de concurrence, encouragée entre autres par de multiples déréglementations du secteur, s'est traduite par une suroffre au chapitre du transport aérien. Néanmoins, selon l'Organisation mondiale du tourisme (OMT) et le World Tourism and Travel Council (WTTC), cette croissance du nombre de voyages se maintiendra au cours des prochaines années, principalement par la demande accrue de produits touristiques par l'ensemble de la population occidentale – démocratisation du voyage – et par les effets bénéfiques de la reprise économique enregistrée dans la plupart des pays occidentalisés (voir graphique 1).

L'industrie du voyage est soumise à de multiples influences externes et internes. D'abord, elle se limite essentiellement à la prestation de services ; l'ensemble de son activité est ainsi de nature intangible. L'expérience du voyage est donc influencée par la perception de la clientèle, ce qui rend l'industrie du voyage tributaire de son image générale (Kendall et Booms, 1989). Elle est particulièrement sensible aux cycles économiques (Tarlow et Muesham, 1992). En effet, les voyages – plus particulièrement ceux d'agrément – sont influencés par la disponibilité des revenus discrétionnaires des ménages. On observe ainsi, en Amérique du Nord, qu'une croissance d'environ 1 % du revenu discrétionnaire n'aura aucun impact sensible sur l'augmentation du nombre de voyages, alors qu'une augmentation de l'ordre de 2,5 % se traduira par une hausse de 4 % des voyages, et qu'une augmentation de 5 % des revenus se soldera par une hausse de 10 % (Cleverdon, 1992). Le revenu disponible constitue souvent le premier incitatif à voyager. Si ce dernier n'est pas suffisamment élevé, la décision de voyager pourra être reportée ou encore substituée par une autre activité récréative ou par d'autres types de dépenses en biens et services. Les variables démographiques exercent, elles aussi, un impact sensible sur l'industrie du voyage en modifiant la composition et les caractéristiques du bassin de population et, par le fait même, de la clientèle voyageuse. Ces variables expliquent certains changements dans les besoins de la clientèle et dans la nature de la demande.

GRAPHIQUE 1

Croissance des voyages à l'échelle internationale

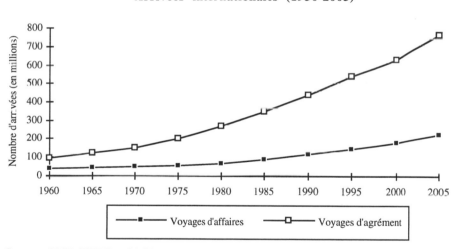

Source : OMT, WTTC et OACI

Aspects méthodologiques

La recherche s'appuie, comme mentionné préalablement, sur les résultats d'un sondage effectué auprès de la main-d'œuvre et des dirigeants des agences de voyages détaillantes et grossistes au Québec. Cette démarche a permis de mieux cerner la nature de l'industrie québécoise du voyage et de dresser un profil socio-économique précis de sa main-d'œuvre. Nous avons préalablement procédé à un échantillonnage par le recoupement de trois sources d'informations provenant de la Direction des ressources humaines du Canada

(DRHC), de l'Office de la protection du consommateur du Québec (OPC) et d'une firme privée (Baxter).

Nous avons, pour tracer un portrait adéquat et statistiquement valable de la main-d'œuvre du réseau de distribution au Québec, construit un questionnaire d'enquête. Composé de quatre sections spécifiques, ce dernier a été administré par voie téléphonique. La première section visait à connaître la structure, les activités et les caractéristiques organisationnelles propres aux entreprises du secteur. La deuxième section touchait les caractéristiques des tâches des répondants et la formation de base et d'appoint reçue par ceux-ci. La troisième section sondait les conditions de travail des répondants ainsi que les avantages liés à l'emploi. Finalement, la quatrième section couvrait les données socio-démographiques des répondants. Trois groupes de discussions – *focus group* –, auprès d'experts reconnus et de décideurs-clés de l'industrie et des secteurs associés, ont permis de valider les tendances, les opportunités et les menaces qui influencent l'industrie, les entreprises et la main-d'œuvre. Les discussions, dirigées par un animateur selon une formule d'entrevue semi-structurée non-directive, ont été enregistrées. Des observateurs externes et visibles ont assisté à ces rencontres.

Pour les fins de l'enquête, 551 entreprises ont été sélectionnées sur les 1 045 permis actifs recensés au Québec. À l'intérieur de ces 551 entreprises, 697 personnes ont été aléatoirement choisies ; cette sélection a été réalisée par un pas d'échantillonnage d'un employé sur quatorze. Suite à cette démarche, 388 questionnaires ont été complétés, soit un taux de réponse de 55,7 %. La marge d'erreur des résultats obtenus est de plus ou moins 4,98 %, 19 fois sur 20.

Résultats : portrait des entreprises québécoises du secteur du voyage

Si plusieurs auteurs se sont intéressés à certains aspects de l'industrie du voyage, principalement aux États-Unis et en Europe, ce sujet demeure toutefois l'objet de peu de recherches approfondies dans le cas particulier du Québec. Quoique de prime abord l'industrie du voyage apparaît très homogène, une analyse plus fine permet de mettre au jour le nombre, la diversité et la dynamique des relations entre ces entreprises. Ce réseau complexe d'interactions se présente alors comme un tout passablement hétérogène. Ainsi, les entreprises québécoises de l'industrie du voyage se distinguent entre elles de manière significative, principalement par le type d'entreprise – grossiste ou détaillante, par la nature de leurs activités – expéditeur ou récepteur, par leurs situations géographiques – urbaine ou régionale, par leurs tailles – petite ou grande, par leurs spécialisations – voyage d'affaires ou de vacances et finalement par leurs modes de regroupement – indépendante ou affiliée.

Au Québec, l'Office de la protection du consommateur (OPC), rattaché au ministère de la Justice, régit l'accès aux activités commerciales d'agence de voyage – détaillante ou grossiste – par l'émission d'un permis. On compte ainsi 1 045 permis en vigueur en 1994 représentant quelque 1 855 points de vente, puisqu'un même permis peut inclure plus d'une succursale. Le graphique 2 illustre l'évolution du nombre de points de vente au Québec depuis 1980 en distinguant les détaillants des grossistes.

GRAPHIQUE 2

Nombre de succursales détaillantes et grossistes au Québec

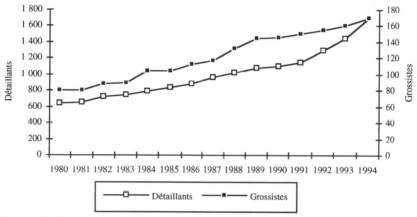

Source : OPC

L'industrie du voyage au Québec se concentre géographiquement dans le pôle métropolitain montréalais avec 53 % des entreprises situées sur l'île de Montréal. Pour l'année 1993, les agences détaillantes québécoises opérant depuis plus de douze mois produisaient un volume de vente de plus de 1,4 milliard de dollars. Pour la même année, le chiffre d'affaires des grossistes s'élève à plus de 797 millions de dollars ; fait à souligner, 20 % des entreprises réalisent 84,4 % du chiffre d'affaires. Le graphique 3 décrit l'évolution du chiffre d'affaires des entreprises du réseau de distribution québécois.

La majorité des employés, soit plus de 87 %, travaillent au sein des agences détaillantes, alors que les grossistes emploient 12,4 % de la main-d'œuvre de l'industrie. Les femmes cumulent 71,9 % de tous les emplois alors que les hommes représentent 28,1 %. Âgé majoritairement entre 26 et 45 ans, le personnel compte en moyenne dix années d'expérience dans cette industrie. L'ensemble des employés possède une formation académique passablement élevée, puisque 68,7 % détiennent un diplôme d'études postsecondaire, soit approximativement 10 % de plus que l'ensemble de la population canadienne[2]. Il s'agit d'une situation paradoxale, puisque les employés du secteur du voyage travaillent en moyenne 18 % plus d'heures[3] par semaine que l'ensemble des travailleurs québécois. En même temps, le niveau de salaire hebdomadaire moyen désaisonnalisé pour l'ensemble de la population active au Canada était de 561,62 $ en 1993, alors que notre recherche situe le salaire hebdomadaire moyen dans le secteur du voyage à 419,42 $ en 1994, soit approximativement 25 % de moins que l'ensemble des travailleurs canadiens.

GRAPHIQUE 3
Croissance du chiffre d'affaires

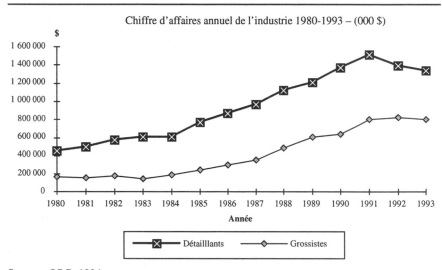

Chiffre d'affaires annuel de l'industrie 1980-1993 – (000 $)

Source : OPC, 1994

Les enjeux du réseau de distribution

Plusieurs enjeux exercent un impact majeur sur le devenir du réseau de distribution traditionnel. Ces derniers s'articulent autour de trois dimensions, à savoir la structure même de l'industrie qui réfère à la raison d'être du réseau de distribution, la technologie qui change la nature et l'intensité de la prestation de services des intermédiaires, et enfin la formation de la main-d'œuvre qui influe sur la qualité et le professionnalisme du service. Ces enjeux ne peuvent être conçus comme mutuellement exclusifs ; ce sont des ensembles complexes de dynamiques interdépendantes.

Les enjeux structurels

Les enjeux structurels sont fondamentaux puisqu'ils réfèrent à l'évolution du réseau de distribution. Malgré le caractère stratégique de ces enjeux, les intervenants de l'industrie les négligent, étant trop engagés dans les impératifs et les aléas de la gestion opérationnelle quotidienne. Néanmoins, certaines des problématiques structurelles interpellent directement les gestionnaires de ce secteur d'activité. En effet, la fin des années 80 et le début des années 90 ont été marqués par une vague de déréglementation massive des activités touristiques et du voyage, vague particulièrement perceptible au chapitre du transport aérien. De nouvelles entreprises importantes se sont alors intéressées par les possibilités offertes de l'industrie. Issues de secteurs d'activités autres que le tourisme et le voyage – souvent du domaine des institutions financières, de la haute technologie ou des télécommunications – elles se posent comme de nouveaux meneurs d'enjeux à très forte capitalisation (Freeman, 1984). Dans cette optique, nous avons identifié trois enjeux :

1. Les changements dans la nature de la demande de la clientèle, qui échappent au contrôle du réseau de distribution, apparaissent comme une source importante de perturbation de l'industrie. Ces changements résultent d'exigences de plus en plus diversifiées et pointues des consommateurs, ce qui exige une spécialisation accrue des entreprises de distribution et un niveau de compétence plus grand au chapitre de l'interface avec la clientèle. Par contre, ces besoins donnent naissance à des créneaux de marché inexploités et favorisent l'émergence de nouvelles niches d'opération. Les changements dans la demande se concrétisent à la fois dans la façon d'acheter du consommateur et dans la modification de ses critères d'achat. Ainsi, le service à la clientèle et sa qualité deviennent un enjeu de taille pour le réseau de distribution. Lewis (1994) précise qu'il existe deux éléments au service : premièrement, l'aspect physique du service, qu'il soit tangible – décor, apparence, etc. – ou périphérique – système de réservation, bandes vidéo, etc. ; deuxièmement, le processus de service lui-même qui inclut les aspects technologiques et humains.

2. Le réseau de distribution souffre d'un problème de crédibilité auprès de ses fournisseurs, de sa clientèle et de sa main-d'œuvre. Il donne souvent l'image d'une industrie « improvisée », dans la mesure où le secteur se présente comme peu structuré. La faible réglementation et le peu de barrières à l'entrée ajoutent à cette perception en favorisant l'ouverture et la fermeture incessante de nombreuses entreprises. Ce roulement excessif est imputable au manque d'expérience des propriétaires ; il est facile d'ouvrir une agence et de s'improviser agent de voyage. Ce manque de professionnalisme représente ainsi une menace puisqu'il affecte l'image de l'industrie vis-à-vis des partenaires et des clientèles.

3. Les regroupements mondiaux sont de plus en plus fréquents et importants. La formation de groupes – fusions et alliances – apparaît comme une opportunité pour le développement de l'industrie, car elle favorise entre autres l'achat massif de technologies de pointe et d'économies de volume entre les différents partenaires (Go et Hedges, 1994 ; Selin, 1993). Wild (1994) ajoute que cette stratégie d'alliances permet également aux grands groupes de mieux contrôler le marché. Par contre, cette situation n'est pas encore généralisée ; ces regroupements étant onéreux, certaines agences choisissent de concentrer leurs activités dans un créneau particulier. Cette stratégie permet alors de miser sur la créativité et la flexibilité que l'on retrouve dans les agences de taille plus modeste.

Les enjeux technologiques

Les changements technologiques ont un impact significatif sur l'industrie ; ils en constituent le centre nerveux (Sheldon, 1994). L'évolution des technologies dans les secteurs des télécommunications et des services bancaires automatisés et informatisés bouleversent l'environnement d'affaires des entreprises du secteur du voyage. De manière générale, les technologies de l'information dépassent le cadre de l'industrie du voyage pour s'étendre à l'ensemble des secteurs de l'activité économique. Dans cette optique, les gestionnaires doivent envisager leurs activités en termes d'interactions entre tous les secteurs, désormais unis par les réseaux informatiques. En effet, le rythme d'introduction de nouvelles technologies de plus en plus rapide, ajoute au climat d'incertitude et de turbulence de l'industrie. Le volet technologique possède deux facettes.

1. La technologie joue un rôle de support majeur pour les entreprises du voyage, tant au niveau de la vente que de la gestion. Depuis les dix dernières années, elle constitue l'élément-clé de la concurrence. Que ce soit par le biais des micro-ordinateurs, des systèmes de télécommunications ou encore des systèmes de réservation, l'informatique s'avère essentielle au fonctionnement des entreprises du voyage. Elle permet de se rapprocher du client et de lui offrir un meilleur service, tout en assurant à l'agent de voyage ou de réservation un accès excessivement rapide à un nombre important de données sur les produits, les départs, les disponibilités, les tarifs, etc. Ainsi, dans la dynamique actuelle du marché du voyage, qui se solde à l'avantage du client, la qualité du service ne peut désormais se concrétiser qu'avec l'aide des diverses technologies de réservation, d'information et de gestion (Deng et Ryan, 1992).

2. L'autoroute de l'information permettra bientôt à la clientèle québécoise d'effectuer ses propres recherches et réservations depuis son domicile, sans l'intermédiaire d'une agence de voyage. En effet, les nouvelles technologies que sont la télématique, l'autoroute informatique ainsi que les fibres optiques, facilitent l'accès aux centrales informatisées des transporteurs aériens et des autres fournisseurs. Cette nouvelle réalité technologique viendra éventuellement accaparer une part de marché du réseau de distribution des produits du voyage. Les règles du jeu changeront dans la mesure où le nombre d'intermédiaires nécessaire à la mise en marché des produits sera limité et que ces systèmes permettront à un plus grand nombre de consommateurs d'accéder rapidement à diverses informations. Néanmoins, ces technologies ne sont pas encore d'un usage courant ; l'expérience américaine démontre que les consommateurs hésitent encore à entreprendre de longues et parfois coûteuses recherches sur ces systèmes alors que les conseillers en voyage, déjà entraînés à cette tâche, leur fournissent ces services gratuitement (Tarlow et Mucsham, 1992). Notons enfin que l'informatique vient changer les habitudes des clientèles d'affaires. On parle désormais de voyages électroniques en référence aux vidéoconférences, aux messageries électroniques, aux transmissions par satellites et par télécopieur qui se substituent aux voyages d'affaires conventionnels. Le Conference Board du Canada estime pour 1994 que 28 % des voyageurs d'affaires ont réalisé moins de voyages dû à l'accessibilité des téléconférences et des télécopieurs[4].

Les enjeux de la formation et de la main-d'œuvre

Le dernier type d'enjeu concerne la formation de la main-d'œuvre. Un profond hiatus existe entre l'offre de formation en voyage au Québec, qui relève de plusieurs niveaux – secondaire, collégial, universitaire, public et privé – et les compétences recherchées par l'industrie. De plus, ce problème s'étend aussi à la gestion des entreprises du voyage.

1. Deux problèmes cohabitent au chapitre de la formation. Premièrement, un manque de main-d'œuvre qualifiée dans l'industrie affecte la qualité des services offerts par les intermédiaires. Cette situation est accentuée par le peu d'intérêt de la main-d'œuvre à investir dans les programmes de formation d'appoint, malgré les besoins ressentis à ce chapitre. Deuxièmement, on observe une dévalorisation de la profession, principalement au niveau secondaire ; les conseillers en orientation proposeront souvent les programmes de tourisme aux élèves moins qualifiés académiquement. Ainsi, les étudiants à fort potentiel vont s'investir là où les opportunités de revenus sont jugées plus élevées.

2. Il existe par ailleurs un problème important d'hétérogénéité de la formation dans le secteur du voyage. En effet, puisqu'elle n'est réglementée que par le biais des agences de voyage, l'industrie ne possède pas de normes minimales de qualification pour œuvrer dans ce secteur. Il n'existe de fait aucun système d'amélioration ou de reconnaissance des compétences qui soit uniformément reconnu par l'industrie. Par ailleurs, la formation des gestionnaires, elle non plus, n'est pas adaptée aux attentes de l'industrie. Les gestionnaires et les cadres doivent ainsi se tourner bien souvent vers les programmes reliés à des domaines connexes pour se perfectionner.

3. Enfin, les entreprises de l'industrie sont confrontées à un enjeu de taille au chapitre de l'éthique et du professionnalisme. On observe actuellement deux situations problématiques. Premièrement, les intermédiaires conçoivent parfois les impératifs de rentabilité en opposition à la qualité des services. Or, ces exigences sont au contraire intimement liées ; la qualité du service se solde souvent par des bénéfices monétaires et intangibles. Deuxièmement, la question de la rémunération s'avère elle aussi centrale ; le niveau des salaires de l'industrie est faible compte tenu des exigences de la semaine de travail. Dans cette perspective, le dilemme se pose entre verser des salaires fixes – qui facilitent la prestation de service mais parfois aussi l'oisiveté – ou encore des salaires à commissions – qui favorisent un niveau de vente élevé, mais ce parfois au détriment de la qualité du service.

Pistes de réflexion

Nous pouvons questionner la volonté ou la possibilité de l'industrie d'agir sur son devenir, vu sa relative faiblesse et sa dépendance face aux fournisseurs – principalement les transporteurs aériens – et à la clientèle. Les expériences antérieures de concertation démontrent que le dialogue s'avère difficile à susciter entre les intervenants du réseau de distribution. De plus, les grandes entreprises, déjà sensibilisées aux enjeux, ne voient pas l'intérêt de se porter au secours des plus petites entreprises – mais néanmoins concurrentes – plus vulnérables dans le climat actuel. Dans cette optique dite de *statu quo*, l'industrie vivra une restructuration « naturelle ». La tendance aux alliances entre les grands groupes se poursuivra et de nouveaux joueurs issus de domaines autres que le voyage apparaîtront. Il est ainsi à craindre que cette restructuration se fasse aux dépens des petites agences indépendantes qui seraient appelées, à moyen ou à long terme, à disparaître. Dans cette hypothèse, le contrôle des entreprises se concentrera entre les mains de grands groupes mondiaux, amenant un exode du contrôle du réseau de distribution vers des pays étrangers. Ces groupes possèdent, contrairement à l'ensemble des entreprises du voyage au Québec, un pouvoir de négociation certain auprès des fournisseurs et bénéficient d'une capitalisation plus saine et plus importante ; ils pourront facilement tenir tête aux nouveaux intrants dans l'industrie.

Par contre, l'industrie peut intervenir au niveau structurel et contrer ces tendances. Ainsi, un système de reconnaissance formelle des compétences de la main-d'œuvre et des gestionnaires pourrait être mis de l'avant. Dans cette optique, le droit d'œuvrer dans l'industrie serait alors accordé aux individus ayant obtenu un permis de conseiller en voyage. Il s'agit à ce chapitre d'un changement majeur dans la mesure où la législation actuelle concède au détenteur d'un permis d'agence de voyage de procéder à l'embauche de n'importe quel individu, quelles que soient ses compétences ou expériences préalables. Le permis de conseiller en voyage serait ainsi octroyé après la réussite d'un programme de cours évalué par un examen uniforme. Le droit d'opérer une agence de voyage se verrait également limité aux détenteurs d'un permis de courtier en voyage, également octroyé après la réussite d'un examen uniforme qui garantirait les compétences en gestion du demandeur. Encore une fois, l'actuelle Loi sur les agences de voyage ne couvre pas cette dimension ; elle focalise à peine sur la solvabilité du demandeur et de son entreprise.

En modifiant les règles du jeu, l'industrie deviendrait moins vulnérable aux changements environnementaux et structurels et aux autres joueurs des diverses industries. L'industrie du voyage se doterait alors d'un code d'éthique ou d'un modèle concernant les règles d'obtention et de maintien des permis de détaillant ou de grossiste pour augmenter le niveau de professionnalisme. L'effort de réflexion menant à cette restructuration constituerait également une occasion pour l'industrie de s'interroger sur son devenir et un moyen d'accroître les compétences de la main-d'œuvre. Cela améliorerait son image et garantirait aux consommateurs un niveau de qualité dans les prestations de services fournis. Finalement, ces nouvelles dispositions auraient un effet positif sur les relations avec les fournisseurs, désormais assurés de la qualité et de la compétence des intermédiaires responsables de la mise en marché de leurs produits.

Conclusion et avenues de recherche

La structure de l'industrie semble inévitablement appelée à se modifier. L'option du statu quo, comme elle se présente aujourd'hui, constitue une invitation pour les entreprises des autres secteurs à s'introduire dans le domaine de la distribution des produits du voyage. Une reconnaissance formelle des compétences de la main-d'œuvre et l'émission de permis s'appliquant à la profession – et non plus à l'entreprise comme c'est actuellement le cas – constituent une deuxième option pour contrer cette situation. Il faut enfin que l'industrie atteigne un niveau de professionnalisme et d'éthique beaucoup plus élevé. L'implication des décideurs-clés et des leaders de l'industrie s'avère primordiale pour donner suite à ces enjeux. La formation de comités spécifiques, la tenue de colloques et le développement d'activités de recherche – principalement dans les champs de la technologie et de la qualité des services – apparaissent opportuns afin d'assurer cette sensibilisation des acteurs de l'industrie.

Cet article proposait les conclusions d'une réflexion plus large sur l'avenir du réseau de distribution du secteur québécois du voyage (Archambault et Arseneault, 1994). Ces constats, nous le croyons, ouvrent la porte à plusieurs recherches qui pourraient approfondir l'un ou l'autre des enjeux proposés. Ainsi, l'enjeu technologique pose déjà de multiples questionnements quant à son impact sur l'industrie du tourisme dans son ensemble. La poursuite de cette recherche aura un impact plus que favorable sur la pratique de la gestion dans l'industrie du voyage caractérisée par un manque de vision à long terme de plusieurs gestionnaires.

NOTES

1. Tant les alliances entre les entreprises du secteur du voyage qu'avec les entreprises des secteurs associés ou complémentaires.
2. Source : Statistique Canada, Recensement 1991, Cat. 71-220
3. D'après les données colligées par les auteurs lors d'un sondage téléphonique auprès de 388 employés.
4. Travel Exclusive : Canadian Tourism Research Institute, hiver 1994.

Bibliographie

ARCHAMBAULT, M. et P. ARSENEAULT (1994). *Diagnostic sectoriel de l'industrie du voyage au Québec*, Comité sectoriel de l'industrie du voyage ; Montréal, 109 p.

BAXTER PUBLICATION (1993). *Personnel guide to Canada's Travel Industry*, Spring/Summer edition.

CROUCH, J. (1991). « Expert Computer Systems in Tourism : Emerging Possibilities », *Journal of Travel Research*, vol. 29 (4), 3-10.

DENG, S. et C. RYAN (1992). « CRS : Tool or Determinant of Management Practice in Canadian Travel Agents ? » », *Journal of Travel & Tourism Marketing*, vol. 1 (1), 19-38.

DUPONT, C. (1993). *Gestion des ressources humaines dans l'industrie touristique : une étude empirique des pratiques innovatrices*, Département d'études urbaines et touristiques (UQAM) – Études, matériaux et documents #3, 175 p.

FREEMAN, R. Edward (1984). *Strategic Management : A Stakeholder Approach*, Pitman, Boston.

GILBERT, D. C. et S. Soni (1991). « UK Tour Operators and Consumer Responsiveness », *Service Industries Journal*, vol. 11 (4), 413-424.

GO, F. M. et A. HEDGES (1994). « Strategic alliances » », in *Tourism Marketing and Management Handbook, Second Edition*, Witt et Mouthino eds., Prentice Hall International, Hertfortshire, 617 p.

HITCHINS, F. (1991). « The Influence of Technology on UK Travel Agents », *EIU Travel & Tourism Analyst*, vol. 12 (3), 88-105.

KENDALL, K. W. et B. H. BOOMS (1989). « Consumer Perceptions of Travel Agencies : Communications, Images, Needs, and Expectations », *Journal of Travel Research*, vol. 27 (1), 29-37.

LEBLANC, G. (1992). « Factors Affecting Customer Evaluation of Service Quality in Travel Agencies : An Investigation of Customer Perceptions », *Journal of Travel Research*, vol. 30 (1), 10-16.

LEWIS, B. R. (1994). « Quality of service and customer care » », in *Tourism Marketing and Management Handbook, Second Edition*, Witt et Mouthino eds., Prentice Hall International, Hertfortshire, 617 p.

MOWLANA, H. et G. SMITH (1990). « Tourism, Telecommunications, and Transnations Banking – A Framework for Policy Analysis », *Tourism Management*, vol. 11 (4), 315-324.

PAWLAK, A (1990). « Bureaucrats or Victims of the Halo Effect : A Sociological Study of Travel Agency Personnel », *Problems of Tourism*, vol. 5 (1-2), 65-72.

POON, A. (1988). « Tourism and Information Technologies », *Annals of Tourism Research*, vol. 15 (4), 531-549.

PRÉMONT, B. (1992). *Structure et stratégie des voyagistes québécois*, travail dirigé de maîtrise, École des HEC, Montréal, 114 p. + annexes.

SELIN, S. (1993). « Collaborative Alliances : New Interorganizational Forms in Tourism », *Journal of Travel & Tourism Marketing*, vol. 2 (2/3), 217-227.

SHELDON, P. J. (1994). « Information technology and computer reservation systems », in *Tourism Marketing and Management Handbook, Second Edition*, Witt et Mouthino eds., Prentice Hall International, Hertfortshire, 617 p.

TARLOW, P. E. et M. J. MUESHAM (1992). « Wide Horizons : Travel and Tourism in the Coming Decades », *Futurist*, vol. 26 (5), september-october, 28-32.

TRUITT, L. J. *et al.* (1991). The role of computer reservations systems : International implications for the travel industry », *Tourism Management*, vol. 8 (1), p.16-36.

WILD, C. N. (1994). « Fragmentation in the tourisme industry », in *Tourism Marketing and Management Handbook, Second Edition*, Witt et Mouthino eds., Prentice Hall International, Hertfortshire, 617 p.

World Travel and Tourism Review (1992). *Indicators, Trends and and Forecast – Special Report on Education, Training and Human-ressources Issues*, CAB International, vol. 2 (5), 179 p.

Michel ARCHAMBAULT et Paul ARSENEAULT
L'industrie du voyage au Québec : les enjeux du réseau de distribution

RÉSUMÉ

L'article repose sur les résultats d'une recherche traçant un bilan situationnel de l'industrie du voyage au Québec. Il décrit l'état actuel de l'industrie et identifie ses particularités à l'aide des résultats d'une enquête menée auprès de 388 cadres et employés ainsi que des conclusions de trois groupes de discussions réalisés auprès d'experts du secteur. Cet article illustre certaines situations caractéristiques de l'industrie et identifie les enjeux risquant de marquer son évolution à moyen et à long terme. Ces enjeux sont articulés autour des dimensions structurelles, technologiques et de la formation. Un portrait succinct de l'industrie est tracé pour exposer par la suite les impacts des enjeux sur celle-ci. Finalement, des pistes de recherche et de solution sont proposées.

Michel ARCHAMBAULT et Paul ARSENEAULT
The Travel Industry in Quebec : the Main Issues for Its Distribution Network

ABSTRACT

The article is based on the findings of a study assessing the overall situation of the travel industry in Quebec. The present state of the industry and its various characteristics are described based both on the findings of a survey carried out among 388 senior management personnel and employees and on the conclusions from three focus groups made up of experts in this area. Some of the situations that are typical of the industry and the issues considered to have short and long term effects on that business are described. The structural, technological and training dimensions of these issues are examined. A brief description of the industry is made, followed by the major influence of these issues. Various research avenues and solutions are pinpointed in conclusion.

Michel ARCHAMBAULT y Paul ARSENEAULT
La industria del viaje en el Quebec: los desafíos de la red de distribución

RESUMEN

El artículo se basa sobre los resultados de una investigación que traza un balance circunstancial de la industria del viaje en Quebec. Se describe el estado actual de la industria y se identifican sus particularidades basándose en los resultados de una encuesta realizada sobre 388 cuadros y empleados, así que en las conclusiones de tres grupos de discusiones realizadas con expertos del sector. Este artículo ilustra ciertas situaciones características de la industria e identifica los desafíos que arriesgan de marcar su evolución a mediano y largo plazo. Estos desafíos están articulados alrededor de las dimensiones estructurales, tecnológicas y de la formación. Un bosquejo sucinto de la industria es trazado para exponer en seguida los impactos de los riesgos sobre esta industria. Finalmente, pistas de investigación y de solución son propuestas.

NOTE DE RECHERCHE / *RESEARCH NOTE*

THE ROLE OF ABORIGINAL WOMEN'S ART IN CULTURAL IDENTITY

Pauline SKY

School of Sport and Leisure Studies
The University of New South Wales
Sydney, Australia

In the important legal decision (Mabo) which led to the Native Title Act 1993, the High Court of Australia has accepted that Aboriginal customary law and culture can be used by courts as a point of reference and a descriptor of traditional land use. This means that together with existing legal title, *cultural affiliation* to land is given consideration in the assessment of native rights. Evidence of these cultural ties is usually dependent on the validation of the claim through historical knowledge of tribal occupation (or usage) of land based on anthropological records. However there are some questions being raised about the accuracy of these accounts in relation to aboriginal women's claims to land. This is because the early history of Aboriginal customary law was almost exclusively recorded in the field by male scholars who, because of the separation of female and male law, were only aware of the male ceremonies and rites. Women inhabited a separate camp and conducted a separate culture in the substantial part of their tribal life. This life created and passed down learning about women's affiliation to specific lands.

A problem then is that the story of women's cultural knowledge passed on between Aboriginal women in the shared songs, dances, and art designs of the women's ceremonies, has been neglected in the main (male) anthropological records which can be used as reference to court judgements. However, the story (culture) does exist through the work of female scholars who have begun to contribute to field work records of women's customary law and art practices, and the picture of land affiliation is being recreated as the early history is pieced together and the female initiates identified.

The Legal Position Established Under Mabo v. Queensland

The telling of the women's claims would have been irrelevant to Australian law up until the recent acknowledgments of cultural recognition resulting from the Mabo case. Because this cultural perspective is so important to an adjudication of women's land rights, and to the story in this paper of women's arts as the key instruments of their culture and so of their inheritance, a background to the evolution of law in Australia is essential to explain why the exclusions of past law have been so thorough.

The High Court of Australia (Mabo v. Queensland, 1992) decision recognising Aboriginal occupation before European settlement, has become the most important confrontation to assumed ownership of Australia in our history. The arguments against Mabo and the subsequent Native Title Act 1993, predominantly reject legislation which appears to recognise Aboriginal title to Australia that could put at risk some non Aboriginal title (for example, mining title). The case, like some others in local history (including Coe 1979), presented the High Court with a claim to land, in this instance, the Murray Islands (Mer, Dawar, and Waier) in the Torres Straits which lies between the Australian continent and New Guinea. Torres Strait Islanders sought to demonstrate that native title has survived European occupation because these islands were not annexed by the British Crown until 1879 when they were conquered by sea through a British naval act of war. The importance of this version of occupation of the islands relates to British Constitutional Law by which colonies were seen to be either (a) conquered or ceded, or (b) settled. Australia has always been treated as (b) because the propositions explicit in (a) have been rendered indefensible in law because there was no invasion of the continent but a slow, systematic settlement. Setting aside the ceded title option under (a) because unlike the New Zealand, Canadian, or American experience there have been no treaties in Australia to guarantee title of occupancy to Aborigines, conquest arguments under (a) have generally failed in the Australian courts because of the presumption of settlement. When Cook claimed Australia for the British Crown as terra nullius (land belonging to no-one), the rights of the Aboriginal inhabitants were presumed extinguished, and the right to the land was vested in the Crown. All land titles were then based on Crown Grants administered under the common law imported with the settlers. Apart from obvious questions to be raised about whether a military penal colony is a settled place, or whether a point of settlement, Port Jackson, would extinguish land rights for the entire country, the crux of the constitutional position to modern Australian debate is the extent by which the common law can recognise customary law (right) or deem it to have been extinguished.

Mabo challenged the doctrine of settlement by winning a case based on (a) possession by conquest, arguing that an act of dispossession by official approval exists. This judgement though, rather than signalling the automatic success of all other indigenous claims, recognises the distinctive scenario of the Murray Islands and the Meriam people who live there. While accepting that native title has continued to exist on the Murray Islands, the High Court justices were clear to protect interests in land held in valid freehold grants (and probable leaseholdings too), limiting native title where statutory title exists. In terms of legal precedent this, in fact, reinforces the view that all legal rights including native title come under Crown laws, and has the affect of protecting Crown Grants.

The landmark in the Mabo case is that the High Court rejected the view that Australia was terra nullius at the time of European settlement (Commonwealth of Australia, 1993 : 14), this judgement amended the common law to recognise native title to land. The decision went so far as to admit that the content of native title should be determined according to the traditional law and customs of the Meriam people involved. The post-Mabo reality that traditional law can be applied to land rights questions in modern Australia, should have us seeking to understand Aboriginal customary law as vigorously as we are grappling with British Constitutional Law, in an attempt to accept jurisdictions. We need to understand if all traditional claimants are enfranchised under customary law and whether it will meter decision (justice) to the approval of claimant populations. How for example, customary law would deal with women's rights to land title, is a fascinating point of interest given the bias in recorded anthropology.

Presuming that the study of Aboriginal tribal law can prepare our viewpoints for the debate on how a legal deference to customary law might apply to land rights questions, the Northern Territory tribes would seem an appropriate starting place. The Territory not only has one of the largest populations of tribal Aborigines in Australia but at around the time of Federation came under the control of the Commonwealth Government who took over the Territory's Aboriginal affairs from the State of South Australia in 1911. Commonwealth legislative controls still apply to the Territories differently than in the other States of Australia which have enacted their own legislation and, on some readings, this situation has benefited Northern Territory Aborigines. That is, the law in the Territory has more closely resembled the position of the Commonwealth Government which has been less self serving than the States who have usually rated Aboriginal populations second to mining or other industrial needs for pasture or waterways.

This legal distinction, together with the anthropological data available about the tribes of Central Australia, provide a rich resource for the exploration of the scope and function of Aboriginal customary law. Happily too, we have in Australia a line of women scholars who have researched Central Aboriginal societies in close detail and have published their findings in contradiction of male work in this field. So a set of female academic perspectives of tribal culture and law has survived to inform us and the courts about land rights. To quote Maurice (1988 : 248) again, « ...it would be impossible for any structured inquiry to begin to duplicate the field work necessary to gather together the ethnographic data required to establish the validity of a land claim. » The Commissioner relies on, amongst other data, anthropological analysis to determine land rights.

When contradictory anthropological records exist, together with well explained accounts in the literature of mainstream disciplines of the way in which female exclusion from the creation of knowledge has systematically occurred in the academy (Sky 1994), it is important that female evidence is not subsumed but used to provide the full story of customary law and land rights. Much of the data collected by women academics has been gathered from Aboriginal women who would not have met the anthropology paternity because of the gender prohibitions in tribal life. In many cases, these women have shared knowledge with white women because of a belief that women belong to the same *dream* mob. The work resulting from this liaison, will be used here to tell the story of the survival of female knowledge through their arts.

Anthropological Records

The coincidence of Federation with a series of detailed university expeditions to Central Australia provides a marvellous means of comparison between the legislative picture of Aboriginal Affairs and Aboriginal life in remote regions. In the early part of this century, the gathering of anthropological accounts of the traditional practices and ceremonial beliefs of indigenous people was driven by the anticipation of their extinction. While at the same time, laws were being passed to manage what was seen in Government circles as the unfortunate annihilation of a primitive culture that was, metaphorically and actually, surrounded by the contemporary demands for the development of the new nation. That indigenous groups have survived would have surprised both academics and legislators alike and the story of this survival is still in the telling ; Mabo is just another remarkable stanza with a pervasive ramification – the overturning of the doctrine of terra nullius. If, as in the Mabo judgement, the content of rights can be referred to customary law then consideration of traditional claim to land or, from an Aboriginal viewpoint the belonging of people to the land, will be of major importance in questions of legal title, and the question of the independent rights of Aboriginal women to land, will reside in their identification with their country in customary law. The anthropological testimony to cultural rights through a recognition of women's law, should help to define their customary ownership and traditional possession of women's land. These investigations though, like feminist work in other fields, will have to surmount the existing biased devaluation of women in scholarly texts.

In reading the accounts of the expeditions during the early 1900's, it is difficult to admire the picture of Aboriginal women portrayed by male anthropologists ; Spencer, Radcliffe-Brown, Strehlow, Hiatt, and Hoebel all treat tribal women as pitiable creatures who occupy a peripheral place in the male-dominated life of Aboriginal society. Indeed, the story they tell is one of total subjugation of women by men. However, on further investigation a different reality begins to emerge ; one of separate women's cultural lifestyle. The men on these expeditions could not, of course, accompany the women to the women's camp which was forbidden to all men, nor could they join in the rites or receive an explanation of the women's ceremonies. All these experiences and secrets have belonged to women and cannot be divulged to men. So most accounts of Aboriginal women's lifestyle are testament to the distance between men's and women's law in tribal systems, and the fact that most bona fide accounts of Aboriginal social order were by men who could not have studied the female law or ceremony. These accounts must be seen for their shortcomings ; the omission of women. We are fortune though, to have some versions of traditional woman's role written by female diarists and scholars from the fieldwork of Daisy Bates at the turn of the century to that of Diane Bell in our own time. It is this work which constructs a powerful and contrasting vision of Aboriginal women that stands against that portrayed by male, and therefore unacknowledged exclusive recordists.

It is appropriate to begin a reconstruction of tribal women's status with the work of Daisy Bates (1944). Her professional story has been commented upon by Rohrlich-Leavitt, Sykes, and Weatherford (1975) as an example of how male anthropological accounts have been foreign to and disputed by women in the same field of study, and how the pioneering work of women has often been represented by senior male scholars as their own. Readers interested in the subsumption of female academic product can pursue the story of Bates to add to their collection but it is her work on, what she saw as, the passing of tribal life that informs our interest here. Bates spent most of her adult life in the Australian outback living with Aborigines. It should be noted that Bates never received financial support from any academic institution although they were aware of her work and, on occasion, used her notes. The work was funded from the slow sale of her property over the period of forty years. She spent some time in Ooldea in South Australia which is an area south of the region and peoples referred to here, but she had many visitors walk in from the desert, including groups from Central Australia and so she provides some insight into their practices. The term *visitors* is deceptive because Bates has an off-hand way of describing time and, for example, talks about having *sat down* with a group for two or three years.

Amidst her story of starvation and increasing dependence as the railway line crept across Aboriginal territory devouring water and game, and traversing sacred sites with permanent constructions, are examples of female autonomy over reproduction and children which escape from the pages of her Christian portrayal as reports of dispassionate infanticide and cannibalism. Women, she observed, gave birth away from the men (1944 : 236) and exercised the decision over the child's survival ; they were neither reprimanded or punished when they returned to the camp with or without the baby. This information is important because it correlates with later work (e.g. Berndt 1981) which emphasises that female choice of birthplace continues or disrupts the totem inheritance of individuals in the group ; the most binding description of social position. To explain this social organisation of Aboriginal groups we must first understand the concept of the Dreaming.

Aboriginal Women's Ritual

By their activities in each place, the ancestors who roamed the featureless world shaped the rivers, ranges, deserts and all life. Aborigines believed they must continue to sing the world into existence by re-enacting rites and other ceremonies at the sacred places and that as the songs, dances and sacred designs retold the story of creation of all things, each thing was revived through the enactment of its own specific performance to renew the spirit. For thousands of years tokens had been buried in sacred places ; places of ritual or birth or death, and each place remembered by some natural feature so that it could be revisited and its spirit sung. A spirit could enter a woman to be reincarnated as her child to carry the totem of the birthplace. This put this child in a particular relationship to the rest of the group and signed her/his place for life. An emu child was responsible for the emu land and its rites but was not charged with dingo responsibilities. This is demonstrated by Bates' (1944 : 183) account of the unwillingness of men of the kangaroo totem to submit to a dingo man as leader. This occasion arose in 1920 when Ooldea Aborigines, incensed by the impending rail visit of the Prince of Wales, announced they wanted their own king. However, the totem loyalties blocked this Aboriginal demonstration of self rule.

A woman could exercise some control over the totem make-up of the group by walking to a particular place to birth or, in some tribes where the totem was ascribed by the place of the announcement of conception, could speak of birth in a particular territory. Bates described women walking thirty miles on the day they gave birth, and wrote about the frequency of child killing, which one may construe was of offspring borne in an undesirable location. Women could therefore have exercised absolute control over the reproduction of spirits, which would appear to indicate significant status. Children were acknowledged by custom to have been dreamed by the mother.

This reverence for spirits also explains why Aborigines were dis-interested in acquiring the country of other groups because it would have already been inhabited by their spirits who were not always friendly to strangers. Indeed, groups would greet one another with suspicion and bravado but did accept transit across their territory so long as no irreverent acts were committed. The burial of their human spirits was also precise to ensure their calm residence in the ground. Sacred rituals, songs and dances performed by women and men reinforced their respect for separate cultural knowledge and individuals were regarded as knowledgable according to the number of performances they knew. There is evidence of this regard for singers still.

Ellis and Barwick (in Brock 1989 : 21) make the point that in the regions of Central Australia, traditional cultural knowledge is centred on song knowledge. The songlines retrace the path of ancestors through the country and define both an individual's right to sing a particular song (status) and group rights to a locality (claim). The song sequence represents a map of the ancestral journey, and the singer revives and shares in the power of the Dreaming by performing the songs. The repetition of songs sustains the world and links people with past history. Ellis' study reveals that women own song rights based primarily on birthplace and family line, or sometimes residence of a site, and the secret women's ceremonies are the means for the continuation of women's cultural knowledge. A woman may own an inherited song in a relatives language from some other territory, and retains the right of performance based on birthplace. Men are not always permitted to hear the secret version of women's songs and women tend to perform the rites in the women's camp or at sites known to be for women.

There appear to be different levels of seriousness of performances and there are playful versions of rites for children ; we might understand these as Sunday School versions. The performers have a clear understanding of the appropriateness of the discrete ceremony to different circumstances, and control knowledge by this discretion. The song owner may also dance the ceremony and this ownership can be accompanied by a right to a ground design or painting which completes the full ceremony. The full power of a ceremony will only be called up in the presence of the entire ritual. Ellis observed that song texts have three levels of meaning ; open or the description of the story itself (a play corroboree), erotic or magical or a purposeful version (e.g. a healing ceremony), and esoteric or dealing with the detail of the ancestral myth (the spiritual version). The knowledge of the viewer often being the controlling factor in the reading of the performance, although the owners of rites can also restrict the audience to women only. So the gender segregation of Dream mob (Hamilton 1981) functions together with level of knowledge initiation to contain cultural education. The most usual way for a song to be passed on is by gender and along totem line which is defined by place of birth.

Aboriginal women traditionally leave the women's camp upon marriage to live in their husband's country. As women are betrothed according to moieties or decent-based relationship this practice disperses women, and their sacred knowledge, into wide areas of the country. They return though to sacred sites for ceremonies or, when this is not possible, perform the rituals away from the site. This adaptation has probable served to continue the knowledge line related to distant land or land locked up by settlement or of other restricted access. This scenario also explains why Aboriginal women's collectives and councils are often anxious to procure four-wheel drive vehicles to enable re-enactments of the Dreaming.

Although the ceremonial repertoires of women and men change as some new songs, designs, and dances are dreamed, Ellis certainly believes that the women's secret rites have survived virtually intact from an earlier stage than men's and that women's singing is recognised as capable of calling up power from the Dreaming. Women sing the sites into being, as well as use ceremony to control individual behaviour, healing or the weather. For example, women in the desert have been observed to stand out in a thunderstorm to sing it into silence.

It is important we realise that despite the portrayal of Aboriginal women in the classical anthropological texts as irrelevant to ritual life, Aboriginal men generally have acknowledged their power as complementary to their own. Bell (1984 : 182) concluded from her study of Central Aborigines that both male and female rituals are a celebration of cultural values, but that the law of each gender tends to exhibit some shared, and retain some separate knowledge of the Dreamtime activities. She also expresses her fear that the autonomy of Aboriginal women is eroding as their society is exposed to the intrusion of white culture. As described earlier, this exposure has only occurred this century and the impact has been slow. Aboriginal women and men in Central Australia still maintain the Dreamtime Law and perform the separate knowledge they inherit. The connection of ceremonies with the sacred sites and to the land in the form of their totem lines of responsibility, speaks unmistakably of the rights of these peoples to their land. Women's rights to land can only be denied in so far as we are willing to accept the exclusion of Aboriginal women's status in the classical anthropology of male academics who were unaware of the women's law, and unexposed to its ceremonies or place in Central Aboriginal society.

Correcting the Future

As Australia moves into a post-Mabo period of the judgement of land rights, the adjudication of rights based on customary law will need to give consideration to women's claims. Such decisions will suffer if a biased anthropological account is used to define traditional possession and if Aboriginal women are alienated from the process of claims through insensitive construction of the mechanism of preparing and hearing claims.

In the discussions of land rights there has been little consideration of the needs of Central Aboriginal women for women's gatherings or their preference for speaking to women representatives on ownership matters. The court's precedent deference to customary law in the Mabo case is an invitation to correcting the story of Aboriginal women's power and status, and to recognise their traditional autonomy.

References

Aboriginal and Torres Strait Islanders (Queensland Reserves and Communities Self-Management) Act 1978 (No.11 of 1978)

BATES, D. (1944). *The Passing of the Aborigines : A Lifetime Spent Among the Natives of Australia.* London : Murray.

BELL, D. (1984). *Daughters of the Dreaming.* Melbourne : McPhee Gribble/Allen & Unwin.

BERNDT, C. H. (1981). Interpretations and « facts » in Aboriginal Australia, in F. Dahlberg (Ed.) *Women the Gatherer.* New Haven and London : Yale University Press. pp 153-203.

BRENNAN, F. (1992). *Land Rights Queensland Style : The Struggle For Aboriginal Self-Management.* St Lucia : University of Queensland Press.

Coe v The Commonwealth of Australia (1979) 53 ALAR 403 ; 24 AIR 118

COMMONWEALTH OF AUSTRALIA. (1988). *Warumunga Land Claim.* Canberra : Australian Government Publishing Service.

COMMONWEALTH OF AUSTRALIA. (1993). *Mabo : The High Court Decision on Native Title.* Discussion Paper. Canberra : Commonwealth Government Printer.

ELLIS, C. J. and BARWICK, L. (1989). Antikirinja women's song knowledge 1963-72, in P. Brock, (Ed.) *Women Rites & Sites.* Sydney : Allen & Unwin. 21-40.

FLOOD, J. (1983). *Archaeology of the Dreamtime.* Sydney : Collins.

HAMILTON, A. (1981). A complex strategical situation : Gender and power in Aboriginal Australia, in N. Grieve and P. Grimshaw (Eds.) *Australian Women : Feminist Perspectives.* Melbourne : Oxford University Press. 69-85.

Mabo and Others v Queensland (No. 2) (1992) 175 CAR 1 ; 107 AIR 1

SKY P. (1994). Feminist leisure theory. *Journal of Leisure Research,* 26 (1), 88-96.

ROHRLICH-LEAVITT, R., SYKES, B., and E. WEATHERFORD (1975). Aboriginal women : male and female anthropological perspectives, in R. R. Reiter, (Ed.) *Towards an Anthropology of Women.* NY : Monthly Review Press. 110-126.

Pauline SKY
Rôle de l'identité artistique et culturelle des femmes autochtones

RÉSUMÉ

Depuis la Loi sur les droits des autochtones (*Native Title Act*) de 1993 adoptée par le Parlement australien, les discussions relatives aux droits de ces
derniers sur le territoire ont dépassé le stade de la simple clarification de la
loi et portent maintenant sur le fondement de leur explication culturelle de
l'affiliation territoriale. Les tribunaux entendent maintenant les témoignages
de ces groupes au sujet de leur utilisation culturelle du territoire afin de ju-
ger des liens (droits) des tribus avec certains espaces particuliers. Pour évaluer le bien-fondé de leurs revendications territoriales, les magistrats
confrontent la version des faits des autochtones avec celles des dossiers an-
thropologiques portant sur les premières habitations du pays. En ce qui concerne les femmes autochtones, cependant, il importe de reconstituer
l'anthropologie des droits culturels afin de combler le vide causé par les
préjugés des chercheurs masculins qui ont retracé l'histoire du pays à ses
débuts. En effet, dans la société autochtone traditionnelle, la culture des femmes est en grande partie séparée des pratiques tribales des hommes. Ainsi,
les anthropologues masculins (et les autres chercheurs) qui ont étudié les
tribus autochtones primitives n'auraient pas pu avoir accès à la vie culturelle
dans les camps de femmes où l'imaginaire collectif au sujet de l'origine
culturelle et de l'appartenance était véhiculé par les rites, les danses, les
chansons et les dessins. De plus, les hommes ainsi que la plupart des femmes autochtones auraient aussi été limités dans leur témoignage au sujet des
rites sacrés.
Bref, nous ne possédons qu'une version tronquée de l'histoire des droits des
femmes. Le présent article explore les connaissances accumulées par les femmes autochtones à propos de leurs rites et de leur art (culture) afin d'étayer
leurs revendications territoriales et en faveur de l'autodétermination.

Pauline SKY
The Role of Aboriginal Women's Art in Cultural Identity

ABSTRACT

Since the Native Title Act 1993 passed through the Australian Parliament,
discussion about Aboriginal right to land has developed beyond the mere

clarification of law, to encompass the question of the accuracy of Aboriginal cultural explanation of land affiliation. Courts are now able to hear evidence from Aboriginal groups about their cultural use of land, to judge the connections (rights) of tribes to specific areas. These are tested against the anthropological records of early habitations, to assess claims to land. For Aboriginal women, an anthropology of cultural rights needs to be reconstructed to fill the gap left due to the gender of the scholars who recorded early history. For in traditional Aboriginal society, women's culture is separated from male tribal practice to a substantial amount. The male anthropologists (and other men) who studied early Aboriginal tribes would not have been admitted to see the cultural life of the women's camps where the stories of women's Dreaming (cultural origin and belonging) were passed on in rites, dance, songs and art designs. Aboriginal men and most women would also have been limited in the form their witness to sacred rites, could be allowed.

In sum then we have a fragmented account of women's law, however, one does exist. This paper explores Central Aboriginal women's knowledge residing in rites and art (culture) to make a case for women's claims to land rights and essential self determination.

Pauline SKY
El papel de la identidad artística y cultural de las mujeres autóctonas

RESUMEN

Después de la adopción por el Parlamento Australiano de ley sobre los derechos de los autóctonos (Native Title Act) en 1993, las discusiones relativas a los derechos de los aborígenes sobre el territorio han superado el estado de la simple clarificación de la ley y ahora tratan sobre el fundamento de su explicación cultural de la afiliación territorial. Los tribunales escuchan en este momento los testimonios de estos grupos con respecto de su utilización cultural del territorio con el propósito de juzgar los vínculos (derechos) de las tribus con ciertos espacios particulares. Para evaluar la legitimidad de sus reivindicaciones territoriales, los magistrados confrontan la versión de los hechos de los autóctonos con las de los expedientes antropológicos que tratan de las primeras habitaciones del país. En lo que concierne a las mujeres autóctonas, sin embargo, es importante reconstituir la antropología de los derechos culturales con el fin de llenar el vacío causado por los prejuicios de los investigadores masculinos que trazaron la historia del país en sus comienzos. En efecto,en la sociedad autóctona tradicional, la cultura de las mujeres se encuentra en gran parte separada de las prácticas tribales de los hombres. Así, los antropólogos masculinos (y los otros investigadores) que han estudiado las tribus autóctonas primitivas no hubiesen podido tener acceso a la vida cultural en el campo de las mujeres donde el imaginario colectivo con respecto al origen cultural y a la pertenencia, era transmitido por los ritos, las danzas, las canciones y los dibujos artísticos. Además, los hombres al igual que la mayor parte de las mujeres autóctonas hubiesen también sido limitados en su testimonio con respecto a los ritos sagrados.

En resumen, nosotros poseemos una versión truncada de la historia de los derechos de las mujeres. El presente artículo explora los conocimientos acumulados por las mujeres autóctonas a propósito de sus ritos y de su arte (cultura) con el fin de apoyar sus reivindicaciones territoriales y en favor de la autodeterminación

COMPTES RENDUS / *BOOK REVIEWS*

GILLES JANSON
Emparons-nous du sport.
Les Canadiens-français et le sport au XIXe siècle
Guérin, 1995

À première vue, le titre apparaît comme un pastiche de l'ouvrage de l'écrivain-essayiste Errol Bouchette, paru en 1901, et intitulé « *Emparons-nous de l'industrie* ». Mais le parallèle ne s'arrête pas là. Le volume constitue, en perspective historique, une interprétation, largement fondée sur des matériaux archivistiques de première main, des visées sociales des premiers promoteurs du sport chez les Canadiens français, bien avant qu'ils deviennent des Québécois, tout en s'inspirant des travaux déjà connus de A. Metcalfe et D. Guay en histoire du sport et de la meilleure littérature de l'époque ayant traité du sujet, soit directement, soit par incidence.

L'ancien « desport » devenu sport par aphérèse, représentait une tradition culturelle de jeux et d'amusements physiques de la « meilleure société », principalement anglaise, que l'empire britannique allait diffuser au XIXe siècle par le truchement de ses colonies anciennes ou actuelles, tout en continuant à en créer de nouveaux selon la couleur et les caractéristiques locales, par exemple, la crosse, la raquette et le hockey au Canada. Certains de ces jeux devenaient des sports lorsque, transcendant les objectifs traditionnels de sociabilité qui leur étaient inhérents, les élites s'avisaient de les codifier dans un espace-temps précis, d'en réglementer la pratique et de les organiser socialement sur base de compétition, que celle-ci soit de type amateur ou professionnel, les couches populaires y ayant accès graduellement sous forme de participants ou de spectateurs. C'est de ces quelques jeux érigés en sports au Canada français dont nous parle l'auteur. L'univers des jeux non sportifs espère encore largement ses historiens.

Le livre illustre le fait qu'avant 1890, le sport au Canada-français et à Montréal en particulier était une « réalité » anglaise (chap. 1) et que les francophones n'y étaient présents que d'une façon marginale, se comportant face à lui comme en regard d'un phénomène culturel, étranger à leurs réalités propres. Jusqu'en 1867, la pratique sportive était le fait de la grande bourgeoisie anglaise, de marchands et de militaires qui s'y adonnaient dans le cadre de cercles et clubs sociaux plutôt hermétiques auxquels participaient à l'occasion quelques Canadiens français de même rang et à titre individuel, c'est-à-dire sans avoir prise sur leur organisation. De 1867 à 1890 apparaissent les premiers clubs sportifs francophones, mais l'auteur, faits à l'appui, qualifie leur existence d'éphémère (pp. 42-45), à l'exception de ce qui touche les courses de chevaux et les clubs de raquettes, ainsi que le baseball américain qui trouve un écho favorable chez les Canadiens français plusieurs années avant l'invention du hockey par des Montréalais anglophones gravitant autour de l'université McGill. Pendant cette période, le dynamisme anglo-saxon s'était étendu au cricket, au curling, aux régates, au canotage, à la crosse, le golf, le tennis, la lutte et la boxe, et ainsi de suite. L'ouvrage de Janson fourmille d'exemples concrets de cette situation. Pour autant que le sport à l'époque intéressait un certain nombre d'adeptes et de promoteurs francophones, ces derniers étaient de toute évidence placés devant une situation de rattrapage et de récupération, d'où le sens du titre de l'ouvrage.

Est aussi mise en évidence la place de l'urbanité dans la naissance et le développement de l'institution sportive. À cet égard, le rôle de Montréal a été capital. À peu près tout ce dont l'auteur nous parle a commencé dans ce que nous appelons aujourd'hui la Communauté Urbaine de Montréal, sans porter préjudice à ce qui a pu exister en d'autres villes du Québec. Il souligne à la fin du XIXᵉ siècle l'inversion démographique en faveur d'une majorité francophone à Montréal, la naissance d'une bourgeoisie issue de ses rangs qui va lutter pour sa place au soleil, en sport comme ailleurs, et va chercher à se doter d'institutions qui soient à l'image de son pouvoir naissant (chap. 3). Il ne voit pas là cependant le signe d'une « participation de masse aux activités sportives » (p. 53). La pratique sportive demeure largement élitaire (par exemple, dans les collèges classiques) et la masse, lorsqu'il y a lieu d'employer ce mot, se retrouve principalement dans les gradins pour des spectacles publicisés avec les moyens de l'époque, notamment le journal « *La Presse* » dans les années 1890. Par contre, qu'il s'agisse de pratique active ou de « spectatoriat », il est évident que la croissance urbaine allait inciter à la réservation d'espaces et à la création d'équipements à des fins récréo-sportives, tout comme c'était le cas dans les domaines des parcs ou des arts à la même époque, où le même dynamisme anglo-saxon était à l'œuvre à Montréal.

Le lecteur est alors amené à poser la question à l'auteur : pourquoi les Canadiens français devaient-ils s'emparer du sport ? Était-ce pour éviter de paraître les parents pauvres d'une société en voie d'urbanisation et d'industrialisation ? Était-ce pour profiter des bienfaits d'appréhendés de la pratique sportive ou jouir de la contemplation de beaux spectacles ? Il y avait certainement un peu de cela, mais dès l'introduction de son livre, l'auteur nous informe que les trois derniers chapitres « *témoignent de la présence constante du nationalisme canadien-français tant chez les promoteurs que chez les commentateurs sportifs* » (p. 4). C'est un fait connu et général dans toute l'histoire du sport que ce phénomène culturel, même dans ses versions contemporaines a vibré au chant des sirènes de l'idéologie nationaliste autant dans sa version chauvine que dans celle de l'affirmation ethnique. Là comme ailleurs, l'idéologie remplit sa fonction de justification de l'action d'un groupe social en mal d'ascension.

L'auteur raconte de nombreux cas d'équipes sportives composées de Canadiens français capables de rivaliser, compétitionner et lancer des défis aux meilleures formations anglo-canadiennes et même américaines dans plusieurs disciplines (pp. 129-156). L'idéologie produit une aura symbolique où se projettent les espoirs d'un groupe ethnique dominé. Par exemple, les hommes forts qui stimulent « la fibre Nationale » et Louis Cyr dont l'auteur dit en citant le journal « *La Presse* » de 1891 : *« celui qui représente avec le plus d'éclat la force physique de notre race »* (p. 91). De plus, le spectacle sportif entraîne chez les spectateurs le début d'un vedettariat francophone (pp. 188-192) qui est alimenté par les chroniqueurs sportifs (pp. 193-196). En d'autres termes, le XIXᵉ siècle a produit des Maurice Richard dont l'excellence sportive a servi à nourrir l'imaginaire d'un petit peuple se confortant et se reconnaissant déjà dans une représentation symbolique de « dieux du stade » issus de ses rangs. De plus, le nationalisme avait l'avantage de servir de paravent vertueux à une certaine élite sportive camouflant sa quête de prestige social dans un amateurisme déjà un peu marron tout en permettant aux marchands et promoteurs de spectacles de consolider leurs intérêts économiques.

Ce que l'ouvrage illustre très bien sans employer le terme, c'est que l'entrée et l'insertion du sport dans la société canadienne française au XIXᵉ siècle ont été un beau cas de ce que les anthropologues appellent « acculturation », c'est-à-dire transfert d'un phénomène culturel propre à une société généralement dominante vers une autre société qui n'en dispose pas, mais qui, sous la pression de certains de ses acteurs internes, tend à se l'approprier. En ce sens, les Canadiens français de l'époque n'ont rien inventé en matière de sport, ils ont récupéré : ils ont assimilé des modèles ou « patterns » exogènes à leur groupe ethnique (clubs, associations, ligues, modes d'organisation, compétitions, spectacles, etc.) et les ont reproduits tels quels, au sein de leur propre groupe social, en lui donnant une couleur locale définie à partir d'éléments plus généraux inspirés de leurs propres caractéristiques socioculturelles que le discours nationaliste pouvait très bien adapter au sport, entre autres objets d'usage de la même idéologie.

Dans sa conclusion, l'auteur formule l'hypothèse qu'une autre mentalité aurait caractérisé les promoteurs du sport à l'époque, composée d'esprit libéral, de modernisme, de pluralisme et même d'universalisme à la Coubertin, parfois en opposition avec les éléments traditionalistes incarnés principalement par l'Église catholique. L'examen de ces questions, sous forme d'un (ou de deux) chapitre supplémentaire, aurait ajouté à la valeur du texte en montrant la complexité du sujet abordé, la conquête du sport par les Canadiens

français ; mais peut-être fallait-il, dans un premier temps, élucider historiquement le discours rassembleur et consensualiste qui a été utilisé pour les insérer dans l'univers des nations sportives. Cela, l'auteur le fait avec brio.

Michel Bellefleur

Département des sciences du loisir
Université du Québec à Trois-Rivières

Roger SUE
Temps et ordre social
Presses universitaires de France, 1994

Dans un ouvrage récent, Roger Sue écrit qu'une étude du temps et de ses ruptures est susceptible de mener à une meilleure compréhension des mutations en cours dans les sociétés modernes. Il écrit encore que l'étude des « structures temporelles » ouvre « une voie royale pour étudier une société, puisqu'elle met en lumière les principales articulations qui rythment la vie sociale » (p. 23). Il écrit plus loin :

> Si toute société peut se caractériser par un certain agencement des temps sociaux, on conçoit qu'une transformation dans cet agencement soit un signe d'une profonde mutation sociale (p. 31).

L'ouvrage comprend deux parties. Dans la première, Sue présente une brève revue des principaux auteurs français qui ont abordé l'étude du temps ; il décrit également les principaux éléments de son cadre sociologique d'analyse auquel il puisera abondamment dans la deuxième partie. Dans celle-ci, l'auteur présente en détail sa thèse selon laquelle les sociétés actuelles sont passées du temps dominant du travail au temps dominant du temps libre.

Le temps « en soi » n'existe pas, c'est une construction culturelle, sociale et historique. La sociologie n'aurait manifesté qu'un intérêt mineur pour l'étude du temps, et il en résume grossièrement les approches autour de deux grands pôles : « le Temps-Histoire » et « le Temps-Objet » (p. 25). Le premier renvoie à une « représentation du temps comme espace de la réalisation de l'Histoire », quelques fondateurs de la sociologie (dont Comte, Durkheim) en sont tributaires ; le second renvoie au temps microsociologique, il désigne « le temps ou la périodisation qui résulte de l'étude de tel ou tel phénomène social » (p. 26).

Ayant dit cela, Sue soutient qu'une sociologie *du* temps n'est pas possible, mais qu'une sociologie *des temps sociaux* peut être féconde. Étudier non pas le temps en général, mais les temps sociaux, Cette approche est très près de ce que j'ai publié dans *The Sociology of Time*, au chapitre 3, sur la diversité des temps sociaux.

Sue se risque ensuite dans une typologie du temps dans les « sociétés primitives ». Il insiste surtout sur la notion de « temps sacré », dont il décrit certaines caractéristiques. Il passe alors en revue quelques « précurseurs » ... qui ont pour trait commun d'être tous Français ! Mauss, Durkheim, Halbwachs, Gurvitch.

Dans un chapitre intitulé « Temps et modernité », Sue retrace trois grands axes de développement de la sociologie du temps.

1. Il construit le premier autour de la sociologie du travail, tout particulièrement Georges Friedmann. Sue précise bien que Friedmann n'a pas une notion explicite de sociologie du temps, mais il pense pouvoir en dégager une en filigrane : caractéristiques du temps industriel, rapports entre temps de travail et autres temps sociaux, tout particulièrement ses propos célèbres sur les rapports travail-loisir.

2. Le second renvoie aux travaux de Rezsohazy et de Grossin, et il en profite pour rappeler ce que j'ai moi-même écrit sur les conceptions actuelles du temps dans les sociétés modernes : valeur du temps, mesure, horizon temporel, etc.

3. Le dernier, très justement à mon avis, insiste sur l'apport décisif de la sociologie du loisir. Je pense qu'il pousse trop fort en la situant dans le prolongement de Friedmann et de la sociologie du travail. Il donne une vision particulièrement courte de la sociologie du loisir et en néglige les développements au plan international. Sue traite bien évidemment des travaux de Joffre Dumazedier, qu'il présente très mal à mon avis, procédant à des critiques faciles du genre « la civilisation du loisir, c'est fini », « la sociologie du loisir a plutôt effectué une rupture avec la sociologie du travail qu'avec le travail lui-même » (p. 111).

Roger Sue laisse entendre qu'un « glissement progressif de la notion de loisir vers celle de temps libre va marquer une nouvelle étape en donnant une plus grande ampleur à cette sociologie qui va se libérer plus radicalement du travail » (p. 112). Il se cite évidemment... puisqu'il est l'auteur de la thèse ! Notons au passage qu'il offre une vision fort réductrice du loisir pour étayer sa thèse, en présentant la notion de temps libre comme sociologique par rapport à celle de loisir, présentée comme psychologique ! Une revue même élémentaire des études sociologiques du loisir ne permet aucunement d'étayer une telle affirmation.

Cette partie s'achève sur un résumé de « quelques principes fondamentaux » essentiels à la sociologie des temps sociaux. La notion de structures du temps est présentée comme essentielle, en ce sens qu'elle permet de poser que les rapports entre les temps sociaux sont structurés et surtout, dans la perspective de Sue, que les temps sociaux sont organisés autour d'un temps dominant. Il propose cinq critères pour établir un temps dominant dans une société particulière, (du point de vue quantitatif, qualitatif, des valeurs sociales, etc.) sur lesquels il reviendra longuement dans la deuxième partie pour étayer sa thèse. Il propose même une sorte de typologie du cycle historique d'un temps dominant (p. 137-141), représentation quelque peu naïve, comme s'il n'existait qu'*un* temps dominant, et comme si *le temps de ce temps* pouvait obéir à une telle linéarité...

Dans la deuxième partie de l'ouvrage, l'auteur présente en détail sa thèse selon laquelle les sociétés actuelles sont passées du temps dominant du travail au temps dominant du temps libre.

Dans le premier chapitre de cette deuxième partie, Sue reprend sa typologie des cycles historiques d'un temps dominant, et propose une « histoire des temps sociaux » : le temps sacré, le Moyen Age (autour des travaux bien connus de Jacques Le Goff), le passage au temps industriel (sans jamais citer Thompson), pour conclure au « déclin du temps dominant de travail », et par voie de conséquence à l'apparition d'un « nouveau temps dominant en gestation, porteur d'un nouvel ordre social et d'un nouveau mode de production de la société par elle-même » (p. 184). Telle est la grande thèse de l'ouvrage.

Or quel serait ce nouveau temps dominant, « porteur d'un nouvel ordre social », rien de moins ? Ce serait le temps libre. Car le travail est en déclin, au plan quantitatif et de la valeur qu'on lui accorde. Le chômage dure et durera ; l'automation est à la fois une libération et un cauchemar pour l'emploi ; les exclus du travail sont quasiment majoritaires.

Sa thèse est rédigée ainsi :

> Ou l'on reste, contre toute évidence, dans une perspective du travail comme temps dominant, principe essentiel de la régulation sociale, et le déclin du temps de travail continuera à se traduire par un chômage accru, une exclusion massive ou encore des emplois artificiels, subventionnés, et une faible productivité, ou l'on considère le temps de travail pour ce qu'il est devenu, un temps marginal qu'il convient de gérer au mieux par des procédures d'aménagement et de réduction du temps de travail et l'on recherche un nouveau principe de régulation dans le nouveau temps dominant, le temps libéré ou temps libre (p. 193).

Pour établir que le temps libre est maintenant devenu le temps dominant, Roger Sue reprend un à un les cinq critères qu'il avait proposés en première partie de son ouvrage :

– un critère quantitatif : le temps de travail en déclin continu ;

– un critère des valeurs dominantes : déclin de la valeur du travail, importance accordée à l'individualité, importance du temps libre chez les jeunes, etc. ;

– un critère de stratification sociale : les classes sociales fondées sur la primauté du travail s'estompent au profit de frontières beaucoup moins nettes, vers de nouveaux types de groupes sociaux (jeunes, personnes âgées ; Sue ne mentionne pas ces exemples), vers une pluralité d'appartenances sociales ;

– un critère du mode de production dominant : le travail ne constitue plus le mode de production dominant, le capital n'est plus réservé aux seuls capitalistes (épargnants, rentiers, etc.), importance de l'éducation et de la formation, de l'économie informelle, des solidarités sociales ;

–   un critère de la représentation sociale du temps dominant : de nombreuses pesanteurs font encore du temps de travail celui qui est pensé comme dominant (idéologies du travail, etc.) ; mais il y a bien vide idéologique, crise d'identité, crise des valeurs, ce qui est une autre manière de montrer que la représentation du temps dominant est en train de basculer.

Le dernier chapitre porte sur ce pourrait être un nouvel ordre social fondé sur ce nouveau temps dominant que serait le temps libre. On passe de l'analyse à l'utopie, de la réflexion sociologique à la futurologie qui de triste mémoire a affligé les études sur le loisir.

Dans ses « Fragments d'un nouvel ordre social » Sue propose quelques mesures du genre suivant : flexibilité du travail ; allocation universelle de revenu assurée pour tous (retour aux utopies du 19ᵉ siècle) ; « revenu d'utilité sociale » pour la participation aux associations.

Il écrit également que nous nous acheminons vers de nouvelles représentations du temps. Ainsi, « le temps libre est désormais investi d'une fonction mythique et sacrée » (p. 293) (on ne peut toucher aux vacances et aux congés, etc.). Il y a la recherche de temps plus flexibles. On observe une plus grande centration sur le temps présent (c'est l'hypothèse de Rezsohazy).

Mais la thèse de Roger Sue n'est pas crédible.

Au seul plan documentaire, son ouvrage pêche par une étroitesse de vue en ce qui concerne les auteurs majeurs en sociologie du temps, ramenés pratiquement à la sociologie *française* du temps. La même étroitesse prévaut dans sa présentation des sciences du loisir. Sa typologie historique des cycles du temps dominant laissera plus d'un historien inquiet des raccourcis et des synthèses abusives. Sa critique de la sociologie du loisir est étroite, réductrice à outrance et constitue un véritable affront à une grande tradition sociologique qui remonte à Lafargue et Veblen, qui a connu de grands noms dont David Riesman, Kenneth Roberts, Joffre Dumazedier. De plus, sa thèse sur le temps libre comme temps dominant se construit au détriment d'une critique facile du travail, dont la sociologie du loisir porte le triste fleuron ; on peut y voir des relents de cette vision négative du travail sur laquelle trop de sociologues du loisir ont tenté de construire leur objet.

Sue nous offre une utopie passéiste et peu crédible d'un temps libre mythique qu'aucun sociologue du temps n'a vraiment envisagé et qu'aucun sociologue actuel du loisir ne reprendra.

Gilles Pronovost
Département des sciences du loisir
Université du Québec à Trois-Rivières

Lecteurs du volume 18, 1995
Referees for Volume 18, 1995

ATTIAS-DONFUT, Claudine, Caisse nationale d'assurance vieillesse, 49, Mirabeau, 75016, Paris, France.

ANNAND, Viki, College of Health and Human Performance, University of Maryland, College Park, MD 20742, United States.

BAILLARGEON, Jean-Paul, Institut national de la recherche scientifique, INRS-Culture et société, 14, rue Haldimand, Québec, Québec, Canada.

BEAUREGARD, Yves, Département des sciences du loisir, Université du Québec à Trois-Rivières, C.P. 500, Trois-Rivières, Québec, Canada.

BOIVIN, Micheline, Direction de la recherche de l'évaluation et des statistiques, ministère de la Culture et des Communications, Gouvernement du Québec, 225, Grande Allée Est, Québec Québec, Canada.

CALDWELL, Linda, Department of Recreation and Leisure Studies, University of Georgia, Athens, Georgia 30602, United States.

CHARETTE, Johanne, Centre d'hébergement et de soins de longue durée de Longueuil, 15, rue Pratt, Longueuil, Québec, Canada.

CHIFFET, Pierre, UFR de STAPS, Université de Grenoble, Grenoble, France.

CLÉMENT, Jean-Paul, UFR de STAPS, Université de Strasbourg, 226, rue Descartes, 670821 Strasbourg, France.

COLBERT, François, Chaire de gestion des arts, École des Hautes Études Commerciales, Université de Montréal, 5255, avenue Decelles, Montréal, Québec, Canada.

COLEMAN, Dennis, Faculty of Health and Behavioral Sciences, Griffith University, Nathan, Brisbane, Queensland 4111, Australia.

DEMERS, Jacques, 605, de Champfleury, Bernières, Québec, Canada.

DENIS, Marie-Claude, Département de psychologie, Université du Québec à Trois-Rivières, C.P. 500, Trois-Rivières, Québec, Canada.

DUBÉ, Micheline, Département de psychologie, Université du Québec à Trois-Rivières, C.P. 500, Trois-Rivières, Québec, Canada.

FREYSINGER, Valeria J., Department of Physical Education, Health and Sport Studies, Miami University, 109 Phillips Hall, Oxford, Ohio 4505, United States.

GAGNON, Nathaly, Département des sciences du loisir, Université Concordia, Loyola Campus, 7141, rue Sherbrooke Ouest, Montréal, Québec, Canada.

HAYLLAR, Bruce, University of Technology, School of Leisure and Tourism Studies, Kuring-Gal, Campus, Eton Road, Lindfield, NSW 2070, Australia.

KLEIBER, Douglas, Department of Recreation and Leisure Studies, University of Georgia, Athens, Georgia 30602, United States.

LABERGE, Suzanne, Département d'éducation physique, Université de Montréal, C.P. 6128, Succursale Centre-ville, Montréal, Québec, Canada.

LACOSTE, Pierre, Département des sciences de l'activité physique, Université du Québec à Trois-Rivières, C.P. 500, Trois-Rivières, Québec, Canada.

LAFORTUNE, Benoît, 2022, rue Théodore, Montréal, Québec, Canada.

LANDREVILLE, Philippe, Département de psychologie, Université Laval, Cité universitaire, Sainte-Foy, Québec, Canada.

LEFRANÇOIS, Richard, Centre de recherche en gérontologie et gériatrie, Hôpital d'Youville, 1036, rue Belvédère, Sherbrooke, Québec, Canada.

MACNEIL, Richard, Department of Leisure Studies, University of Iowa, Field House, Iowa City, Iowa 52242 , United States.

MARCOTTE, Gaston, Sciences de l'activité physique, Université Laval, Cité universitaire, Sainte-Foy, Québec, Canada.

MOBILY, Ken, Department of Leisure Studies, University of Iowa, Field House, Iowa City, Iowa 52242 , United States.

MORVAL, Monique, Département de psychologie, Université de Montréal , C.P. 6128, succursale Centre-ville, Montréal, Québec, Canada.

PAGEOT, Jean-Claude Sciences du loisir, Faculté des sciences sociales, Université d'Ottawa, 550, Cumberland, Ottawa, Ontario, Canada.

PARÉ, Claude, Département des sciences de l'activité physique, Université du Québec à Trois-Rivières, C.P. 500, Trois-Rivières, Québec, Canada.

PARÉ, Jean-Louis, Département des sciences du loisir, Université du Québec à Trois-Rivières, C.P. 500, Trois-Rivières, Québec, Canada.

PARENT, Ghislain, Département des sciences de l'éducation, Université du Québec à Trois-Rivières, C.P. 500, Trois-Rivières, Québec, Canada.

POIRIER, Sylvie, Département d'anthropologie, Université Laval, Cité universitaire, Sainte-Foy, Québec, G1R 4N4.

RAGHEB, Mounir G., Leisure Services and Studies, 15 Stone Building, The Florida State University, Tallahassee, FL 32306-3001, United States.

ROY, Benoît, Sciences de l'activité physique, Université Laval, Cité universitaire, Sainte-Foy, Québec, Canada.

SAMDAHL, Diane, Department of Recreation and Leisure Studies of Georgia, Hardman Hall, Athens Georgia 30609-4066, United States.

SEARLE, Mark S., Health, Leisure & Human Performance, Research Institute – Max Bell Centre, University of Manitoba, Winnipeg, Manitoba, Canada.

SMITH, Ralph, Department of Leisure Studies, Penn State University, Henderson Bldg, University Park PA 16802, United States.

SOUBRIER, Robert, Département des sciences du loisir, Université du Québec à Trois-Rivières, C.P. 500, Trois-Rivières, Québec, Canada.

STEWART, William, Department of Recreation, Park and Tourism Sciences, Texas A & M University, College Station TX 77843-2261, United States.

VALOIS, Pierre, Département des sciences de l'éducation, Université du Québec à Trois-Rivières, C.P. 500, Trois-Rivières, Québec, Canada.

WALKIN, M., Department of Recreation, Southern Illinois University, 121, Quigley Hall, Carbondale, Illinois 62901, United States.

WANKEL, Léonard M., Faculty of Physical Education and Recreation, University of Alberta, Edmonton, Alberta, Canada.

WITT, Peter, North Texas State University, P.O. Box 5447, Denton, Texas 76203, United States.

INDEX DU VOLUME 18, 1995
CONTENT TO VOLUME 18, 1995

ARTICLES / *ARTICLES*

NOTES DE RECHERCHE / *RESEARCH NOTES*

COMPTES RENDUS / *BOOK REVIEWS*

À PARAÎTRE
FORTHCOMING ISSUES

TEMPS DE TRAVAIL ET TEMPS HORS-TRAVAIL
Vol. 19, nº 2, automne 1996
Éditeurs invités : Jean-Yves BOULIN et Diane-Gabrielle TREMBLAY

Vers les années 60, on annonçait l'arrivée de la société des loisirs. Les récessions des années 80 et 90 ont cependant diminué la pertinence de ce concept, la situation de chômage amenant la majorité des gens à se préoccuper davantage de s'assurer un emploi. On observe en fait une polarité de situations. Bon nombre de personnes se trouvent exclues de l'emploi ou sont dans des situations transitoires (temps partiel, stages, contrats à durée déterminée) qui se prolongent. Elles connaissent de ce fait une situation de « loisir forcé ». À l'inverse, un certain nombre de personnes travaillent apparemment plus que ne l'indiquent leurs horaires officiels et d'autres font un grand nombre d'heures supplémentaires ou cumulent deux emplois à temps partiel ou réduit pour obtenir un salaire convenable.

Par ailleurs, la progression des ménages à deux revenus, et donc à deux travailleurs, de même que celle des foyers monoparentaux, entraîne des contraintes sur le plan du temps hors travail ; les tâches domestiques se substituent souvent au loisir proprement dit, entraînant parfois une redéfinition du concept du temps hors-travail, sinon du « loisir » proprement dit. Le caractère plus proprement ludique du loisir cède le pas à celui de l'utilité.

Le chômage chronique élevé que connaissent bon nombre de pays industrialisés fait émerger de nouveau le débat sur le partage du temps de travail dont les effets sur l'utilisation du temps hors travail sont parfois soulignés de façon positive. En effet, si certains mettent l'accent sur la réduction du chômage que permettrait une telle mesure, d'autres soulignent qu'elle favoriserait un nouvel équilibre des temps sociaux, considérant cette évolution préférable au présent partage entre le travail et le non-emploi. Aux yeux des premiers, le travail constitue un élément positif et enrichissant de la vie, alors que pour les seconds, il est plutôt pénible, contraignant et peu susceptible de conduire à l'épanouissement humain.

Ce numéro de *Loisir et Société* abordera différents aspects associés à l'articulation du temps de travail et du temps hors-travail. Les articles présentant les faits, les enjeux, les facteurs explicatifs des évolutions observées en ces matières sont donc les bienvenus ; ils peuvent être à caractère sociologique, économique ou politique. On pourra ainsi traiter de sujets tels que :

- l'évolution historique du temps de travail et du temps hors-travail ;
- le temps de travail par rapport au cycle de vie, notamment l'articulation entre la formation, le travail et la retraite ;
- le temps choisi, la diversification des temps de travail et des statuts d'emploi ;
- les aspirations au regard du temps libre ;
- la structuration des comportements en matière de temps de travail et de temps hors-travail par rapport à l'évolution des valeurs dont l'un et l'autre sont porteurs ;

- les rapports sociaux de sexe, ou différences hommes-femmes, relativement à ces comportements ;
- une comparaison du contenu du temps hors-travail dans différents pays ;
- etc.

Soumission des manuscrits

Les thèmes suggérés ci-dessus ne sont aucunement limitatifs ; d'autres perspectives de recherche peuvent également être abordées sur les plans méthodologique ou théorique. Les éditeurs invitent plus particulièrement les auteurs à présenter des textes portant sur des comparaisons internationales.

Les manuscrits devront être soumis aux deux éditeurs invités avant le 30 mai 1996 et inclure :

1) Quatre exemplaires du manuscrit, dactylographiés à double interligne ; la première page du manuscrit ne doit pas comporter le nom ou les coordonnées de l'auteur ;

2) Une page titre contenant le titre de l'article, le nom de l'auteur ou des auteurs, numéros de téléphone et de télécopieur ainsi que l'affiliation institutionnelle de chacun ;

3) Un résumé d'au plus 150 mots.

Si le manuscrit est accepté est également exigée une copie du texte sur disquette portant la mention du logiciel utilisé ainsi que sa version.

Les tableaux, figures et notes doivent être présentés sur des feuillets séparés ; on indiquera leur emplacement dans le texte (par ex. : insérer ici Fig. 1).

Adopter le style APA (*American Psychological Association*) pour les références.

Faire parvenir à : Diane-Gabrielle Tremblay
Télé-Université
C.P. 5250, succursale C
Montréal (Québec)
Canada
H2X 3M4
Fax : (514) 522-3608

ou   Jean-Yves Boulin
Institut de recherche et d'information socio-économique
Université Paris Dauphine
Place Maréchal de Lattre Tassigny
75775 Paris
Cedex 16
France

WORKING TIME AND NON-WORK TIME
Vol. 19, No. 2, Fall 1996
Guest Editors: Jean-Yves BOULIN and Diane-Gabrielle TREMBLAY

In the 60's we were said to be at the threshold of the *society of leisure*. However, owing to the slumps of the 80's and 90's, people now tend to focus more on having or keeping their jobs, reducing by the same token the emphasis on leisure The situation has now dichotomized. On the one hand, numerous people either do not have a job at all, or else have a temporary one (part time, field training, limited contracts) for a more or less extended period of time, thus experiencing a *forced state* of leisure. On the other hand, other people are working more and more, extending their regular working schedule, doing considerable amount of overtime or cumulating two part-time jobs in order to get a decent salary.

There are also new constraints on the non-work time of people, since they tend to either have a double income when they live as a couple or else be in a single-parent situation. In both cases, the hours formerly spent in recreational activities are now often dedicated to family chores. Thus the need of a new definition of the concept of non-work time and *leisure* itself. It seems that leisure is losing its *play* content at the expense of its *purpose* content.

With chronic unemployment being so high in numerous industrialized societies, the debate on work or employment sharing has resurfaced, and consequences of reduced working time on the use of non-work time are sometimes given a positive emphasis. For those who think that work is a positive and enriching element of life, such a measure is welcome since it would favour a decrease in unemployment. For those who consider work as hard, constraining and rarely fulfilling, such a measure would have the advantage of creating a new balance between social times and would, at any rate, be preferable to the present dichotomy between work and unemployment.

This issue of *Society and Leisure* will focus on the interrelation between working time and non-work time. Papers dealing with facts, issues and factors affecting changes in this area are welcomed. They may be of a sociological, economical or political character. Subjects such as the following will be accepted:

- The historical evolution of working time and non-work time;
- Working time in relation to life cycle, and the relationship between education, work and retirement;
- Selected time, diversification of working times and of job;
- Aspirations concerning free time;
- Structuration of behaviour with respect to working time and non-work time behaviour in relation to the implied evolution of values;
- Gendered social relationships regarding this type of behaviour;
- Comparison of the content of non-work time within different countries;
- Etc.

These subjects only provide examples of the types of papers that are expected. Other topics may be addressed either from a methodological or a theoretical perspective. The editors are particularly interested in papers reporting on international comparisons in this area.

Submission of Manuscripts

Manuscripts should be submitted to guest editors before May 30, 1996, and should include:

1) Four copies of the manuscript, typed double-spaced; the first page must not bear the name, address or telephone number of the author or authors;

2) A title page containing the title of the article, the name or names of the authors, their telephone and Fax numbers as well as the name of their institution;

3) An abstract of 150 words maximum.

Should the manuscript be accepted, a copy of the text on a diskette identifying software and version will be mandatory.

Tables, figures and notes should be presented on separate sheets with their location noted in the text (e.g. insert Fig. 1 about here).

References should be cited according to the American Psychological Association format.

Mail to: Diane-Gabrielle Tremblay
                    Télé-Université
                    C.P. 5250, succursale C
                    Montréal (Québec)
                    Canada
                    H2X 3M4
                    Fax: (514) 522-3608

or   Jean-Yves Boulin
                    Institut de recherche et d'information socio-économique
                    Université Paris Dauphine
                    Place Maréchal de Lattre Tassigny
                    75775 Paris
                    Cedex 16
                    France

RECOMMANDATIONS AUX AUTEURS

Les manuscrits doivent être soumis à la rédaction et doivent inclure :

1) Quatre copies du manuscrit, dactylographiées à double interligne ; la première page du manuscrit ne doit pas comporter le nom ou les coordonnées de l'auteur ;

2) Une page titre contenant le titre de l'article, le nom de l'auteur ou des auteurs, numéros de téléphone et de télécopieur ainsi que l'affiliation institutionnelle de chacun ;

3) Un résumé d'au plus 150 mots.

Si le manuscrit est accepté, est également exigée une copie du texte sur disquette avec la mention du logiciel utilisé ainsi que sa version.

Les tableaux, figures et notes doivent être présentés sur des feuillets séparés ; on indiquera leur emplacement dans le texte (par ex. : insérer ici Fig. 1).

Adopter le style APA (*American Psychological Association*) pour les références et la bibliographie.

Faire parvenir à :

Le Directeur
Loisir et Société / Society and Leisure
Département des sciences du loisir
Université du Québec à Trois-Rivières
C.P. 500, Trois-Rivières (Québec)
CANADA   G9A 5H7

INSTRUCTIONS FOR AUTHORS

Manuscripts should be submitted to the editor and should include :

1) Four copies of the manuscript, typed double-spaced ; the first page must not bear the name, address or telephone number of the author or authors ;

2) A title page containing the title of the article, the name or names of the authors, their telephone and fax numbers as well as the name of their institution ;

3) An abstract of 150 words, at most.

If accepted, a copy of the text on a diskette, identifying software and version will be required.

Tables, figures and notes should be presented on separate sheets with their location noted in the text (e.g. insert Fig. 1 about here).

References should be styled according to the American Psychological Association format.

Mail to :

The Editor
Loisir et Société / Society and Leisure
Département des sciences du loisir
Université du Québec à Trois-Rivières
P.O. Box 500, Trois-Rivières (Québec)
CANADA   G9A 5H7

NUMÉROS DISPONIBLES
NUMBERS AVAILABLE

LOISIR ET SOCIÉTÉ / *SOCIETY AND LEISURE*

Abonnez-vous pour trois ans et recevez **GRATUITEMENT** un exemplaire du livre
Répertoire des établissements de formation et de recherche en loisir, culture et tourisme,
sous la direction de Max D'Amours, ouvrage multilingue, 1991, 602 pages. Une valeur de 35 $.

Ask for a three year subscription and receive a **FREE** book
International Directory of Academic Institutions in Leisure, Recreation and Related Fields,
edited by Max D'Amours, multilingual, 1991, 602 pages. A $35 value.

FEUILLE DE COMMANDE / *ORDER FORM*

	CANADA (Taxes incluses / *Taxes included*)		ÉTRANGER *OTHER COUNTRIES*
	RÉGULIER / *REGULAR*	ÉTUDIANT (Preuve requise) / *STUDENT (Requested proof)*	
3 ans (6 n^os)	85 $ ☐	62 $ ☐	95 $ ☐
2 ans (4 n^os)	68 $ ☐	50 $ ☐	75 $ ☐
1 an (2 n^os)	38 $ ☐	28 $ ☐	43 $ ☐

VENTES À L'UNITÉ / *SINGLE COPY*   **26,75 $** (TPS incluse / *GST included*)

Faites-moi parvenir les titres suivants déjà parus :
Please send me the following back numbers

Nombre de copies / *Copies*	Volume	Numéro	Total ($)
_____	_____	_____	_____
_____	_____	_____	_____
_____	_____	_____	_____
		TOTAL	_____

C-81

Nom / *Name* _____

Adresse / *Address* _____

Ville / *City* _____

Code postal / *Postal Code* _____ Téléphone / *Phone Number* _____

RETOURNEZ CETTE FEUILLE DE COMMANDE AVEC VOTRE PAIEMENT
PAYMENT IS REQUESTED WITH THIS ORDER FORM

☐ Visa   ☐ MasterCard   N° de compte / *Account Number* _____

Date d'expiration / *Expiration Date* _____ Signature _____

À l'extérieur du Canada, les abonnés sont invités à utiliser leur carte de crédit pour faciliter l'échange des monnaies étrangères. *Foreign subscribers are advised to use credit card in order to facilitate currency exchange.*

Postez à / *Mail to* : **Presses de l'Université du Québec**
2875, boul. Laurier, Sainte-Foy (Québec) Canada G1V 2M3

ACCELERATING LEISURE ?

Leisure, Time and Space in a Transitory Society

LEISURE STUDIES ASSOCIATION (LSA)
VERENIGING VAN DE VRIJETIJDSSECTOR (VVS)
1996 CONFERENCE
12 - 14 SEPTEMBER 1996

Society as a whole and leisure in particular is changing at ever greater velocity. Leisure products and services not only circulate along routes of greater and greater distance, but also with ever quickening turnover time. For example: technological changes, the ever emerging of new forms of production and consumption in leisure, processes of globalization and localisation, the growing of various kinds of mobility and migration of people and the building up of numbers of (socio-cultural and land use) conflicts in the countryside and in the cities are causing important transformations in the use of time and space in leisure.

During the LSA-VVS-conference attention will be given to transitions in a.o.:
* the relation between leisure and the culture industry, e.g. the (new) media (from 'word' to 'image'?);
* the public and private provision of leisure (from state to market?);
* the land use in the countryside (from agriculture tot nature and/or recreation and tourism?);
* leisure and tourism attractions (from authenticity to hyper-real?);
* ethics of leisure and tourism

Sub-themes

The aim of the conference is to analyze, understand and explain these and other transformations and their consequences from several points of view. Therefore, the transitions will be dealt with from the point of view of:

* Policy, planning and designing of leisure products and services in time and space;

* Management of leisure products and services

* Research in leisure, time and space: new paradigms?

Ideas for additional themes are invited

Landbouwuniversiteit   Wageningen

LSA
LEISURE STUDIES ASSOCIATION

Werkgroep Recreatie en Toerisme

Vereniging voor de
Vrijetijdssector

Journal of
APPLIED
RECREATION
RESEARCH

The *Journal of Applied Recreation Research* is prepared quarterly by the Ontario Research Council on Leisure and is devoted to applied research articles on a wide array of topics concerning recreation and leisure. Of interest to both academic researchers and practitioners, the *Journal of Applied Recreation Research* emphasizes the practical implications of empirical and conceptual recreation and leisure research.

Ontario Research Council on Leisure

Conseil ontarien de recherche en loisir

The Ontario Research Council on Leisure (ORCOL) was founded in 1975 and is devoted to the promotion and dissemination of research on all aspects of leisure and recreation including sports, fitness, culture, and tourism. The Council is composed of researchers in the leisure field drawn from government, academe, consult-ancies, and other agencies, and membership is open to any individual with interests in leisure and recreation research.

Editor: **Mark E. Havitz**, Department of Recreation and Leisure Studies, University of Waterloo, Waterloo, ON   N2L 3G1

Editorial Policy: Open to contributors from Canada and abroad, the *Journal of Applied Recreation Research* publishes articles and reviews in all areas of leisure, recreation, and tourism. All manu-scripts are refereed anonymously by three reviewers.

Subscription Information: The *Journal of Applied Recreation Research* is published four times per year by Wilfrid Laurier University Press. A subscription for each volume of four issues is $50.00 (or US$50.00 outside Canada) per year.

Subscriptions and address changes should be sent to:
    Wilfrid Laurier University Press
    Wilfrid Laurier University
    Waterloo, ON, Canada   N2L 3C5
    Telephone: (519) 884-0710, ext. 6124
    Fax: (519) 725-1399
Make cheques payable to **Wilfrid Laurier University Press**.

Sixth International Symposium on Society and Resource Management :

Call for papers

All individuals interested in presenting a paper, poster, or organizing a roundtable discussion at the Sixth International Symposium on Society and Natural Resource Management are encouraged to submit an abstract by November 1, 1995 to the address listed below.

The Sixth Symposium is being hosted by the Department of Agricultural Economics and Rural Sociology and The School of Forestry of the College of Agricultural Sciences and the Department of Hotel, Restaurant, and Recreation Management of the School of Health and Human Development at The Pennsylvania State University. It is scheduled for May 18-23, 1996 and will be held on the Penn State campus.

This year's symposium will focus on a better integration of social and natural resource sciences in addressing resource and environmental issues. A commitment to the role of social perspectives in policy development and managing natural resources is underscored.

Symposium activities include concurrent paper and poster sessions, plenary theme addresses, roundtables and dialogue sessions, exhibits, field trips and receptions. Special efforts are being made to encourage and accommodate participation by students this year.

Those wishing to present at the conference should submit abstracts no longer than two, double-spaced, typewritten pages to:

> A.E. Luloff, Program Co-Chair
> Department of Agricultural Economics and Rural Sociology
> 111 Armsby Building
> The Pennsylvania State University
> University Park, PA 16802

The organizers of the Symposium have arranged a variety of publication outlets for some of the papers being presented at the conference. For more information about publication opportunities or topics being addressed at the Symposium, write to the above address.

10^E CONGRÈS DE L'IASI

L'Association Internationale pour l'Information Sportive (IASI), groupement mondial pour la promotion et le développement de l'information et de la documentation dans le domaine du sport, organise tous les quatre ans un Congrès Scientifique dont la prochaine session se déroulera à Paris, du 10 au 12 juin 1997.

À l'aube des autoroutes de l'information, le 10e Congrès de l'IASI constituera le grand rendez-vous international pour tous les acteurs des milieux de l'information et de la documentaiton sportive. À ce titre, plus de 250 participants en provenance d'une soixantaine de pays sont attendus.

Les objectifs de ce forum international ont pour priorité de :

– favoriser la coopération entre professionnels,

– faciliter l'accès aux sources d'information,

– encourager les échanges scientifiques et techniques entre pays et institutions,

– promouvoir la gestion des ressources technologiques et la veille technologique.

Le titre du Congrès « L'information sportive : au-delà des frontières », manifeste la volonté du comité scientifique d'élargir les champs d'application de l'information.

Contat pour toute demande de renseignements et recevoir les documents d'inscription :

10^c Congrès de l'IASI – Paris 1997
Comité d'Organisation
11, avenue du Tremblay – 75012 – Paris – France
Tél. :   33 (1) 41 74 41 07
Tlc. :   33 (1) 48 08 19 60
Email :   FRA7501@CRIUC.UNICAEN.FR

10TH IASI CONGRESS

The International Association for Sports Information (IASI), worldwide organisation for the promotion and development of information and documentation in the field of sports, holds a Scientific Congress every four years. The next session will take place in Paris, on June 10th to 12th 1997.

On the eve of information highways, the 10th IASI Congress will be a major international event for all those who are interested in sports information and documentation. Over 250 participants are expected from about sixty different countries.

The main objects of this international forum are :

– to promote cooperation between professionals,

– to facilitate access to sources of information,

– to encourage scientific and technical exchanges between countries and organisations,

– to promote the management of technological resources and awareness technology.

The name of the Congress « Sports Information : without borders », expresses the Scientific Committee's will to broaden the fields of application of information.

For all inquiries regarding information and registration documents please contact :

10th IASI Congress – Paris 1997
Organizing Committee
11, avenue du Tremblay – 75012 – Paris – France
Tel.:   33 (1) 41 74 41 07
Fax :   33 (1) 48 08 19 60
Email :   FRA7501@CRIUC.UNICAEN.FR